PREFACE FROM US

The built environment has a profound impact on our natural environment, economy, health, and productivity. Breakthroughs in building science, technology, and operations are now available to designers, builders, operators, and owners who want to build green and maximize both economic and environmental performance.

Through the LEED® green building certification program, the U.S. Green Building Council (USGBC) is transforming the built environment. The green building movement offers an unprecedented opportunity to respond to the most important challenges of our time, including global climate change, dependence on non sustainable and expensive sources of energy, and threats to human health. The work of innovative building professionals is a fundamental driving force in the green building moment. Such leadership is a critical component to achieving USGBC's mission of a sustainable built environment for all within a generation.

USGBC MEMBERSHIP

USGBC's greatest strength is the diversity of our membership. USGBC is a balanced, consensus-based nonprofit with more than 18,000 member companies and organizations representing the entire building industry. Since its inception in 1993, USGBC has played a vital role in providing a leadership forum and a unique, integrating force for the building industry. USGBC's programs have three distinguishing characteristics:

Committee-based

The heart of this effective coalition is our committee structure, in which volunteer members design strategies that are implemented by staff and expert consultants. Our committees provide a forum for members to resolve differences, build alliances, and forge cooperative solutions for influencing change in all sectors of the building industry.

Member-driven

Membership is open and balanced and provides a comprehensive platform for carrying out important programs and activities. We target the issues identified by our members as the highest priority. We conduct an annual review of achievements that allows us to set policy, revise strategies, and devise work plans based on members' needs.

Consensus-focused

We work together to promote green buildings, and in doing so, we help foster greater economic vitality and environmental health at lower costs. We work to bridge ideological gaps between industry segments and develop balanced policies that benefit the entire industry.

Contact the U.S. Green Building Council
2101 L Street, NW
Suite 500
Washington, DC 20037
(800) 795-1747 Office
(202) 828-5110 Fax
www.usgbc.org

TRADEMARK

LEED® is a registered trademark of the U.S. Green Building Council.
LEED Reference Guide for Green Interior Design and Construction
For the Design, Construction and Renovation of Commercial and Institutional Interiors Projects
2009 Edition
ISBN # 978-1-932444-15-5

ACKNOWLEDGMENTS

The LEED Reference Guide for Green Interior Design and Construction, 2009 Edition, has been made possible only through the efforts of many dedicated volunteers, staff members, and others in the USGBC community. The Reference Guide drafting was managed and implemented by USGBC staff and consultants and included review and suggestions by many Technical Advisory Group (TAG) members. We especially extend our deepest gratitude to all of our LEED committee members who participated in the development of this guide, for their tireless volunteer efforts and constant support of USGBC's mission:

LEED Steering Committee

Scot Horst, Chair, LSC	Horst, Inc
Joel Ann Todd, Vice-Chair, LSC	Joel Ann Todd
Muscoe Martin	M2 Architecture
Stuart Carron	JohnsonDiversey, Inc.
Holley Henderson	H2 Ecodesign, LLC
Christine Magar	Greenform
Kristin Shewfelt	Architectural Energy Corporation
Jessica Millman	Agora DC
Bryna Dunn	Moseley Architects
Neal Billetdeaux	JJR
Greg Kats	Managing Good Energies
Mark Webster	Simpson Gumpertz & Heger
Bob Thompson	EPA Indoor Environment Management Branch
Malcolm Lewis	Constructive Technologies Group, Inc.
John Boecker	7Group
Sara O'Mara	Choate Construction Company
Alex Zimmerman	Rep Canada Green Building Council
Ian Theaker	Rep Canada Green Building Council

Sustainable Sites TAG

Bryna Dunn, Chair	Moseley Architects
Stewart Comstock, Vice-Chair	Maryland Department of the Environment
Michele Adams	Cahill Associates
Gina Baker	Burt Hill
Ted Bardacke	Global Green USA
Stephen Benz	Sasaki
Mark Brumbaugh	Brumbaugh & Associates
Laura Case	Emory University Campus Services
Zach Christeson	the HOK Planning Group
Jay Enck	Commissioning & Green Building Services
Ron Hand	E/FECT. Sustainable Design Solutions

Richard Heinisch	Acuity Lighting Group
Michael Lane	Lighting Design Lab
Marita Roos	HNTB
Zolna Russell	Hord Coplan Macht, Inc.
Alfred Vick	Ecos Environmental Design, Inc.

Water Efficiency TAG

Neal Billetdeaux, Chair	JJR
John Koeller, Vice-Chair	Alliance for Water Efficiency
David Carlson	Columbia University
Bill Hoffman	H.W. Hoffman and Associates, LLC
Geoff Nara	Civil & Environmental Consultants
Stephanie Tanner	U.S. Environmental Protection Agency
Daniel Yeh	University of South Florida
David Bracciano	Tampa Bay Water
Robert Rubin	NCSU-BAE and McKim & Creed
Winston Huff	SSR Engineers
Robert Benazzi	Jaros Baum & Bolles
Gunnar Baldwin	TOTO USA, INC
Heather Kinkade	Forgotten Rain, LLC
Shabbir Rawalpindiwala	Kohler Company
Bill Wall	Clivus New England, Inc.

Energy and Atmosphere TAG

Greg Kats, Chair	GoodEnergies
Marcus Sheffer, Vice-Chair	7group
Drury Crawley	US Department of Energy
Jay Enck	Commissioning & Green Building Solutions, Inc.
Ellen Franconi	IPMVP and AEC
Mark Frankel	New Buildings Institute
Nathan Gauthier	Harvard Green Campus Initiative
Rusty Hodapp	Dallas/Fort Worth, Energy & Transportation Management
John Hogan	City of Seattle Department of Planning & Development
Bion Howard	Building Environmental Science and Technology
Dan Katzenberger	Engineering, Energy, and the Environment
Bob Maddox	Sterling Planet
Brenda Morawa	BVM Engineering, Inc.
Erik Ring	LPA, Inc.
Michael Rosenberg	Oregon Department of Energy
Mick Schwedler	Trane
Gord Shymko	IPMVP and G.F. Shymko & Associates
Gail Stranske	CTG Energetics
Michael Zimmer	Thompson Hine LLP

Materials and Resources TAG

Mark Webster, Chair	Simpson Gumpertz & Heger Inc.
Steven Baer, Vice-chair	Five Winds International
Paul Bertram	NAIMA
Chris Dixon	NBBJ
Ann Edminster	Design AVEnues

Lee Gros	Lee Gros Architect and Artisan, Inc
Theresa Hogerheide-Reusch	Reusch Design Services
Nadav Malin	BuildingGreen, LLC.
Nancy Malone	Siegel & Strain Architects
Kirsten Ritchie	Gensler
Wayne Trusty	Athena Sustainable Materials Institute
Denise Van Valkenburg	MASCO Retail Cabinet Group
Gabe Wing	Herman Miller, Inc.

Indoor Environmental Quality TAG

Bob Thompson, Chair	EPA Indoor Environment Management Branch
Steve Taylor, Vice-Chair	Taylor Engineering
Nancy Clanton	Clanton and Associates
Alexis Kurtz	Ove Arup &Partners
George Loisos	Loisos+ Ubelohde
Prasad Vaidya	The Weidt Group
Daniel Bruck	BRC Acoustics & Tech.
David Lubman	David Lubman & Associates
Charles Salter	Salter Associates
Ozgem Ornektekin	DMJM Harris
Jude Anders	Shoreline Concepts, LLC
Brian Cloward	Mithun Architects+Designers+Planners
Larry Dykhuis	Herman Miller, Inc
Francis (Bud) Offerman	Indoor Environmental Engineering
Christopher Schaffner	The Green Engineer
Dennis Stanke	Trane Company

This edition of the reference guide builds on the work of those who helped create previous versions:

LEED for Commercial Interiors Version 2.0 Core Committee

Penny Bonda	Environmental Communications
Keith Winn	Catalyst Partners
Gina Baker	Burt Hill Kosar Rittelmann Associates
Kirsten Childs	Croxton Collaborative Architects, P.C.
Holley Henderson, Chair	H2 Ecodesign, LLC
Don Horn	U.S. General Services Administration
Scot Horst	Horst, Inc
Liana Kallivoka	Austin Energy Green Building Program
Jill Kowalski	EwingCole
Fran Mazarella	U.S. General Services Administration
Roger McFarland	HOK
Denise Van Valkenburg, Vice Chair	Steelcase Inc.
Ken Wilson	Envision Design
Elaine Aye	Green Building Services
Carlie Bullock-Jones	Thompson, Ventulett, Stainback & Associates
Rico Cedro	Krueck & Sexton
Hellen Kessler	HJKessler Associates, Inc
Mehran Khazra	Guttmann & Blaevoet Consulting Engineer

Laurie McMahon   Cassidy & Pinkard Colliers
Ralph Muehliesen   Illinois Institute of Technology
Georgina Sikorski   INVISTA

A special thanks to USGBC staff for their invaluable efforts in developing this LEED Reference Guide especially Sonia Punjabi for her technical expertise and extraordinary commitment, Lauren Riggs for her dedication and hard work, and Brendan Owens and Peter Templeton for their vision and guidance.

TABLE OF CONTENTS

LEED 2009 for Commercial Interiors

100 base points; 6 possible Innovation in Design and 4 Regional Priority points

Certified	40–49 points
Silver	50–59 points
Gold	60–79 points
Platinum	80 points and above

INTRODUCTION

I. WHY MAKE YOUR BUILDING GREEN?

The environmental impact of the building design, construction, and operations industry is enormous. Buildings annually consume more than 30% of the total energy and more than 60% of the electricity used in the United States. In 2006, the commercial building sector produced more than 1 billion metric tons of carbon dioxide, an increase of more than 30% over 1990 levels.[1] Each day 5 billion gallons of potable water are used solely to flush toilets. A typical North American commercial building generates about 1.6 pounds of solid waste per employee per day[2]; in a building with 1,500 employees, that can amount to 300 tons of waste per year. Development alters land from natural, biologically diverse habitats to hardscape that is impervious and devoid of biodiversity. The far-reaching influence of the built environment necessitates action to reduce its impact.

Green building practices can substantially reduce or eliminate negative environmental impacts through high-performance, market-leading design, construction, and operations practices. As an added benefit, green operations and management reduce operating costs, enhance building marketability, increase workers' productivity, and reduce potential liability resulting from indoor air quality problems.

Examples abound. Energy efficiency measures have reduced operating expenses of the Denver Dry Goods building by approximately $75,000 per year. Students in day-lit schools in North Carolina consistently score higher on tests than students in schools using conventional lighting fixtures. Studies of workers in green buildings reported productivity gains of up to 16%, including less absenteeism and higher work quality, based on "people-friendly" green design. Karges Faulconbridge, Inc., renovated a former grocery store for its new headquarters and diverted 88% of the construction waste from landfills through reuse and recycling. The largest high-rise real estate project in Sacramento, the Joe Serna Jr. Environmental Protection Agency Headquarters Building (Cal/EPA), was able to save $610,000 a year by implementing energy efficiency measures, making it 34% more energy efficient than required by California's 1998 energy code. In short, green design, construction, and operations have environmental, economic, and social elements that benefit all building stakeholders, including owners, occupants, and the general public.

II. LEED® GREEN BUILDING RATING SYSTEM

Background on LEED®

Following the formation of the U.S. Green Building Council (USGBC) in 1993, the organization's members quickly realized that the sustainable building industry needed a system to define and measure "green buildings." USGBC began to research existing green building metrics and rating systems. Less than a year after formation, the members acted on the initial findings by establishing a committee to focus solely on this topic. The composition of the committee was diverse; it included architects, real estate agents, a building owner, a lawyer, an environmentalist, and industry representatives. This cross section of people and professions added a richness and depth both to the process and to the ultimate product.

The first LEED Pilot Project Program, also referred to as LEED Version 1.0, was launched at the USGBC Membership Summit in August 1998. After extensive modifications, LEED Green Building

Rating System Version 2.0 was released in March 2000, with LEED Version 2.1 following in 2002 and LEED Version 2.2 following in 2005.

As LEED has evolved and matured, the program has undertaken new initiatives. In addition to a rating system specifically devoted to building operational and maintenance issues (LEED for Existing Buildings: Operations & Maintenance), LEED addresses the different project development and delivery processes that exist in the U.S. building design and construction market, through rating systems for specific building typologies, sectors, and project scopes: LEED for Core & Shell, LEED for New Construction, LEED for Schools, LEED for Neighborhood Development, LEED for Retail, LEED for Healthcare, LEED for Homes, and LEED for Commercial Interiors.

Project teams interact with the Green Building Certification Institute (GBCI) for project registration and certification. GBCI was established in 2008 as a separately incorporated entity with the support of the U.S. Green Building Council. GBCI administers credentialing and certification programs related to green building practice. These programs support the application of proven strategies for increasing and measuring the performance of buildings and communities as defined by industry systems such as LEED.

The green building field is growing and changing daily. New technologies and products are being introduced into the marketplace, and innovative designs and practices are proving their effectiveness. The LEED rating systems and reference guides will evolve as well. Project teams must comply with the version of the rating system that is current at the time of their registration.

USGBC will highlight new developments on its website on a continual basis at www.usgbc.org.

Features of LEED®

The LEED Green Building Rating Systems are voluntary, consensus-based, and market-driven. Based on existing and proven technology, they evaluate environmental performance from a whole-building perspective over a building's life cycle, providing a definitive standard for what constitutes a green building in design, construction, and operation.

The LEED rating systems are designed for rating new and existing commercial, institutional, and residential buildings. They are based on accepted energy and environmental principles and strike a balance between known, established practices and emerging concepts. Each rating system is organized into 5 environmental categories: Sustainable Sites, Water Efficiency, Energy and Atmosphere, Materials and Resources, and Indoor Environmental Quality. An additional category, Innovation in Design, addresses sustainable building expertise as well as design measures not covered under the 5 environmental categories. Regional bonus points are another feature of LEED and acknowledge the importance of local conditions in determining best environmental design and construction practices.

The LEED Credit Weightings

In LEED 2009, the allocation of points between credits is based on the potential environmental impacts and human benefits of each credit with respect to a set of impact categories. The impacts are defined as the environmental or human effect of the design, construction, operation, and maintenance of the building, such as greenhouse gas emissions, fossil fuel use, toxins and carcinogens, air and water pollutants, indoor environmental conditions. A combination of approaches, including energy modeling, life-cycle assessment, and transportation analysis, is used to quantify each type of impact. The resulting allocation of points among credits is called credit weighting.

LEED 2009 uses the U.S. Environmental Protection Agency's TRACI[3] environmental impact categories as the basis for weighting each credit. TRACI was developed to assist with impact evaluation for life-cycle assessment, industrial ecology, process design, and pollution prevention.

LEED 2009 also takes into consideration the weightings developed by the National Institute of Standards and Technology (NIST); these compare impact categories with one another and assign a relative weight to each. Together, the 2 approaches provide a solid foundation for determining the point value of each credit in LEED 2009.

The LEED 2009 credit weightings process is based on the following parameters, which maintain consistency and usability across rating systems:

- All LEED credits are worth a minimum of 1 point.

- All LEED credits are positive, whole numbers; there are no fractions or negative values.

- All LEED credits receive a single, static weight in each rating system; there are no individualized scorecards based on project location.

- All LEED rating systems have 100 base points; Innovation in Design (or Operations) and Regional Priority credits provide opportunities for up to 10 bonus points.

Given the above criteria, the LEED 2009 credit weightings process involves 3 steps:

1. A reference building is used to estimate the environmental impacts in 13 categories associated with a typical building pursuing LEED certification.

2. The relative importance of building impacts in each category are set to reflect values based on the NIST weightings.[4]

3. Data that quantify building impacts on environmental and human health are used to assign points to individual credits.

Each credit is allocated points based on the relative importance of the building-related impacts that it addresses. The result is a weighted average that combines building impacts and the relative value of the impact categories. Credits that most directly address the most important impacts are given the greatest weight, subject to the system design parameters described above. Credit weights also reflect a decision by LEED to recognize the market implications of point allocation. The result is a significant change in allocation of points compared with previous LEED rating systems. Overall, the changes increase the relative emphasis on the reduction of energy consumption and greenhouse gas emissions associated with building systems, transportation, the embodied energy of water, the embodied energy of materials, and where applicable, solid waste.

The details of the weightings process vary slightly among individual rating systems. For example, LEED for Existing Buildings: O&M includes credits related to solid waste management but LEED for New Construction does not. This results in a difference in the portion of the environmental footprint addressed by each rating system and the relative allocation of points. The weightings process for each rating system is fully documented in a weightings workbook.

The credit weightings process will be reevaluated over time to incorporate changes in values ascribed to different building impacts and building types, based on both market reality and evolving scientific knowledge related to buildings. A complete explanation of the LEED credit weightings system is available on the USGBC website, at www.usgbc.org.

III. OVERVIEW AND PROCESS

The LEED Green Building Rating System for Commercial Interiors is a set of performance standards for certifying the design and construction of commercial or institutional buildings and high-rise residential buildings of all sizes, both public and private. The intent is to promote healthful, durable, affordable, and environmentally sound practices in tenant space design and construction.

Prerequisites and credits in the LEED Green Building Rating Systems address 7 topics:

- Sustainable Sites (SS)
- Water Efficiency (WE)
- Energy and Atmosphere (EA)
- Materials and Resources (MR)
- Indoor Environmental Quality (IEQ)
- Innovation in Design (ID)
- Regional Priority (RP)

LEED prerequisites and credits have identical structures; see Section X of this Introduction.

When to Use LEED for Commercial Interiors

LEED for Commercial Interiors is appropriate for interior spaces that are undergoing alteration work. Please see the Rating System Selection Policy, located in the LEED Resources and Tools section of www.usgbc.org/projecttools, for more information about choosing a rating system.

Multiple Buildings and On-Campus Projects

The 2010 LEED Application Guide for Multiple Buildings and On-Campus Building Projects (available at www.usgbc.org/campusguidance) provides guidance on applying the LEED rating systems to multiple-building and on-campus projects that are on a shared site under the control of a single entity; for example, a corporate or educational campus or government installation. The 2010 LEED Application Guide for Multiple Buildings and On-Campus Building Projects provides guidance for the certification of projects under the Design and Construction and Interior Design and Construction rating systems as well as the LEED for Existing Buildings: Operations & Maintenance rating system. The guidance does not create a new rating system. Users may follow this guidance and apply it to existing rating system requirements for projects on a campus.

Minimum Program Requirements

A project must adhere to LEED's Minimum Program Requirements (MPRs), or possess minimum characteristics in order to be eligible for certification under LEED 2009. These requirements define the categories of buildings that the LEED rating systems were designed to evaluate, and taken together serve three goals: (1) give clear guidance to customers, (2) protect the integrity of the LEED program, and (3) reduce challenges that occur during the LEED certification process. The MPRs will evolve over time in tandem with the LEED rating systems. In order to be eligible for certification under any LEED 2009 Rating System, projects must comply with each associated MPR. The MPRs can be found in the LEED 2009 Rating Systems. To view the MPRs and the MPR Supplemental Guidance, visit the LEED Resources and Tools section of www.usgbc.org/projecttools.

The Green Building Certification Institute (GBCI) reserves the right to revoke LEED certification from any LEED 2009 project upon gaining knowledge of non-compliance with any applicable MPRs. If such a circumstance occurs, no registration or certification fees paid to GBCI will be refunded.

NOTE: Exceptions to all the MPRs will be considered on a case-by-case basis for special circumstances. Direction on the nature of allowable exceptions is given in the Supplemental Guidance document.

Registration

Project teams interested in earning LEED for Commercial Interiors certification for their buildings must first register the project with GBCI. Projects can be registered on the GBCI website (www.gbci. org). The website also has information on registration costs for USGBC national members as well as nonmembers. Registration is an important step that establishes contact with GBCI and provides access to software tools, addenda, critical communications, and other essential information.

LEED Online

LEED Online is the primary resource for managing the LEED documentation process. From LEED Online, project teams can manage project details, complete documentation requirements for LEED credits and prerequisites, upload supporting files, submit applications for review, receive reviewer feedback, and ultimately earn LEED certification. LEED Online provides a common space where members of a project team can work together to document compliance with the LEED rating system. All project teams pursuing LEED certification are required to use LEED Online and its submittal documentation paths. LEED submittals are instrumental in demonstrating credit compliance because they contain all the documentation requirements for each LEED credit. Additionally, LEED Online contains embedded calculators and tables to ensure that the submittal package delivered to GBCI is complete and accurate.

LEED Online also features several support capabilities. It enables team members to view and submit credit interpretation requests, contact customer service, generate project-specific reports, and consult supplementary LEED resources, such as FAQs, tutorials, offline calculators, and sample documentation. Applicants with multiple projects will have access to reporting tools that use data from projects across their entire LEED portfolio. LEED certificates for successful projects are also issued through using LEED Online.

Credit Interpretation Requests and Rulings

In some cases, a LEED project team may encounter challenges when interpreting the requirements of a prerequisite or credit for their project, perhaps because the reference guide does not sufficiently address a specific issue or a conflict requires resolution. To address such issues, a credit interpretation ruling process has been established for each LEED rating system. See the GBCI website for more information, at www.gbci.org.

Credit interpretation requests must be submitted online. Provide a brief but clear description of the challenge encountered, refer to the prerequisite or credit information found in the rating system and reference guide, and emphasize the intent of the prerequisite or credit. If possible, the project team should offer potential solutions to the problem or a proposed interpretation. Follow the detailed instructions in LEED Online.

Communications related to credit interpretation requests will be in electronic format.

Review and Certification

To earn LEED for Commercial Interiors certification, the applicant project must satisfy all the prerequisites and credits worth the minimum number of points to warrant the desired project rating. Projects must comply with the version of the rating system that is current in LEED Online at the time of project registration.

Appeals

Appeals may be filed after the design phase review, the construction phase review, or the full application review. Please see the GBCI website for more information on appeals.

Fees

Information on certification fees can be found on the GBCI website. GBCI will acknowledge receipt of the application and proceed with application review when all project documentation and payments have been received and processed. Registration fees, appeal review fees, and any additional fees required to expedite LEED certification are not refundable.

Updates and Addenda

This is the first edition of the LEED Reference Guide for Green Building Interior Design and Construction, 2009. As LEED for Commercial Interiors continues to improve and evolve, updates and addenda will be made available. USGBC cannot be held liable for any criteria set forth herein that may not be applicable to later versions of LEED rating systems, and GBCI reserves the right to modify its policies from time to time. Updates and addenda will be accumulated between revisions and will be formally incorporated in major revisions. In the interim, between major revisions, USGBC may issue updates or addenda to clarify criteria.

Project teams are subject to Rating System addenda requirements based on registration date. It is strongly recommended that project teams adhere to the Reference Guide and Reference Guide addenda based on registration date. Rating System and Reference Guide addenda can be found on the USGBC's LEED Addenda website, www.usgbc.org/addenda.

Information Privacy and Policy Guidelines

For more information on the privacy policy of the U.S. Green Building Counil, Inc. (USGBC), refer to the Policies and Guidelines section of the USGBC website, at www.usgbc.org. With the support of its members, volunteers, and other stakeholders, USGBC is the developer of the LEED rating systems.

Green Building Certification Institute, Inc. (GBCI) implements the LEED rating systems and carries out credentialing programs relating to LEED. For more information on the privacy policy of GBCI including the privacy policy on documentation submitted through LEED Online, refer to the Policies and Guidelines section of the GBCI website, at www.gbci.org. Projects whose information should be treated as confidential may select this option during registration; project confidentiality status may be changed at any time through LEED Online. Please review the GBCI privacy policy for further details.

IV. LEED ONLINE DOCUMENTATION REQUIREMENTS

All LEED for Commercial Interiors certification applications must include the required LEED Online documentation: general documentation requirements, documentation requirements for all prerequisites, and documentation requirements for all pursued credits.

General Requirements

LEED certification application requires the submission of an overall project narrative with the completed LEED Online documentation requirements. The project narrative describes the applicant's organization, building, site, and team. This narrative helps the LEED review team understand the major elements of the project and building performance, and it also aids in highlighting projects in future communications efforts. General documentation also requires the basic details pertaining to project site conditions, construction scope and timeline, occupant and usage data, and project team identification. Project teams must address all the elements in the general documentation requirements, providing details and clarifications where appropriate, and they may include any optional elements that are helpful in describing the project.

Credit Substitution

The LEED 2009 rating systems do not allow credit substitution using another version. Currently registered LEED projects that want to use LEED 2009 credits need to switch to the new version in entirety. USGBC expects that most projects will find this switch feasible and advantageous.

Units of Measurement Guidance

In order to facilitate certification review by U.S.-based reviewers, it is necessary to submit pertinent aspects of review-related documentation in English and convert units to U.S. Standard (i.e. Imperial) units of measure, unless noted otherwise in the credit or prerequisite description. It is not necessary to translate every aspect of every construction document into English and imperial units, but only those necessary for evaluation of LEED criteria. The project team should be prepared to provide additional translation(s) if requested by the reviewer in their preliminary review comments.

V. CERTIFICATION APPLICATION

To earn LEED certification, the applicant project must satisfy all the prerequisites and qualify for a minimum number of points to attain the established project ratings as listed below. Having satisfied the basic prerequisites of the program, applicant projects are then rated according to their degree of compliance within the rating system.

After registration, the project design team should begin to collect information and perform calculations to satisfy the prerequisite and credit documentation requirements. Because documentation should be gathered throughout design and construction, it is helpful to designate a LEED team leader who will be responsible for managing its compilation.

LEED for Commercial Interiors provides the option of splitting a certification application into two phases, design and construction, in lieu of a combined design and construction review. Documentation for design phase credits, identified in LEED Online, can be submitted for review at the end of the design phase; the submittals for these credits can be fully evaluated based on documentation available during this phase of the project. For example, if a project site meets the requirements of LEED for Commercial Interiors SS Credit 3.1, Alternative Transportation—Public Transportation Access, the likelihood of credit achievement can be assessed prior to the completion of construction. The LEED credit itself, however, is not awarded at the design review stage.

Design Phase Review

Each project is allotted a design phase review that consists of a preliminary design phase review and a final design phase review. GBCI formally rules on the design phase application by designating each attempted credit as either anticipated or denied. Participating in a design phase review does not guarantee award of any credit and will not result in LEED certification. This process enables project teams to assess the likelihood of credit achievement and requires follow-through to ensure the design is executed in the construction phase according to design specifications.

Construction Phase Review

At the completion of construction, the project team submits all attempted credits for review, including any newly attempted design credits. If the project team has had a design phase review and any of the design phase anticipated credits have since changed, additional documentation must be submitted to substantiate continued compliance with credit requirements. Upon receipt of the full certification application and fee, a final review will be conducted. All applicant-verified design phase credits that were designated as anticipated and have not changed since the design phase review will be declared as awarded. All other credits will be designated as either awarded or denied.

Project teams should refer to LEED Online and the rating system scorecards to get information on credits that can be submitted for design phase review and credits that must be submitted for construction phase review.

LEED for Commercial Interiors certifications are awarded according to the following scale:

Certified	40–49 points
Silver	50–59 points
Gold	60–79 points
Platinum	80 points and above

GBCI recognizes buildings that achieve 1 of the rating levels with a formal letter of certification.

Design or Construction Phase Submittal

LEED-CI v2009:		
Credit		**D/C**
PIf1	Minimum Program Requirements	D
PIf2	Project Summary Details	D
PIf3	Occupant and Usage Data	D
PIf4	Schedule and Overview Documents	D
PIf5	Previously LEED Certified Details	D
SSc1	Site Selection	D
SSc2	Development Density and Community Connectivity	D
SSc3.1	Alternative Transportation—Public Transportation Access	D
SSc3.2	Alternative Transportation—Bicycle Storage and Changing Rooms	D
SSc3.3	Alternative Transportation—Parking Availability	D
WEp1	Water Use Reduction	D
WEc1	Water Use Reduction	D
EAp1	Fundamental Commissioning of Building Energy Systems	C
EAp2	Minimum Energy Performance	D
EAp3	Fundamental Refrigerant Management	D
EAc1.1	Optimize Energy Performance—Lighting Power	D
EAc1.2	Optimize Energy Performance—Lighting Controls	D
EAc1.3	Optimize Energy Performance—HVAC	D
EAc1.4	Optimize Energy Performance—Equipment and Appliances	D
EAc2	Enhanced Commissioning	C
EAc3	Meaurement and Verification	D
EAc4	Green Power	C
MRp1	Storage and Collection of Recyclables	D
MRc1.1	Tenant Space—Long-Term Commitment	D
MRc1.2	Building Reuse—Maintain Interior Nonstructural Components	C
MRc2	Construction Waste Management	C
MRc3.1	Materials Reuse	C
MRc3.2	Materials Reuse—Furniture and Furnishings	C
MRc4	Recycled Content	C

LEED-CI v2009:		
Credit		**D/C**
MRc5	Regional Materials	C
MRc6	Rapidly Renewable Materials	C
MRc7	Certified Wood	C
IEQp1	Minimum Indoor Air Quality Performance	D
IEQp2	Environmental Tobacco Smoke (ETS) Control	D
IEQc1	Outdoor Air Delivery Monitoring	D
IEQc2	Increased Ventilation	D
IEQc3.1	Construction Indoor Air Quality Management Plan-During Construction	C
IEQc3.2	Construction Indoor Air Quality Management Plan-Before Occupancy	C
IEQc4.1	Low-Emitting Materials—Adhesives and Sealants	C
IEQc4.2	Low-Emitting Materials—Paints and Coatings	C
IEQc4.3	Low-Emitting Materials—Flooring Systems	C
IEQc4.4	Low-Emitting Materials—Composite Wood and Agrifiber Products	C
IEQc4.5	Low-Emitting Materials—Systems Furniture and Seating	C
IEQc5	Indoor Chemical and Pollutant Source Control	D
IEQc6.1	Controllability of Systems—Lighting	D
IEQc6.2	Controllability of Systems—Thermal Control	D
IEQc7.1	Thermal Comfort—Design	D
IEQc7.2	Thermal Comfort—Verification	D
IEQc8.1	Daylight and Views—Daylight	D
IEQc8.2	Daylight and Views—Views for Seated Spaces	D
IDc1	Innovation in Design	D/C
IDc2	LEED® Accredited Professional	C

VI. CERTIFICATION STRATEGY

Timeline and Project Design Phases

Project teams should study the principles and objectives of LEED as early in the site selection and design process as possible. The project design phases mentioned throughout this reference guide correspond to the architectural design and planning steps commonly used in the construction industry:

1. **Predesign** entails gathering information, recognizing stakeholders' needs, and establishing project goals.

2. **Schematic design** explores several design options and alternatives, with the intent of establishing an agreed-upon project layout and scope of work.

3. **Design development** begins the process of spatial refinement and usually involves the first design of a project's energy systems.

4. **Construction documents** carry the design into the level of details for all spaces and systems and materials so that construction can take place.

5. **Construction.**

6. **Substantial completion** is a contractual benchmark that usually corresponds to the point at which a client could occupy a nearly completed space.

7. **Final completion.**

8. **Certificate of occupancy** is the official recognition by a local building department that a building conforms to applicable building and safety codes.

Related Credits

When pursuing LEED certification, it is important to consider how credits are interconnected and how their synergies and trade-offs will ultimately affect both the project and the other credits the team may consider pursuing. Consult the Related Credits section of each prerequisite and credit to help inform design and construction decisions leading to certification.

Consistent Documentation across Credits

Several kinds of project information are required for consistent LEED documentation across various credits. If the number of full-time employees (FTEs) is used in one credit, it should be used consistently throughout all credits. LEED Online contains many features specifically designed to assist project teams with this process. Pay special attention to overlapping project data; doing so will help the application and review process go smoothly.

Operations and Maintenance in LEED for Commercial Interiors

The LEED Reference Guide for Green Building Interior Design and Construction contains information on operations and maintenance to help project teams streamline green O&M practices once the LEED design and construction project has been completed. Although not required as part of the LEED certification process, upfront planning for green operations and maintenance can help building owners, operators, and maintenance staff ensure that the commercial interiors space continues to operate in a sustainable manner.

VII. EXEMPLARY PERFORMANCE STRATEGIES

Exemplary performance strategies result in performance that greatly exceeds the performance level or expands the scope required by an existing LEED for Commercial Interiors credit. To earn exemplary performance credits, teams must meet the performance level defined by the next step in the threshold progression. For credits with more than 1 compliance path, an Innovation in Design point can be earned by satisfying more than 1 compliance path if their benefits are additive. See the Innovation in Design credit section for further details.

The credits for which exemplary performance points are available through expanded performance are noted throughout this reference guide and in LEED Online by the logo shown below.

The list for exemplary performance points available is as follows:

Sustainable Sites

SS Credit 1	Site Selection
SS Credit 2	Development Density and Community Connectivity
SS Credit 3	Alternative Transportation

Water Efficiency

WE Credit 1	Water Use Reduction

Energy and Atmosphere

EA Credit 1	Optimize Energy Performance
EA Credit 4	Green Power

Materials and Resources

MR Credit 1.2	Building Reuse—Maintain Interior Nonstructural Components
MR Credit 2	Construction Waste Management
MR Credit 3	Materials Reuse
MR Credit 4	Recycled Content
MR Credit 5	Regional Materials
MR Credit 6	Rapidly Renewable Materials
MR Credit 7	Certified Wood

Indoor Environmental Quality

IEQ Credit 8.2	Daylight and Views—Views for Seated Spaces

VIII. REGIONAL PRIORITY

To provide incentive to address geographically specific environmental issues, USGBC regional councils and chapters have identified 6 credits per rating system that are of particular importance to specific areas. Each Regional Priority credit is worth an additional 1 point, and a total of 4 additional points may be earned by achieving Regional Priority credits, with 1 point earned per credit. Upon project registration, LEED Online automatically determines a project's Regional Priority credits based on its zip code. If the project achieves more than 4 Regional Priority credits, the team can choose the credits for which these points will apply. The USGBC website also contains a searchable database of Regional Priority credits.

IX. TOOLS FOR REGISTERED PROJECTS

LEED offers additional resources for LEED project teams on the USGBC website, at www.usgbc. org/projecttools. The Registered Projects Tools website provides resources for starting the project, including rating system addenda, documentation requirements, and referenced industry standards. Also consult the website for the following:

Declarant definitions and other definitions. This resource describes the team members who are required to sign off on certain documentation requirements and indicates the prerequisites and credits for which each team member is responsible. The required declarant is noted in the corresponding credit documentation section of LEED Online.

Licensed Professional Exemption Form. Licensed Professional Exemptions (LPEs) can be used by a project team's registered professional engineer, registered architect, registered interior designer, or registered landscape architect as a streamlined path for documenting certain credits, or bypassing otherwise-required submittals. License information and an Exemption Signature in LEED Online are required to document each exemption the project team wishes to claim. Licensed Professional Exemptions are noted in the corresponding credit documentation section of LEED Online.

X. HOW TO USE THIS REFERENCE GUIDE

The LEED Reference Guide for Green Building Interior Design and Construction is a supporting document to the LEED for Commercial Interiors Rating System. The guide helps project teams understand the criteria, the reasons behind them, strategies for implementation, and documentation requirements. It includes examples of strategies that can be used in each category and additional resources. It does not provide an exhaustive list of strategies for meeting the criteria or all the information that a project team needs to determine the applicability of a credit to the project.

Rating System Pages

The rating system, published in its entirety on the USGBC website, is imbedded in this reference guide. Each prerequisite and credit discussion begins with a gray page that mirrors the rating systems' Intent and Requirements. This Reference guide addresses the Intents and Requirements for the LEED 2009 Commercial Interiors Rating System. The Potential Technologies and Strategies included in the rating systems are not explicitly called out in the reference guide, refer to the published rating systems as desired.

Prerequisite and Credit Format

Each prerequisite or credit is organized in a standardized format for simplicity and quick reference. The first section summarizes the main points regarding the green measure and includes the intent, requirements, required submittals for certification, and a summary of any referenced industry standard. Subsequent sections provide supporting information to help interpret the measure and offer links to resources and examples. The sections for each credit are described in the following paragraphs.

Intent identifies the main sustainability goal or benefit of the prerequisite or credit.

Requirements specifies the criteria that satisfy the prerequisite or credit and the number of points available. The prerequisites must be achieved; the credits are optional, but each contributes to the overall project score. Some credits have 2 or more paths with cumulative points. Other credits have several options from which the project team must choose. For example, Energy & Atmosphere Credit 1, Optimize Energy Efficiency Performance, has 3 options, but a project can apply for only 1, depending on the type of building.

Benefits and Issues to Consider addresses the environmental benefits of the activity encouraged by the prerequisite or credit, and economic considerations related to first costs, life-cycle costs, and estimated savings.

Related Credits acknowledges the trade-offs and synergies within the LEED rating system credit categories. Achieving a particular credit may make it worthwhile and comparatively easy to pursue related credits; the converse is also possible.

The **Summary of Referenced Standards**, where applicable, introduces the required standards used to measure achievement of the credit intent. Teams are strongly encouraged to review the full standard and not rely on the summary.

Implementation discusses specific methods or assemblies that facilitate achievement of the requirements.

Timeline and Team guides the project team by identifying who should lead an effort and when the tasks should begin.

Calculations offers sample formulas or computations that determine achievement of a particular prerequisite or credit. Most calculations are facilitated in LEED Online.

The **Documentation Guidance** section provides the first steps in preparing to complete the LEED Online documentation requirements.

Examples illustrates strategies for credit achievement.

Exemplary Performance, if applicable, details the level of performance needed for the award of points in addition to those for credit achievement.

Regional Variations outlines concerns specific to the geographic location of the building.

Resources offers suggestions for further research and provide examples or illustrations, detailed technical information, or other information relevant to the prerequisite or credit. The resources include websites, online materials, and printed books and articles that can be obtained directly from the organizations listed.

Definitions clarifies the meaning of certain terms relevant to the prerequisite or credit. These may be general terms or terms specific to LEED for Commercial Interiors. A complete glossary is found at the end of this reference guide.

Endnotes

[1] Energy Information Administration. "Emissions of Greenhouse Gas Report." Report #DOE/EIA-0573(2006). Released 28 November 2007. http://www.eia.doe.gov/oiaf/1605/ggrpt/carbon.html#commercial

[2] Office of the Federal Environmental Executive. http://ofee.gov/wpr/wastestream.asp Last modified 24 April 2008.

[3] Tools for the Reduction and Assessment of Chemical and Other Environmental Impacts (TRACI). U.S. Environmental Protection Agency, Office of Research and Development. http://www.epa.gov/nrmrl/std/sab/traci/.

[4] Relative impact category weights based on an exercise undertaken by NIST (National Institute of Standards and Technology) for the BEES program. http://www.bfrl.nist.gov/oae/software/bees/.

Overview

The selection of a building site and its development in accordance with sustainable building practices are of fundamental importance. Environmental damage to a site, either during or as a result of construction, can take years to remedy.

This credit section addresses environmental concerns relating to building landscape, hardscape, and exterior building issues and promotes the following measures:

Selecting a Building That Has Developed Its Site Wisely

Buildings affect ecosystems in a variety of ways. Development of greenfields, or previously undeveloped sites, consumes land. Development projects can also encroach on agricultural lands and wetlands or water bodies and compromise wildlife habitats. Choosing a building on a previously developed site or even a damaged site that can be remediated reduces pressure on undeveloped land.

Selecting a Building with Sustainable Landscapes

Conventional planting and landscape maintenance often require irrigation and chemicals. Sustainable practices minimize the use of irrigation, fertilizers, and pesticides and can prevent soil erosion and sedimentation. Erosion from precipitation and wind causes degradation of property as well as sedimentation of local water bodies, and building sites can be major sources of sediment. Loss of nutrients, soil compaction, and decreased biodiversity of soil organisms can severely limit the vitality of landscaping. Sedimentation increases turbidity levels, which degrades aquatic habitats, and the buildup of sediments in stream channels can lessen flow capacity, increasing the possibility of flooding. Sustainable landscaping involves using or restoring native and adapted plants, which require less irrigation and maintenance and fewer or no applications of chemical fertilizers and pesticides compared with most introduced species.

Selecting a Building That Protects Surrounding Habitats

Commercial building sites can encroach on agricultural lands and/or adversely affect wildlife habitat. As animals are displaced by development, they become crowded into increasingly smaller spaces, and eventually the population exceeds the carrying capacity of the area. Overall biodiversity, as well as individual plant and animal species, may be threatened. Restoring native and adapted vegetation and other ecological features to the site provides wildlife habitat.

Selecting a Building That Manages Stormwater Runoff

As areas developed and urbanized, surface permeability is reduced, which in turn increases the runoff transported via pipes and sewers to streams, rivers, lakes, bays, and oceans. Stormwater runoff harms water quality, aquatic life, and recreation opportunities in receiving waters. For instance, parking areas contribute to stormwater runoff that is contaminated with oil, fuel, lubricants, combustion by-products, material from tire wear, and deicing salts. Runoff also accelerates the flow rate of waterways, causing erosion downstream and altering aquatic habitat. Effective strategies exist to control, reduce, and treat stormwater runoff before it leaves the project site.

Selecting a Building That Reduces Heat Island Effects

The use of dark, nonreflective surfaces for parking areas, roofs, walkways, and other surfaces contributes to the heat island effect. These surfaces absorb incoming solar radiation and radiate that heat back to the surrounding areas, increasing the ambient temperature. In addition to being detrimental to site habitat, this increase raises a building's external and internal temperatures, requiring more energy for cooling. The Lawrence Berkeley National Laboratory estimates that 1/6 of the electricity consumed in the United States is used to cool buildings. By installing reflective surfaces and vegetation, the nation's homes and businesses could save $4 billion a year in reduced cooling energy demand by 2015.[1]

Selecting a Building That Reduces Light Pollution

Poorly designed exterior lighting may exacerbate nighttime light pollution, which can interfere with nocturnal ecology, reduce observation of night skies, cause roadway glare, and hurt relationships with neighbors by causing light trespass. Reducing light pollution encourages nocturnal wildlife to inhabit the building site and causes less disruption to birds' migratory patterns. Thoughtful exterior lighting may also reduce infrastructure costs and energy use over the life of the building.

Selecting a Building with Water-Efficient Landscaping

Landscape irrigation in the United States consumes large quantities of potable water. Outdoor uses, primarily landscaping, account for 30% of the 26 billion gallons of water consumed daily.[2] Improved landscaping practices can dramatically reduce and even eliminate irrigation needs. Maintaining or reestablishing native plants on building sites fosters a self-sustaining landscape that requires minimal supplemental water and has other environmental benefits.

Landscaping with native plants can reduce the amount of water needed for irrigation and attract native wildlife, creating a building site integrated with its natural surroundings. In addition, native plants tend to require less fertilizer and pesticides, which minimizes the degradation of water quality and other negative environmental impacts.

Selecting a Building That Uses On-site Renewable Energy

Energy generation from renewable sources, such as solar, wind, and biomass, avoids air and water pollution and other environmental impacts associated with producing and using coal, nuclear energy, oil, and natural gas. Although hydropower is considered renewable, it can have harmful environmental effects, such as degrading water quality, altering fish and bird habitat, and endangering species. Low-impact hydropower, if available, is recommended.

Renewable energy minimizes acid rain, smog, climate change, and human health problems from air contaminants. In addition, using renewable resources avoids the consumption of fossil fuels, the production of nuclear waste, and the operation of environmentally damaging hydropower dams.

Selecting a Building That Reduces Potable Water Consumption

Reducing indoor potable water consumption may require using alternative water sources for nonpotable applications and installing water-efficient fixtures, flow restrictors, electronic controls, composting toilet systems, and waterless urinals. Lowering potable water use in fixtures can reduce the total amount of water drawn from natural bodies of water. A commercial building in Boston replaced 126 3.5-gallons-per-flush (gpf) toilets with low-flow 1.6-gpf toilets and reduced total water consumption by 15%. With an initial cost of $32,000 and estimated annual savings of $22,800, the payback period was 1.4 years. Another Boston building installed 30 faucet aerators and reduced annual indoor water consumption by 190,000 gallons. The cost of the equipment and labor totaled $300 and is estimated to save $1,250 per year, with a payback period of 2 months.[3]

Selecting a Building That Helps Reduce Emissions Associated with Transportation

Environmental concerns related to buildings include vehicle emissions and the need for vehicle infrastructure as building occupants travel to and from the site. Emissions contribute to climate change, smog, acid rain, and other air quality problems. Parking lots, roadways, and building surfaces increase stormwater runoff and contribute to the urban heat island effect. In 2006, 76% of commuters in America ages 16 and older drove to work alone. Of the remaining 24% who used alternative means of transportation (including working from home), only 5% used public transportation and 11% carpooled.[4] Locating the project near residential areas and providing bicycle racks, changing facilities, preferred parking, access to mass transit, and alternative-fuel refueling stations can all encourage the adoption of alternative forms of transportation. Use of mass transit reduces the energy demand for transportation as well as the space needed for parking lots, which encroach on green space and contribute to the heat island effect.

Summary

The LEED for Commercial Interiors SS credits promote responsible, innovative, and practical site designs that are sensitive to plants, wildlife, water, and air quality and that mitigate some of the negative effects buildings have on the local and regional environment. Project teams selecting sites and undertaking building projects should be cognizant of the impact of development on land consumption, ecosystems, natural resources, and energy use. Preference should be given to buildings with high-performance attributes in locations that enhance existing neighborhoods and make use of existing transportation networks and urban infrastructures. LEED encourages the selection of sites and land-use plans that preserve natural ecosystems and enhance the health of the surrounding community.

CREDIT	TITLE
SS Credit 1	Site Selection
SS Credit 2	Development Density and Community Connectivity
SS Credit 3.1	Alternative Transportation—Public Transportation Access
SS Credit 3.2	Alternative Transportation—Bicycle Storage and Changing Rooms
SS Credit 3.3	Alternative Transportation—Parking Availability

LEED REFERENCE GUIDE FOR GREEN INTERIOR DESIGN AND CONSTRUCTION 2009 EDITION

SITE SELECTION

	CI
Credit	SS Credit 1
Points	1-5 points

Intent

To encourage tenants to select buildings that employ best practices systems and green strategies.

Requirements

OPTION 1

Select a LEED certified building (5 points).

OR

OPTION 2

Locate the tenant space in a building that has in place 1 or more of the following characteristics at time of submittal (1–5 points). Each of the following options may also be met by satisfying the requirements of the corresponding LEED 2009 for New Construction credit.

PATH 1. Brownfield Redevelopment (1 point)

A building developed on a site documented as contaminated (by an ASTM E1903-97 Phase II Environmental Site Assessment or a local voluntary cleanup program) OR

A building on a site classified as a brownfield by a local, state or federal government agency.

Effective remediation of site contamination must have been completed.

PATH 2. Stormwater Design—Quantity Control (1 point)

A building that prior to its development had less than or equal to 50% imperviousness and has implemented a stormwater management plan that is equal to or is less than the predevelopment 1/2 year 24-hour rate and quantity discharge.

OR

A building that prior to its development had more than 50% imperviousness and has implemented a stormwater management plan that reduced predevelopment 1 1/2 year 24-hour rate and quantity discharge by 25% of the annual on-site stormwater load. This mitigation can be achieved through a variety of measures such as perviousness of site, stormwater retention ponds, and harvesting of rainwater for reuse.

Stormwater values are based on actual local rainfall unless the actual exceeds the 10-year annual average local rainfall, in which case the 10-year annual average should be used.

PATH 3. Stormwater Design—Quality Control (1 point)

A building that has in place site stormwater treatment systems designed to remove at least 80% of the average annual site area's total suspended solids (TSS) and 40% of the average annual site area's total phosphorus (TP).

These values are based on the average annual loadings from all storms less than or equal to the 2-year 24-hour storm. The building must implement and maintain best management practices (BMPs) outlined in Chapter 4, Part 2 Urban Runoff, of the EPA Guidance Specifying Management Measures for Sources of Nonpoint Pollution in Coastal Waters, January 1993 (EPA 840B92002) or the local government's BMP document, whichever is more stringent.

PATH 4. Heat Island Effect—NonRoof (1 point)

A building that provides shade (or will provide shade within 5 years of landscape installation); and/ or uses light-colored or high-albedo materials with a solar reflectance index (SRI)[1] of at least 29; and/ or has open-grid pavement areas that individually or in total equals at least 30% of the site's nonroof impervious surfaces, such as parking areas, walkways, plazas, and fire lanes.

OR

A building that has placed a minimum of 50% of parking spaces underground or covered by structured parking.

OR

A building that has an open-grid pavement system (less than 50% impervious) for 50% of the parking lot area.

PATH 5. Heat Island Effect—Roof (1 point)

A building whose roofing has a solar reflectance index (SRI) of the following minimum values for at least 75% of the roof surface;

Roof Type	Slope	SRI
Low-sloped roof	≤ 2:12	78
Steep-sloped roof	> 2:12	29

OR

A building that has installed a vegetated roof for at least 50% of the roof area.

OR

A building that has both high SRI roofs and vegetated roofs that satisfy the following area requirement:

$$\text{Total Roof Area} \leq \left[\left(\text{Area of SRI Roof} \times 1.33 \right) + \left(\text{Area of Vegetated Roof} \times 2 \right) \right]$$

[1] The solar reflectance index (SRI) is a measure of the constructed surface's ability to reflect solar heat, as shown by a small temperature rise. It is defined so that a standard black surface (reflectance 0.05, emittance 0.90) is 0 and a standard white surface (reflectance 0.80, emittance 0.90) is 100. To calculate the SRI for a given material, obtain the reflectance value and emittance value for the material. SRI is calculated according to ASTM E 1980. Reflectance is measured according to ASTM E 903, ASTM E 1918 or ASTM C 1549. Emittance is measured according to ASTM E 408 or ASTM C 1371.

PATH 6. Light Pollution Reduction (1 point)

A building whose nonemergency interior luminaires with a direct line of sight to any openings in the envelope (translucent or transparent) must have their input power reduced (by automatic device) by at least 50% between 11 p.m. and 5 a.m. After-hours override may be provided by a manual or occupant-sensing device provided the override lasts no more than 30 minutes.

OR

A building whose openings in the envelope (translucent or transparent) with a direct line of sight to any nonemergency luminaires must have shielding (with transmittance of less than 10%) that is controlled or closed by automatic device between 11 p.m. and 5 a.m.

PATH 7. Water Efficient Landscaping—Reduce by 50% (2 points)

A building that employs high-efficiency irrigation technology OR uses harvested rainwater or recycled site water to reduce potable water consumption for irrigation by at least 50% over conventional means.

PATH 8. Water Efficient Landscaping—No Potable Water Use or No Irrigation (2 points in addition to Path 7)

A building that uses only harvested rainwater or recycled site water to eliminate all potable water use for site irrigation (except for initial watering to establish plants), OR does not have permanent landscaping irrigation systems.

PATH 9. Innovative Wastewater Technologies (2 points)

A building that reduces the use of municipally provided potable water for building sewage conveyance by at least 50%, OR treats 100% of wastewater on-site to tertiary standards.

PATH 10. Water Use Reduction—30% Reduction (1 point)

A building that meets the 30% reduction in water use requirement for the entire building and has an ongoing plan to require future occupants to comply.

PATH 11. On-site Renewable Energy (1-2 points)

A building that supplies at least 2.5% (1 point) or 5% (2 points) of the building's total energy use (expressed as a fraction of annual energy cost) from on-site renewable energy systems.

PATH 12. Other Quantifiable Environmental Performance (1 point)

A building that has in place at the time of selection other quantifiable environmental benefits.

OPTION 1: SELECT LEED-CERTIFIED BUILDING

1. Benefits and Issues to Consider

Environmental Issues

The built environment has a tremendous impact on our natural resources and the health of our communities. In 2006, the U.S. Department of Energy reported that U.S. buildings accounted for 72.4% of electricity consumption.[5] According to the Energy Information Administration, in 2008, buildings in the United States were responsible for 38% of all CO_2 emissions.[6] In 2000, the U.S. Geological Survey reported that the nation's buildings used 13.6% of all potable water, or 15 trillion gallons per year.[7]

Certification of a building under LEED for New Construction, LEED for Schools, LEED for Core & Shell, or LEED for Existing Buildings Operations & Maintenance signifies that building owners have already taken significant steps to protect ecosystems and biodiversity, conserve valuable resources, and provide healthful indoor environments for building occupants.

Economic Issues

The commercial real estate industry has begun to document the increased market appeal of space in LEED-certified buildings, based on recognition that LEED-certified base buildings deliver many economic benefits to tenants, such as reduced operating costs and improved productivity of building occupants. Cost analyses can project and weigh the impact of these reductions on the possibly higher lease values of such buildings.

2. Related Credits

Selecting a LEED-certified base building will link the LEED for Commercial Interiors project to the credits the base building earned under its original certification. Such projects are likely to be well situated to earn credits under the LEED for Commercial Interiors Rating System.

3. Summary of Referenced Standards

There are no standards referenced for this credit.

4. Implementation

Select tenant space in an existing LEED-certified building. If possible, obtain the base building LEED certification review documents early in the project development phase. The certification documents from the base building can serve as a resource for identifying credits and base building systems and will make it much easier to earn certain LEED for Commercial Interiors credits.

Establishing project goals that maximize use of base building systems early on is crucial. Clearly communicate to real estate and leasing agents that space in a LEED-certified building is a priority. Consult the USGBC website for a list of completed LEED-certified projects. Local USGBC chapters can also serve as valuable resources for identifying leasable space in LEED-certified buildings and for finding buildings currently seeking LEED certification.

5. Timeline and Team

During the building selection process, work with real estate brokers and leasing agents to identify LEED-certified buildings with tenant space. The building owner or manager should supply a copy of the final LEED scorecard.

6. Calculations

There are no calculations required for this credit.

7. Documentation Guidance

As a first step in preparing to complete the LEED Online documentation requirements, work through the following measure. Refer to LEED Online for the complete descriptions of all required documentation.

- Assemble information about the base building's LEED certification from the building owner or manager.

8. Examples

There are no examples for this credit.

9. Exemplary Performance

This option is not eligible for exemplary performance under the Innovation in Design section.

10. Regional Variations

There are no regional variations associated with this credit.

11. Operations and Maintenance Considerations

There are no operations and maintenance considerations for this credit.

12. Resources

Please see the USGBC website, at http://www.usgbc.org, for a database of LEED-registered and certified buildings and a list of regional USGBC chapters.

13. Definitions

Tenant space is the area within the LEED project boundary. For more information on what can and must be in the LEED project boundary see the Minimum Program Requirements (MPRs) and LEED 2009 MPR Supplemental Guidance. Note: tenant space is the same as project space.

OPTION 2, PATH 1: BROWNFIELD REDEVELOPMENT

1. Benefits and Issues to Consider

Environmental Issues

The EPA estimates that there are more than 450,000 brownfields in the United States.[8] Buildings located on brownfield sites have undergone remediation efforts to remove or stabilize hazardous materials from the sites' soil and groundwater, reducing the exposure of humans and wildlife to health risks associated with environmental pollution. Brownfield redevelopment can contribute to social and economic revitalization of depressed or disadvantaged neighborhoods, and can renew and augment a sense of community pride in local residents.

Economic Issues

Investors who develop brownfield sites often take advantage of government grants, tax incentives, existing infrastructure, and ready availability of labor. These cost savings may be reflected in lower lease rates for these properties. Additionally, because many brownfield sites are in or near urban areas, they are well served by existing transportation networks and other infrastructure.

2. Related Credits

There are no related credits.

3. Summary of Referenced Standards

U.S. EPA Definition of Brownfields
The EPA Sustainable Redevelopment of Brownfields Program
http://www.epa.gov/brownfields
With certain legal exclusions and additions, brownfield site means real property, the expansion, redevelopment, or reuse of which may be complicated by the presence or potential presence of a hazardous substance, pollutant, or contaminant (Public Law 107-118, H.R. 2869, Small Business Liability Relief and Brownfields Revitalization Act). See the EPA website for additional information and resources.

ASTM E1903-97, Phase II Environmental Site Assessment, effective 2002
ASTM International
http://www.astm.org
A Phase II environmental site assessment is an investigation that collects original samples of soil, groundwater, or building materials to analyze for quantitative values of various contaminants. This investigation is normally undertaken when a Phase I assessment has determined a potential for site contamination. The substances most frequently tested are petroleum hydrocarbons, heavy metals, pesticides, solvents, asbestos, and mold.

4. Implementation

Select a base building that was constructed on a site formerly classified as a brownfield. Former brownfield sites and remediation activities may be catalogued by the federal, state, or local authorities. Projects where asbestos is found and remediated may also earn this credit. Testing should be done in accordance with EPA Reg 40CFR part 763, when applicable.

5. Timeline and Team

The project team should make the selection of a base building constructed on a remediated brownfield a requirement of its selection process. Work with real estate brokers and leasing agents to identify buildings that meet the requirements.

6. Calculations

There are no calculations required for this credit.

7. Documentation Guidance

As a first step in preparing to complete the LEED Online documentation requirements, work through the following measure. Refer to LEED Online for the complete descriptions of all required documentation.

- Assemble information about the previous site contamination and remediation efforts undertaken.

- For projects where asbestos is found, prepare executive summary-level content from the investigation's report explaining the extent of the contamination and required action as well as documentation indicating an acceptable level of remediation was achieved based on an acceptable standard, such as RCRA or NESHAPs.

8. Examples

There are no examples for this credit.

9. Exemplary Performance

This path is not eligible for exemplary performance under SS Credit 1 Path 12 Other Quantifiable Environmental Performance.

10. Regional Variations

Preliminary screening levels or remediation criteria may differ by state or region.

11. Operations and Maintenance Considerations

Some remediation efforts may require ongoing activities. The project team and owner should keep careful records of remediation activities and develop a plan for ongoing compliance with monitoring and reporting requirements as defined by the relevant federal, state or local regulatory agency.

12. Resources

Please see USGBC's LEED Resources & Tools (www.usgbc.org/projecttools) for additional resources and technical information.

Websites

U.S. EPA, Asbestos

http://www.epa.gov/asbestos/index.html

This website provides information on the health effets of asbestos, where it is commonly found, and the laws and regulations governing testing of sites containing asbestos.

U.S. EPA, Preliminary Remediation Goals for EPA Region 9

http://www.epa.gov/region09/waste/sfund/prg/files/04prgtable.pdf

Preliminary remediation goals are tools for evaluating and cleaning up contaminated sites. They are intended to help risk assessors and others perform initial screening-level evaluations of environmental measurement results. The remediation goals for Region 9 are generic; they are calculated without site-specific information. However, they may be recalculated using site-specific data.

U.S. EPA, Sustainable Redevelopment of Brownfields

http://www.epa.gov/brownfields

This is a comprehensive website on brownfields that includes projects, initiatives, tools, tax incentives and other resources to address brownfield remediation and redevelopment. For information by phone, contact the regional EPA office.

13. Definitions

A **brownfield** is real property whose use may be complicated by the presence or possible presence of a hazardous substance, pollutant, or contaminant.

Remediation is the process of cleaning up a contaminated site by physical, chemical, or biological means. Remediation processes are typically applied to contaminated soil and groundwater.

A **site assessment** is an evaluation of a site's aboveground and subsurface characteristics, including its structures, geology, and hydrology. Site assessments are typically used to determine whether contamination has occurred, as well as the extent and concentration of any release of pollutants. Information generated during a site assessment is used to make remedial action decisions.

OPTION 2, PATH 2: STORMWATER DESIGN—QUANTITY CONTROL

1. Benefits and Issues to Consider

Environmental Issues

Stormwater is a major source of pollution for all types of water bodies in the United States.[9] Soil compaction caused by site development and the expanse of impervious surfaces, such as roads and parking lots, produce stormwater runoff that contains sediment and other contaminants, including atmospheric deposition, pesticides, fertilizers, vehicle fluid leaks, and mechanical equipment waste. Increased stormwater runoff can overload pipes and sewers and damage water quality, affecting navigation and recreation. Furthermore, municipal systems that convey and treat runoff require significant infrastructure improvements and maintenance.

The health of streams is closely linked to stormwater runoff velocities and volumes. Increases in the frequency and magnitude of stormwater runoff due to development can increase bankfull events and erosion, widen channels, and cause downcutting in streams. Effective on-site management practices let stormwater infiltrate the ground, thereby reducing the volume and intensity of stormwater flows.[10] Additionally, reducing stormwater runoff helps maintain the natural aquifer recharge cycle and restore depleted stream base flows. By selecting a building that has met the requirements of SS Credit 1, Option 2, Path 2, the project team is recognizing the importance of reducing stormwater runoff and the associated environmental benefits.

2. Related Credits

A building's efforts to reduce the rate and quantity of stormwater runoff may involve the use of pervious pavements, native or adapted vegetation, and increased on-site infiltration strategies, assisting projects with earning the following credits:

- SS Credit 1, Option 2, Path 3: Stormwater Management—Quality Control

- SS Credit 1, Option 2, Path 4: Heat Island Reduction—Nonroof

Efforts to capture and reuse rainwater for irrigation or in nonpotable applications inside the building, such as toilets and urinals, can help projects earn the following credits:

- SS Credit 1, Option 2, Path 7: Water-Efficient Landscaping—Reduce by 50%

- SS Credit 1, Option 2, Path 8: Water-Efficient Landscaping—No Potable Water Use or No Irrigation

- SS Credit 1, Option 2, Path 10: Water Use Reduction—30% Reduction

3. Summary of Referenced Standards

There are no standards referenced for this credit.

4. Implementation

Identify a space in a building that has implemented 1 of the 2 compliance paths or that can meet equivalent performance requirements. Include this requirement in the criteria for selecting a base building. Local permitting agencies may have detailed information on the stormwater control techniques implemented or in use at the base building. Check the application for the building's stormwater management permit for this information.

5. Timeline and Team

Because tenants may not be able to influence the base building and site infrastructure design, LEED for Commercial Interiors projects may require a different approach than LEED for New Construction or Core & Shell projects. Work with building owners or facility managers to first assess the base building for compliance with the LEED requirements. Since many local jurisdictions have comparable requirements, part of this process may include consulting with local permitting officials to determine whether the local stormwater requirements at the time of the base building construction were adequately stringent to meet this credit. If the existing system does not meet the credit requirements, investigate opportunities to modify the site design. This may include modification of existing stormwater management systems and replacing site hardscapes with vegetated areas that decrease site runoff.

6. Calculations

The following calculation illustrates one method that can be used to support the credit submittals. Stormwater runoff volumes are affected by surface characteristics on the site as well as rainfall intensity over a specified time period. Stormwater volumes generated are directly related to the net imperviousness of the project site. By reducing the amount of impervious surface on the site, stormwater volumes are reduced. Estimate the imperviousness of the project site as follows:

1. Identify the different surface types on the site: roof, pavement (e.g., roads and sidewalks), landscaping, and other areas.

2. Determine the total area for each of these surface types using site drawings. Use Table 1 to assign a runoff coefficient to each surface type. If a surface type is not included in the table, use a "best estimate" or manufacturer information. For instance, if pervious paving is used, consult the manufacturer to determine the imperviousness (the percentage of the surface that does not allow infiltration).

3. Summarize the area and runoff coefficient for each surface type on a spreadsheet. Multiply the runoff coefficient by the area to obtain an impervious area for each surface type. This figure represents the square footage of each surface area that is 100% impervious (Equation 1).

4. Add the impervious areas for each surface type to obtain a total impervious area for the site.

5. Divide the total impervious area by the total site area to obtain the imperviousness of the site (Equation 2). For sites with 50% imperviousness or less, imperviousness discharge must not increase from predevelopment to postdevelopment conditions. For previously developed sites with imperviousness greater than 50%, imperviousness discharge must be reduced by 25% from predevelopment to postdevelopment conditions.

Table 1. Typical Runoff Coeffiicient

Surface Type	Runoff Coefficient	Surface Type	Runoff Coefficient
Pavement, Asphalt	0.95	Turf, Flat (0 - 1% slope)	0.25
Pavement, Concrete	0.95	Turf, Average (1 - 3% slope)	0.35
Pavement, Brick	0.85	Turf, Hilly (3 - 10% slope)	0.40
Pavement, Gravel	0.75	Turf, Steep (> 10% slope)	0.45
Roofs, Conventional	0.95	Vegetation, Flat (0 - 1% slope)	0.10
Roof, Garden Roof (< 4 in)	0.50	Vegetation, Average (1 - 3% slope)	0.20
Roof, Garden Roof (4 - 8 in)	0.30	Vegetation, Hilly (3 - 10% slope)	0.25
Roof, Garden Roof (9 - 20 in)	0.20	Vegetation, Steep (> 10% slope)	0.30
Vegetation, Steep (> 10% slope)	0.10		

Equation 1

$$\text{Impervious Area (sf)} = \text{Surface Area (sf)} \times \text{Runoff Coefficient}$$

Equation 2

$$\text{Imperviousness (\%)} = \frac{\text{Total Impervious Area (sf)}}{\text{Total Site Area (sf)}}$$

7. Documentation Guidance

As a first step in preparing to complete the LEED Online documentation requirements, work through the following measures. Refer to LEED Online for the complete descriptions of all required documentation.

- Determine the rates and quantities for pre- and postdevelopment conditions for the required storm events.

- Prepare a stormwater plan assessment from design documentation, or have one completed by a civil engineer or other professional.

- List stormwater management strategies and record the percentage of rainfall that each is designed to handle.

8. Example

Site Imperviousness

The project is an office renovation with site improvements to an existing concrete parking lot of average slope. Surface types include sidewalks, parking areas, landscaping, and the roof. The roof area is assumed to be equal to the building footprint, as determined from site drawings. Table 2 shows calculations for the design case. To reduce imperviousness, some concrete sidewalks and asphalt parking areas can be replaced with pervious paving and vegetation. The building footprint is reduced and vegetated roofs are installed to reduce runoff. Next, calculations are done for the baseline case (the existing site conditions; Table 3). The calculations demonstrate that the design case has an imperviousness of 47% and the baseline case has an imperviousness of 95%, or a 49% reduction. The project has exceeded the 25% minimum, thus earning 1 point.

Table 2. Design Case Imperviousness

Surface Type	Runoff Coefficient	Area (sf)	Impervious Area (sf)
Pavement, Asphalt	0.95	5,075	4,821
Pavement, Pervious	0.60	1,345	807
Roof, Garden Roof (4 - 8 in)	0.30	8,240	2,472
Vegetation, Average (1 - 3% slope)	0.20	4,506	901
Total Area			19,166
Total Impervious Area			9,001
Imperviousness			47%

Table 3. Baseline Case Imperviousness

Surface Type	Runoff Coefficient	Area (sf)	Impervious Area (sf)
Pavement, concrete	0.95	19,166	18,208
Total area			19,166
Total impervious area			18,208
Imperviousness			95%

9. Exemplary Performance

This path is not eligible for exemplary performance under SS Credit 1, Path 12, Other Quantifiable Environmental Performance.

10. Regional Variations

The approach to this credit varies dramatically across different regions and climate zones because the 1 1/2 year 24-hour design storms are particular to a given location. Local stormwater management requirements also differ. The strategies employed in an urban environment where water is discharged to a municipal master system will be much different from the approach for a rural project that discharges to streams or lakes with high water quality standards.

11. Operations and Maintenance Considerations

Though unlikely to be within the control of the tenant, operations best practices include developing an ongoing inspection and maintenance plan to ensure the proper upkeep of all aspects of the stormwater management system, including desired levels of vegetation and mulching, repair of washouts, and proper functioning of any system controls. Silting in infiltration trenches or dry retention wells, for example, may impair performance. At a minimum, the maintenance plan should include periodic visual site inspections to identify unsatisfactory conditions and recommendations for typical corrective actions. If stormwater harvesting systems are used, period checks for leaks and blockages should be scheduled, and occasional cleaning may be necessary to keep the system operating effectively. Prevention of on-site erosion will extend the life of the installed measures.

12. Resources

Please see USGBC's LEED Resources & Tools (http://www.usgbc.org/projecttools) for additional resources and technical information.

Websites
Center for Watershed Protection
http://www.cwp.org
A nonprofit dedicated to disseminating watershed protection information to community leaders and watershed managers, the center offers online resources, training seminars, and watershed protection techniques.

Stormwater Manager's Resource Center
http://www.stormwatercenter.net
This site for practitioners and local government officials provides technical assistance on stormwater management issues.

U.S. EPA Office of Wetlands, Oceans, and Watersheds
http://www.epa.gov/owow
This website has information about watersheds and information about water resource protection, water conservation, landscaping practices, and water pollution reduction.

U.S. EPA, Post-Construction Stormwater Management in New Development and Redevelopment
http://cfpub.epa.gov/npdes/stormwater/menuofbmps/index.cfm
This EPA website provides information about catch basins as a tool for sediment control.

U.S. National Oceanic and Atmospheric Administration, National Climate Data Center
http://www.ncdc.noaa.gov/oa/ncdc.html
This website provides historical rainfall data and isohyetal maps for various storm events.

13. Definitions

An **aquifer** is an underground water-bearing rock formation that supplies groundwater, wells, and springs.

Retention ponds capture stormwater runoff and clear it of pollutants before its release. Some retention pond designs use gravity only; others use mechanical equipment, such as pipes and pumps, to facilitate transport. Some ponds are dry except during storm events; others permanently store water.

Erosion is a combination of processes or events by which materials of the earth's surface are loosened, dissolved, or worn away and transported by natural agents (e.g., water, wind, or gravity).

Impervious surfaces have a perviousness of less than 50% and promote runoff of water instead of infiltration into the subsurface. Examples include parking lots, roads, sidewalks, and plazas.

Infiltration basins and **trenches** are devices used to encourage subsurface infiltration of runoff volumes through temporary surface storage. Basins are ponds that can store large volumes of stormwater. They need to drain within 72 hours to maintain aerobic conditions and be available for future storm events. Trenches are similar to infiltration basins but are shallower and function as a subsurface reservoir for stormwater volumes. Pretreatment to remove sediment and oil may be necessary to avoid clogging infiltration devices. Infiltration trenches are more common in areas where infiltration basins are not possible.

Porous pavement and **permeable surfaces** allow runoff to infiltrate into the ground.

Stormwater runoff consists of water from precipitation that flows over surfaces into sewer systems or receiving water bodies. All precipitation that leaves project site boundaries on the surface is considered stormwater runoff.

OPTION 2, PATH 3: STORMWATER DESIGN—QUALITY CONTROL

1. Benefits and Issues to Consider

Environmental Issues

As areas are developed and urbanized, surface permeability is reduced, resulting in increased stormwater runoff that is transported via gutters, pipes, and sewers to receiving waters. This stormwater contains sediment and other contaminants that have negative effects on water quality, navigation, and recreation. Furthermore, conveyance and treatment of stormwater require significant municipal infrastructure and maintenance.

Sources of stormwater pollution include atmospheric deposition, vehicle fluid leaks, and mechanical equipment wastes. During storm events, these pollutants are washed away and discharged to downstream waters, damaging aquatic habitats and decreasing biological diversity of aquatic species.

2. Related Credits

A building's efforts to capture and treat stormwater runoff may involve the use of pervious pavements, native or adapted vegetation, and increased on-site infiltration strategies, assisting projects with earning these credits:

- SS Credit 1, Option 2, Path 2: Stormwater Management—Quantity Control

- SS Credit 1, Option 2, Path 4: Heat Island Reduction—Nonroof

Efforts to capture and reuse rainwater for irrigation or in nonpotable applications inside the building, such as toilet and urinals, can help projects earn the following credits:

- SS Credit 1, Option 2, Path 7: Water-Efficient Landscaping—Reduce by 50%

- SS Credit 1, Option 2, Path 8: Water-Efficient Landscaping—No Potable Water Use or No Irrigation

- SS Credit 1, Option 2, Path 10: Water Use Reduction—30% Reduction

3. Summary of Referenced Standard

U.S. EPA 840B92002, Guidance Specifying Management Measures for Sources of Non-Point Pollution in Coastal Waters, effective January 1993
http://www.epa.gov/owow/nps/MMGI

Hardcopy or microfiche (836 pages): National Technical Information Service (PB93-234672),
http://www.ntis.gov,
The EPA Office of Water, http://www.epa.gov/OWOW

This document discusses a variety of management practices that can remove pollutants from stormwater volumes. Chapter 4, Part II, addresses urban runoff and suggests strategies for treating and filtering stormwater volumes after construction is completed.

4. Implementation

Choose a base building that has in place a stormwater treatment system that meets the requirements of SS Credit 1, Option 2, Path 3. Since underground systems usually aren't visible, some research into the building's history may be required to determine whether the stormwater system complies with the credit requirements.

Consult facility personnel, design documents, manufacturer information, and code officials about the base building's stormwater treatment systems. Building management and permitting authority may have the information needed to demonstrate that the credit requirements are met. For physical components, such as extractors, manufacturers' cut sheets can confirm that the installed system can remove suspended solids and phosphorus as required by the referenced standard.

Facilities can be constructed to remove contaminants from the portion of stormwater that cannot be contained or reused on-site. Possible strategies include constructed wetlands, stormwater filtering systems, bioswales, retention basins, and vegetated filter strips. While evaluating potential buildings for commercial interior projects, see whether the base building site design incorporates compliant systems.

5. Timeline and Team

Because tenants may not be able to influence the base building and site infrastructure design, LEED for Commercial Interiors projects may require a different approach than LEED for New Construction or Core & Shell projects. Work with building owners or facility managers to assess the base building for compliance with the LEED requirements. Since many local jurisdictions have comparable requirements, consult with local permitting officials to determine whether the local stormwater requirements at the time of the base building construction were adequate to meet this credit. If the existing system does not meet the credit requirements, investigate opportunities to modify the site design. This may include modification of existing stormwater management systems and replacing site hardscapes with vegetated areas that decrease site runoff.

6. Calculations

In most cases, buildings that have implemented standard EPA or local best management practices will not need to complete any calculations to demonstrate compliance with the requirements. If designs far different from accepted best management practices have been developed and implemented, detailed engineering calculations may be required to demonstrate the reductions in total suspended solids (TSS) and total phosphorus (TP).

7. Documentation Guidance

As a first step in preparing to complete the LEED Online documentation requirements, work through the following measures. Refer to LEED Online for the complete descriptions of all required documentation.

- List the best management practices used to treat stormwater and record the percentage of annual rainfall that each is designed to handle.

- For structural controls, list and describe the measures, and determine the percentage of annual rainfall that each is designed to handle.

8. Examples

There are no examples for this credit

9. Exemplary Performance

This credit is not eligible for exemplary performance under SS Credit 1, Path 12, Other Quantifiable Environmental Performance.

10. Regional Variations

The approach to this credit varies dramatically across different regions and climate zones because the 1-year and 2-year 24-hour design storms are particular to a given location. Local stormwater management requirements also differ. The strategies employed in an urban, coastal environment where water is discharged to concrete channels and then the ocean will be much different from the approach for a rural, inland project that discharges to streams or lakes.

11. Operations and Maintenance Considerations

Ideally, the landlord has implemented a maintenance plan that includes periodic visual site inspections to identify any erosion and recommendations for typical corrective actions. Preventing erosion will extend the life of installed stormwater measures, since silting of infiltration trenches or dry retention wells may impair long-term performance.

Further, this plan should address maintenance of any pervious pavement systems. This might include quarterly vacuuming or washing. The tenant should consider requiring periodic inspection and maintenance of these systems during lease negotiations

12. Resources

Please see USGBC's LEED Resources & Tools (http://www.usgbc.org/projecttools) for additional resources and technical information.

13. Definitions

A **constructed wetland** is an engineered system designed to simulate natural wetland functions for water purification. In LEED, constructed wetlands are essentially treatment systems that remove contaminants from wastewater.

Retention ponds capture stormwater runoff and clear it of pollutants before its release. Some retention pond designs use gravity only; others use mechanical equipment, such as pipes and pumps, to facilitate transport. Some ponds are dry except during storm events; others permanently store water.

Impervious surfaces have a perviousness of less than 50% and promote runoff of water instead of infiltration into the subsurface. Examples include parking lots, roads, sidewalks, and plazas.

Infiltration basins and **trenches** are devices used to encourage subsurface infiltration of runoff volumes through temporary surface storage. Basins are ponds that can store large volumes of stormwater. They need to drain within 72 hours to maintain aerobic conditions and be available for future storm events. Trenches are similar to infiltration basins but are shallower and function as a subsurface reservoir for stormwater volumes. Pretreatment to remove sediment and oil may be necessary to avoid clogging infiltration devices. Infiltration trenches are more common in areas where infiltration basins are not possible.

Porous pavement and **permeable surfaces** allow runoff to infiltrate into the ground.

Stormwater runoff consists of water from precipitation that flows over surfaces into sewer systems or receiving water bodies. All precipitation that leaves project site boundaries on the surface is considered stormwater runoff.

Total phosphorus (**TP**) consists of organically bound phosphates, polyphosphates, and orthophosphates in stormwater, the majority of which originates from fertilizer application. Chemical precipitation is the typical removal mechanism for phosphorus.

Total suspended solids (**TSS**) are particles that are too small or light to be removed from stormwater via gravity settling. Suspended solid concentrations are typically removed via filtration.

OPTION 2, PATH 4: HEAT ISLAND EFFECT—NONROOF

1. Benefits and Issues to Consider

Environmental Issues

The use of dark, nonreflective surfaces for parking, roofs, walkways, and other hardscapes contributes to the heat island effect by absorbing the sun's warmth, which then radiates into the surroundings. Because of heat island effect, ambient temperatures in urban areas are artificially elevated by 2° to 10°F compared with surrounding suburban and undeveloped areas.[11] The result is increased cooling loads in the summer, requiring larger heating, ventilating, and air-conditioning (HVAC) equipment and greater electricity consumption, both of which generate greenhouse gases and pollution. Heat islands are detrimental to site habitat, wildlife, and animal migration corridors. Plants and animals are also sensitive to large fluctuations in daytime and nighttime temperatures and may not thrive in areas affected by heat islands.

Economic Issues

The energy used to cool a building represents a substantial portion of the operating budget over its lifetime. Reducing heat islands can significantly lower cooling costs and HVAC equipment needs. According to the Department of Energy's Lawrence Berkeley National Laboratory, the annual energy savings potential of heat island reduction measures, studied in the metropolitan areas of Sacramento, Baton Rouge, and Salt Lake City, range from $4 million to $15 million.[12] By selecting base buildings that have taken steps to reduce heat island effect from nonroof surfaces, tenants can benefit from lower operating costs associated with space cooling.

2. Related Credits

Properly designed and installed open-grid pavements increase stormwater infiltration on the site and reduce stormwater runoff, assisting projects with earning the following credits:

- SS Credit 1, Option 2, Path 2: Stormwater Design—Quantity Control

- SS Credit 1, Option 2, Path 3: Stormwater Design—Quality Control

If the base building uses vegetation to shade hardscapes, refer to the landscape irrigation requirements in these 2 credits:

- SS Credit 1, Option 2, Path 7: Water Efficient Landscaping—Reduce by 50%

- SS Credit 1, Option 2, Path 8: Water-Efficient Landscaping—No Potable Water Use or No Irrigation

3. Summary of Referenced Standards

There are no standards referenced for this credit.

4. Implementation

Choose a base building with physical characteristics that reduce its contribution to heat island effect. LEED for Commercial Interiors SS Credit 1, Option 4, has 3 compliance paths, all of which aim to reduce the potential for nonroof building surfaces to absorb and retain heat.

5. Timeline and Team

The project team should make shaded, reflective, or open-grid site hardscapes a criterion for site selection. Real estate brokers and leasing agents can help identify buildings that comply.

6. Calculations

Shading of Nonroof Impervious Surfaces

1. Identify all nonroof hardscape surfaces on the project site and sum the total area (T).

   Hardscapes must include all roads, sidewalks, courtyards, and parking lots within the LEED project boundary.

2. Identify all hardscape surfaces that are shaded by trees or other landscape features (or will be shaded within 5 years from the date of installation). Shade coverage must be calculated at 10 a.m., 12 noon, and 3 p.m. on the summer solstice. The arithmetic mean of these 3 values will be used as the effective shaded area. Calculated the effective shaded area (S).

3. Identify all hardscape surfaces shaded by solar energy panels and sum the total area (E). The shaded area can be considered equivalent to the area covered by the panels on the site plan (from a direct overhead aerial perspective).

4. Identify all hardscape surfaces shaded by architectural devices or structures that have an SRI of at least 29 and sum the total area (A). The shaded area can be considered equivalent to the area covered by the architectural devices or structures on the site plan (from a direct overhead aerial perspective).

5. Identify all the hardscape surfaces that have an SRI of at least 29 and sum the total area (R).

SRI can be calculated from emissivity and solar reflectance values. Emissivity is calculated by the manufacturer according to ASTM E 408 or ASTM C 1371, and solar reflectance is calculated according to ASTM E 903, ASTM E 1918 or ASTM C 1549. Alternatively, use the SRI values for typical paving materials listed in Table 1 in lieu of obtaining specific emissivity and solar reflectance measurements for the listed materials.

Table 1. Solar Reflectance Index (SRI) for Standard Paving Materials

Material	Emissivity	Reflectance	SRI
Typical new gray concrete	0.9	0.35	38
Typical weathered* gray concrete	0.9	0.20	19
Typical new white concrete	0.9	0.7	86
Typical weathered* white concrete	0.9	0.4	45
New asphalt	0.9	.05	0
Weathered asphalt	0.9	.10	6

* Reflectance of surfaces can be maintained with cleaning. Typical pressure washing of cementitious materials can restore reflectance close to original value. Weathered values are based on no cleaning.

6. Identify all hardscape surfaces that have an open grid paving system that is at least 50% pervious and sum the total area (O).

7. Sum the area of all qualifying surfaces to determine the total qualifying area (Q), using Equation 1.

Equation 1

$$Q = (S + E + A + R + O)$$

8. The total qualifying area must be at least 30% of the total hardscape area (T), as in Equation 2.

Equation 2

$$Q > T \times 0.3$$

Underground or Covered Parking

1. Determine the total number of parking spaces within the project boundary.

2. Determine the number of parking spaces that are under cover (include underground, under deck, under roof, or under building). This number must be at least 50% of the total number of parking spaces.

3. A base building with no parking is not eligible for this credit path.

Open-Grid Parking Areas

1. Identify the total parking lot area on the project site (T).

2. Identify all hardscape surfaces that are open-grid paving that is at least 50% pervious and sum the total area (O).

3. The total qualifying area (O) must be at least 50% of the total parking lot area, as in Equation 3.

Equation 3

$$O > \frac{T}{2}$$

7. Documentation Guidance

As a first step in preparing to complete the LEED Online documentation requirements, work through the following measures. Refer to LEED Online for the complete descriptions of all required documentation.

- If surfaces are shaded, prepare a site plan that highlights all nonroof hardscape areas. Clearly label each portion of hardscape that counts toward credit achievement. List material information about the compliant surfaces (e.g., SRI values of reflective paving materials).

- If parking spaces are placed under cover, determine the total number of parking spaces and the portion covered. If applicable, assemble SRI values for the roofs that cover parking areas.

- If hardscapes are open-grid paving, prepare a site plan that highlights the areas covered by the open-grid pavement system. Assemble information about the open-grid system used.

8. Examples

The tenant space is in a building situated on a 25,000-square-foot site, of which 15,000 square feet is occupied by the building footprint and vegetated areas. Deciduous trees shade parking and driveway areas, and light-colored concrete with an SRI of 35 is in place for the driving aisles and walkways (Figure 1). Areas that contain both light-colored hardscapes and are shaded by trees are counted only once. Table 2 lists the areas of qualifying surfaces.

Table 2. Sample Areas of Qualifying Surfaces

Description	Area (sf)
Total nonroof hardscapes	10,000
Shaded areas	3,000
Areas of hardscapes with minimum SRI-29	4,000
Total qualifying surfaces	7,000

In this example, the total area of qualifying surfaces is greater than 50% of the total area of nonroof hardscapes, and the project earns 1 point.

Figure 1. Shading and SRI for Credit Compliance

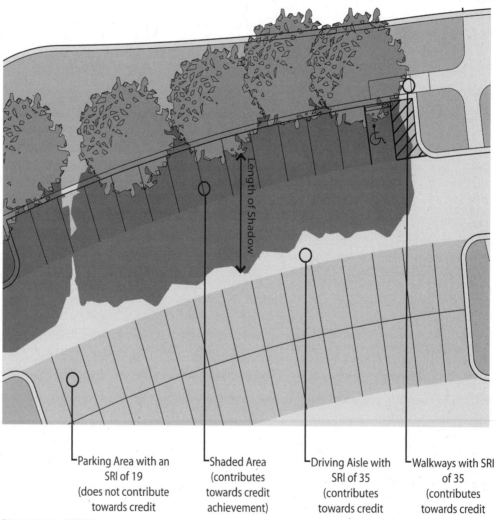

Parking Area with an SRI of 19 (does not contribute towards credit

Shaded Area (contributes towards credit achievement)

Driving Aisle with SRI of 35 (contributes towards credit

Walkways with SRI of 35 (contributes towards credit

Diagram courtesy of OWP/P

9. Exemplary Performance

Projects may earn credit for exemplary performance under SS Credit 1, Path 12, Other Quantifiable Environmental Performance, by demonstrating that 2 or more of the compliance paths described above have been met.

10. Regional Variations

Heat island intensities depend on an area's weather and climate, proximity to water bodies, and topography.[13] Buildings in very cold climates or at high latitudes may not experience the same rise of surface and ambient temperatures. Buildings in urban areas and those in climate zones 1, 2, and 3 (as defined by ASNI/ASHRAE/IESNA Standard 90.1–2007) are most affected by heat islands and are likely to benefit from measures to decrease cooling loads by avoiding additional heat absorption. In sunny climates, building tenants may need to mitigate glare from reflective pavements into the building by providing shading devices.

11. Operations and Maintenance Considerations

Tenants who have located in a building that uses the strategies described in this credit should be aware of the need to maintain materials and systems. Surface materials with high reflectivity should be cleaned at least every 2 years to maintain good reflectance.

Some open-grid pavement systems require special maintenance to remain pervious. If this is the responsibility of the tenant, project teams should request maintenance information from product manufacturers and installers and make sure this information is given to the operations team.

12. Resources

Please see USGBC's LEED Resources & Tools (http://www.usgbc.org/projecttools) for additional resources and technical information.

Websites

American Concrete Pavement Association

http://www.pavement.com

This national association represents concrete pavement contractors, cement companies, equipment and material manufacturers, and suppliers. See Albedo: A Measure of Pavement Surface Reflectance, R&T Update (3.05) (June 2002): http://www.pavement.com/Downloads/RT/RT3.05.pdf.

Lawrence Berkeley National Laboratory, Heat Island Group

http://eetd.lbl.gov/HeatIsland/

Lawrence Berkeley National Laboratory conducts heat island research to find, analyze, and implement solutions to minimize heat island effect. Current research efforts focus on the study and development of more reflective surfaces for roadways and buildings.

U.S. EPA, Heat Island Effect

http://www.epa.gov/heatisland/index.htm

This website offers basic information about heat island effect, its social and environmental costs, and reduction strategies.

13. Definitions

Albedo is synonymous with **solar reflectance.**

Emissivity is the ratio of the radiation emitted by a surface to the radiation emitted by a black body at the same temperature.

Greenhouse gases are relatively transparent to the higher-energy sunlight but trap lower-energy infrared radiation (e.g., carbon dioxide, methane, and CFCs).

Hardscape consists of the inanimate elements of the building landscaping. Examples include pavement, roadways, stone walls, concrete paths and sidewalks, and concrete, brick, and tile patios.

Heat island effect refers to the absorption of heat by hardscapes, such as dark, nonreflective pavement and buildings, and its radiation to surrounding areas. Particularly in urban areas, other sources may include vehicle exhaust, air-conditioners, and street equipment; reduced airflow from tall buildings and narrow streets exacerbates the effect.

Impervious surfaces have a perviousness of less than 50% and promote runoff of water instead of infiltration into the subsurface. Examples include parking lots, roads, sidewalks, and plazas.

Infrared (or thermal) emittance is a parameter between 0 and 1 (or 0% and 100%) that indicates the ability of a material to shed infrared radiation (heat). The wavelength range for this radiant energy is roughly 5 to 40 micrometers. Most building materials (including glass) are opaque in this part of the spectrum and have an emittance of roughly 0.9. Materials such as clean, bare metals are the most important exceptions to the 0.9 rule. Thus clean, untarnished galvanized steel has low emittance, and aluminum roof coatings have intermediate emittance levels.

On-site wastewater treatment systems transport, store, treat, and dispose of wastewater volumes generated on the project site.

Perviousness is the percentage of the surface area of a paving system that is open and allows moisture to soak into the ground below.

Solar reflectance, or **albedo,** is a measure of the ability of a surface material to reflect sunlight—visible, infrared, and ultraviolet wavelengths—on a scale of 0 to 1. Black paint has a solar reflectance of 0; white paint (titanium dioxide) has a solar reflectance of 1.

The **solar reflectance index (SRI)** is a measure of a material's ability to reject solar heat, as shown by a small temperature rise. Standard black (reflectance 0.05, emittance 0.90) is 0 and standard white (reflectance 0.80, emittance 0.90) is 100. For example, a standard black surface has a temperature rise of 90°F (50°C) in full sun, and a standard white surface has a temperature rise of 14.6°F (8.1°C). Once the maximum temperature rise of a given material has been computed, the SRI can be calculated by interpolating between the values for white and black. Materials with the highest SRI values are the coolest choices for paving. Because of the way SRI is defined, particularly hot materials can even take slightly negative values, and particularly cool materials can even exceed 100. (Lawrence Berkeley National Laboratory Cool Roofing Materials Database)

Tenant space is the area within the LEED project boundary. For more information on what can and must be in the LEED project boundary see the Minimum Program Requirements (MPRs) and LEED 2009 MPR Supplemental Guidance. Note: tenant space is the same as project space.

Undercover parking is underground or under a deck, roof, or building; its hardscape surfaces are shaded.

OPTION 2, PATH 5: HEAT ISLAND EFFECT—ROOF

	SS
CI	Credit 1 OPTION 2: PATH 5

1. Benefits and Issues to Consider

Environmental Issues

The use of dark, nonreflective roofing surfaces contributes to the heat island effect by absorbing the sun's warmth, which then radiates into the surroundings. Because of the heat island effect, ambient temperatures in urban areas are artificially elevated, resulting in increased cooling loads, greater electricity consumption, and higher emissions of greenhouse gases and pollution. Heat islands are also detrimental to site habitat, wildlife, and the migration corridors of various species. Plants and animals are sensitive to large fluctuations in daytime and nighttime temperatures and may not thrive in areas affected by heat islands. In addition, base buildings that have vegetated roofs provide habitat for birds, insects, and other wildlife.

Economic Issues

Tenants can benefit from reduced costs associated with cooling and HVAC equipment by selecting base buildings that have vegetated roofing and/or highly reflective roofing materials.

2. Related Credits

Properly designed and installed vegetated roofs increase stormwater infiltration on the site and help reduce stormwater runoff, assisting projects with earning these 2 credits:

- SS Credit 1, Option 2, Path 2: Stormwater Design—Quantity Control
- SS Credit 1, Option 2, Path 3: Stormwater Design—Quality Control

Vegetated roofs also reduce the availability of rainwater that can be harvested for nonpotable purposes, making the following water-efficiency credits more challenging to achieve:

- SS Credit 1, Option 2, Path 7: Water-Efficient Landscaping—Reduce by 50%
- SS Credit 1, Option 2, Path 8: Water-Efficient Landscaping—No Potable Water Use or No Irrigation
- SS Credit 1, Option 2, Path 10: Water Use Reduction—30% Reduction

3. Summary of Referenced Standards

ASTM International Standards

http://www.astm.org

ASTM E1980–01, Standard Practice for Calculating Solar Reflectance Index of Horizontal and Low-Sloped Opaque Surfaces

This standard describes how surface reflectivity and emissivity are combined to calculate a solar reflectance index (SRI) for a roofing material or other surface. The standard also describes a laboratory and field testing protocol that can be used to determine SRI.

ASTM E408–71(1996)e1, Standard Test Methods for Total Normal Emittance of Surfaces Using Inspection-Meter Techniques

This standard describes how to measure total normal emittance of surfaces using a portable inspection-meter instrument. The test methods are intended for large surfaces where nondestructive testing is required. See the standard for testing steps and a discussion of thermal emittance theory.

ASTM E903–96, Standard Test Method for Solar Absorptance, Reflectance, and Transmittance of Materials Using Integrating Spheres

Referenced in the ENERGY STAR® roofing standard, this test method uses spectrophotometers and need be applied only for initial reflectance measurement. It specifies methods of computing solar-weighted properties using the measured spectral values. This test method is applicable to materials having both specular and diffuse optical properties. Except for transmitting sheet materials that are heterogeneous, patterned, or corrugated, this test method is preferred over Test Method E1084. The ENERGY STAR® roofing standard also allows the use of reflectometers to measure roofing materials' solar reflectance. See the roofing standard for more details.

4. Implementation

Choose a base building that has incorporated highly reflective roof surfaces or vegetated roofs. Use the LEED-certified buildings database to find local projects that have achieved LEED credit for roof heat island reduction and include this requirement in the criteria for selecting a base building. Local roofing product representatives may be able to identify buildings where their compliant products have been installed.

5. Timeline and Team

The project team should make an installed vegetated roof or reflective roofing a criterion for site selection. Real estate brokers and leasing agents can help identify buildings that comply.

6. Calculations

1. Determine the total roof surface area of the project building (square feet).

2. Determine the area of the roof covered by mechanical equipment, solar energy panels, and appurtenances, and deduct these areas from the total roof surface area.

3. Determine whether the areas of qualifying reflective and vegetated roofing are adequate to meet the credit requirements, using Equation 1. Table 1 provides SRI values for typical roofing materials. Project teams may use these values to determine compliance if manufacturers' data are not available for existing installed materials.

Equation 1

$$\left(\frac{\text{Area of Low}-\text{Slope SRI Material}}{78 \times \frac{0.75}{\text{SRI Value}}} + \frac{\text{Area of Steep}-\text{Slope SRI Material}}{29 \times \frac{0.75}{\text{SRI Value}}} + \frac{\text{Vegetated Roof Area}}{0.5} \right) \geq \left(\text{Total Roof Area} - \text{Deducted Area} \right)$$

Table 1. Solar Reflectance Index (SRI) for Typical Roofing Materials

Example SRI Values for Solar Infrared Temperature Solar	Solar Reflectance	Infrared Emittance	Temperature Rise	SRI
Gray EPDM	0.23	0.87	68°F	21
Gray asphalt shingle	0.22	0.91	67°F	22
Unpainted cement tile	0.25	0.9	65°F	25
White granular surface bitumen	0.26	0.92	63°F	28
Red clay tile	0.33	0.9	58°F	36
Light gravel on built-up roof	0.34	0.9	57°F	37
Aluminum coating	0.61	0.25	48°F	50
White-coated gravel on built-up roof	0.65	0.9	28°F	79
White coating on metal roof	0.67	0.85	28°F	82
White EPDM	0.69	0.87	25F	84
White cement tile	0.73	0.9	21F	90
White coating, 1 coat, 8 mils	0.8	0.91	14F	100
PVC white	0.83	0.92	11F	104
White coating, 2 coats, 20 mils	0.85	0.91	9F	107
Source: LBNL Cool Roofing Materials Database				

7. Documentation Guidance

As a first step in preparing to complete the LEED Online documentation requirements, work through the following measures. Refer to LEED Online for the complete descriptions of all required documentation.

- Prepare roof drawings that show the total roof area and the areas of reflective materials or vegetated roof systems.

- List the roofing products and their emittance percentages, reflectance percentages, SRI values, and slopes. Retain product specifications that verify product characteristics.

8. Examples

The project has selected tenant space in an office building that has a 10,000-square-foot low-slope roof with both high-reflectance roofing materials and a vegetated roof system. The vegetated roof makes up 35% of the roof area. White EPDM roofing with a SRI of 85 covers 60% of the roof area, and the remaining 5% is covered by rooftop mechanical equipment. Table 2 summarizes the roofing types.

Table 2. Roofing Area Summary, by Type

Roofing Type	Area (sf)
Vegetated roof area	3,500
White EPDM roof area (SRI-85), low slope	6,000
Mechanical equipment	500
Total roof area	10,000

Using Equation 1,

$$\left(\frac{6000}{78 \times \frac{0.75}{85}} + \frac{3500}{0.5} \right) = 15{,}718 \geq \left(10{,}000 - 500 \right)$$

In this example, the white EPDM roofing plus the vegetated roofing meets the requirements of this credit, and the project earns 1 point.

9. Exemplary Performance

Projects may earn credit for exemplary performance under SS Credit 1, Path 12, Other Quantifiable Environmental Performance, by demonstrating that 100% of the building's roof area (excluding mechanical equipment, photovoltaic panels, and skylights) consists of a vegetated roof system.

10. Regional Variations

Heat island intensities depend on an area's weather and climate, proximity to water bodies, and topography.[14] Buildings in very cold climates or at high latitudes may not experience the same rise of surface and ambient temperatures. Projects in urban areas and those in climate zones 1, 2, and 3 (as defined by ASNI/ASHRAE/IESNA Standard 90.1–2007) are most affected by heat islands and are likely to benefit from measures to decrease cooling loads by avoiding additional heat absorption.

11. Operations and Maintenance Considerations

Tenants who have located in a building that uses the strategies described in this credit may not be responsible for their upkeep but should nevertheless be aware of the need to maintain materials and systems. Surface materials with high reflectivity should be cleaned at least every 2 years to maintain good reflectance.

SS	
CI	Credit 1 OPTION 2: PATH 5

Building operators must have the necessary information to maintain any vegetated roofing system. An operations plan should specify the schedule for inspecting the roof membrane and plantings and maintaining drainage paths. Until plants are fully established, watering and fertilization may be necessary. Properly designed green roofs do not require mowing or cutting, though occasional weeding may be required.

12. Resources

Please see USGBC's LEED Resources & Tools (http://www.usgbc.org/projecttools) for additional resources and technical information.

Websites

Cool Roof Rating Council

http://www.coolroofs.org

This nonprofit organization is dedicated to implementing and communicating fair, accurate, and credible radiative energy performance rating systems for roof surfaces; supporting research into roofing surfaces' energy-related radiative properties, including durability; and providing education and objective support to parties interested in understanding and comparing various roofing options.

ENERGY STAR® Reflective Roofing Products

http://www.energystar.gov/index.cfm?c=roof_prods.pr_roof_products

This website provides solar reflectance levels required to meet ENERGY STAR® requirements for qualified roof products.

Green Roofs for Healthy Cities

http://www.greenroofs.com

This nonprofit industry association consists of individuals and public and private organizations committed to developing a market for green roof infrastructure products and services across North America.

Lawrence Berkeley National Laboratory, Heat Island Group, Cool Roofs

http://eetd.lbl.gov/HeatIsland/CoolRoofs/

This site offers a wealth of information about cool roof research and technology, including links to the cool roofing materials database.

Pennsylvania State University, Center for Green Roof Research

http://hortWeb.cas.psu.edu/research/greenroofcenter/

The center aims to demonstrate and promote green roof research, education, and technology transfer in the Northeastern United States.

Whole Building Design Guide, Extensive Green Roofs

http://www.wbdg.org/resources/greenroofs.php

This article by Charlie Miller, PE, details the features and benefits of constructing green roofs.

13. Definitions

Albedo is synonymous with **solar reflectance.**

Emissivity is the ratio of the radiation emitted by a surface to the radiation emitted by a black body at the same temperature.

Greenhouse gases are relatively transparent to the higher-energy sunlight but trap lower-energy infrared radiation (e.g., carbon dioxide, methane, and CFCs).

Heat island effect refers to the absorption of heat by hardscapes, such as dark, nonreflective pavement and buildings, and its radiation to surrounding areas. Particularly in urban areas, other sources may include vehicle exhaust, air-conditioners, and street equipment; reduced airflow from tall buildings and narrow streets exacerbates the effect.

Infrared (or thermal) emittance is a parameter between 0 and 1 (or 0% and 100%) that indicates the ability of a material to shed infrared radiation (heat). The wavelength range for this radiant energy is roughly 5 to 40 micrometers. Most building materials (including glass) are opaque in this part of the spectrum and have an emittance of roughly 0.9. Materials such as clean, bare metals are the most important exceptions to the 0.9 rule. Thus clean, untarnished galvanized steel has low emittance, and aluminum roof coatings have intermediate emittance levels.

Solar reflectance, or albedo, is a measure of the ability of a surface material to reflect sunlight—visible, infrared, and ultraviolet wavelengths—on a scale of 0 to 1. Black paint has a solar reflectance of 0; white paint (titanium dioxide) has a solar reflectance of 1.

The **solar reflectance index (SRI)** is a measure of a material's ability to reject solar heat, as shown by a small temperature rise. Standard black (reflectance 0.05, emittance 0.90) is 0 and standard white (reflectance 0.80, emittance 0.90) is 100. For example, a standard black surface has a temperature rise of 90°F (50°C) in full sun, and a standard white surface has a temperature rise of 14.6°F (8.1°C). Once the maximum temperature rise of a given material has been computed, the SRI can be calculated by interpolating between the values for white and black. Materials with the highest SRI values are the coolest choices for paving. Because of the way SRI is defined, particularly hot materials can even take slightly negative values, and particularly cool materials can even exceed 100. (Lawrence Berkeley National Laboratory Cool Roofing Materials Database)

Tenant space is the area within the LEED project boundary. For more information on what can and must be in the LEED project boundary see the Minimum Program Requirements (MPRs) and LEED 2009 MPR Supplemental Guidance. Note: tenant space is the same as project space.

OPTION 2, PATH 6: LIGHT POLLUTION REDUCTION

1. Benefits and Issues to Consider

Environmental Issues

This credit option seeks to recognize projects that minimize their contribution to light pollution from interior lighting. Light pollution consists of both light trespass (affecting adjacent sites) and sky glow (affecting the sky). Poorly designed interior perimeter lighting can affect the nocturnal ecosystem on the site if interior light passes through translucent or transparent openings in the building envelope and unnecessarily illuminates the exterior environment. This light pollution can hinder enjoyment of the night sky for both the building occupants and neighbors.

Minimizing light pollution encourages nocturnal wildlife to thrive at the building site and permits observations of the night sky. Another benefit is better visual comfort and improved visibility. Sensitively designed lighting systems that minimize glare and provide more uniform light at lower levels create aesthetically pleasing, more secure environments. A carefully designed and maintained lighting system can help a project be a nonintrusive member of the community.

Economic Issues

Well-controlled lighting provides the right amount of lighting in the right place at the right times, thereby saving energy. By selecting high-efficiency luminaries and light sources, the project team can maximize energy and maintenance savings over the lifetime of the building.

2. Related Credits

By lighting areas only as necessary, designers avoid wasting light by spilling it through openings in the envelope (translucent or transparent). These efforts, along with the integration of lighting controls, support the achievement of the following credits:

- EA Credit 1.1: Optimize Energy Performance—Lighting Power

- EA Credit 1.2: Optimize Energy Performance—Lighting Controls

Development of a comprehensive lighting design that has individual and group controls should also include automatic occupancy controls to shut off interior perimeter lighting when spaces are not occupied. These considerations relate to the following credit:

- IEQ Credit 6.1: Controllability of Systems—Lighting

3. Summary of Referenced Standards

There are no standards referenced for this credit.

4. Implementation

Locate the project in a building with interior and exterior lighting equipment designed to eliminate light trespass from the building and the site, and include this requirement in the base building selection criteria. Local USGBC chapters or the Illuminating Engineering Society of North America (IESNA) may have detailed information on projects that have achieved light pollution reduction requirements.

Project teams can meet the requirements of this credit through 1 of 2 options:

OPTION 1

All nonemergency interior lighting fixtures must be automatically controlled and programmed to turn off or have their input power reduced by at least 50% following regular business hours. Controls may be automatic sweep timers, occupancy sensors, or programmed master lighting control panels. Manual or occupancy-based override capabilities that enable lights to be turned on for after-hours use should be included in the design.

Projects operating 24 hours a day are exempt from the after-hours override automatic shutoff and thus must use Option 2.

OPTION 2

All exterior openings, such as windows, must have shielding that can be automatically controlled and programmed to close from 11:00 p.m. to 5:00 a.m. Shielding options include automatic shades that have less than 10% transmittance.

An example is a rolling shade that controls light transmittance and is operated automatically, with a timer.

5. Timeline and Team

During the design phase, the project team should consider strategies that will reduce or eliminate light from exiting the building through openings in the building envelope (translucent or transparent). During construction administration, the architect or design team should verify that the shop drawings are compliant with the intended design. Field verification and adjustment of fixtures and fixture heads should take place during installation. After construction is complete, commissioning will ensure that automatic lighting controls or shading devices are operating according to the design intent.

6. Calculations

There are no calculations required for this credit.

7. Documentation Guidance

As a first step in preparing to complete the LEED Online documentation requirements, work through the following measures. Refer to LEED Online for the complete descriptions of all required documentation.

- If automatic controls are used for interior lighting, prepare drawings showing their location and incorporate the sequence of operation for lighting into drawings and specifications or the building operation plan.

- If automatic shading devices are used to control interior lighting, prepare drawings of shading devices, assemble specifications or product data showing that the shading devices result in transmittance of less than 10%, and incorporate the sequence of operation for automatic shading devices into drawings and specifications or the building operation plan.

8. Examples

There are no examples for this credit.

9. Exemplary Performance

This path is not eligible for exemplary performance under SS Credit 1, Path 12, Other Quantifiable Environmental Performance.

10. Regional Variations

There are no regional variations associated with this credit.

11. Operations and Maintenance Considerations

The project team should ensure that automatic control schedules for lighting or shading devices are documented in the building's operation plan.

12. Resources

Please see USGBC's LEED Resources & Tools (http://www.usgbc.org/projecttools) for additional resources and technical information.

Websites

Illuminating Engineering Society of North America

http://www.iesna.org

The mission of IESNA is to benefit society by promoting knowledge and disseminating information for the improvement of the lighted environment.

International Dark-Sky Association

http://www.darksky.org/ida/ida_2/index_html

This nonprofit agency is dedicated to educating about and providing solutions to light pollution.

Rensselaer Polytechnic Institute, Lighting Research Center

http://www.lrc.rpi.edu

This leading university-based research center is devoted to providing objective information about lighting technologies, applications, and products.

Sky and Telescope

http://skyandtelescope.com

This site Includes facts on light pollution and its effect on astronomy and information about purchasing light pollution-minimizing light fixtures.

Print Media

The IESNA Lighting Handbook, ninth edition, edited by Mark S. Rea (Illuminating Engineering Society of North America, 2000).

Lighting for Exterior Environments RP-33-99, by The IESNA Outdoor Environment Lighting Committee (Illuminating Engineering Society of North America, 1999).

Concepts in Practice Lighting: Lighting Design in Architecture, by Torquil Barker (B.T. Batsford Ltd., 1997).

The Design of Lighting, by Peter Tregenza and David Loe (E & FN Spon, 1998).

13. Definitions

Emergency lighting as defined by the Illuminating Engineering Society of North America is lighting designed to supply illumination essential to the safety of life and property in the event of failure of the normal supply.

Light pollution is waste light from building sites that produces glare, is directed upward to the sky, or is directed off the site. Waste light does not increase nighttime safety, utility, or security and needlessly consumes energy.

Light trespass is obtrusive light that is unwanted because of quantitative, directional, or spectral attributes. Light trespass can cause annoyance, discomfort, distraction, or loss of visibility.

Sky glow is caused by stray light from unshielded light sources and light reflecting off surfaces that then enter the atmosphere and illuminate and reflect off dust, debris, and water vapor. Sky glow can substantially limit observation of the night sky, compromise astronomical research, and adversely affect nocturnal environments.

OPTION 2, PATH 7: WATER EFFICIENT LANDSCAPING—REDUCE BY 50%, AND PATH 8: WATER EFFICIENT LANDSCAPING—NO POTABLE WATER USE OR NO IRRIGATION

1. Benefits and Issues to Consider

Environmental Issues

Landscape irrigation practices in the United States consume large quantities of potable water. Outdoor uses, primarily landscaping, account for 30% of the 26 billion gallons of water consumed daily in the United States.[15] Improved landscaping practices can dramatically reduce and even eliminate irrigation needs. Maintaining or reestablishing native or adapted plants on building sites fosters a self-sustaining landscape that requires minimal supplemental water and provides other environmental benefits as well, such as attracting native wildlife and creating a building site integrated with its natural surroundings. In addition, native or adapted plants tend to require less fertilizer and pesticides, and therefore reduce water quality degradation and other environmental impacts.

Water-efficient landscaping helps conserve local and regional potable water resources. Maintaining natural aquifer conditions is important to providing reliable water sources for future generations. Consideration of water issues during planning can encourage development where resources can support it and prevent development if it would exceed the resource capacity.

Economic Issues

A water-efficient landscape design can lower municipal water use and maintenance requirements for the base building. The resulting cost savings may be reflected in lower lease rates.

2. Related Credits

In addition to reducing potable water consumption, rainwater capture systems can be used to manage stormwater runoff and can help projects earn points under these credits:

- SS Credit 1, Option 2, Path 2: Stormwater Design—Quantity Control
- SS Credit 1, Option 2, Path 3: Stormwater Design—Quality Control

Landscape plantings that shade hardscapes can help achieve the following credit:

- SS Credit 1, Option 2, Path 4: Heat Island Effect—Nonroof

Additionally, landscape plantings can mitigate climate conditions and reduce building energy consumption (for example, by shading south-facing windows), contributing to this credit:

- EA Credit 1: Optimize Energy Performance

The use of a vegetated roof may contribute to the achievement of another SS credit:

- SS Credit 1, Option 2, Path 5: Heat Island Effect—Roof

3. Summary of Referenced Standards

There are no standards referenced for this credit.

4. Implementation

Choose a base building with water-efficient landscape irrigation that is designed to reduce or eliminate the use of potable water by incorporating features such as these:

- Landscaping with indigenous plants.

- Rainwater collection systems.

- High-efficiency irrigation strategies, such as microirrigation systems, moisture sensors, timers, and weather database controllers.

- Graywater systems used for site irrigation.

Landscape irrigation using "nuisance" groundwater (i.e., groundwater that must be pumped away from the building's basement or foundation) is an example of a strategy to achieve this option. However, a well installed specifically to collect groundwater for irrigation does not meet the intent of this credit. Additionally, a project site that has no landscaping is not eligible.

Buildings without vegetation or other ecologically appropriate features on the grounds can nevertheless earn points by reducing the use of potable water for watering any roof or courtyard garden space or outdoor planters, provided the planters or garden space cover at least 5% of the building site area (including building footprint, hardscape area, parking footprint, etc.). If the planters or garden space cover less than 5% of the building site area, the project is ineligible for this credit.

5. Timeline and Team

The project team should make installed native landscaping, rainwater collection systems, high-efficiency irrigation strategies, or graywater systems a criterion for site selection. Real estate brokers and leasing agents can help identify buildings that comply.

6. Calculations

The following calculation methodology is used to support the credit submittals for Options 7 and 8. To quantify water-efficient landscaping measures, determine the irrigation volumes for the designed landscape irrigation system for July and compare these with irrigation volumes required for a baseline landscape irrigation system. The resulting water savings is the difference between the 2 systems. The factors that must be calculated to determine irrigation volumes are explained in detail in the following paragraphs and summarized in Table 1.

To calculate the percentage reduction in potable or natural water use for this credit, establish a baseline water use rate for the project and then calculate the as-designed water use rate according to the steps listed below.

Standard Assumptions and Variables

- All calculations are based on irrigation during July.

- The landscape coefficient (K_L) indicates the volume of water lost through evapotranspiration. It varies with the plant species, microclimate, and planting density. The formula for determining the landscape coefficient is given in Equation 3.

- The species factor (k_s) accounts for variation in water needs by different plant species, divided into 3 categories (high, average, and low water need). To determine the appropriate category for a plant species, use plant manuals and professional experience. This factor is somewhat subjective, but landscape professionals know the general water needs of plant species. Landscapes can be maintained in acceptable condition at about 50% of the reference evapotranspiration (ET_o) value, and thus the average value of k_s is 0.5. If a species does not require irrigation once it is established, then the effective $k_s = 0$ and the resulting $K_L = 0$.

- The density factor (k_d) accounts for the number of plants and the total leaf area of a landscape. Sparsely planted areas will have less evapotranspiration than densely planted areas. An average k_d is applied to areas where shading from trees is 60% to 100%. This is equivalent to shrubs and groundcover that shade 90% to 100% of the landscape area. Low k_d values are found where shading from trees is less than 60%, or where shrub and groundcover shading is less than 90%. For instance, a 25% ground shading from trees results in a k_d value of 0.5. In mixed plantings, where the tree canopy shades understory shrubs and groundcover, evapotranspiration increases. This represents the highest level of landscape density, and the kd value is 1.0 to 1.3.

- The microclimate factor (k_{mc}) accounts for environmental conditions specific to the landscape, including temperature, wind, and humidity. For instance, parking lots increase wind and temperature effects on adjacent landscapes. The average k_{mc} is 1.0; this refers to conditions where evapotranspiration is unaffected by buildings, pavements, reflective surfaces, or slopes. High-k_{mc} conditions occur where evaporative potential is increased by heat-absorbing and reflective surfaces or exposure to high winds; examples include parking lots, west sides of buildings, and the west and south-facing slopes, medians, and areas experiencing wind tunnel effects. Low-k_{mc} landscapes include shaded areas and areas protected from wind, such as north sides of buildings, courtyards, areas under wide building overhangs, and north-facing slopes.

STEP 1. Create a Design Case

Determine the landscape area for the project. This number must represent the as-designed landscape area and must use the same project boundary as is used in all other LEED credits. Sort the total landscape area into the major vegetation types (trees, shrubs, groundcover, mixed, and turf grass), listing the area for each.

Determine the following characteristics for each landscape area: species factor (k_s), density factor (k_d), and microclimate factor (k_{mc}). Recommended values for each are provided in Table 1. Select the low, average, or high value for each parameter as appropriate for the site. Explain any variance from these recommended values in the credit narrative.

Table 1. Landscape Factors

Vegetation type	Species Factor (k_s)			Density Factor (k_d)			Microclimate Factor (k_{mc})		
	Low	Average	High	Low	Average	High	Low	Average	High
Trees	0.2	0.5	0.9	0.5	1.0	1.3	0.5	1.0	1.4
Shrubs	0.2	0.5	0.7	0.5	1.0	1.1	0.5	1.0	1.3
Groundcover	0.2	0.5	0.7	0.5	1.0	1.1	0.5	1.0	1.2
Mixed trees, shrubs, groundcover	0.2	0.5	0.9	0.6	1.1	1.3	0.5	1.0	1.4
Turf grass	0.6	0.7	0.8	0.6	1.0	1.0	0.8	1.0	1.2

Calculate the landscape coefficient (K_L) by multiplying the 3 area characteristics, as shown in Equation 1.

Equation 1

$$K_L = k_s \times k_d \times k_{mc}$$

Determine the reference evapotranspiration rate (ET_o) for the region. This rate is a measurement of the total amount of water needed to grow a reference plant (such as grass or alfalfa), expressed in millimeters or inches. The values for ET_o in various regions throughout the United States can be found in regional agricultural data (see Resources). The ET_o for July is used in the LEED calculation because this is typically the month with the greatest evapotranspiration effects and, therefore, the greatest irrigation demands.

Calculate the project-specific evapotranspiration rate (ET_L) for each landscape area by multiplying the (ET_O) by the K_L, as shown in Equation 2.

Equation 2

$$ET_L \text{ (in)} = ET_O \; \mathbf{X} \; K_L$$

Determine the irrigation efficiency (IE) by listing the type of irrigation used for each landscape area and the corresponding efficiency. Table 2 lists irrigation efficiencies for different irrigation systems. Calculations will be accepted that include water use reduction and efficiencies from rotating heads, pressure-regulating heads, and "smart" irrigation controls. These numbers must be supported by either manufacturers' documentation or detailed calculations by the landscape designer.

Table 2. Irrigation Types and Efficiencies

Type	Efficiency
Sprinkler	0.625
Drip	0.90

Determine, if applicable, the controller efficiency (CE), the percentage reduction in water use from any weather-based controllers or moisture sensor-based systems. This number must be supported by either manufacturers' documentation or detailed calculations by the landscape designer.

Determine, if applicable, the volume of reuse water (harvested rainwater, recycled graywater, or treated wastewater) available in July. Reuse water volumes may depend on rainfall volume and frequency, building-generated graywater and wastewater, and on-site storage capacity. On-site reuse systems must be modeled to predict volumes generated on a monthly basis as well as optimal storage capacity. For harvested rainwater calculations, project teams may either use the collected rainwater total for July based on historical average precipitation, or use historical data for each month to model collection and reuse throughout the year. The latter method allows the project team to determine the volume of water that can be expected in the storage cistern at the beginning of July and add it to the expected rainwater volume collected during the month; it also allows the team to determine the optimal size of the rainwater cistern.

To calculate the total water applied (TWA) and total potable water applied (TPWA) for each landscape area and the installed case, use Equations 3 and 4.

Equation 3

$$\text{Design Case TWA (gal)} = \left(\text{Area (sf)} \; \mathbf{X} \; \frac{ET_L \text{ (in)}}{IE} \right) \mathbf{X} \; CE \; \mathbf{X} \; 0.6233 \text{ (gal/sf/in)}$$

Equation 4

$$\text{Design Case TPWA (gal)} = \text{TWA (gal)} - \text{Reuse Water (gal)}$$

STEP 2. Create the Baseline Case

In the baseline case, the species factor (k_s), density factor (k_d), and irrigation efficiency (IE) are set to average values representative of conventional equipment and design practices. The same microclimate factors (k_{MC}) and the reference evapotranspiration rate (ET_O) are used in both cases. If the project substitutes low-water-using plants (such as shrubs) for high-water-using types (such as turf grass), the landscape areas can be reallocated in the baseline case, but the total landscape area must remain the same. The baseline cannot be 100% turf grass if typical landscaping practices in the region include trees, shrubs, and planting beds.

Calculate the TWA for the baseline case using Equation 5.

Equation 5

$$\text{Baseline Case TWA (gal)} = \text{Area (sf)} \times \frac{ET_L \text{ (in)}}{IE} \times 0.6233 \text{ (gal/sf/in)}$$

STEP 3

Calculate the percentage reduction in total irrigation water use (potable and reuse)

AND

the percentage reduction of potable water use for irrigation.

Calculate the percentage reduction of potable water use according to Equation 6.

Equation 6

$$\text{Percentage Reduction of Potable Water (\%)} = \left(1 - \frac{\text{Design TPWA}}{\text{Baseline TWA}} \right) \times 100$$

If the percentage reduction of potable water use for irrigation achieved is 50% or more, it meets the requirements for Option 7. If the percentage reduction of potable water use for irrigation achieved is 100% and the percentage reduction of total water use for irrigation is 50% or more, it meets the requirements for Option 8 as well as Option 7.

If the percentage reduction of potable water use for irrigation is 100%, also calculate the percentage reduction of total water (potable plus reuse), according to Equation 7.

Equation 7

$$\text{Percentage Reduction of Total Water (\%)} = 1 - \frac{\text{Design TWA}}{\text{Baseline TWA}} \times 100$$

7. Documentation Guidance

As a first step in preparing to complete the LEED Online documentation requirements, work through the following measures. Refer to LEED Online for the complete descriptions of all required documentation.

- Estimate the amounts of potable and nonpotable water used for landscape irrigation.

- Estimate the percentage reduction in water demand, and report on the portion of irrigation that will come from each nonpotable source (if any).

- Prepare a landscape plan showing a planting schedule and irrigation system.

8. Examples

EXAMPLE 1. OPTION 2, PATH 7

An office building in Austin, Texas, has a total site area of 6,000 square feet. The site comprises 3 landscape types: shrubs, mixed vegetation, and turf grass. All are irrigated with a combination of potable water and graywater harvested from the building. The reference evapotranspiration rate (ET_0) for Austin in July, obtained from the local agricultural data service, is 8.12. The high-efficiency irrigation system utilizes drip irrigation with an efficiency of 90% and reuses an estimated 4,200 gallons of graywater during July. Table 3 shows the calculations to determine total potable water use for the designed case.

The baseline case uses the same reference evapotranspiration rate and total site area. However, it uses sprinklers for irrigation (IE = 0.625), does not take advantage of graywater harvesting, and irrigates only shrubs and turf grass. Calculations to determine total water use for the baseline case are presented in Table 4.

The design case has an irrigation water demand of 14,632 gallons. Graywater reuse provides 4,200 gallons toward the demand, and this volume is treated as a credit in the water calculation. Thus, the total potable water use in July is 10,432 gallons. The baseline case has an irrigation demand of 38,967 gallons and uses no graywater. The project thus achieves a potable water savings of 73% and earns SS Credit 1, Path 7.

Table 3. Design Case (July)

Landscape Type	Area (sf)	Species Factor (k_s)	Density Factor (k_d)	Microclimate Factor (k_{mc})	K_L	ET_L	IE	TWA (gal)
Shrubs	1,200	Low 0.2	Avg 1.0	High 1.3	0.26	2.11	Drip	1,754.5
Mixed	3,900	Low 0.2	Avg 1.1	High 1.4	0.31	2.50	Drip	6,755
Turf grass	900	Avg 0.7	Avg 1.0	High 1.2	0.84	6.82	Sprinkler	6,122
Subtotal TWA (gal)								14,632
July rainwater and graywater harvest (gal)								(4,200)
TPWA (gal)								10,432

Table 4. Baseline Case (July)

Landscape Type	Area (sf)	Species Factor (k_s)	Density Factor (k_d)	Microclimate Factor (k_{mc})	K_L	ET_L	IE	TWA (gal)
Shrubs	1,200	Avg 0.5	Avg 1.0	High 1.3	0.65	5.28	Sprinkler	6,316.4
Turf grass	4,800	Avg 0.7	Avg 1.0	High 1.2	0.84	6.82	Sprinkler	32,650.8
Subtotal TWA (gal)								38,967

EXAMPLE 2. OPTION 2, PATH 8

The project team could achieve Path 8 by completely eliminating the need for potable water. One strategy is to rely on native plants and harvest rainwater for irrigation use, as shown in Figure 1.

Figure 1. A sketch of potential areas for rainwater collection and native plantings on-site to eliminate the need for potable water for irrigation.

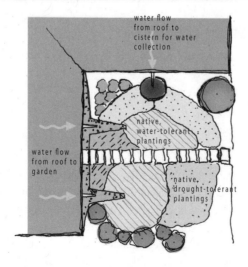

Figure 2. A site section showing the cistern for rainwater harvesting which feeds a drip irrigation system to eliminate any potable water needed for irrigation.

	SS
CI	Credit 1 OPTION 2: PATH 7, PATH 8

9. Exemplary Performance

This path is not eligible for exemplary performance under SS Credit 1, Path 12, Other Quantifiable Environmental Performance.

10. Regional Variations

Much of the United States is faced with increasing demands on existing water supplies, and it is therefore important to landscape sites appropriately for the climate. Appropriately designed landscaping should take into account climate and microclimate, sun exposure, soil type, site drainage, topography, and irrigation options.

In hot, dry climates, use drought-tolerant plants and xeriscape designs. Reducing or eliminating turf grass will lessen the demand on potable water. Rocks and stones can be incorporated into the landscape instead. If turf grass is desired, select a species that can endure drought.

In hot, humid, and temperate climates, use native plants combined with rain or moisture sensors to avoid unnecessary watering in the wet seasons. The use of captured rainwater can help eliminate the use of potable water for irrigation needs.

In cold climates, install hardy native plants and trees. Rain or moisture sensors will prevent excessive watering.

11. Operations and Maintenance Considerations

The building's facility manager will typically be responsible for the operations and maintenance of the water-efficient landscaping systems. A simple way to increase the efficiency of a conventional system is to schedule watering early or late in the day when evaporation is minimal. This allows more water to soak into the ground and reach the roots of the plants. Irrigation systems and controllers must be commissioned to work optimally. This includes inspecting, maintaining, and adjusting the systems on a regular basis.

Resources

Please see USGBC's LEED Resources & Tools (http://www.usgbc.org/projecttools) for additional resources and technical information.

Websites

American Water Works Association, WaterWiser: The Water Efficiency Clearinghouse
http://www.awwa.org/waterwiser
This clearinghouse includes articles, reference materials, and papers on all forms of water efficiency.

California State University at Fresno, Center for Irrigation Technology
http://cati.csufresno.edu/cit

CIT is an independent research and testing facility providing information to designers, manufacturers, and users of irrigation equipment.

Irrigation Association

http://www.irrigation.org

This nonprofit organization promotes products that efficiently use water in irrigation applications.

Rain Bird® ET Manager™ Scheduler

http://www.rainbird.com/landscape/products/controllers/etmanager.htm

This free software provides sufficient local evapo-transpiration data for the United States and Canada. Use data from the closest or most climate-appropriate location.

University of Missouri Extension, Water-Efficient Gardening and Landscaping

http://muextension.missouri.edu/xplor/agguides/hort/g06912.htm

This website has general descriptions and strategies for water efficiency in gardens and landscapings.

Print Media

Evapotranspiration and Irrigation Water Requirements, ASCE Manuals and Reports on Engineering Practice No. 70 (ASCE, 1990).

Efficient Irrigation: A Reference Manual for Turf and Landscape, by Geoff Connellan (University of Melbourne, 2002).

Estimating Irrigation Water Needs of Landscape Plantings in California (University of California Cooperative Extension and California Department of Water Resources, 1999).
This guide explains the landscaping coefficient method established by the University of California.
http://www.owue.water.ca.gov/docs/wucols00.pdf.

Landscape Irrigation: Design and Management, by Stephen W. Smith (John Wiley & Sons, 1996).

Turf Irrigation Manual, fifth edition, by Richard B. Choate (Telsco Industries, 1994).

Water-Efficient Landscaping: Preventing Pollution and Using Resources Wisely (the *EPA*, 2002).
This EPA manual describes ways to reduce water consumption through creative landscaping techniques.

13. Definitions

An **aquifer** is an underground water-bearing rock formation that supplies groundwater, wells, and springs.

Conventional irrigation refers to the most common irrigation system used in the region where the project is located. A common conventional irrigation system uses pressure to deliver water and distributes it through sprinkler heads above the ground.

Drip irrigation delivers water at low pressure through buried mains and submains. From the submains, water is distributed to the soil through a network of perforated tubes or emitters. Drip irrigation is a high-efficiency type of microirrigation.

Evapotranspiration is the loss of water by evaporation from the soil and by transpiration from plants. It is expressed in millimeters per unit of time.

Graywater is defined by the Uniform Plumbing Code (UPC) in its Appendix G, Gray Water Systems for Single-Family Dwellings, as "untreated household waste water which has not come into contact with toilet waste. Greywater includes used water from bathtubs, showers, bathroom wash basins, and water from clothes-washer and laundry tubs. It must not include waste water from kitchen sinks or dishwashers." The International Plumbing Code (IPC) defines graywater in its Appendix C, Gray

Water Recycling Systems, as "waste water discharged from lavatories, bathtubs, showers, clothes washers and laundry sinks." Some states and local authorities allow kitchen sink wastewater to be included in graywater. Other differences with the UPC and IPC definitions can likely be found in state and local codes. Project teams should comply with graywater definitions as established by the authority having jurisdiction in the project area.

The **landscape area** is the total site area less the building footprint, paved surfaces, water bodies, and patios.

Potable water meets or exceeds the EPA's drinking water quality standards and is approved for human consumption by the state or local authorities having jurisdiction; it may be supplied from wells or municipal water systems.

Xeriscaping is a landscaping method that makes routine irrigation unnecessary. It uses drought-adaptable and low-water plants as well as soil amendments such as compost and mulches to reduce evaporation.

OPTION 2, PATH 9: INNOVATIVE WASTEWATER TECHNOLOGIES

1. Benefits and Issues to Consider

Environmental Issues

Water closets and urinals do not require the same high level of water quality that is necessary for fixtures such as faucets and showerheads. Reducing the amount of water needed for the potable water supply reduces the total amount withdrawn from natural water bodies. Similarly, reducing or eliminating the volume of sewage that leaves the site reduces public infrastructure, chemical inputs, energy use, and emissions at municipal water treatment works. Water efficiency and reuse can greatly reduce these environmental impacts, and project teams should consider comparing the environmental impacts of off-site treatment and supply versus on-site treatment.

On-site wastewater treatment systems transform perceived "wastes" into resources that can be used on the building site and provide opportunities to enhance occupants' understanding of nutrient cycles. These resources include treated water volumes for potable and nonpotable use, as well as nutrients that can be applied to the site to improve soil conditions.

Economic Issues

Facilities and spaces that generate large amounts of wastewater can realize considerable savings by reducing the amount of potable water needed for sewage conveyance. High-efficiency toilets and urinals may have a minimal cost premium depending on the building type, but other strategies, such as recycling graywater or rainwater harvesting, require added initial investment by the building developer and may be reflected in the lease rates for these properties. Choosing space in a building with high-efficiency plumbing systems, or incorporating them into tenant spaces where applicable, can reduce water utility costs for the tenant.

2. Related Credits

Efforts to reduce potable water for sewage conveyance can contribute to achieving the following credits:

- SS Credit 1 Option B, Path 10: Water Use Reduction—30%

- WE Prerequisite 1: Water Use Reduction

- WE Credit 1: Water Use Reduction

Water treatment systems, if included in the tenant scope of work, require commissioning and are related to the following credits:

- EA Prerequisite 1: Fundamental Commissioning of Building Energy Systems

- EA Credit 2: Enhanced Commissioning

3. Summary of Referenced Standards

U.S. Energy Policy Act (EPAct) of 1992 (and as amended)
This act addresses energy and water use in commercial, institutional, and residential facilities.

U.S. Energy Policy Act (EPAct) of 2005
This statute became U.S. law in August 2005.

International Association of Plumbing and Mechanical Officials Uniform Plumbing Code,
Section 402.0: Water-Conserving Fixtures and Fittings, effective 2006

Publication IAPMO/ANSI UPC 1-2006
http://www.iapmo.org
The Uniform Plumbing Code defines water-conserving fixtures and fittings for water closets,

urinals, and metered faucets. This code, accredited by the American National Standards Institute, safeguards life, health, property, and public welfare by regulating and controlling the design, construction, installation, quality, location, operation, maintenance, and use of plumbing systems. International Code System, International Plumbing Code, Section 604, Design of Building Water Distribution System, effective 2006

International Code Council

http://www.iccsafe.org

The International Plumbing Code defines maximum flow and consumption rates for plumbing fixtures and fittings for use in public and private lavatories, showerheads, sink faucets, urinals, and water closets.

4. Implementation

Choose a base building with wastewater technologies that are designed to reduce the use of municipal potable water. Either the municipal potable water used for sewage conveyance should be reduced by 50%, or 100% of the on-site wastewater should be treated to tertiary standards. Include one of these requirements in the criteria for selecting a base building.

Potable water is used for many functions that do not require high-quality water, such as toilet and urinal flushing and landscape irrigation. Effective methods for reducing potable water use for sewage conveyance include installation of low-consumption flush fixtures, such as high-efficiency water closets and urinals, nonwater urinals and toilet fixtures, and the harvesting of rainwater or reuse of graywater.

Graywater systems collect the wastewater from sinks, showers, and other sources to reuse for flushing of toilets and urinals, to irrigate landscape, and to serve other functions that do not require potable water. Graywater treatment may be required prior to reuse depending on the intended end use and the local codes. If it is likely that a graywater system will be used in the future, install dual plumbing lines during the initial project construction to avoid the substantial costs and difficulty of adding them later.

When reusing graywater volumes from the building, model the system on an annual basis to determine graywater volumes, generated storage capacity of the system, and any necessary treatment processes before reusing the water volumes. Graywater may not be consistently available throughout the year, depending on building occupants' activities. For instance, graywater volumes in typical office buildings will change only slightly with vacation schedules and holidays, but the volume in a school building will fall during the summer recess, and sufficient water may not be available for irrigation.

When considering an on-site rainwater, graywater, or blackwater collection system, first check with local government agencies for regulations and required permits. Each state has its own standards and requirements for the installation and operation of rainwater, graywater, and water treatment systems. Texas and California, for example, have standards that encourage the use of graywater systems, whereas other states have regulations that may limit or prohibit using graywater. In many areas, irrigation with graywater must be subsurface, although some regions allow aboveground irrigation.

Projects that plan to treat wastewater on-site should consider constructed wetlands, mechanical recirculating sand filters, and anaerobic biological treatment reactors.

The quality of rainwater is typically higher than that of collected graywater, so rainwater systems have significantly fewer code requirements and are often less expensive than graywater systems. Stormwater retention systems can be designed with cisterns to hold rainwater runoff for nonpotable use.

Local climate and weather patterns should be factored into determining the feasibility of harvesting rainwater to reduce potable water for plumbing fixture flushing and landscape irrigation. When precipitation is evenly spread out throughout the year, rainwater harvesting systems may not require large storage capacities.

5. Timeline and Team

The project team should make innovative wastewater systems a criterion for site selection. Real estate brokers and leasing agents can help identify buildings that comply.

6. Calculations

The following calculations are based on the annual generation of blackwater volumes from plumbing fixtures such as water closets and urinals. The calculations compare the design case with a baseline case and are based on occupancy conditions and fixtures and fittings for the entire building in which the tenant space is located.

User Groups

It may be advantageous when performing the water use calculations to divide the facility into separate user groups, calculate water use for each, and sum the values to determine whole building performance. User groups are populations within the building that use a specific subset of washroom facilities. Indicate which fixtures are available to each. If all occupants within the building have access to all fixtures, or if all fixtures are standard throughout the building, enter only a single user group. That is the simpler approach, but it may be more appropriate to define two or more groups to account for different fixtures in one area of the building or special usage patterns by a population within the building. For example, if fixture usage patterns are different on the first floor, enter a separate fixture group for the first floor.

The following scenario illustrates the application of different fixture usage groups.

The Riggs Hotel is in an urban center. The ground floor includes a restaurant open to the public, the hotel lobby, and administrative offices. The upper floors contain guest rooms. Restaurant, back-of-house, and guestroom restroom facilities have different fixture and fitting models. The project team has identified 3 distinct populations in the building and the specific restroom facilities they use: (1) restaurant (including customers and restaurant staff), (2) administrative back-of-house (including hotel administrators and operations staff), and (3) guest rooms (including hotel guests).

Calculating Occupancy

Calculate the FTE for regular building occupants, based on a standard 40-hour weekly occupancy period. An 8-hour occupant has an FTE value of 1.0, and part-time and overtime occupants have an FTE value based on their hours per day divided by 8 (FTE calculations for each shift of the project must be used consistently for all LEED credits). In buildings with multiple shifts, use the number of FTEs from all shifts. For residential projects, use the number of residents.

Estimate the transient building occupants, such as students, visitors, and customers. Transient occupants can be reported as either a daily total or a full-time equivalent. When using daily totals for transients, match the fixture uses for each occupancy type with the values shown in Table 3 (e.g., for the daily total of students, assume 0.5 lavatory faucet uses per daily student visitor). If transients are reported as a daily full-time equivalent value, fixture uses for FTEs must be assumed regardless of the transient population's identity (e.g., for students reported as FTEs, assume 3 lavatory faucet uses per student FTE). Use a transient occupancy number that is a representative daily average over the course of a year.

If occupancy is not known, see Appendix 1, Default Occupancy Counts, for requirements and guidance. If the number of transient visitors per day for retail facilities is unknown, estimate the FTE value of this population based on the default values presented in Table 2.

Table 1 provides default fixture use values for different occupancy types. These values should be used in the calculations for this credit unless special circumstances warrant modifications. Most buildings with students, visitors, and retail customers will also have FTE occupants. Half of all students and visitors occupants are assumed to use a flush fixture and a lavatory faucet in the building and are not expected to use a shower or kitchen sink. A fifth of retail customers are assumed to use a flush and a flow fixture in the building and no shower or kitchen sink. The default for residential occupants is 5 uses per day of water closet and lavatory faucet, 1 shower, and 4 kitchen sink uses.

For consistency across LEED projects, the calculations require the use of a balanced, 1-to-1 gender ratio unless specific project conditions warrant an alternative. For these special situations, provide a narrative description to explain the unique circumstances.

Table 1. Standard Fixture Uses, by Occupancy Type

Fixture Type	FTE	Student/Visitor	Retail Customer	Resident
	Uses/Day			
Water Closet				
— Female	3	0.5	0.2	5
— Male	1	0.1	0.1	5
Urinal				
— Female	0	0	0	n/a
— Male	2	0.4	0.1	n/a
Lavatory Faucet — duration 15 sec; 12 sec with autocontrol — residential, duration 60 sec	3	0.5	0.2	5
Shower — duration 300 sec — residential, duration 480 sec	0.1	0	0	1
Kitchen Sink, — duration 15 sec — residential, duration 60 sec	1 n/a	0 n/a	0 n/a	n/a 4

Table 2. Default Values for Transient Retail Occupants

Retail space	FTE per 100 (sf)
Large-format retailer (greater than 50,000 square feet)	0.91
Grocery store	0.87
Restaurant	1.05
Small retailer	0.67
Service	0.77
Sources: 2001 Uniform Building Code, 2004–2005 Database for Energy Efficiency Resources (DEER) Update Study; field investigation work performed by LEED Retail Core Committee Members; ASNI/ASHRAE/IESNA 90.1–2007; LEED Reference Guide for Green Interior Design and Construction, 2009 Edition.	

Design Case

The design case annual water use is determined by totaling the annual volume of each fixture type and subtracting any nonpotable water supply. The design case must use the rated flow rates and flush volumes for installed plumbing fixtures and fittings. Obtain water consumption data from manufacturers' published product literature.

Perform calculations for each type of blackwater-generating fixture (Table 3).

Table 3. Sample Blackwater-Generating Fixtures and Fittings and Water Consumption

Flush fixture	Flow rate (gpf)
Conventional water closet	1.6
High-efficiency toilet (HET), single-flush gravity	1.28
HET, single-flush pressure assist	1.0
HET, dual flush (full-flush)	1.6
HET, dual flush (low-flush)	1.1
HET, foam flush	0.05
Non-water toilet	0.0
Conventional urinal	1.0
High-efficiency urinal (HEU)	0.5
Nonwater urinal	0.0

If rainwater or graywater harvested on-site is used for sewage conveyance, enter the estimated quantity in the calculation. Subtract the total annual quantity of nonpotable water from the total annual design case water usage. Calculations are required to demonstrate that the reuse volumes of rainwater or graywater are sufficient to meet water closet demands.

Baseline Case

The baseline case annual water use is determined by setting the fixture flush rates and flow rates to default values (as opposed to actual installed values in the design case).

Eligible Fixtures

This credit is limited to savings generated by water using flush fixtures (i.e., urinals and water closets).

7. Documentation Guidance

As a first step in preparing to complete the LEED Online documentation requirements, work through the following measures. Refer to LEED Online for the complete descriptions of all required documentation.

- Determine the number of occupants of each type (e.g., FTEs, retail customers, visitors).

- Retain plumbing fixture schedules and manufacturer data showing the water consumption rates, manufacturer, and model of each fixture and fitting.

- List plumbing fixtures by usage groups, if appliable.

- Define each usage group used.

- If applicable, retain information about system schematics and capacity of rainwater or graywater systems.

8. Examples

EXAMPLE 1. Wastewater Treatment System

On-site biological treatment transforms waste into resources that can be used on the building site. Figure 1 shows the steps for on-site treatment. As solids settle in the aerobic septic tank, microbes begin to feed and break down the waste. The closed aerobic reactor is aerated by pumps to help remove aromatic compounds. The open aerobic reactors contain plants, algae, snails, and fish that further break down the organic waste. In the constructed wetland, aerobic and anaerobic reactions remove the remaining impurities and nitrates. This creates clean, nonpotable water that can be used in irrigation systems, water closets, or cooling towers.

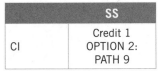
Figure 1. On-site Biological Treatment of Wastewater

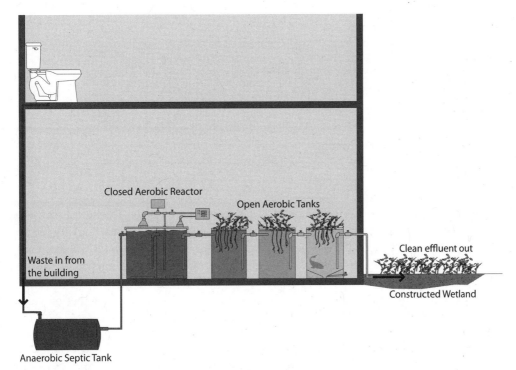

EXAMPLE 2. Calculating Design and Baseline Cases

Table 4 shows sample potable water calculations for sewage conveyance for a 2-story office building with 300 occupants. The calculations are based on a typical 8-hour workday. It is assumed that building occupants are 50% male and 50% female. Male occupants are assumed to use water closets once and urinals twice in a typical workday. Female occupants are assumed to use water closets 3 times.

Table 4. Design Case

Fixture Type	Daily Uses	Flowrate (gpf)	Occupants	Sewage Generation (gal)
Low-Flow Water Closet (Male)	0	1.1	150	0
Low-Flow Water Closet (Female)	3	1.1	150	495
Composting Toilet (Male)	1	0.0	150	0
Composting Toilet (Female)	0	0.0	150	0
Waterless Urinal (Male)	2	0.0	150	0
Waterless Urinal (Female)	0	0.0	150	0
Total Daily Volume (gal)				495
Annual Work Days				260
Annual Volume (gal)				128,700
Rainwater or Graywater Reuse Volume (gal)				(36,000)
Total Annual Volume (gal)				92,700

First, the design case is considered to determine annual potable water usage for sewage conveyance. The building uses either nonpotable rainwater for sewage conveyance or no water for sewage conveyance (i.e., fixtures are waterless urinals and composting toilets). Table 4 summarizes the sewage generation rates; 92,700 gallons of potable water are used annually for sewage conveyance. In the example, 36,000 gallons of rainwater are harvested and directed to water closets for flushing.

Table 5. Baseline Case

Fixture Type	Daily Uses	Flowrate (gpf)	Occupants	Sewage Generation (gal)
Water Closet (Male)	1	1.6	150	240
Water Closet (Female)	3	1.6	150	720
Urinal (Male)	2	1.0	150	300
Urinal (Female)	0	1.0	150	0
Total Daily Volume (gal)				1,260
Annual Work Days				260
Total Annual Volume (gal)				327,600

Table 5 summarizes baseline calculations. The baseline case estimates that sewage conveyance requires 327,600 gallons of potable water per year. Comparison of the baseline with the design case indicates that the building realizes a 72% reduction in potable water volumes used for sewage conveyance (1 – 92,700/327,600). Thus, this strategy earns 2 points under this credit. When developing the baseline, only the fixtures, sewage generation rates, and the water reuse credit are different from the design case; usage rates, occupancy, and number of workdays remain the same.

9. Exemplary Performance

This path is not eligible for exemplary performance under SS Credit 1, Path 12, Other Quantifiable Environmental Performance.

10. Regional Variations

The necessity and availability of wastewater reuse and treatment strategies vary by region. Where aquifers cannot meet the needs of the population, rainwater and other recovered water is the least expensive alternative source. In drought-prone regions, on-site graywater and blackwater treatment may provide an alternative to using potable water for faucets and showers.

Local and regional building and health codes and ordinances govern on-site water treatment and the use of harvested rainwater and graywater; these strategies are prohibited in some states. Additionally, codes differ in their handling of alternative plumbing fixtures, such as dual-flush or low-flow water closets, composting toilets, and waterless urinals. Confirm the legality of nontraditional approaches with code officials prior to making a commitment to specific water-saving strategies.

11. Operations and Maintenance Considerations

To ensure continued water savings as well as owner and occupant satisfaction, maintenance staff must be trained in the operations and maintenance of any specialized equipment. For example, waterless urinals generally need to be cleaned according to manufacturers' specifications and their chemical traps appropriately maintained, and 0.5-gallon and 0.2-gallon flushing urinals must also be maintained according to manufacturers' specifications.

Resources

Please see USGBC's LEED Resources & Tools (http://www.usgbc.org/projecttools) for additional resources and technical information.

Websites

American Rainwater Catchment Systems Association

http://www.arcsa-usa.org

This website includes a variety of publications such as the Texas Guide to Rainwater Harvesting.

Choosing a Toilet

http://www.taunton.com/finehomebuilding/pages/h00042.asp

This article in *Fine Homebuilding* describes several types of water-efficient toilets.

***Environmental Building News,* Water: Doing More with Less**

http://www.buildinggreen.com/auth/article.cfm/2008/2/3/Water-Doing-More-With-Less

This article describes building water efficiency.

National Oceanic and Atmospheric Administration, National Climatic Data Center

http://www.ncdc.noaa.gov/oa/ncdc.html

This site is useful for researching local climate data such as rainfall amounts. It also includes links to state climate offices.

Rocky Mountain Institute (RMI), Water

http://www.rmi.org/sitepages/pid128.php

This portion of RMI's website is devoted to water conservation and efficiency. The site contains information on commercial, industrial, and institutional water use, watershed management, and articles on policy and implementation.

Terry Love's Consumer Toilet Reports

http://www.terrylove.com/crtoilet.htm

This website offers a plumber's perspective on many of the major toilets used in commercial and residential applications.

U.S. EPA, Constructed Wetlands for Wastewater Treatment and Wildlife Habitat: 17 Case Studies, 1993

http://www.epa.gov/owow/wetlands/construc

The case studies in this document, Publication 832/B-93-005, describe 17 wetland treatment systems that improve water quality and wildlife habitat. The projects described include systems with constructed and natural wetlands; created and restored habitats; and municipal effluent, urban stormwater, and river water quality improvements.

U.S. EPA, How to Conserve Water and Use It Effectively

http://www.epa.gov/owow/NPS/chap3.html

This website provides guidance for commercial, industrial, and residential water-users on saving water and reducing sewage volumes.

U.S. EPA, On-Site Wastewater Treatment Systems Manual

http://www.epa.gov/OW-OWM.html/septic/pubs/septic_management_handbook.pdf

This manual provides a focused, performance-based approach to on-site wastewater treatment and system management, including information on a variety of on-site sewage treatment options.

U.S. EPA, WaterSense

http://www.epa.gov/watersense

The WaterSense Program is intended to make it easy for U.S. consumers to save water and protect the environment. Look for the WaterSense label to help choose high-quality, water-efficient products. A variety of products is available, and they do not require a change in lifestyle.

Water Closet Performance Testing

http://www.ebmud.com/conserving_&_recycling/toilet_test_report/default.htm
This site provides 2 reports of independent test results on flush performance and reliability for a variety of toilets.

Print Media

Constructed Wetlands for Wastewater Treatment and Wildlife Habitat: 17 Case Studies (EPA 832/B-93-005) (U.S. EPA, 1993).

Mechanical & Electrical Equipment for Buildings, eighth edition, by Benjamin Stein and John Reynolds (John Wiley and Sons, 1992).

Sustainable Building Technical Manual (Public Technology, Inc., 1996).

On-Site Wastewater Treatment Systems Manual (U.S. EPA, 2002).
http://www.epa.gov/owm/septic/pubs/septic_2002_osdm_all.pdf
This manual provides a focused and performance-based approach to on-site wastewater treatment and system management. The document provides valuable information on various on-site sewage treatment options.

13. Definitions

Aquatic systems are ecologically designed treatment systems in which a diverse community of biological organisms (e.g., bacteria, plants, fish) treat wastewater.

An **aquifer** is an underground water-bearing rock formation that supplies groundwater, wells, and springs.

Blackwater definitions vary, but wastewater from toilets and urinals is always considered blackwater. Wastewater from kitchen sinks (perhaps differentiated by the use of a garbage disposal), showers, or bathtubs is considered blackwater under some state or local codes.

Composting toilet systems utilize foam flush or nonwater toilet fixtures to treat human waste via biological processes, producing biologically stable end products.

Graywater is defined by the Uniform Plumbing Code (UPC) in its Appendix G, Gray Water Systems for Single-Family Dwellings, as "untreated household waste water which has not come into contact with toilet waste. Greywater includes used water from bathtubs, showers, bathroom wash basins, and water from clothes-washer and laundry tubs. It must not include waste water from kitchen sinks or dishwashers." The International Plumbing Code (IPC) defines graywater in its Appendix C, Gray Water Recycling Systems, as "waste water discharged from lavatories, bathtubs, showers, clothes washers and laundry sinks." Some states and local authorities allow kitchen sink wastewater to be included in graywater. Other differences with the UPC and IPC definitions can likely be found in state and local codes. Project teams should comply with graywater definitions as established by the authority having jurisdiction in the project area.

Nonpotable water. See **potable water.**

On-site wastewater treatment systems transport, store, treat, and dispose of wastewater volumes generated on the project site.

Potable Water is water that is suitable for drinking and is supplied from wells or municipal water systems. Potable Water is water that meets drinking water quality standards and is approved for human consumption by the state or local authorities having jurisdiction.

Process water is used for industrial processes and building systems such as cooling towers, boilers, and chillers. It can also refer to water used in operational processes, such as dishwashing, clothes washing, and ice making.

Tenant space is the area within the LEED project boundary. For more information on what can and must be in the LEED project boundary see the Minimum Program Requirements (MPRs) and LEED 2009 MPR Supplemental Guidance. Note: tenant space is the same as project space.

Tertiary treatment is the highest form of wastewater treatment and includes removal of organics, solids, and nutrients as well as biological or chemical polishing, generally to effluent limits of 10 mg/L biological oxygen demand (BOD) 5, and 10 mg/L total suspended solids (TSS).

Wastewater is the spent or used water from a home, community, farm, or industry that contains dissolved or suspended matter. (Federal Remediation Technologies Roundtable)

Waterless urinals are dry plumbing fixtures that use advanced hydraulic design and a buoyant fluid to maintain sanitary conditions.

OPTION 2, PATH 10: WATER USE REDUCTION—30% REDUCTION

1. Benefits and Issues to Consider

Refer to the Benefits and Issues section of WE Credit 1: Water Use Reduction. Option 2, Path 10 of SS Credit 1 differs from WE Credit 1 in that it applies to whole buildings, rather than to occupant spaces within buildings.

2. Related Credits

For information on related credits, refer to the Related Credits section in WE Credit 1.

3. Summary of Referenced Standards

The Energy Policy Act (EPAct) of 1992 (and as amended)
This act addresses energy and water use in commercial, institutional, and residential facilities.

The Energy Policy Act (EPAct) of 2005
This statute became U.S. law in August 2005.

International Association of Plumbing and Mechanical Officials, Uniform Plumbing Code, Section 402.0, Water-Conserving Fixtures and Fittings, effective 2006
Publication IAPMO/ANSI UPC 1-2006
http://www.iapmo.org
The Uniform Plumbing Code defines water-conserving fixtures and fittings for water closets, urinals, and metered faucets. This ANSI-accredited code safeguards life, health, property, and public welfare by regulating and controlling the design, construction, installation, quality, location, operation, maintenance, and use of plumbing systems.

International Code Council, International Plumbing Code, Section 604, Design of Building Water Distribution System, effective 2006
http://www.iccsafe.org
The International Plumbing Code defines maximum flow and consumption rates for plumbing fixtures and fittings for use in public and private lavatories, sink faucets, urinals, and water closets.

4. Implementation

Choose a base building that is equipped with water-conserving plumbing fixtures for the entire building. The building owner is required to demonstrate that these fixtures use 30% less water compared with the baseline fixture performance, and must also have an ongoing plan to require future occupants to comply. This path applies to LEED projects that use 50% or less of the building's total square footage; this requirement prevents large projects that occupy the majority of the building from getting double credit here and under WE Credit 1.

See WE Prerequisite 1 for more information.

5. Timeline and Team

The project team should make water-conserving fixtures and fittings a criterion for site selection. Real estate brokers and leasing agents can help identify buildings that comply.

See WE Prerequiste 1 for more information.

6. Calculations

The following section describes the calculation methodology for determining water use savings under this credit. The water use reduction for the project is the difference between the calculated design case and a baseline case. The percentage is determined by dividing the design case usage by the baseline usage. The methodology differs from traditional plumbing design, in which the calculations are based on fixture counts; under this credit, the water use calculation is based on fixture and fitting water consumption rates and estimated usage by the occupants. Estimated occupant usage is determined by calculating full-time equivalent (FTE) and transient occupants and applying appropriate fixture use rates to each occupant type. For this credit, occupancy is based on the entire facility, not just the tenant space occupied by the LEED project.

User Groups

It may be advantageous when performing the water use calculations to divide the facility into separate user groups, calculate water use for each, and sum the values to determine whole building performance. User groups are populations within the building that use a specific subset of washroom facilities. Indicate which fixtures are available to each. If all occupants within the building have access to all fixtures, or if all fixtures are standard throughout the building, enter only a single user group. That is the simpler approach, but it may be more appropriate to define two or more groups to account for different fixtures in one area of the building or special usage patterns by a population within the building. For example, if fixture usage patterns are different on the first floor, enter a separate fixture group for the first floor.

Calculating Occupancy

Calculate the FTE for regular building occupants, based on a standard 40-hour weekly occupancy period. An 8-hour occupant has an FTE value of 1.0, and part-time and overtime occupants have an FTE value based on their hours per day divided by 8 (FTE calculations for each shift of the project must be used consistently for all LEED credits). In buildings with multiple shifts, use the number of FTEs from all shifts. For residential projects, the number of residents is the occupancy number.

Estimate the transient building occupants, such as students, visitors, and customers. Transient occupants can be reported as either a daily total or a full-time equivalent. When using daily totals for transients, match the fixture uses for each occupancy type with the values shown in Table 3 (e.g., for the daily total of students, assume 0.5 lavatory faucet uses per daily student visitor). If transients are reported as a daily full-time equivalent value, fixture uses for FTEs must be assumed regardless of the transient population's identity (e.g., for students reported as FTEs, assume 3 lavatory faucet uses per student FTE). Use a transient occupancy number that is a representative daily average over the course of a year.

If the number of transient visitors per day for retail facilities is unknown, estimate the FTE value of this population based on the default values presented in Table 1.

Table 2 provides default fixture use values for different occupancy types. These values should be used in the calculations for this credit unless special circumstances warrant modification. Most buildings with students, visitors, and retail customers will also have FTE occupants. Half of all students and visitors are assumed to use a water closet or urinal and a lavatory faucet in the building and are not expected to use a shower or kitchen sink. A fifth of retail customer occupants are assumed to use a water closet or urinal and lavatory faucet in the building and no shower or kitchen sink. The default for residential occupants is 5 uses per day of water closet and lavatory faucet, 1 shower, and 4 kitchen sink uses.

For consistency across LEED projects, the calculations require the use of a balanced, 1-to-1 gender ratio unless specific project conditions warrant an alternative. For these special situations, provide a narrative description to explain the unique circumstances.

Table 1. Default Values for Transient Retail Occupants

Retail space	FTE per 100 (sf)
Large-format retailer (greater than 50,000 square feet)	0.91
Grocery store	0.87
Restaurant	1.05
Small retailer	0.67
Service	0.77

Sources: 2001 Uniform Building Code, 2004–2005 Database for Energy Efficiency Resources (DEER) Update Study; field investigation work performed by LEED Retail Core Committee Members; ASNI/ASHRAE/IESNA 90.1–2007; LEED Reference Guide for Green Interior Design and Construction, 2009 Edition.

Table 2. Standard Fixture Uses, by Occupancy Type

Fixture Type	FTE	Student/Visitor	Retail Customer	Resident
	Uses/Day			
Water Closet				
— Female	3	0.5	0.2	5
— Male	1	0.1	0.1	5
Urinal				
— Female	0	0	0	n/a
— Male	2	0.4	0.1	n/a
Lavatory Faucet — duration 15 sec; 12 sec with autocontrol — residential, duration 60 sec	3	0.5	0.2	5
Shower — duration 300 sec — residential, duration 480 sec	0.1	0	0	1
Kitchen Sink, — duration 15 sec — residential, duration 60 sec	1 n/a	0 n/a	0 n/a	n/a 4

Design Case Water Consumption Calculations

The design case annual water use is determined by totaling the annual volume of each fixture type and subtracting any nonpotable water supply. The design case must use the rated flow rates and flush volumes for installed plumbing fixtures and fittings. Obtain water consumption data should be obtained from manufacturers' published product literature. Table 3 shows examples of typical water consumption rates for different fixture and fitting technologies.

If rainwater or graywater harvested on-site is used for sewage conveyance, enter the estimated quantity in the calculation. Subtract the total annual quantity of nonpotable water from the total annual design case water usage. Calculations are required to demonstrate that the reuse volumes of rainwater or graywater are sufficient to meet water closet demands.

Table 3. Sample Plumbing Fixtures and Fittings and Water Consumption

Flush fixture	Flow rate (gpf)	Flow fixture	Flow rate
Conventional water closet	1.6	Conventional private lavatory	2.2 gpm
High-efficiency toilet (HET), single-flush gravity	1.28	Conventional public lavatory	0.5 gpm or ≤ 0.25 gpc
HET, single-flush pressure assist	1.0	Conventional kitchen sink	2.2 gpm
HET, dual flush (full-flush)	1.6	Low-flow kitchen sink	1.8 gpm
HET, dual flush (low-flush)	1.1	Conventional shower	2.5 gpm
HET, foam flush	0.05	Low-flow shower	1.8 gpm
Nonwater toilet	0.0		
Conventional urinal	1.0		
High-efficiency urinal (HEU)	0.5		
Nonwater urinal	0.0		

Facilities in residences and apartments, private bathrooms in hotels and hospitals, and restrooms in commercial establishments where the fixtures are intended for the use of a family or an individual are considered private or private-use facilities. All other facilities are considered public or public use. If the classification for public or private use is unclear, default to public-use flow rates in performing the calculations associated with this credit.

Baseline Case Water Consumption Calculations

The baseline case annual water use is determined by setting the fixture and fitting water consumption rates to the baseline values (as opposed to actual installed values in the design case).

Eligible Fixtures

This prerequisite is limited to savings generated by water-using fixtures as shown in Table 1.

7. Documentation Guidance

As a first step in preparing to complete the LEED Online documentation requirements, work through the following measures. Refer to LEED Online for the complete descriptions of all required documentation.

- Determine the number of occupants of each type (e.g., FTEs, retail customers, visitors).

- Retain plumbing fixture schedules and manufacturers' data showing the water consumption rates, manufacturer, and model of each fixture and fitting.

- List plumbing fixtures by usage group, if appliable.

- Define each usage group used.

- Retain information about system schematics and capacity of any rainwater or graywater systems.

8. Examples

There are no examples for this credit.

9. Exemplary Performance

Projects may earn an exemplary performance credit under SS Credit 1, Path 12, Other Quantifiable Environmental Performance, by demonstrating a 40% water use reduction for the whole building.

10. Regional Variations

Refer to the Regional Variations section in WE Prerequisite 1.

11. Operations and Maintenance Considerations

To ensure continued water savings and satisfaction for owners and occupants, maintenance staff should be trained in the operations and maintenance of any specialized equipment. For example, waterless urinals generally need to be cleaned according to manufacturers' specifications and their chemical traps appropriately maintained, and 0.5-gallon and 0.2-gallon flushing urinals, must also be maintained according to manufacturers' specifications.

Water saving opportunities through operations and maintenance should include metering and data recording efforts.

12. Resources

Please see USGBC's LEED Resources & Tools (http://www.usgbc.org/projecttools) for additional resources and technical information. Also refer to the Resources section of WE Prerequisite 1.

13. Definitions

Refer to the Definitions section of WE Prerequisite 1.

OPTION 2, PATH 11: ON-SITE RENEWABLE ENERGY

1. Benefits and Issues to Consider

Environmental Issues

Energy production contributes significantly to air pollution in the United States, releasing such pollutants as sulfur dioxide, nitrogen oxide, and carbon dioxide—primary contributors to acid rain, smog, and climate change—that have widespread and adverse effects on humans, especially respiratory health.

The overall environmental benefits of renewable energy depend on the energy source and the process by which energy is generated. For example, utilization of biomass can reduce the estimated 136 million tons of woody waste from construction, demolition, and land-clearing that is sent to landfills annually,[16] but if these wastes are not processed properly, their combustion could result in harmful air quality. Although renewably generated electricity is not entirely benign, it greatly decreases the negative environmental impacts of power generation. Renewable energy generated on-site is an excellent way for owners to reduce the environmental impacts associated with a building's energy requirements.

Economic Issues

Selecting space in a building that uses on-site renewable energy technologies can result in energy cost savings. Utility rebates are often available to reduce initial costs of renewable energy equipment. The initial costs of installing or providing renewable energy on-site can be offset by savings on energy costs accrued over a period of time. A life-cycle cost analysis of the potential savings that could accrue over the life-cycle of the renewable energy source can help project teams in their decision-making process. In some states, first costs can also be offset by net metering, in which excess energy is sold back to the utility, and through programs that provide incentives for using renewable energy. Project teams must ascertain whether these options are available locally, particularly for the type of renewable energy they plan to use.

Research on the available technologies is essential; consider climatic, geographical, and other regional factors that influence the appropriateness of an on-site renewable source for the building's energy use.

2. Related Credits

Renewable energy equipment installed as a part of the tenant scope will require commissioning and measurement and verification efforts, as described in the following credits:

- EA Prerequisite 1: Fundamental Commissioning of Building Energy Systems
- EA Credit 3: Measurement and Verification

3. Summary of Referenced Standard

ANSI/ASHRAE/IESNA 90.1-2007, Energy Standard for Buildings Except Low-Rise Residential
American Society of Heating, Refrigerating and Air-Conditioning Engineers
American National Standards Institute http://www.ashrae.org

Illuminating Engineers Society of North America
On-site renewable or site-recovered energy that might be used to achieve EA Credit 2, Enhanced Commissioning, is handled as a special case in the modeling process. If either renewable or recovered energy is produced at the site, the energy cost budget method considers it free energy and it is not included in the design energy cost. See the Calculation section for details.

4. Implementation

Choose a base building that is equipped with an on-site renewable energy system. Demonstrate the technology's contribution to the total energy requirements of the building (expressed as a fraction of annual energy cost).

Technologies

Eligible technologies within the base building include photovoltaic, solar thermal, geothermal, wind, biomass, and biogas energy. Eligible systems produce either electric power or thermal energy for use on-site and should, where possible, deliver power to the grid when their output exceeds the site demand. Contact local utilities or electric service providers to determine whether net metering is available.

Energy savings from the use of on-site renewables should be based on either the metered renewable energy produced and used on-site, or the metered renewable energy produced and used on-site or sent to the grid. Energy produced on-site that is not captured and used, whether on-site or via the grid, cannot be included in the credit calculations. For example, if a project building uses photovoltaic panels to generate electricity on-site but does not store energy when output exceeds demand or use net metering, only the portion of renewable electricity actually consumed on-site counts. Renewable energy produced on-site and then sold to the grid is not eligible.

Eligible On-site Systems

On-site renewable energy technologies eligible for Option 11 include these:

- Photovoltaic systems.
- Wind energy systems.
- Solar thermal systems.
- Biofuel-based energy systems (see list of eligible biofuels, below).
- Geothermal energy systems.
- Low-impact hydroelectric power systems.
- Wave and tidal power systems.

There are some restrictions for geothermal energy systems, solar thermal energy systems, and biofuel-based electrical systems. Geothermal energy systems using deep-earth water or steam sources (but not vapor compression systems for heat transfer) may be eligible for this credit. These systems may either produce electric power or provide thermal energy for primary use at the building.

Active solar thermal energy systems that employ collection panels, heat transfer mechanical components such as pumps or fans, and defined heat storage systems such as hot water tanks are eligible for this credit. Thermosiphon solar and storage tank "batch heaters" are also eligible.

The following biofuels are considered renewable energy under this credit:

- Untreated wood waste, including mill residues.
- Agricultural crops or waste.
- Animal waste and other organic waste.
- Landfill gas.

Ineligible On-site Systems

These types of on-site systems are not eligible for this credit:

- Architectural features.

- Passive solar strategies.

- Daylighting strategies.

- Geo-exchange systems (e.g., geothermal or ground-source heat pumps).

Architectural passive solar and daylighting strategies provide significant energy savings. Their contributions are reflected in project-wide energy efficiency levels and facilitate the achievement of EA Prerequisite 2 and EA Credit 1.

Geo-exchange systems are earth-coupled heating, ventilating, and air-conditioning (HVAC) applications that use vapor-compression systems for heat transfer and do not obtain significant quantities of deep-earth heat. They are not eligible as renewable energy systems. The contributions of these systems are reflected in project-wide energy efficiency levels and facilitate the achievement of EA Prerequisite 2 and EA Credit 1.

Energy production based on the following biofuels is not eligible for this credit:

- Combustion of municipal solid waste.

- Forestry biomass waste other than mill residue.

- Wood coated with paints, plastics, or formica.

- Wood treated for preservation with materials containing halogens, chlorine compounds, halide compounds, chromated copper arsenate, or arsenic. If more than 1% of the wood fuel has been treated with these compounds, the energy system is ineligible.

Retention of Renewable Energy Environmental Attributes

For renewable energy coming from on-site sources, the associated environmental attributes must be retained or retired; they cannot be sold. Project teams should understand and value the positive effect of on-site renewables on the surrounding ecosystems. For on-site renewables, energy that exceeds the project building's demand may be sold at fees equivalent to the market rate of nonrenewable energy, but no premium may be charged for the renewable nature of the energy. Such a premium indicates that these attributes have not been retained, and therefore the project team cannot take credit for that energy as renewable.

To encourage the greater development of on-site renewable energy systems, the sale of renewable energy certificates (RECs) is allowed from an on-site renewable energy system that claims credit if the building owner or energy system owner, either separately or acting together, meets the following conditions:

- RECs equal to 200% of the system's annual rated energy output each year are purchased from another source, which must be Green-e eligible. The system's rated output must reflect all system performance characteristics as well as actual local site conditions (e.g., climate, mounting location, and angles). The rationale for the 1-for-2 ratio is that many states have set renewable portfolio standards and in-state renewable energy targets that can be traded in the form of credits. These in-state RECs are typically more expensive to achieve and usually cost more (e.g., $0.05/kWh for New England wind power vs. $0.01/kWh for RECs from West Texas or Dakotas wind). From an environmental and financial perspective, these are not the same for 2 reasons:

- In-state and out-of-state RECs reduce carbon dioxide emissions by the same amount, but out-of-state RECs result in fewer reductions of other emissions than in-state RECs, where the population is concentrated and where RECs are largely purchased.

- Distant renewable energy generation may be stranded by limited technical and design capacities.

Given that in-state RECs create more benefits than out-of-state RECs for non-CO_2 impact but are equal in their CO_2 impacts, in-state credits may be replaced by out-of-state credits on a 1-for-2 basis. This allows green building projects to capture the value of RECs created by on-site renewables while reducing net CO_2.

- The seller of the on-site RECs must follow all established guidelines for the sale of RECs and not claim any of the environmental attributes for the on-site system.

5. Timeline and Team

The project team, with the owner, architect, and engineer, should first estimate the potential energy use of the building so that renewable technologies with adequate capacity can be identified. Systems producing on-site renewable electrical power should be designed to facilitate net metering back to the grid for periods when the renewable energy system output exceeds the site demand. Ask local utilities and electric service providers about incentive and rebate programs.

The project team should make on-site renewable energy generation a criterion for site selection. Real estate brokers and leasing agents can help identify buildings that comply. The LEED-certified buildings database can help identify local buildings that have achieved LEED credit for on-site renewable energy, and local USGBC chapters may also have detailed information on such projects.

6. Calculations

Determining On-site Renewable Quantity

The quantity of energy generated on-site by renewable systems may be predicted using a bin type calculation or determined through submetering. Projects that use a bin calculation are required to account for the contribution of variables associated with the renewable source. For example, a building-integrated photovoltaic (BIPV) design would include the effects of sunny, partly cloudy, and overcast conditions, the orientation and altitude of the array, and system losses. Table 1 shows the factors that affect calculation of the energy generated by a BIPV array.

Once the amount of energy generated by the renewable system is calculated, an energy cost must be computed to establish the LEED level of achievement. The renewable energy cost is calculated by multiplying the renewable energy contribution by either the local utility rate or the Energy Information Administration (EIA) 2003 average energy cost for the renewable fuel type. Multiply the quantity of on-site energy produced by the applicable energy rate for this fuel type.

Determining Whole Building Energy Consumption

The fraction of energy cost supplied by the renewable energy features is calculated against existing utility data (for buildings in operation at least 12 months), energy costs calculated by the U.S. Department of Energy (EIA 2003 Commercial Sector Average Energy Costs by State) in conjunction with the Commercial Buildings Energy Consumption Survey (CBECS) database of annual electricity and natural gas usage per square foot, or total energy costs as calculated by a whole building simulation.

Calculations based on existing utility data

Existing buildings with a utility history may use recent annual utility bills as a basis for the calculating renewable energy contribution. Divide renewable energy cost (renewable energy generated multiplied by utility rate) for a 12-month period by the 12-month total utility costs for the building.

Calculations based on CBECS data

Use the Department of Energy's Commercial Buildings Energy Consumption Survey database to determine the estimated electricity use. This database provides electricity intensity factors (kWh/sf/yr) for various building types in the United States.

To determine the building's annual energy cost, multiply total energy consumption by the average cost for electricity and natural gas (from EIA commercial sector rates for the state). Dividing the renewable energy cost by the building annual energy cost yields the percentage renewable energy.

Calculations based on energy simulation

Projects that complete a whole building simulation in accordance with Option B of EA Credit 1.3, Optimize Energy Performance—HVAC, may use the simulated total building energy consumption as a basis for calculating the renewable energy contribution.

Table 1. BIPV Renewable Energy Calculation

BIPV System Design	
Number of stories	5
Length of south façade	525 (lf)
Depth of awning	.2 (lf)
Gross area of awning	5,250 (sf)
Shading effects	85%
Net area of awning	4,463 (sf)
PV capacity	5.5 (w/sf)
Awning peak capacity	25 (kW)
Average daily output	4.03 (kWh)/100 (sf)
Average annual output	65,641 (kWh)

7. Documentation Guidance

As a first step in preparing to complete the LEED Online documentation requirements, work through the following measures. Refer to LEED Online for the complete descriptions of all required documentation.

- Determine energy use for the project, demonstrate the portion of that supplied by on-site renewable energy systems, and identify a back-up energy source.

- Prepare documentation from the project owner verifying the performance of on-site renewable systems, confirming system capacity, and confirming that renewable energy is not double-counted.

8. Examples

There are no examples for this credit.

9. Exemplary Performance

Projects may earn an exemplary performance credit under SS Credit 1, Path 12, Other Quantifiable Environmental Performance, by demonstrating that on-site renewable energy accounts for 10% or more of the annual building energy cost.

10. Regional Variations

The availability and appropriateness of a renewable energy technology for a building varies by region. Factors like climate, geography, and location can greatly affect a building's choice of the renewable source. For maximum energy savings, project teams should look for buildings that draw from on-site renewable energy sources most efficient for their region, such as solar energy in the southwestern United States, biomass in regions with agricultural land, or wind power in coastal regions.

11. Operations and Maintenance Considerations

There are no operations and maintenance considerations for this credit.

12. Resources

Please see the USGBC's LEED Resources & Tools (http://www.usgbc.org/projecttools) for additional resources and technical information.

Websites

American Wind Energy Association

http://www.awea.org

AWEA is a national trade association representing wind power plant developers, wind turbine manufacturers, utility companies, consultants, insurers, financiers, researchers, and others involved in the wind industry.

ENERGY Guide

http://www.energyguide.com

This website includes information on different power types, including green power, and general information on energy efficiency and tools for selecting power providers based on economic, environmental, and other criteria.

National Renewable Energy Laboratory, National Center for Photovoltaics

http://www.nrel.gov/ncpv

This website provides clearinghouse information on all aspects of photovoltaic systems.

North Carolina Solar Center, Database of State Incentives for Renewable Energy (DSIRE)

http://www.dsireusa.org

This database contains all available information on state financial and regulatory incentives (e.g., tax credits, grants, and special utility rates) that are designed to promote the application of renewable energy technologies. DSIRE also offers additional services such as the preparation and printing of reports that detail the incentives state-by-state.

U.S. Department of Energy, EERE, Renewable Energy Maps and Data

http://www1.eere.energy.gov/maps_data

The maps and data section of DOE's EERE website provides information on regional distribution of renewable energy sources and technologies in the United States.

U.S. Department of Energy, National Renewable Energy Laboratory

http://www.nrel.gov

NREL is a leader in the U.S. Department of Energy's effort to ensure that the nation's energy future is environmentally and economically sustainable.

U.S. Department of Energy, Energy Efficiency and Renewable Energy

http://www.eere.energy.gov

The EERE website includes information on all types of renewable energy technologies and energy efficiency.

U.S. EPA, Green Power Partnership

http://www.epa.gov/greenpower/index.htm

EPA's Green Power Partnership provides assistance and recognition to organizations that demonstrate environmental leadership by choosing green power. It includes a buyer's guide with listings of green power providers by state.

Print Media

Wind and Solar Power Systems, by Mukund Patel (CRC Press 1999).

Wind Energy Comes of Age, by Paul Gipe (John Wiley & Sons 1995).

13. Definitions

Biofuel-based energy systems are electrical power systems that run on renewable fuels derived from organic materials, such as wood by-products and agricultural waste. In LEED, biofuels include untreated wood waste (e.g., mill residues), agricultural crops or waste, animal waste and other organic waste, and landfill gas.

Biomass is plant material from trees, grasses, and crops that can be converted to heat energy to produce electricity.

The **environmental attributes of green power** include the emissions reduction benefits that result from the substitution of renewable energy sources for conventional power sources.

Geothermal energy is electricity generated by harnessing hot water or steam from within the earth.

Geothermal heating systems use pipes to transfer underground heat for heating, cooling, and hot water. These systems retrieve heat from the earth during cool months and return heat in summer months. **Photovoltaic (or solar) energy** is produced by photovoltaic cells that convert sunlight energy into electricity.

Hydro energy is electricity produced from the downhill flow of water from rivers or lakes.

Net metering is a metering and billing arrangement that allows on-site generators to send excess electricity flows to the regional power grid. These electricity flows offset a portion of those drawn from the grid. For more information on net metering in individual states, visit the DOE's Green Power Network website at http://www.eere.energy.gov/greenpower/netmetering.

On-site renewable energy is derived from renewable sources, including solar, wind, geothermal, low-impact hydro, biomass, and biogas, and is integrated into the building energy use and present within the project site perimeter.

Renewable energy comes from sources that are not depleted when used. This includes energy from the sun, wind, and small (low-impact) hydropower.

Renewable energy certificates (**RECs**) are tradable environmental commodities representing proof that a unit of electricity was generated from a renewable energy resource. RECs are sold separately from the electricity itself and thus allow the purchase of green power by a user of conventionally generated electricity.

Solar thermal systems collect or absorb sunlight via solar collectors and heat water that is then circulated to the building's hot water tank. The hot water can be used to warm swimming pools or provide domestic hot water for residential and commercial use.

Wave and tidal power systems capture energy from waves and the diurnal flux of tidal power, respectively. The captured energy is commonly used for desalination, water pumping, and electricity generation.

Wind energy is electricity generated by wind turbines.

OPTION 2, PATH 12: OTHER QUANTIFIABLE ENVIRONMENTAL PERFORMANCE

An "other quantifiable environmental performance" characteristic is any green feature that was implemented according to (1) the requirements of another LEED rating system credit or (2) the exemplary performance criteria of any of the above paths in this credit. A green feature selected from another LEED rating system must be different from those addressed under the LEED for Commercial Interiors Rating System.

1. Benefits and Issues to Consider

Path 12 rewards properties that employ the highest and best green building strategies—innovations that go beyond those covered in this credit. Path 12 thus accommodates credits from other LEED rating systems not specifically itemized in Paths 1 through 11. For example, the exemplary performance criteria under SS Credit 5.1, Site Development—Protect or Restore Habitat, in LEED for New Construction awards 1 innovation point for restoring or protecting a minimum of 75% of the site area (excluding the building footprint) with native or adapted vegetation on previously developed or graded sites. Projects that implement such a program at a LEED-certified building site may apply for this option. Path 12 may also be used when the selected building meets the exemplary performance criteria specified for a requirement of SS Credit 1, Paths 1 through 11; project teams should refer to the information under Exemplary Performance in Paths 1 through 11 to determine the performance level needed to achieve an additional point.

2. Related Credits

Refer to the Related Credits section in the credit from the other rating system or under Paths 1 through 11.

3. Summary of Referenced Standards

Refer to the standards referenced for the credit from the other rating system or under Paths 1 through 11.

4. Implementation

Choose a base building that has achieved an environmental performance characteristic for at least 1 credit found in another LEED rating system, but not listed in Option2, Paths 1 through 11 or that has achieved an additional point for exemplary performance, as appropriate, in the credit listed in Option2, Paths 1 through 11. Innovation in Design credits that are not addressed by existing credits in other LEED rating systems will also be considered.

For projects attempting to earn a point for this path by achieving an environmental performance characteristic for at least 1 credit not listed in listed in Option2, Paths 1 through 11. The Eligibility Criteria that selected credits must meet include:

- Applicability to the entire building or site;

- Demonstration of an ongoing performance impact (environmental, health, etc.); and

- Selection of credits that are unaddressed by the LEED for Green Interior Design and Construction, 2009 Edition and found in the applicable LEED 2009 Rating Systems, such as LEED for Green Building Design and Construction, 2009 Edition and LEED for Green Building Operations and Maintenance, 2009 Edition or that have overlapping strategies with credits found in the LEED-CI Rating System, but are qualified by the notes provided below to prevent double-counting.

Per the criteria listed on the previous page, specific guidance has been provided for select credits below:

Table 1. Pre-approved credits for use with LEED-CI SSc1, Option 2, Path 12

LEED 2009 for New Construction Credits		Conditions for Use
SSc4.3	Alternative Transportation—Low-Emitting and Fuel Efficient Vehicles	No special conditions apply
EAp1	Fundamental Commissioning of Building Energy Systems	Eligible if project meets the following conditions: 1. The project is located within a building that is less than 5 years old. 2. The project scope (tenant scope) does not include HVAC&R systems as they are a part of the base building system. 3. Project area is less than 50% of the total building area.
EAc3	Enhanced Commissioning	Eligible if project meets the following conditions: 1. The project is located within a building that is less than 5 years old. 2. The project scope (tenant scope) does not include HVAC&R systems as they are a part of the base building system. 3. Project area is less than 50% of the total building area.
EAc4	Enhanced Refrigerant Management	No special conditions apply
EAc5	Measurement and Verification	Eligible if project meets the following conditions: 1. The project scope (tenant scope) does not include HVAC&R systems as they are part of the base building system. 2. Project area is less than 75% of the total building area. 3. The tenant shares common spaces in the building, such as lobby, corridors, and restrooms.
LEED 2009 for Existing Buildings: Operations and Maintenance Credits		**Conditions for Use**
SSc2	Building Exterior and Hardscape Management Plan	No special conditions apply
SSc3	Integrated Pest Management, Erosion Control, and Landscape Management Plan	No special conditions apply
SSc5	Site Development—Protect or Restore Open Habitat	No special conditions apply
WEc4	Cooling Tower Water Management	No special conditions apply
EAp1	Energy Efficiency Best Management Practices—Planning, Documentation, and Opportunity Assessment	Eligible if project meets the following conditions: 1. The project is located within a building that is 5 years or older. 2. The project scope (tenant scope) does not include HVAC&R systems as they are a part of the base building system. 3. Project area is less than 50% of the total building area.
EAc1	Optimize Energy Performance	No special conditions apply
EAc2.1	Existing Building Commissioning—Investigation and Analysis	Eligible if project meets the following conditions: 1. The project is located within a building that is 5 years or older. 2. The project scope (tenant scope) does not include HVAC&R systems as they are a part of the base building system. 3. Project area is less than 50% of the total building area.
MRc4	Sustainable Purchasing—Reduced Mercury in Lamps	No special conditions apply
MRc5	Sustainable Purchasing—Food	No special conditions apply
MRc6	Solid Waste Management—Waste Stream	No special conditions apply
MRc7	Solid Waste Management—Ongoing Consumables	No special conditions apply
MRc8	Solid Waste Management—Durable Goods	No special conditions apply
IEQp3	Green Cleaning Policy	No special conditions apply
IEQc1.1	Indoor Quality Best Management Practices—Indoor Air Quality Management Program	No special conditions apply
IEQc3.6	Green Cleaning—Indoor Integrated Pest Management	No special conditions apply

For projects attempting to earn a point for this credit by achieving exemplary performance for eligible credits in SS Credit 1, Option 2, Paths 1 through 11, documentation of exemplary performance must be provided. The same approach can be taken for Innovation in Design credits that are not included in Option 2, Paths 1 through 11, however, these credits must meet the 4 Eligibility Criteria listed on the previous page.

A maximum of 1 additional point can be awarded if the specified threshold is achieved.

5. Timeline and Team

Refer to the Timeline and Team information under the selected credit.

6. Calculations

Refer to the Calculations section under the selected credit.

7. Documentation Guidance

As a first step in preparing to complete the LEED Online documentation requirements, work through the following measure. Refer to LEED Online for the complete descriptions of all required documentation.

- Prepare a brief narrative, calculations, or other information that demonstrates the nature of the other environmental benefits delivered. Refer to the Documentation Guidance section under the selected credit.

8. Examples

Refer to the Examples section under the selected credit.

9. Exemplary Performance

Projects earning SS Credit 1, Path 12, Other Quantifiable Environmental Performance, through exemplary performance of any of the SS Credit 1 compliance paths are not eligible for additional exemplary performance under the Innovation in Design section.

10. Regional Variations

Refer to the Regional Variations section under the selected credit.

11. Operations and Maintenance Considerations

Refer to the Operations and Maintenance section under the selected credit.

12. Resources

Please see the USGBC's LEED Resources & Tools (http://www.usgbc.org/projecttools) for additional resources and technical information.

13. Definitions

There are no definitions associated with this credit.

DEVELOPMENT DENSITY AND COMMUNITY CONNECTIVITY

	CI
Credit	SS Credit 2
Points	6 points

Intent

To channel development to urban areas with existing infrastructure, protect greenfields and preserve habitat and natural resources.

Requirements

OPTION 1. Development Density

Select space in a building that is located in an established, walkable community with a minimum density of 60,000 square feet per acre net. The density calculation is based on a typical two-story downtown development and must include the area of the project being built.

OR

OPTION 2. Community Connectivity

Select space in a building on a site that meets the following criteria:

- Is located within 1/2-mile of a residential area or neighborhood with an average density of 10 units per acre net
- Is within 1/2-mile of at least 10 basic services
- Has pedestrian access between the building and the services.

For mixed-use projects, no more than 1 service within the project boundary may be counted as 1 of the 10 basic services, provided it is open to the public. No more than 2 of the 10 services required may be anticipated (i.e. at least 8 must be existing and operational). In addition, the anticipated services must be documented appropriately to demonstrate that they will be operational in the locations indicated within 1 year of occupation of the applicant project.

Examples of basic services include the following:

- Bank
- Place of Worship
- Convenience Grocery
- Day Care Center
- Cleaners
- Fire Station
- Beauty Salon

- Hardware
- Laundry
- Library
- Medical or Dental Office
- Senior Care Facility
- Park
- Pharmacy

- Post Office
- Restaurant
- School
- Supermarket
- Theater
- Community Center
- Fitness Center
- Museum

Proximity is determined by drawing a 1/2-mile radius around a main building entrance on a site map and counting the services within that radius.

Greenfield developments and projects that do not use existing infrastructure are not eligible.

1. Benefits and Issues to Consider

Environmental Issues

Consider proximity to transportation and community services. Selecting base buildings located within walking distance of existing or planned basic services reduce transportation impacts, such as air pollution and greenhouse gas emissions.

Many cities have existing buildings that could be rehabilitated, an approach that reduces the demand for new materials. The potential trade-offs for sites in dense areas include limited open space and factors that may compromise indoor environmental quality, such as contaminated soils, undesirable air quality, or limited daylighting opportunities.

Economic Issues

Locating a Commercial Interiors project on an infill site helps control urban sprawl and uses existing infrastructure, including roads, utility services, and other amenities that benefit the local economy. If a site is close to mass transit, significant cost reductions may be achieved by downsizing parking space for building occupants. In addition, making access to basic services walkable may improve the productivity and health of building occupants by reducing the time spent driving and increasing their levels of physical activity both of which translate into reduced costs for tenants. The redevelopment of urban areas helps restore, invigorate, and sustain established urban living patterns, creating a more stable and interactive community.

2. Related Credits

By selecting buildings located in urban areas, tenants can increase the likelihood of providing building occupants with access to public transportation, thus assisting project teams with earning the following credit:

- SS Credit 3.1: Alternative Transportation—Public Transportation Access

3. Summary of Referenced Standards

There are no standards referenced for this credit.

4. Implementation

The most common approach for achieving this credit is to give preference to sites within an existing urban fabric. Work with local jurisdictions to follow the urban development plan and meet or exceed density goals. When choosing sites based on infrastructure, transportation, and quality of life, explore opportunities for alliances and innovations with neighboring spaces. Look at locations with redevelopment plans that will achieve the required development density by the completion of the project. Choose a building in an area where community revitalization is already underway and the required development density will be met by the time the project is completed.

OPTION 1. Development Density

To determine the development density, assess the density of the LEED project site, as well as the densities of surrounding developments. Determine the total area of the project site and the total square footage of the building. For projects that are part of a larger property (such as a campus), define the project area (outlined in the LEED project's scope). The project area must be defined consistently throughout LEED documentation.

Calculate the density of the project site and the density radius using the equations below. Overlay the density radius on a site map that includes the project site and surrounding areas, originating from the center of the LEED project site. This is the density boundary. For each property within the density boundary (including the LEED project site and any properties that intersect the density boundary), create a table with the building square footage and site area of each property. Include all properties except for undeveloped public areas, such as parks and water bodies. Do not include public roads and right-of-way areas. Information on neighboring properties can be obtained from your city or county zoning department.

OPTION 2. Community Connectivity

Consider both residential and commercial neighbors when determining the community connectivity of a project. Prepare a site map (Figure 1) and draw a 1/2-mile radius around the main building entrance. Radii may be drawn around multiple entrances for projects with multiple buildings or more than 1 main entrance. The combination of the area in these radii would then be considered the project radius.

Figure 1. Sample Map for Community Connectivity

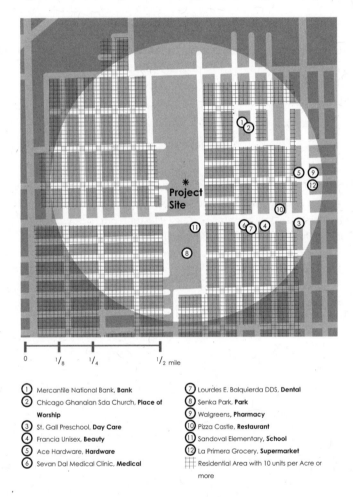

① Mercantile National Bank, **Bank**
② Chicago Ghanaian Sda Church, **Place of Worship**
③ St. Gall Preschool, **Day Care**
④ Francia Unisex, **Beauty**
⑤ Ace Hardware, **Hardware**
⑥ Sevan Dal Medical Clinic, **Medical**
⑦ Lourdes E. Balquierda DDS, **Dental**
⑧ Senka Park, **Park**
⑨ Walgreens, **Pharmacy**
⑩ Pizza Castle, **Restaurant**
⑪ Sandoval Elementary, **School**
⑫ La Primera Grocery, **Supermarket**
▦ Residential Area with 10 units per Acre or more

Mark all residential developments within the radius. For the project to earn this credit, a residential area with a minimum density of 10 units per acre must be present within the radius.

Mark all commercial buildings within the radius. At least 10 basic services must be present within the radius for the project to earn this credit. Services other than those listed in the credit requirements will be considered on a project-by-project basis.

List each of the identified services, the business name. and the service type to confirm compliance. Table 1 illustrates an example.

Table 1. Sample Community Connectivity Tabulation

Service Identification (Corresponds to uploaded Vicinity Plan)	Business Name	Service Type
1	Restaurant 1	Restaurant
2	Grocery 1	Convenience Grocery
3	Urgent Care 1	Medical
4	Pharmacy 1	Pharmacy
5	Gym 1	Fitness
6	Hair Care 1	Beauty
7	Bank 1	Bank
8	Restaurant 2	Restaurant
9	Cleaners 1	Cleaners
10	Post Office 1	Post Office

With the exception of restaurants, no service may be counted more than once in the calculation. Up to 2 restaurants may be counted toward achievement of this credit. Count only those services for that can be accessed by pedestrians from the project; that is, pedestrians must be able to walk to the services without being blocked by walls, highways, or other barriers.

The project building itself cannot be considered 1 of the 10 basic services; however, in a mixed-use building, a maximum of 1 service within the building may be counted as 1 of the 10. A service in a mixed-use project must be open to the public.

Up to 2 services that are anticipated to be built in the near future can count toward this credit; at least 8 services must be existing and operational. Any anticipated services must be documented by lease agreements or other appropriate documentation (e.g., a letter from the owner or other appropriate party) to demonstrate that they will be operational in the locations indicated within a year of occupation of the project building.

5. Timeline and Team

The project team should make development density or community connectivity a criterion for site selection. Real estate brokers and leasing agents can help identify buildings that comply.

6. Calculations

OPTION 1. Development Density

To determine the development density of a project, both the project density and the densities of surrounding developments must be considered. The calculations detailed below refer to the base building in which the LEED for Commercial Interiors project is located, the base building site area, and the buildings surrounding the base building. The density calculation process is described in the following steps:

STEP 1

Determine the total area of the project site and the total square footage of the building.

For projects that are part of a larger property (such as a campus), define the project area as the area that is defined in the project's scope. The project area must be defined consistently throughout LEED documentation.

STEP 2

Calculate the development density for the project by dividing the total square footage of the building by the total site area in acres.

This development density must be 60,000 square feet or more per acre (Equation 1).

Equation 1

$$\text{Development Density} \; \frac{\text{(sf)}}{\text{(acre)}} \; = \; \frac{\text{Building Square Footage (sf)}}{\text{Site Area (acres)}}$$

STEP 3

Convert the total site area from acres to square feet and calculate the square root of this number.

Then multiply the square root by 3 to determine the appropriate density radius (Equation 2). The square root function is used to normalize the calculation by removing effects of site shape.

Equation 2

$$\text{Density Radius (lf)} \; = \; 3 \; \times \; \sqrt{\left[\text{Site Area (acres)} \; \times \; 43{,}560 \; \text{(sf/acre)} \right]}$$

STEP 4

Calculate the average property density within the density boundary by adding up the square footage values and site areas of each property and dividing the total square footage by the total site area. The average property density of the properties within the density boundary must be 60,000 square feet or more per acre. If this requirement is met, LEED for New Construction and LEED for Core & Shell projects earn 5 points under this credit. LEED for Schools projects earn 4 points.

Equation 3

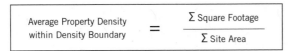

$$\text{Average Property Density within Density Boundary} \; = \; \frac{\Sigma \, \text{Square Footage}}{\Sigma \, \text{Site Area}}$$

OPTION 2. Community Connectivity

There are no calculations required for this option.

7. Documentation Guidance

As a first step in preparing to complete the LEED Online documentation requirements, work through the following measures. Refer to LEED Online for the complete descriptions of all required documentation.

- For development density, develop a project site vicinity plan that includes the development density radius.

- For community connectivity, develop a project site vicinity plan that indicates the half-mile radius and the locations of qualifying services and residential areas; list the services and identify them by type.

8. Examples

Development Density

A 30,000-square-foot office building is located on a 0.44-acre urban site. The building density, calculated by dividing the square footage of the building space by the site area in acres, is 68,182 square feet per acre (Table 2). the density thus exceeds the 60,000 square feetminimum required by the credit.

Table 2. Building Density Calculations

Project Buildings	Building Space (sf)	Site Area (acres)
Project	30,000	0.44
Density (sf/acre)	a	68,182

Next, the density radius is calculated to be 415 feet using the following equation.

Equation 2

$$\text{Density Radius (lf)} = 3 \times \sqrt{\left[0.44 \text{ (acres)} \times 43{,}560 \text{ (sf/acre)} \right]} = 415 \text{ (ft)}$$

The density radius of 415 feet is applied to an area plan of the project site and surrounding area. The plan identifies all properties that are within or are intersected by the density radius. The plan includes a scale and a north indicator (Figure 2).

Figure 2. An illustration of a Sample Area Plan

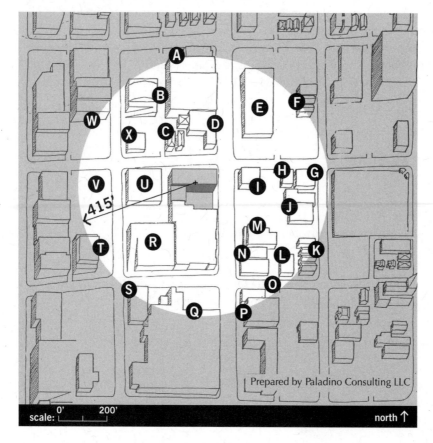

Prepared by Paladino Consulting LLC

scale: 0'   200'

north ↑

For each property located within the density radius, list the building space and site area (Table 3). These values are summed and the average density is calculated by dividing the total building square footage by the total site area.

Table 3. Sample Area Properties

Properties within Density Radius	Building Space (sf)	Site Area (acres)		Properties within Density Radius	Building Space (sf)	Site Area (acres)
Project Site	30,000	0.44		M	24,080	0.64
A	33,425	0.39		N	28,740	0.3
B	87,500	1.58		O	6,690	0.15
C	6,350	0.26		P	39,000	0.39
D	27,560	0.32		Q	348,820	2.54
E	66,440	1.17		R	91,250	1.85
F	14,420	1.36		S	22,425	0.27
G	12,560	0.2		T	33,650	0.51
H	6,240	0.14		U	42,400	0.52
I	14,330	0.22		V	—	0.76
J	29,570	0.41		W	19,200	0.64
K	17,890	0.31		X	6,125	0.26
L	9,700	0.31				
Total Building Space (sf)				1,018,365		
Total Site Area (acres)				5	15.94	
Average Density (sf/acre)					63,887	

For this example, the average building density of the surrounding area is greater than 60,000 square feet per acre, so the example qualifies for 6 points under this credit.

9. Exemplary Performance

The following exemplary performance paths are available for projects that have earned Option 1 under SS Credit 2:

1. The project building itself must have a density at least double that of the average density within the calculated area, OR

2. The average density within an area twice as large as that for the base credit achievement must be at least 120,000 square feet per acre. To double the area, use equation 2 but double the project site area first.

10. Regional Variations

There are no regional variations associated with this credit.

11. Operations and Maintenance Considerations

Densely developed communities may have poor air quality, making it difficult for building occupants and operators to address health and comfort issues. Consider optimizing the mechanical systems for air quality protection by using superior filtration media and selecting materials that do not contribute to indoor air quality issues. Encourage building operators to actively manage for high indoor air quality through the use of the EPA's Indoor Air Quality Building Education and Assessment Model (I-BEAM) or other strategies.

12. Resources

Please see USGBC's LEED Resources & Tools (http://www.usgbc.org/projecttools) for additional resources and technical information.

Websites

Congress for New Urbanism

http://www.cnu.org

The Congress for the New Urbanism promotes pedestrian-friendly, neighborhood-based development as an alternative to sprawl.

Urban Land Institute

ULI Washington

http://washington.uli.org

The Urban Land Institute is a nonprofit organization based in Washington, D.C., that promotes the responsible use of land to enhance the total environment.

The International Union for the Scientific Study of Population

http://www.iussp.org

IUSSP promotes scientific studies of demography and population-related issues.

Print Media

Changing Places: Rebuilding Community in the Age of Sprawl, by Richard Moe and Carter Wilkie (Henry Holt & Company, 1999).

Density by Design: New Directions in Residential Development, by Steven Fader (Urban Land Institute, 2000).

Green Development: Integrating Ecology and Real Estate, by Alex Wilson, et al. (John Wiley & Sons, 1998).

Once There Were Greenfields: How Urban Sprawl Is Undermining America's Environment, Economy, and Social Fabric, by F. Kaid Benfield, et al. (Natural Resources Defense Council, 1999).

Suburban Nation: The Rise of Sprawl and the Decline of the American Dream, by Andres Duany, et al. North Point Press, 2000).

13. Definitions

Building density is the floor area of the building divided by the total area of the site (square feet per acre).

Building footprint is the area on a project site used by the building structure, defined by the perimeter of the building plan. Parking lots, landscapes, and other nonbuilding facilities are not included in the building footprint.

Greenfields are sites not previously developed or graded that could support open space, habitat, or agriculture.

A **mixed-use** project involves a combination of residential and commercial or retail components.

Neighborhood is synonymous with **residential area.**

Pedestrian access allows people to walk to services without being blocked by walls, freeways, or other barriers.

Previously developed sites once had buildings, roadways, parking lots, or were graded or otherwise altered by direct human activities.

Property area is the total area within the legal property boundaries of a site; it encompasses all areas of the site, including constructed and nonconstructed areas.

Public transportation consists of bus, rail, or other transit services for the general public that operate on a regular, continual basis.

A **residential area** is land zoned primarily for housing at a density of 10 units per acre or greater. These areas may have single-family and multifamily housing and include building types such as townhomes, apartments, duplexes, condominiums, or mobile homes.

Site area is synonymous with **property area.**

ALTERNATIVE TRANSPORTATION—PUBLIC TRANSPORTATION ACCESS

	CI
Credit	SS Credit 3.1
Points	6 points

Intent

To reduce pollution and land development impacts from automobile use.

Requirements

OPTION 1. Rail Station Proximity

Locate the project in a building within 1/2-mile walking distance (measured from a main building entrance) of an existing (or planned and funded) commuter rail, light rail or subway station.

OR

OPTION 2. Bus Stop Proximity

Locate the project within 1/4-mile walking distance (measured from a main building entrance) of 1 or more stops for 2 or more public campus or private bus lines usable by tenant occupants.

1. Benefits and Issues to Consider

Environmental Issues

The extensive use of single-occupancy vehicles and their heavy reliance on petroleum contribute to environmental problems. Fortunately, alternatives to conventional transportation methods exist. Many people are willing to use other options if they are convenient. The use of mass transit helps reduce energy demand for transportation and associated greenhouse gas emissions, as well as the space needed for parking lots that encroach on the green space of a building site. Minimizing parking lots reduces the building footprint and sets aside more space for natural areas or greater development densities.

Reductions in single-occupancy vehicle use directly affect fuel consumption and reduce air and water pollution from vehicle exhaust. On the basis of passenger miles traveled, public transportation is twice as fuel efficient as private vehicles and annually saves 45 million barrels of oil.[17] Another benefit of public transportation is the associated reduction in the need for infrastructure used by vehicles. Parking facilities and roadways for automobiles have negative impacts on the environment because impervious surfaces, such as asphalt, increase stormwater runoff while contributing to urban heat island effects.

Economic Issues

Many occupants view proximity to mass transit as a benefit, and this can influence the value and marketability of the building. For building occupants, costs associated with traveling to and from the workplace can be significantly reduced through access to public transportation. Not only is this an economic benefit for building occupants, it helps business owners attract and retain employees.

Reducing the size of parking areas based on anticipated use of public transportation by building occupants may alter operating costs associated with parking lot maintenance. If local utilities charge for stormwater based on impervious surface area, minimizing these areas can result in lower stormwater fees.

2. Related Credits

Sites close to existing public transportation infrastructure tend to be in more densely developed areas. The following credit may be more likely achievable for projects in such locations:

- SS Credit 2: Development Density and Community Connectivity

3. Summary of Referenced Standards

There are no standards referenced for this credit.

4. Implementation

Choose a base building that has convenient access to existing transportation networks to minimize the need for new transportation lines. Local transit authorities can provide maps and directories that will help identify the available transportation options.

Consider developing a transportation management plan that evaluates anticipated transportation use patterns and offers alternatives aimed at reducing commuting in single-occupancy vehicles. This management plan could be considered a comprehensive approach to addressing the 4 credits within SS Credit 4, Alternative Transportation. This is particularly useful for large buildings, buildings that are part of a master plan implementation, and developments with multiple buildings.

If possible, survey future potential building occupants about whether the available public transportation options meet their needs. Look for functional sidewalks, paths, and walkways that lead directly to existing mass transit stops.

If a light rail or subway station is sited, planned, and funded at the time the project is completed, it satisfies the intent of this credit. If private shuttle buses will be used to meet the requirements, they must connect to public transportation and operate during the most frequent commuting hours.

5. Timeline and Team

The project team should make proximity to public transportation a criterion for site selection. Real estate brokers and leasing agents can help identify buildings that comply.

6. Calculations

OPTION 1 and OPTION 2

Use an area drawing, aerial photograph, or map to calculate the walking distance to the transit stops. If the building has multiple main or public entrances, project teams can measure walking distances from multiple building entrances. Software tools like Google™ Maps Pedometer (www. gmap-pedometer.com) may be useful for determining walking distance.

7. Documentation Guidance

As a first step in preparing to complete the LEED Online documentation requirements, work through the following measures. Refer to LEED Online for the complete descriptions of all required documentation.

- Identify local rail stations or bus routes serving the project building.

- Develop a site vicinity plan, to scale, and label walking paths between the project building's main entrance and rail stations or bus stops.

- If the team anticipates rail development, obtain verification of funding for the rail project.

8. Examples

LEO Enterprise, Inc., has selected tenant space in a downtown office building. The building is within walking distance of public transportation. Figure 1 shows a rail station within 1/2-mile walking distance from the building's main entrance, the entrance used by the tenant. The map includes a scale bar and a north indicator.

Figure 1: Sample Area Drawing: Distance to Rail

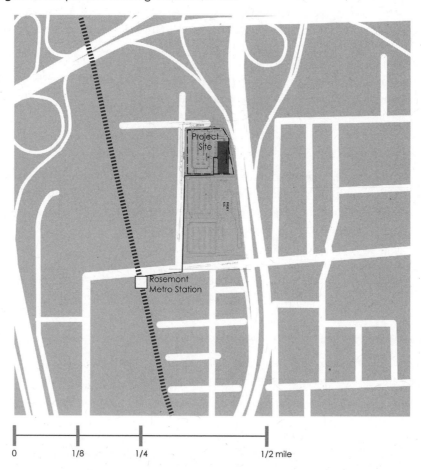

| 0 | 1/8 | 1/4 | 1/2 mile |

9. Exemplary Performance

Projects may earn an exemplary performance credit under the Innovation in Design section for SS Credit 3.1, Alternative Transportation—Public Transportation Access by complying with the requirements of 1 of the 2 options described below.

OPTION 1. Comprehensive Transportation Management Plan

Institute a comprehensive transportation management plan that demonstrates a quantifiable reduction in personal automobile use by providing multiple transportation alternatives. Only 1 exemplary performance credit is available for implementing a comprehensive transportation management plan for any of the SS Credit 3, Alternative Transportation, credits.

OPTION 2. Double Transit Ridership

Because projects in locations with good mass transit can achieve substantially and quantifiably higher environmental benefits, meeting the following threshold qualifies a project for exemplary performance. The Center for Clean Air Policy has found that average transit ridership increases by 0.5% for every 1.0% increase in growth of transit service levels, which leads to the conclusion that quadrupling transit service generally doubles transit ridership.

To achieve exemplary performance, meet the following minimum requirements:

- Locate the tenant space in a building that is within 1/2 mile of at least 2 existing commuter rail, light rail, or subway lines.

OR

- Locate the tenant space in a building that is within 1/4 mile of at least 2 or more stops for 4 or more public or campus (private) bus lines usable by tenants.

AND

- Frequency of service must be at least 200 transit rides per day, total, at these stops. A combination of rail and bus lines is allowable. This strategy is based on the assumption that the threshold of the base credit would provide, in most cases, at least 50 transit rides per day (half-hourly service 24 hours per day or more frequent service for less than 24 hours per day). If, on average, transit ridership increases by 0.5% for every 1.0% increase in transit service, then quadrupling the number of rides available would, on average, double the transit ridership: 4 x 50 rides = 200 rides. Include a transit schedule and map with the LEED certification submittal.

10. Regional Variations

There are no regional variations associated with this credit.

11. Operations and Maintenance Considerations

Transit infrastructure can be underutilized if building occupants are not informed about public transportation opportunities or encouraged to use these systems. Consider working with building owners, tenants and operators to develop ongoing programs to support transit use and infrastructure. Appropriate strategies will vary by building ownership, tenant organization and occupancy type. For example, a multitenant facility with third-party management is less likely to provide subsidized transit passes than an owner-occupied facility, but it could establish a program to inform occupants about transit opportunities.

Programming options to consider include the following examples:

- Providing financial incentives or subsidized passes for public transit.

- Instituting a "free ride home" program for public transit commuters who need to work unexpected hours.

- Promoting the use of mass transit by providing information on transportation options, routes, services, and incentives.

- Participating in local or regional transportation planning to ensure that building occupants' needs are considered.

- Establishing a method for tracking public transit ridership.

12. Resources

Please see USGBC's LEED Resources & Tools (http://www.usgbc.org/projecttools) for additional resources and technical information.

Websites

U.S. EPA and Department of Transportation, Best Workplaces for Commuters
http://www.bestworkplaces.org/index.htm
This program publicly recognizes employers who have exemplary commuter benefits programs. It provides tools, guidance, and promotions to help employers give commuter benefits, reap the financial gains, and achieve national recognition.

U.S. EPA, Office of Transportation and Air Quality

http://www.epa.gov/otaq

This EPA website provides information about the types and effects of air pollution associated with automobile use and links to resources for organizations interested in promoting commuter-choice programs.

13. Definitions

A **campus** or **private bus** is a bus or shuttle service that is privately operated and not available to the general public. In LEED, a campus or private bus line that falls within 1/4 mile of the project site and provides transportation service to the public can contribute to earning credits.

Mass transit is designed to transport large groups of persons in a single vehicle, such as a bus or train.

Public transportation consists of bus, rail, or other transit services for the general public that operate on a regular, continual basis.

Tenant space is the area within the LEED project boundary. For more information on what can and must be in the LEED project boundary see the Minimum Program Requirements (MPRs) and LEED 2009 MPR Supplemental Guidance. Note: tenant space is the same as project space.

Walking distance is the length of the walkable pathway between the building and public transportation.

ALTERNATIVE TRANSPORTATION—BICYCLE STORAGE AND CHANGING ROOMS

	CI
Credit	SS Credit 3.2
Points	2 points

Intent

To reduce pollution and land development impacts from automobile use.

Requirements

Provide secure bicycle racks and/or storage (within 200 yards of a main building entrance) for 5% or more of tenant occupants (measured at peak periods).

Provide shower and changing facilities in the building, or within 200 yards of a building entrance, for 0.5% of full-time equivalent (FTE) occupants.

1. Benefits and Issues to Consider

Environmental Issues

The environmental effects of automobile use include vehicle emissions that contribute to smog and air pollution, as well as environmental impacts from oil extraction and petroleum refining. Bicycling as an alternative to personal vehicle use offers a number of environmental benefits. Bicycle commuting produces no emissions, has zero demand for petroleum-based fuels, relieves traffic congestion, reduces noise pollution, and requires far less infrastructure for roadways and parking lots. Roadways and parking lots, on the other hand, produce stormwater runoff, contribute to the urban heat island effect, and encroach on green space.

Bicycles are more likely to be used for relatively short commuting trips. Displacing vehicle miles with bicycling, even for short trips, carries a large environmental benefit because a large portion of vehicle emissions occur in the first few minutes of driving. Following a cold start, emissions control equipment is less effective because of cool operating temperatures.

Economic Issues

The initial cost of building bike storage areas and changing facilities or showers is typically low relative to the overall project cost. When buildings accommodate bicycling infrastructure, occupants can realize health benefits through bicycle and walking commuting strategies. Bicycling and walking also expose people to the community, encouraging interaction among neighbors and allowing for enjoyment of the area in ways unavailable to automobile passengers.

2. Related Credits

There are no related credits.

3. Summary of Referenced Standards

There are no standards referenced for this credit.

4. Implementation

Choose a base building that has convenient access to safe bicycle pathways and secure bicycle storage areas for cyclists. Work with building owners to provide shower and changing areas for cyclists that are easily accessible from bicycle storage areas.

Survey potential building occupants and determine whether the available bike routes and their compatibility with mass transit options meet their needs. Look for functional and direct paths that can be used by bicycle commuters.

Shower facilities may be either within the tenant's space or in a common facility within 200 yards of the main building entrance.

If changing rooms and showers are not within the tenant space, demonstrate that the required capacity will not be compromised by other users. Show that the arrangements are permanent and are not subject to lease revisions or other circumstances beyond the control of the tenant.

If the required bicycle-rack capacity cannot be reserved for the specific tenant space, the quantity must be based on the entire building population.

Shower and changing rooms can be provided by health club memberships if those facilities are provided free of charge and if sufficient shower and changing facilities are available to satisfy the credit requirements of 0.5% of the tenant FTE. A minimum of a 2-year contract is required between the tenant and the health club.

5. Timeline and Team

Bicycle storage and shower facilities should be incorporated into design concepts during schematic design and design development. By considering cycling early on, the project team can implement a successful alternative transportation program. For example, when selecting a base building, the project team can include proximity to existing bicycle commuting infrastructure as a criterion. Coordination among the architect, plumbing engineer, civil engineer and/or landscape architect may be required for locating and designing bicycle storage and shower facilities. The project team should also consider future expansion opportunities.

6. Calculations

To determine the number of secure bicycle spaces and changing and shower facilities required, follow the steps below.

STEP 1

Identify the total number of occupants for each of the following occupancy types:

a. Full-time staff

b. Part-time staff

c. Peak transients (students, volunteers, visitors, customers, etc.)

Include only occupants from the tenant space pursuing LEED certification; do not include occupants from the entire building. In tenant spaces with multiple shifts, use only the highest-volume shift in the calculation but consider shift overlap when determining peak users.

STEP 2

For full-time and part-time staff, calculate the FTE tenant occupants based on a standard 8-hour occupancy period. An 8-hour occupant has an FTE value of 1.0, while a part-time occupant has a FTE value based on her/his hours per day divided by 8 (see Equation 1). FTE calculations for the project must be used consistently for all LEED credits.

Equation 1. FTE Staff Occupants

$$\text{Total FTE Staff Occupants} = \frac{\text{Total Staff Occupant Hours}}{8}$$

STEP 3

Calculate the number of secure bicycle spaces required for each group of occupants according to Equation 2.

Equation 2a. Secure Bike Spaces

$$\text{Staff Occupant Spaces} = \text{FTE Staff Occupants} \times 0.05$$

Equation 2b. Secure Bike Spaces

$$\text{Transient Spaces} = \text{Peak Transients} \times 0.05$$

Certain types of transient populations can be excluded from these calculations if they cannot reasonably be expected to arrive by bicycle and thus use on-site storage facilities. For example, air travelers arriving at an airport will not need bicycle storage. Project teams should be prepared to justify the exclusion of any transients from the calculations.

STEP 4

Calculate the number of showers required for staff using Equation 3.

Equation 3. Staff Showering Facilities

$$\text{Showering Facilities} = \text{FTE Staff} \times 0.005$$

Transient occupants are not counted in the showering facility calculation.

7. Documentation Guidance

As a first step in preparing to complete the LEED Online documentation requirements, work through the following measures. Refer to LEED Online for the complete descriptions of all required documentation.

- Determine the number of occupants of each type and calculate the number of bicycle storage and showering facilities required.

- Develop a plan showing the location and quantity of bicycle storage and shower facilities and determine the distance between facilities and the building entry.

8. Examples

A building houses a company with 2 shifts. The first shift includes 240 full-time workers and 90 part-time workers. The second shift includes 110 full-time workers and 60 part-time workers. There are no visitors or transient occupants who use the tenant space. Calculations to determine the total FTE staff occupants for each shift are shown in Table 1.

Table 1. Sample FTE Calculation

Shift	Full-time Staff		Part-time Staff		Full-time Equivalent Staff
	Staff	(hr)	Staff	(hr)	Staff
First Shift	240	8	90	4	285
Second Shift	110	8	60	4	140

The first shift is used for determining the peak number of bicycling occupants because it has the greatest FTE tenant occupant total. Based on a total of 285 FTE-tenant occupants, the estimated number of cycling occupants is 14.25 (285 x 0.05 = 14.25); 15 secure bicycle spaces are required. The result for changing and showering facilities is 1.4 (285 x .005 = 1.4); 2 changing and showering facilities are required.

9. Exemplary Performance

Projects may earn an innovation credit for exemplary performance by instituting a comprehensive transportation management plan that demonstrates a quantifiable reduction in personal automobile use by providing multiple transportation alternatives. Only 1 exemplary performance credit is available for implementing a comprehensive transportation management plan for any of the SS Credit 3, Alternative Transportation, credits. Projects that are awarded exemplary performance for SS Credit 3.1, Alternative Transportation—Public Transportation Access, using the double transit ridership option are not eligible for exemplary performance under this credit.

10. Regional Variations

There are no regional variations associated with this credit.

11. Operations and Maintenance Considerations

Project teams should consider working with tenants, building owners, and operators to develop ongoing programs that support bicycle use. Appropriate strategies will vary by tenant organization, building ownership, and occupancy type but could include these:

- Providing financial incentives for commuting via bicycle.

- Instituting a "free ride home" program for bicycle riders who need to work unexpected hours.

- Promoting the use of a bicycle to the community by providing information on safe bike routes, locations of secure bicycle parking, lockers, showers, etc.

- Providing discounts on bicycle accessories and maintenance at local bike shops.

- Participating in local or regional transportation planning to ensure that building occupants' needs are considered. Provision of bike lanes and paths along corridors leading to the project can significantly influence ridership levels.

- Establishing a method for tracking bicycle ridership.

12. Resources

Please see USGBC's LEED Resources & Tools (http://www.usgbc.org/projecttools) for additional resources and technical information.

Websites

Bicycle Coalition of Maine, An Employer's Guide to Encouraging Bicycle Commuting
http://www.bikemaine.org/btwemployer.htm
This website from the Bicycle Coalition of Maine, this site suggests ways to encourage and facilitate bicycle commuting to employees.

Commuting Guide for Employers
http://www.self-propelled-city.com
This website outlines strategies employers can use as they try to encourage employees to commute by bicycle.

Federal Highway Administration, Office of Human and Natural Environment, Bicycle & Pedestrian Program
http://www.fhwa.dot.gov/environment/bikeped
This program of the Federal Highway Administration's Office of Human and Natural Environment promotes access to and use and safety of bicycle and pedestrian transportation.

Pedestrian and Bicycle Information Center
http://www.bicyclinginfo.org
The Pedestrian and Bicycle Information Center provides information and resources for issues related to bicycle commuting, including health and safety, engineering, advocacy, education, and facilities. Information and links for bicycle parking issues can be found at http://www.bicyclinginfo.org/engineering/parking.cfm.

U.S. EPA and Department of Transportation, Best Workplaces for Commuters
http://www.bestworkplaces.org/index.htm
Now managed by the Center for Urban Transportation Research at the University of South Florida, this program publicly recognizes employers who have exemplary commuter benefits programs. It provides tools, guidance, and promotions to help employers give commuter benefits, reap the financial gains, and achieve national recognition.

U.S. EPA, Office of Transportation and Air Quality

http://www.epa.gov/otaq

EPA's website provides information about the types and effects of air pollution associated with automobile use and links to resources for organizations interested in promoting commuter-choice programs.

13. Definitions

Bicycle racks, in LEED, include outdoor bicycle racks, bicycle lockers, and indoor bicycle storage rooms.

Full-time equivalent (FTE) represents a regular building occupant who spends 40 hours per week in the project building. Part-time or overtime occupants have FTE values based on their hours per week divided by 40. Multiple shifts are included or excluded depending on the intent and requirements of the credit.

Secure bicycle storage is an internal or external space that keeps bicycles safe from theft. It may include lockers and storage rooms.

Tenant space is the area within the LEED project boundary. For more information on what can and must be in the LEED project boundary see the Minimum Program Requirements (MPRs) and LEED 2009 MPR Supplemental Guidance. Note: tenant space is the same as project space.

Transient users are occupants who do not use a facility on a consistent, regular, daily basis. Examples include students in higher education settings, customers in retail settings, and visitors in institutional settings.

ALTERNATIVE TRANSPORTATION—PARKING AVAILABILITY

	CI
Credit	SS Credit 3.3
Points	2 point

Intent

To reduce pollution and land development impacts from automobile use.

Requirements

CASE 1. Projects with an Area Less Than 75% of the Total Building Area

OPTION 1

Parking spaces provided to tenant must meet but not exceed minimum number required by local zoning regulations.

Preferred parking[1] must be provided for carpools or vanpools capable of serving 5% or more of tenant occupants.

OR

OPTION 2

No parking is provided or subsidized for tenant occupants.

CASE 2. Projects with an Area 75% or More of the Total Building Area

OPTION 1

Parking capacity must meet but not exceed minimum local zoning requirements.

Preferred parking must be provided for carpools or vanpools, capable of serving 5% of the building occupants.

OR

OPTION 2

No new parking is added for rehabilitation projects.

Preferred parking must be provided for carpools or vanpools, capable of serving 5% of the building occupants.

---

1 Preferred parking refers to the parking spots that are closest to the main entrance of the project (exclusive of spaces designated for handicapped persons) or parking passes provided at a discounted price.

1. Benefits and Issues to Consider

Environmental Issues

Reducing private automobile use saves energy and avoids associated environmental problems, such as vehicle emissions that contribute to smog, air pollution, and greenhouse gas emissions, as well as the environmental impacts associated with oil extraction and petroleum refining. The environmental benefits of carpooling are significant. For example, 100 people who carpooled (2 people per car) 10 miles to work and 10 miles home instead of driving separately would prevent emissions of about 970 pounds of carbon dioxide per day and would save about 50 gallons of gas per day.[18]

Parking facilities also have negative impacts on the environment because asphalt surfaces increase stormwater runoff and contribute to urban heat island effects. By restricting the size of parking lots and promoting carpooling, project teams can reduce these effects and provide such benefits as more green space.

Economic Issues

Carpooling reduces the size of parking areas needed to support building occupants, allowing the building to accommodate more occupants without enlarging the parking area. Carpooling also helps reduce building costs, since less land is needed for parking and less infrastructure is needed to support vehicles. Smaller parking areas can decrease the amount of impervious surfaces on a site. This may result in reduced stormwater costs if the local utility bases its fees on impervious surface area. Moreover, because fewer cars on the road means less pollution, traffic congestion, and wear and tear to roadways, many municipalities and state governments offer tax incentives for carpooling programs.

2. Related Credits

There are no related credits.

3. Summary of Referenced Standards

There are no standards referenced for this credit.

4. Implementation

Limit the availability of parking to encourage the use of alternative forms of transportation to and from the site. Real estate brokers can help identify buildings with easy access to public transportation and construct lease agreements so that the number of parking spaces guaranteed to tenants does not exceed minimums established by local zoning regulations.

Research the parking requirements for the local zoning ordinances before completing lease negotiations. Determine the minimum number of spaces required by the code for the project's actual area and use building types and multipliers. For example, 20,000 square feet of offices requires 100 spaces, and 10,000 square feet of warehouses requires 10 spaces, etc.

Confirm that the lease does not guarantee more spaces than the calculation requirement. The criteria for "guaranteed" includes the following items:

- Assigned spaces reserved only for the tenant's use, including tenant's guests.
- The portion of a restricted parking area reserved for the tenant's use (i.e., the number of access cards issued to tenant).

"Guaranteed" does not require that the payment for parking be included in the lease. When the tenant organization makes separate payments (e.g., for parking that is a concession of the building or at another facility), the applicant must demonstrate that the spaces reserved for the occupants are fewer than the calculated requirement.

This credit also requires the provision of preferred parking spaces for carpools to serve 5% of the occupants.

5. Timeline and Team

Discussions regarding the reduction of parking capacity are often most productive at the project concept phase. This may entail discussions with zoning and civic officials and could include community and neighborhood organizations. A traffic study can be a valuable tool for evaluating traffic patterns and expected commuting in single-occupancy vehicles. Projects may require an additional team member, possibly a specialist or consultant, to develop this traffic study.

Because of their size or location or because of regulatory requirements, many projects may entail zoning negotiations over the parking requirements. Planned developments may have unique parking requirements; project teams must consider these as part of overall alternative transportation strategies.

Design solutions to reduce parking capacity for the project site should be incorporated during the schematic design and design development phases. The architect, design team, and project owner should coordinate decision making to choose the most appropriate approach for future occupants.

6. Calculations

For projects providing designated preferred parking for carpools or van pools, calculate the number of required preferred parking spaces using the steps below.

STEP 1

Calculate the FTE tenant occupants based on a standard 8-hour occupancy period. An 8-hour occupant has an FTE value of 1.0, while a part-time occupant has a FTE value based on her/his hours per day divided by 8 (see Equation 1). FTE calculations for the project must be used consistently for all LEED credits. In buildings with multiple shifts, use only the highest volume shift in the calculation, but consider shift overlap when determining peak building users.

Equation 1. FTE Staff Occupants

$$\text{Total FTE Staff Occupants} = \frac{\text{Total Staff Occupant Hours}}{8}$$

STEP 2

Use Equation 2 to determine the required number of preferred parking spaces. Equation 2 assumes that all such spaces are for carpools (serving 2 occupants per vehicle). If carpools are known to serve more riders per car or if van pools achieve the same end, the outcome may be adjusted to reflect the increased volume of tenants served per space. In all cases, fractions of a space must be rounded up.

Equation 2

$$\text{Required Spaces} = \frac{\text{FTE Occupants} \times .05}{2}$$

7. Documentation Guidance

As a first step in preparing to complete the LEED Online documentation requirements, work through the following measures. Refer to LEED Online for the complete descriptions of all required documentation.

- For projects providing designated preferred parking for carpool or vanpool users, develop a site plan showing parking spaces for tenants and the location and quantity of preferred spaces.

- Provide adequate communication to occupants about the location and purpose of preferred parking spaces.

- Assemble information about parking provided to the tenant space as well as zoning regulations and lease agreements, if applicable.

8. Examples

Haller Industries occupies 50% of a building and has 100 full-time and 50 part-time employees. The total FTE occupants value is 125 (Table 1).

Table 1. Sample FTE Calculation

Full-Time Staff		Part-Time Staff		Full-Time Equivalent (FTE) Staff
	(hr)		(hr)	
100	8	50	4	125

The required number of preferred parking spaces for carpools or vanpools, based on Equation 2 and rounding up, is 4.

9. Exemplary Performance

Projects may earn an innovation credit for exemplary performance by instituting a comprehensive transportation management plan that demonstrates a quantifiable reduction in personal automobile use by providing multiple transportation alternatives. Only 1 exemplary performance credit is available for implementing a comprehensive transportation management plan for any of the SS Credit 3, Alternative Transportation, credits. Projects that are awarded exemplary performance for SS Credit 3.1, Alternative Transportation—Public Transportation Access, using the double transit ridership option are not eligible for exemplary performance under this credit.

10. Regional Variations

There are no regional variations associated with this credit.

11. Operations and Maintenance Considerations

For project buildings that include preferred parking, establish procedures for the use of this amenity, communicate them to building occupants, and assign operations staff for their administration. The procedures might include establishing a system for enforcing use of designated spaces (e.g, a permitting system), discounting paid parking, and tracking use of preferred parking.

12. Resources

Please see USGBC's LEED Resources & Tools (http://www.usgbc.org/projecttools) for additional resources and technical information.

Websites
Association for Commuter Transportation (ACT)

http://www.actweb.org/mc/page.do

ACT is an association of professionals who specialize in creating a more workable transportation and commuting system. ACT provides information and advocacy on transportation issues involving commute alternatives and offers its members networking and professional development opportunities.

Research Triangle Park, Smart Commute

http://www.smartcommute.org

Smart Commute has valuable information about telecommuting and carpool programs useful for any organization.

State of Arizona Telecommuting Program

http://www.teleworkarizona.com

This website provides background information on the significance of telecommuting and examples of the development, implementation, and results of telecommuting programs.

Teletrips

http://www.secure-teletrips.com

Teletrips helps create, implement, and manage public-private partnership programs to reduce commuter congestion, improve air quality, and reduce energy consumption.

Victoria Transport Policy Institute, Online Transportation Demand Management Encyclopedia

http://www.vtpi.org/tdm

Transportation demand management is a general term for strategies that result in more efficient use of transportation resources. This online encyclopedia is a comprehensive source of information about innovative management solutions to transportation problems.

13. Definitions

A carpool is an arrangement by which 2 or more people share a vehicle for transportation.

Parking subsidies are the costs of providing occupant parking that are not recovered in parking fees.

Preferred parking, available to particular users, includes designated spaces close to the building (aside from designated handicapped spots), designated covered spaces, discounted parking passes, and guaranteed passes in a lottery system.

Tenant space is the area within the LEED project boundary. For more information on what can and must be in the LEED project boundary see the Minimum Program Requirements (MPRs) and LEED 2009 MPR Supplemental Guidance. Note: tenant space is the same as project space.

Endnotes

[1] U.S. Environmental Protection Agency. "Heat Island Effect." http://www.epa.gov/heatisland/index.htm (accessed November 2008).

[2] U.S. Environmental Protection Agency, Office of Water. *Water-Efficient Landscaping.* 2002. http://www.epa.gov/owm/water-efficiency/final_final.pdf (accessed January 2005).

[3] Massachusetts Water Resources Authority. "Water Efficiency and Management for Commercial Buildings." http://www.mwra.state.ma.us/04water/html/bullet4.htm (accessed May 2008).

4   U.S. Census Bureau. "2006 American Community Survey: Selected Economic Characteristics." http://factfinder.census.gov/servlet/ADPTable?_bm=y&-qr_name=ACS_2006_EST_G00_DP3&-geo_id=01000US&-context=adp&-ds_name=&-tree_id=305&-_lang=en&-redoLog=false&-format (accessed May 2008).

5   U.S. Department of Energy, Office of Energy Efficiency and Renewable Energy. "Figure 6.1.1 Building Share of U.S. Electricity Consumption/Sales (Percent)." *2008 Buildings Energy Data Book.* 2008. http://www.btscoredatabook.net/TableView.aspx?table=6.1.1 (accessed November 2008).

6   Energy Information Administration. *Assumptions to the Annual Energy Outlook 2008.* 2008. http://www.eia.doe.gov/oiaf/aeo/assumption/ (accessed November 2008).

7   Hutson, Susan S., Nancy L. Barber, Joan F. Kenny, Kristin S. Linsey, Deborah S. Lumia, and Molly A. Maupin. *Estimated Use of Water in the United States in 2000.* U.S. Geological Survey, 2004. http://pubs.usgs.gov/circ/2004/circ1268/ (accessed November 2008).

8   http://www.epa.gov/brownfields/about.htm.

9   U.S. Environmental Protection Agency. *Reducing Stormwater Costs through Low Impact Development (LID) Strategies and Practices.* **2007.** www.epa.gov/owow/nps/lid/costs07/factsheet.html (accessed May 2008).

10 Ibid.

11 U.S. Environmental Protection Agency. "Heat Island Effect." http://www.epa.gov/heatisland/index.htm (accessed May 2008).

12 U.S. Environmental Protection Agency. "Heat Island Effect: Urban Heat Island Pilot Project (UHIPP)." www.epa.gov/hiri/pilot/index.html (accessed May 2008).

13 U.S. Environmental Protection Agency. "Heat Island Effect: Basic Information." http://www.epa.gov/hiri/about/index.html (accessed November 2008).

14 U.S. Environmental Protection Agency. "Heat Island Effect: Basic Information." http://www.epa.gov/hiri/about/index.html (accessed November 2008).

15 Georgia Department of Natural Resources, Pollution Prevention Assistance Division. "The Sustainable Office Toolkit." http://www.p2ad.org/toolkit/modules_4_1.html (accessed May 2008).

16 U.S. Environmental Protection Agency, Office of Solid Waste. "Wastes—Resource Conservation—Reduce, Reuse, Recycle—Construction & Demolition Materials." http://www.epa.gov/osw/conserve/rrr/imr/cdm/ (accessed November 2008).

17 American Public Transportation Association. "Use of Public Transportation by One in Ten Americans Would Lead to Cleaner Air and Reduce U.S. Oil Dependency by 40 Percent." *APTA News Release* (July 17, 2002), http://www.apta.com/media/releases/energystudy.cfm (accessed November 2008).

18 U.S. Environmental Protection Agency. *Emission Facts: Greenhouse Gas Emissions from a Typical Passenger Vehicle.* 2005. http://www.epa.gov/otaq/climate/420f05004.htm (accessed November 2008).

Overview

Americans' consumption of the public water supply continues to increase. The U.S. Geological Survey estimates that between 1990 and 2000, this consumption increased 12%, to 43.3 billion gallons per day.[1] The public water supply is delivered to users for domestic, commercial, industrial, and other purposes and is the primary source of water for most buildings. In 2000, these uses represented about 11% of total withdrawals and slightly less than 40% of groundwater withdrawals, constituting the third-largest category of water use in the United States, behind thermoelectric power (48% of total withdrawals) and irrigation (34% of total withdrawals). This high demand for water is straining supplies, and in some parts of the United States, water levels in underground aquifers have dropped more than 150 feet since the 1940s.[2]

Only about 14% of withdrawn water is lost to evaporation or transpiration or incorporated into products or crops; the rest is used, treated, and discharged to the nation's water bodies.[3] Discharged water contaminates rivers, lakes, and potable water with bacteria, nitrogen, toxic metals, and other contaminants.[4] The U.S. Environmental Protection Agency (EPA) estimates that 1/3 of the nation's lakes, streams, and rivers are now unsafe for swimming and fishing.[5] Even so, water bodies in the United States are 50% cleaner[6] today than in the mid-1970s. And although consumption is rising, total U.S. withdrawals from the public water supply declined by nearly 9% between 1980 and 1985 and have varied by less than 3% for each 5-year interval since then.[7]

Those achievements can be largely attributed to the Clean Water Act and reductions in industrial, irrigation, and thermoelectric power withdrawals since 1980. Although the statistics show improvement, we are still far from sustainably using water. If total commercial building water consumption for all uses in the United States fell by just 10%, we could save more than 2 trillion gallons of water each year.[8]

Using large volumes of water increases maintenance and life-cycle costs for building operations and also increases consumers' costs for additional municipal supply and treatment facilities. Conversely, buildings that use water efficiently can reduce costs through lower fees, less sewage volume, reductions in energy and chemical use, and lower capacity charges and limits.

Efficiency measures can easily reduce water use in average commercial buildings by 30% or more.[9] In a typical 100,000-square-foot office building, low-flow plumbing fixtures coupled with sensors and automatic controls will save a minimum of 1 million gallons of water per year.[10] In addition, nonpotable water can be used for landscape irrigation, toilet and urinal flushing, custodial purposes, and building systems. Depending on local water costs, utility savings can be tens of thousands of dollars per year. Real estate firm Cushman and Wakefield, for example, implemented a comprehensive water management strategy at its Adobe headquarters in San Jose, California, in 2002 and achieved a 22% reduction in water use.[11]

The LEED for Commercial Interiors Water Efficiency (WE) prerequisite and credit encourage the use of strategies and technologies that reduce the amount of potable water consumed in buildings. Many water conservation strategies are no-cost or provide a rapid payback. Some, such as biological wastewater treatment systems and graywater plumbing systems, require more substantial investment and are cost-effective only under certain building and site conditions.

The WE prerequisite and credit address environmental concerns related to building water use and disposal and promote the following measures:

Monitoring Water Consumption Performance

The first step to improving water efficiency is to understand current performance. Tracking water use alongside energy use can help organizations better understand how these resources relate to each other, make integrated management decisions that increase overall efficiency, and verify savings from improvement projects in both energy and water systems. Organizations that manage water and energy performance together can take advantage of this relationship to create greener, more sustainable buildings.

Reducing Indoor Potable Water Consumption

Reducing indoor potable water consumption may require using alternative water sources for nonpotable applications and installing building upgrades, such as water-efficient fixtures, flow restrictors on existing fixtures, electronic controls, dry composting toilet systems, and waterless urinals. Lowering potable water use for toilets, showerheads, faucets, and other fixtures can reduce the total amount withdrawn from natural water bodies. A commercial building in Boston replaced 126 3.5-gallons-per-flush (gpf) toilets with low-flow, 1.6-gpf toilets and reduced total water use by 15%. With an initial cost of $32,000 and estimated annual savings of $22,800, payback for the renovation was 1.4 years. Another Boston building installed 30 faucet aerators and reduced annual indoor water consumption by 190,000 gallons. The cost of the materials and labor totaled $300, and the change is estimated to save $1,250 per year, with a simple payback of 2 months.[12]

Reducing Water Consumption to Save Energy and Improve Environmental Well-Being

In many buildings, the most significant savings associated with water efficiency result from reduced energy costs. Water efficiency cuts costs by reducing the amount of water that must be treated, heated, cooled, and distributed—all of which require energy. Because water heating in commercial buildings accounts for nearly 15% of total building energy use,[13] the efficient use of hot water results in significant energy savings. For this reason, water conservation that reduces the use of hot water also conserves energy and reduces energy-related pollution. For example, U.S. government office buildings use an estimated 244 billion to 256 billion gallons of water each year. Approximately 138.3 billion Btus of energy is required to process this water annually, 98% of which is used to heat water. By implementing water-efficiency efforts, federal buildings could conserve approximately 40% of their total water consumption and reduce related energy use by approximately 81.32 billion Btus per year.[14]

Practicing water conservation measures can also help improve both environmental and human well-being. A recent government survey showed that at least 36 states are anticipating local, regional, or statewide water shortages by 2013.[15] Human health and environmental welfare are affected when reservoirs and groundwater aquifers are depleted, since lower water levels can concentrate both natural contaminants, such as radon and arsenic, and human pollutants, such as agricultural and chemical wastes. Increasing water efficiency helps keep contaminants at safe levels.

Water efficiency also reduces energy consumption in the water supply and wastewater infrastructure. American public water supply and treatment facilities consume about 56 billion kilowatt-hours (kWh) each year[16]—enough electricity to power more than 5 million homes for an entire year.[17] Better water efficiency in commercial buildings will reduce the amount of energy consumed by water treatment facilities.

CREDIT	TITLE
WE Prerequisite 1	Water Use Reduction
WE Credit 1	Water Use Reduction

WATER USE REDUCTION

	CI
Prerequisite	WE Prerequisite 1
Points	Required

Intent

To increase water efficiency within the tenant space to reduce the burden on municipal water supply and wastewater systems.

Requirements

Employ strategies that in aggregate use 20% less water than the water use baseline calculated for the tenant space (not including irrigation).

Calculate the baseline according to the commercial and/or residential baselines outlined below.[1] Calculations are based on estimated occupant usage and must include only the following fixtures and fixture fittings located within the tenant space: water closets, urinals, lavatory faucets, showers, kitchen sink faucets and prerinse spray valves.[2]

Commercial Fixtures, Fittings, and Appliances	Current Baseline
Commercial toilets	1.6 gallons per flush (gpf)* Except blow-out fixtures: 3.5 (gpf)
Commercial urinals	1.0 (gpf)
Commercial lavatory (restroom) faucets	2.2 gallons per minute (gpm) at 60 pounds per square inch (psi), private applications only (hotel or motel guest rooms, hospital patient rooms) 0.5 (gpm) at 60 (psi)** all others except private applications 0.25 gallons per cycle for metering faucets
Commercial prerinse spray valves (for food service applications)	Flow rate ≤ 1.6 (gpm) (no pressure specified; no performance requirement)

Residential Fixtures, Fittings, and Appliances	Current Baseline
Residential toilets	1.6 (gpf)***
Residential lavatory (bathroom) faucets	2.2 (gpm) at 60 psi
Residential kitchen faucet	2.2 (gpm) at 60 psi
Residential showerheads	2.5 (gpm) at 80 (psi) per shower stall****

* EPAct 1992 standard for toilets applies to both commercial and residential models.
** In addition to EPAct requirements, the American Society of Mechanical Engineers standard for public lavatory faucets is 0.5 gpm at 60 psi (ASME A112.18.1-2005). This maximum has been incorporated into the national Uniform Plumbing Code and the International Plumbing Code.
*** EPAct 1992 standard for toilets applies to both commercial and residential models.
**** Residential shower compartment (stall) in dwelling units: The total allowable flow rate from all flowing showerheads at any given time, including rain systems, waterfalls, bodysprays, bodyspas and jets, must be limited to the allowable showerhead flow rate as specified above (2.5 gpm) per shower compartment, where the floor area of the shower compartment is less than 2,500 square inches. For each increment of 2,500 square inches of floor area thereafter or part thereof, an additional showerhead with total allowable flow rate from all flowing devices equal to or less than the allowable flow rate as specified above must be allowed. Exception: Showers that emit recirculated nonpotable water originating from within the shower compartment while operating are allowed to exceed the maximum as long as the total potable water flow does not exceed the flow rate as specified above.

1 Tables adapted from information developed and summarized by the U.S. Environmental Protection Agency (EPA) Office of Water based on requirements of the Energy Policy Act (EPAct) of 1992 and subsequent rulings by the Department of Energy, requirements of the EPAct of 2005, and the plumbing code requirements as stated in the 2006 editions of the Uniform Plumbing Code or International Plumbing Code pertaining to fixture performance.
2 Projects where fixtures or fixture fittings are not within the tenant space are exempt from WE Prerequisite 1.

The following fixtures, fittings and appliances are outside the scope of the water use reduction calculation:

- Commercial Steam Cookers
- Commercial Dishwashers
- Automatic Commercial Ice Makers
- Commercial (family-sized) Clothes Washers
- Residential Clothes Washers
- Standard and Compact Residential Dishwashers

1. Benefits and Issues to Consider

Environmental Issues

Reducing water use in buildings for urinals, toilets, showerheads, and faucets decreases the total amount withdrawn from rivers, streams, underground aquifers, and other water bodies. These strategies protect the natural water cycle and save water resources for future generations. In addition, water use reductions, in aggregate, allow municipalities to reduce or defer the capital investment needed for water supply and wastewater treatment infrastructure.

Conserving municipally supplied water also reduces chemical inputs at the water treatment works, as well as reduces energy use and the associated greenhouse gas emissions from treatment and distribution. The energy use and emissions generated to supply municipal water vary greatly across the United States and depend on the utility's water sources, the distance water is transported, and the type of water treatment applied. End-use water efficiency can greatly reduce negative environmental impacts. Comparing the environmental impacts of off-site treatment and supply with those of on-site treatment is a worthwhile exercise. Because water heating in commercial buildings accounts for nearly 15% of building energy use,[18] conservation measures will also reduce end-use energy and energy-related pollution.

Economic Issues

Reductions in water consumption decrease building operating costs and bring about wider economic benefits. Reduced water consumption allows municipalities to lessen or defer the capital investment needed for water supply and wastewater treatment infrastructure, thereby leading to more stable municipal taxes and water rates.

Many cost-effective systems and fixtures currently on the market support compliance with the requirement, but the cost of water efficiency measures varies widely. For example, installing tamper-proof faucet aerators on existing fixtures is a small expense compared with a rainwater-harvesting or graywater-recycling system. High-efficiency toilets and dry fixtures, such as composting toilet systems, often have higher initial costs than standard models.

Newer technologies may also have higher costs and limited availability because of production constraints, and they may entail different maintenance and repair expenses, such as special cartridge components and cleaning and sealing fluids. Teams should perform a full cost-benefit and life-cycle study before installing such products.

2. Related Credits

Efforts to increase rainwater harvesting, increase graywater use, and decrease the demand on local water aquifers may support the following credits:

- SS Credit 1, Option 2, Path 2: Site Selection, Stormwater Design—Quantity Control
- SS Credit 1, Option 2, Path 3: Site Selection, Stormwater Design—Quality Control
- SS Credit 1, Option 2, Paths 7 and 8: Site Selection, Water-Efficient Landscaping
- SS Credit 1, Option 2, Path 9: Site Selection—Innovative Wastewater Technologies
- SS Credit 1, Option 2, Path 10: Site Selection—Water Use Reduction
- WE Credit 1: Water Use Reduction

Additional energy use may be needed for certain reuse strategies. Active systems also require commissioning, if within the tenant scope of work, and should be considered in relation to the following credits:

- EA Prerequisite 1: Fundamental Commissioning of Building Energy Systems

- EA Credit 3: Enhanced Commissioning
- EA Credit 5: Measurement and Verification

3. Summary of Referenced Standards

The Energy Policy Act (EPAct) of 1992 (and as amended)
This act addresses energy and water use in commercial, institutional, and residential facilities.

The Energy Policy Act (EPAct) of 2005
This statute became U.S. law in August 2005.
International Association of Plumbing and Mechanical Officials, Publication IAPMO/American National Standards Institute UPC 1–2006

Uniform Plumbing Code 2006, Section 402.0, Water-Conserving Fixtures and Fittings
http://www.iapmo.org
UPC defines water-conserving fixtures and fittings for water closets, urinals, and metered faucets. This ANSI-accredited code safeguards life, health, property, and public welfare by regulating and controlling the design, construction, installation, materials, location, operation, and maintenance or use of plumbing systems.

International Code Council, International Plumbing Code 2006, Section 604, Design of Building Water Distribution System
http://www.iccsafe.org
IPC defines maximum flow rates and consumption for plumbing fixtures and fittings, including public and private lavatories, showerheads, sink faucets, urinals, and water closets.

4. Implementation

The water use reduction credit calculation is based on occupancy. For example, when restrooms are not a part of the tenant space, it is important to evaluate the plumbing in common areas of the building that will be used to meet the needs of the occupants. If the base building does not have high-performance fixtures, the project team should encourage building owners to consider upgrades to existing fixtures as part of the lease negotiations in order to pursue additional water use savings and potential credit under WE Credit 1.

Effective ways to reduce potable water use include installing flow restrictors and reduced flow aerators on lavatory, sink, and shower fixtures; installing and maintaining metering faucets; installing high-efficiency fixtures such as high-efficiency water closets and urinals.

In certain cases, faucets with low-flow rates are not appropriate. For example, in kitchen sinks, faucets are used to fill pots and buckets. Using a low-flow rate for tasks where the volume of water is predetermined does not save water and will likely cause user dissatisfaction and inefficiencies. Consider alternative strategies to reduce water use, such as installing special-use pot fillers and high-efficiency faucets or foot pedal–operated faucets.

WaterSense, a partnership program sponsored by EPA, helps consumers identify water-efficient products and programs. WaterSense-labeled products exceed the requirements of the Uniform Plumbing Code and the International Plumbing Code standards for some high-efficiency fixtures or fittings. A variety of WaterSense labeled products and other high-efficiency plumbing fixtures, fittings, and appliances can be installed in the same way as conventional EPAct plumbing fixtures and fittings, as well as ENERGY STAR® appliances.

Although water-efficient dishwashers, laundry machines, and other water-consuming fixtures are not counted in the calculations for this credit, they may be included in exemplary performance calculations for WE Credit 1, Water Use Reduction.

To determine the most effective strategies for a particular condition, analyze the water efficiency options available to the project based on location, code compliance (plumbing and safety), and overall project function. Determine where in the building the most water is used, evaluate potential alternative water-saving technologies, and examine the impacts of alternative fixtures and technologies. Compare the design case water use with the calculated EPAct baseline to determine the optimal water savings for plumbing fixtures and fittings. Perform a detailed climate analysis to determine the availability of on-site resources and choose strategies that are appropriate and cost-effective.

Table 1. UPC and IPC Standards for Plumbing Fixture Water Use

Fixture	UPC and IPC Standards	EPA WaterSense Standards
Water closets (gallons per flush, gpf)	1.60	1.28
Urinals (gpf)	1.00	0.5[a]
Showerheads (gallons per minute, gpm*)	2.50	2.0[b]
Public lavatory faucets and aerators (gpm**)	0.5	
Private lavatory faucets and aerators (gpm**)	2.2	1.5
Public metering lavatory faucets (gallons per metering cycle)	0.25	
Kitchen sink faucets	2.20	
Metering faucets (gallons per cycle)	0.25	

*When measured at a flowing water pressure of 80 pounds per square inch (psi).
**When measured at a flowing water pressure of 60 pounds per square inch (psi).
[a] On May 22, 2008, EPA issued a notification of intent to develop a specification for high-efficiency urinals. WaterSense anticipates establishing a maximum allowable flush volume of 0.5 gpf.
[b] On August 30, 2007, EPA issued a notification of intent to develop a specification for showerheads. WaterSense anticipates establishing a single maximum flow rate between 1.5 gpm and 2.0 gpm.

Some water-saving technologies affect on-site energy performance and require commissioning; this task should be addressed by a project's measurement and verification plan. Calibration is necessary for projects using automatic sensors or flow valves. See EA Prerequisite 1, Fundamental Commissioning of Building Energy Systems, and EA Credit 5, Measurement and Verification, for more information. Space constraints or characteristics of the plumbing fixtures and fittings in existing buildings may hinder water efficiency efforts.

5. Timeline and Team

During predesign, setting water-use goals and strategy involves the owner, architect, and engineers. Identify local water utilities and governing authorities, research codes and applicable water laws, learn the process for obtaining permits and approval, and set water use goals and strategy.

In construction documents, the architect, working with the owner, should specify efficient fixtures and appliances and complete LEED calculations and documentation.

During construction, the design team and owner should confirm proper selection, installation, and operation of water fixtures, fittings, and systems.

6. Calculations

The following section describes the calculation methodology for determining water savings. The calculated water use reduction for the project is the difference between the calculated design case and a baseline case. The percentage is determined by dividing the design case use by the baseline use. The methodology differs from traditional plumbing design, in which calculations are based on fixture counts; under this prerequisite, the water use calculation is based on fixture and fitting water consumption rates and estimated use by the occupants. Occupants' estimated use is determined by calculating full-time equivalent (FTE) and transient occupants within the tenant space and applying appropriate fixture use rates to each.

Fixture Usage Groups

Fixture usage groups are subsets of washroom facilities used by different types of occupants. For each group, complete the template calculator. Indicate which fixtures are involved and which occupants they serve. If all occupants within the building have access to all fixtures, or if all fixtures are standard throughout the building, enter only a single fixture usage group. That is the simpler approach, but the project team may specify multiple groups to reflect different fixtures and usage patterns. For example, if washrooms on the first floor are used primarily by transient retail customers and washrooms on the second floor are used by office workers, calculate each separately.

The following scenario illustrates the application of different fixture usage groups.

In a retail store, employees use back-of-house restrooms exclusively; these restrooms have different fixture and fitting types and water consumption rates from those in the customer restrooms. The project team establishes 2 usage groups to account for the distinct populations in the space and the specific restroom facilities they use: (1) back-of-house (employees), and (2) customer restrooms (customers).

Calculating Occupancy

Identify the number of building occupants by occupancy type. In buildings with multiple shifts, use the number of FTEs from all shifts. Include the following:

- Full-time staff

- Part-time staff

- Transients (students, visitors, retail customers)

Calculate the FTE number of occupants based on a standard 8-hour daily occupancy period (40 hours per week). An 8-hour occupant has an FTE value of 1.0, and part-time occupants have an FTE value based on their hours per day divided by 8. FTE calculations for each shift of the project must be used consistently for all LEED credits.

Estimate the transient building occupants, such as students, visitors, and customers. Transient occupants can be reported as either daily totals or full-time equivalents. When using daily totals for transients, match the fixture uses for each occupancy type with the values shown in Table 2 (e.g., for the daily total of students, assume 0.5 lavatory faucet uses per daily student visitor). If transients are reported as a daily full-time equivalent value, fixture uses for FTEs must be assumed regardless of the transient population's identity (e.g., for students reported as FTEs, assume 3 lavatory faucet uses per student FTE). Use a transient occupancy number that is a representative daily average over the course of a year. If the number of transient visitors per day for retail facilities is unknown, estimate the FTE value of this population based on the default values presented in Table 3.

Table 2 provides default fixture use values for different occupancy types. These values should be used in the calculations for this credit unless special circumstances warrant modifications. Most buildings with students, visitors, and retail customers will also have FTE occupants. Half of all students and visitors are assumed to use a flush fixture and a lavatory faucet in the building and are not expected to use a shower or kitchen sink. A fifth of retail customers are assumed to use a flush and a flow fixture in the building and no shower or kitchen sink. The default for residential occupants is 5 uses per day of water closet and lavatory faucet, 1 shower, and 4 kitchen sink uses.

For consistency across LEED projects, the calculations require the use of a balanced, 1-to-1 sex ratio unless specific project conditions warrant an alternative. Provide a narrative description to explain any special circumstances.

Table 2a. Non-residential Default Fixture Uses, by Occupancy Type

Fixture Type	Duration (sec)	Uses / Day		
		FTE	Transient (Student / Visitor)	Retail Customer
Water Closet (Female)	n/a	3	0.5	0.2
Water Closet (Male)	n/a	1	0.1	0.1
Urinal (Female)	n/a	0	0	0
Urinal (Male)	n/a	2	0.4	0.1
Lavatory Faucet *	30*	3	0.5	0.2
Shower	300	0.1	0	0
Kitchen Sink	15	1	0	0

* Default duration for the metering type / autocontrol faucet is 15 seconds for the baseline and 12 seconds for the design case.

Table 2b. Residential Default Fixture Uses

Fixture Type	Duration (sec)	Uses / Day
Water Closet (Female)	n/a	5
Water Closet (Male)	n/a	5
Lavatory Faucet	60	5
Shower	480	1
Kitchen Sink	60	4

Table 3. Default Values for Transient Retail Occupants

Retail Space	FTE per 100 (sf)
Large-format retailer (greater than 50,000 square feet)	0.91
Grocery store	0.87
Restaurant	1.05
Small retailer	0.67
Service	0.77

Sources: 2001 Uniform Building Code, 2004–2005 Database for Energy Efficiency Resources (DEER) Update Study; field investigation work performed by LEED Retail Core Committee Members; ASNI/ASHRAE/IESNA 90.1–2007; LEED Reference Guide for Green Interior Design and Construction, 2009 Edition.

Design Case Water Consumption

The design case annual water use is determined by totaling the annual volume of each fixture type. The design case must use the rated flow rates and flush volumes for installed plumbing fixtures and fittings. Obtain water consumption data from the manufacturers' product literature.

In addition to the typical fixtures shown in Table 4, the project team may add others regulated by the referenced standards, as applicable.

Table 4. Sample Plumbing Fixtures and Fittings and Water Consumption

Flush Fixture	Flow Rate (gpf)	Flow Fixture	Flow Rate
Conventional water closet	1.6	Conventional private lavatory	2.2 gpm
High-efficiency toilet (HET), single-flush gravity	1.28	Conventional public lavatory	0.5 gpm or ≤ 0.25 gpc
HET, single-flush pressure assist	1.0	Conventional kitchen sink	2.2 gpm
HET, dual flush (full-flush)	1.6	Low-flow kitchen sink	≤ 2.2 gpm
HET, dual flush (low-flush)	1.1	Conventional shower	2.5 gpm
HET, foam flush	0.05	WaterSense shower	≤ 2.0 gpm
Nonwater toilet	0.0		
Conventional urinal	1.0		
High-efficiency urinal (HEU)	0.5		
Nonwater urinal	0.0		

Private or private use applies to plumbing fixtures in residences, apartments, and dormitories, to private (non-public) bathrooms in transient lodging facilities (hotels and motels), and to private bathrooms in hospitals and nursing facilities. All other facilities are considered public or public use. If the classification for public or private use is unclear, default to public-use flow rates in performing the calculations associated with this credit.

Baseline Case Water Consumption
The baseline case annual water use is determined by setting the fixture and fitting water consumption to baseline rates listed in the requirements (as opposed to actual installed values in the design case).

Eligible Fixtures
The "Kitchen sinks" category encompasses all sinks in public or private buildings that are used with patterns and purposes similar to a sink in a residential kitchen; break room sinks would be included. However professional grade / commercial faucets such as those used in a commercial kitchen would not be included. The "Public lavatory faucets" and "Private lavatory faucets" categories encompass all sinks used primarily for hand-washing regardless of location. Faucets whose usage patterns and flow rates are regulated for medical or industrial purposes (e.g. laboratory sinks) and do not fall under the definition of private or public use are not included. Faucets used exclusively for filling operations (e.g. pot-filler) can be excluded. All other fixtures and fixtures fittings must be included in the calculations unless there are special circumstances that justify excluding them.

7. Documentation Guidance
As a first step in preparing to complete the LEED Online documentation requirements, work through the following measures. Refer to LEED Online for the complete descriptions of all required documentation.

- Determine the type and number of occupants.
- Retain manufacturers' data showing the water consumption rates, manufacturer, and model of each fixture and fitting.
- List plumbing fixtures by usage group, if applicable.
- Define each usage group used.

8. Examples
There are no examples for this credit.

9. Exemplary Performance

This prerequisite is not eligible for exemplary performance under the Innovation in Design section.

10. Regional Variations

Local building and health codes differ in their treatment of alternative plumbing fixtures, such as nonwater urinals, dual-flush or low-flow water closets, and nonwater toilet systems. Confirm the legality of nontraditional approaches with code officials before committing to specific water-saving strategies.

11. Operations and Maintenance Considerations

Consider installing submetering for water delivered to fixture and fittings to help operators manage water consumption and identify problems within the system. Integrating electronic data logging will facilitate consumption trend analysis.

Some water conservation technologies may require special cleaning or maintenance procedures. For example, nonwater urinals generally need to be cleaned according to the manufacturer's specifications and their chemical traps appropriately maintained. Project teams should provide facility managers with appropriate maintenance information, manufacturers' contact information, and product specifications to facilitate proper operation.

A preventive maintenance program that includes plumbing fixture and fitting inspection and testing ensures that flow valves do not leak and that any sensors are calibrated correctly so that the fixtures flush and/or flow the appropriate amounts at the proper time.

12. Resources

Please see USGBC's LEED Resources & Tools (http://www.usgbc.org/projecttools) for additional resources and technical information.

Websites

Alliance for Water Efficiency

http://www.allianceforwaterefficiency.org/

The Alliance for Water Efficiency provides information and assistance on water conservation efforts.

American Rainwater Catchment Systems Association

http://www.arcsa.org

ARCSA was founded to promote rainwater catchment systems in the U.S. The ARCSA website includes a compilation of publications such as the Texas Guide to Rainwater Harvesting.

American Water Works Association, Water Wiser: The Water Efficiency Clearinghouse

http://www.awwa.org/waterwiser%20

This web clearinghouse provides articles, reference materials, and papers on all forms of water efficiency.

Environmental Building News, **Water: Doing More with Less**

http://www.buildinggreen.com/auth/article.cfm/2008/2/3/Water-Doing-More-With-Less

The site presents an article on building water efficiency.

National Oceanic and Atmospheric Administration, National Climatic Data Center

http://www.ncdc.noaa.gov/oa/ncdc.html

This site is useful for researching local climate data such as rainfall amounts. It also includes links to state climate offices.

North Carolina Division of Pollution Prevention and Environmental Assistance, Water Efficiency Manual for Commercial, Industrial, and Institutional Facilities

http://www.p2pays.org/ref/01/00692.pdf

This straightforward manual on water efficiency draws from a number of different North Carolina governmental departments.

Rocky Mountain Institute, Water

http://www.rmi.org/rmi/pid172

This portion of RMI's website is devoted to water resource efficiency.

Terry Love's Consumer Toilet Reports

http://www.terrylove.com/crtoilet.htm

This Website offers a plumber's perspective on many of the major toilets used in commercial and residential applications.

U.S. Department of Energy, Smart Communities Network

http://www.smartcommunities.ncat.org

This project website provides information about water efficiency, national and regional water efficiency assistance programs, and links to additional resources.

U.S. Department of the Interior, Water Measurement Manual: A Water Resources Technical Publication

http://www.usbr.gov/pmts/hydraulics_lab/pubs/wmm

This publication is a guide to effective water measurement practices for better water management.

U.S. EPA, How to Conserve Water and Use It Effectively

http://www.epa.gov/OWOW/nps/chap3.html

This document guides commercial, industrial, and residential water users in saving water and reducing sewage volumes.

U.S. EPA, WaterSense

http://www.epa.gov/watersense

The WaterSense Program helps U.S. consumers save water and protect the environment. Look for the WaterSense label to help choose high-quality, water-efficient products. A variety of products are available, and they do not require a change in lifestyle.

Water Studies

http://www.ebmud.com/resource-center/publications/studies

The site provides a variety of studies related to water.

Print Media

Constructed Wetlands for Wastewater Treatment and Wildlife Habitat: 17 Case Studies, EPA 832/B-93-005 (U.S. EPA, 1993).

On-site Wastewater Treatment Systems Manual (U.S. EPA, 2002): http://www.epa.gov/nrmrl/pubs/625r00008/html/625R00008.htm.
This document provides a focused, performance-based approach to on-site wastewater treatment and system management as well as valuable information on a variety of on-site sewage treatment options.

Water, Sanitary and Waste Services for Buildings, fifth edition, by A. Wise and J. Swaffield (Longman Scientific & Technical, 1995).

13. Definitions

An **aquifer** is an underground water-bearing rock formation or group of formations that supply groundwater, wells, or springs.

Automatic fixture sensors are motion detectors that automatically turn on and turn off lavatories, sinks, water closets, and urinals. Sensors can be hard wired or battery operated.

Blackwater definitions vary, but wastewater from toilets and urinals is always considered blackwater. Wastewater from kitchen sinks (perhaps differentiated by the use of a garbage disposal), showers, or bathtubs is considered blackwater under some state or local codes.

Composting toilet system. See **nonwater toilet system**.

Metering controls limit the flow time of water. They are generally manual-on and automatic-off devices, most commonly installed on lavatory faucets and showers.

Nonpotable water. See **potable water.**

Nonwater (or composting) toilet systems are dry plumbing fixtures and fittings that contain and treat human waste via microbiological processes.

A **nonwater (or dry) urinal**, replaces a water flush with a trap containing a layer of buoyant liquid that floats above the urine, blocking sewer gas and odors.

On-site wastewater treatment is the transport, storage, treatment, and disposal of wastewater generated on the project site.

Potable water meets or exceeds EPA's drinking water quality standards and is approved for human consumption by the state or local authorities having jurisdiction; it may be supplied from wells or municipal water systems.

Tenant space is the area within the LEED project boundary. For more information on what can and must be in the LEED project boundary see the Minimum Program Requirements (MPRs) and LEED 2009 MPR Supplemental Guidance. Note: tenant space is the same as project space.

WATER USE REDUCTION

	CI
Credit	WE Credit 1
Points	6-11 points

Intent

To further increase water efficiency within tenant spaces to reduce the burden on municipal water supply and wastewater systems.

Requirements

Employ strategies that in aggregate use less water than the water use baseline calculated for the tenant spaces (not including irrigation). The minimum water savings percentage for each point threshold is as follows:

Percentage Reduction	Points
30%	6
35%	8
40%	11

Calculate the baseline according to the commercial and/or residential baselines outlined below.[1] Calculations are based on estimated occupant usage and must include only the following fixtures and fixture fittings necessary to meet the needs of the occupants including fixtures and fixture fittings that may be outside the tenant space: water closets, urinals, lavatory faucets, showers, kitchen sink faucets and pre-rinse spray valves.

Commercial Fixtures, Fittings, and Appliances	Current Baseline
Commercial toilets	1.6 gallons per flush (gpf)* Except blow-out fixtures: 3.5 (gpf)
Commercial urinals	1.0 (gpf)
Commercial lavatory (restroom) faucets	2.2 gallons per minute (gpm) at 60 pounds per square inch (psi), private applications only (hotel or motel guest rooms, hospital patient rooms) 0.5 (gpm) at 60 (psi)** all others except private applications 0.25 gallons per cycle for metering faucets
Commercial prerinse spray valves (for food service applications)	Flow rate ≤ 1.6 (gpm) (no pressure specified; no performance requirement)

Residential Fixtures, Fittings, and Appliances	Current Baseline
Residential toilets	1.6 (gpf)***
Residential lavatory (bathroom) faucets	2.2 (gpm) at 60 psi
Residential kitchen faucet	
Residential showerheads	2.5 (gpm) at 80 (psi) per shower stall****

   *   EPAct 1992 standard for toilets applies to both commercial and residential models.

  ** In addition to EPAct requirements, the American Society of Mechanical Engineers standard for public lavatory faucets is 0.5 gpm at 60 psi (ASME A112.18.1-2005). This maximum has been incorporated into the national Uniform Plumbing Code and the International Plumbing Code.

 *** EPAct 1992 standard for toilets applies to both commercial and residential models.

**** Residential shower compartment (stall) in dwelling units: The total allowable flow rate from all flowing showerheads at any given time, including rain systems, waterfalls, bodysprays, bodyspas and jets, must be limited to the allowable showerhead flow rate as specified above (2.5 gpm) per shower compartment, where the floor area of the shower compartment is less than 2,500 square inches. For each increment of 2,500 square inches of floor area thereafter or part thereof, an additional showerhead with total allowable flow rate from all flowing devices equal to or less than the allowable flow rate as specified above must be allowed. Exception: Showers that emit recirculated nonpotable water originating from within the shower compartment while operating are allowed to exceed the maximum as long as the total potable water flow does not exceed the flow rate as specified above.

1 Tables adapted from information developed and summarized by the U.S. Environmental Protection Agency (EPA) Office of Water based on requirements of the Energy Policy Act (EPAct) of 1992 and subsequent rulings by the Department of Energy, requirements of the EPAct of 2005, and the plumbing code requirements as stated in the 2006 editions of the Uniform Plumbing Code or International Plumbing Code pertaining to fixture performance.

The following fixtures, fittings and appliances are outside the scope of the water use reduction calculation:

- Commercial Steam Cookers
- Commercial Dishwashers
- Automatic Commercial Ice Makers
- Commercial (family-sized) Clothes Washers
- Residential Clothes Washers
- Standard and Compact Residential Dishwashers

1. Benefits and Issues to Consider

See the Benefits and Issues section in WE Prerequisite 1.

2. Related Credits

See the Related Credits section in WE Prerequisite 1.

3. Summary of Referenced Standards

Seethe Referenced Standards section in WE Prerequisite 1

4. Implementation

See the Implementation section in WE Prerequisite 1.

5. Timeline and Team

See the Timeline and Team section in WE Prerequisite 1.

6. Calculations

See the Calculations section in WE Prerequisite 1.

7. Documentation Guidance

See the Documentation Guidance section in WE Prerequisite 1.

8. Examples

See the Examples section in WE Prerequisite 1.

9. Exemplary Performance

Projects may earn an innovation point for exemplary performance by demonstrating 45% reduction in projected potable water use.

10. Regional Variations

See the Regional Variations section in WE Prerequisite 1.

11. Operations and Maintenance Considerations

See the Operations and Maintenance section in WE Prerequisite 1.

12. Resources

See the Operations and Maintenance section in WE Prerequisite 1.

13. Definitions

See the Definitions section in WE Prerequisite 1.

Endnotes

[1] Hutson, Susan S., Nancy L. Barber, Joan F. Kenny, Kristin S. Linsey, Deborah S. Lumia, and Molly A. Maupin. Estimated Use of Water in the United States in 2000. U.S. Geological Survey, 2004. http://water.usgs.gov/pubs/circ/2004/circ1268/htdocs/text-trends.html (accessed May 2008).

[2] U.S. Geological Survey. "USGS Study Documents Water Level Changes in High Plains Aquifer." U.S. Geological Survey News Release, (February 9, 2004). http://www.usgs.gov/newsroom/article.asp?ID=121 (accessed May 2008).

[3] Solley, Wayne B., Robert R. Pierce, and Howard A. Perlman. Estimated Use of Water in the United States in 1995. U.S. Geological Survey, 1998. http://water.usgs.gov/watuse/pdf1995/html (accessed May 2008).

4 U.S. Environmental Protection Agency, Office of Ground Water and Drinking Water. "List of Drinking Water Contaminants & MCLS." http://www.epa.gov/safewater/mcl.html (accessed May 2008).

5 U.S. Environmental Protection Agency, Office of Wastewater Management. Water Permitting 101. 2002. http://www.epa.gov/npdes/pubs/101pape.pdf (accessed May 2008).

6 Ibid.

7 Hutson, Susan S., Nancy L. Barber, Joan F. Kenny, Kristin S. Linsey, Deborah S. Lumia, and Molly A. Maupin. Estimated Use of Water in the United States in 2000. U.S. Geological Survey, 2004. http://water.usgs.gov/pubs/circ/2004/circ1268/htdocs/text-trends.html (accessed May 2008).

8 U.S. Environmental Protection Agency, Office of Wastewater Management. Water Permitting 101. 2002. http://www.epa.gov/npdes/pubs/101pape.pdf (accessed May 2008).

9 U.S. Green Building Council. "LEED Certified Project List." http://www.usgbc.org/LEED/Project/CertifiedProjectList.aspx (accessed May 2008).

10 Based on 650 building occupants, each using an average of 20 gallons per day.

11 Knox III, Randy H. Case Study: Adobe's "Greenest Office in America" Sets the Bar for Corporate Environmentalism. U.S. Green Building Council. http://www.fmlink.com/ProfResources/Sustainability/Articles/article.cgi?USGBC:200707-16.html, (accessed November 2008).

12 Massachusetts Water Resources Authority. "Water Efficiency and Management for Commercial Buildings." http://www.mwra.state.ma.us/04water/html/bullet4.htm (accessed May 2008).

13 Energy Information Administration. "1999 Commercial Buildings Energy Consumption Survey." Commercial Buildings Energy Consumption Survey. http://www.eia.doe.gov/emeu/cbecs/background.html (accessed May 2008).

14 U.S. Department of Energy. "Water Efficiency: Water Efficiency Basics." http://www1.eere.energy.gov/femp/water/water_basics.html (accessed May 2008).

15 U.S. Environmental Protection Agency, WaterSense. "Why Water Efficiency?" http://www.epa.gov/owm/water-efficiency/water/why.htm (accessed May 2008).

16 U.S. Environmental Protection Agency, WaterSense. "WaterSense." http://www.epa.gov/watersense (accessed May 2008).

17 Ibid.

18 Energy Information Administration, "1999 Commercial Buildings Energy Consumption Survey," Commercial Buildings Energy Consumption Survey. http://www.eia.doe.gov/emeu/cbecs/ (accessed May 2008).

Overview

Buildings consume approximately 39% of the energy and 74% of the electricity produced annually in the United States, according to the U.S. Department of Energy.[1] Generating electricity from fossil fuels, such as oil, natural gas, and coal, negatively affects the environment at each step of production and use, beginning with extraction and transportation, followed by refining and distribution, and ending with consumption. For example, coal mining disrupts natural habitats and can devastate landscapes. Acidic mine drainage degrades regional ecosystems. Coal is rinsed with water, producing billions of gallons of sludge that must be stored in ponds. Mining itself is a dangerous occupation in which accidents and the long-term effects of breathing coal dust can shorten the life spans of coal miners.

Electricity is most often generated by burning fossil fuels, whose combustion releases carbon dioxide and other greenhouse gases that contribute to climate change. Coal-fired plants accounted for more than half of U.S. electricity generation in 2006.[2] Burning coal releases harmful pollutants, such as carbon dioxide, sulfur dioxide, nitrogen oxides, small particulates, and mercury. Each megawatt of coal-generated electricity releases into the atmosphere an average of 2,249 pounds of carbon dioxide, 13 pounds of sulfur dioxide, and 6 pounds of nitrogen oxides.[3] More than 65% of the sulfur dioxide released into the air, or more than 13 million tons per year, comes from electricity generation, primarily coal-burning generators.[4] Mining, processing, and transporting coal to power plants create additional emissions, including methane vented from the coal during transport.

Natural gas, nuclear fission, and hydroelectric generators all have adverse environmental consequences as well. Natural gas is a major source of nitrogen oxide and greenhouse gas emissions. Nuclear power increases the potential for catastrophic accidents and raises significant waste transportation and disposal issues. Hydroelectric generating plants disrupt natural water flows and disturb aquatic habitats.

Green buildings address those issues in two ways. First, they reduce the amount of energy required for building operations, and second, they use more benign forms of energy. The better the energy performance of a building, the fewer greenhouse gases are emitted from energy production. Electricity generation using sources other than fossil fuels also reduces the environmental impacts from a building's energy use. Additionally, improved energy performance results in lower operating costs. As global competition for fuels accelerates, the rate of return on energy efficiency measures improves.

Energy Performance

The energy performance of a commercial interior depends on both its design and that of the base building. Materials, construction methods, building envelope, and water efficiency as well as the heating, ventilating, and air-conditioning (HVAC) and lighting systems all play a role in determining how efficiently the building uses energy. The most effective way to optimize energy performance is to use an integrated, whole-building approach. Collaboration among all team members and base building operators, beginning at project inception, is necessary when designing for efficiency.

The Energy and Atmosphere (EA) section of the LEED Reference Guide for Green Building Interior Design and Construction promotes three kinds of activities:

Tracking Building Energy Performance—Design, Commissioning, Monitoring

Projects that achieve any level of certification must at a minimum perform better than the average building. Specific levels of achievement beyond the minimum are awarded a proportional number of points. First, the commercial interior must be designed to operate at a high performance level. Next, it must be commissioned to ensure that the chosen systems are performing to meet the design intent. Third, a process for ongoing measurement and verification should be established to ensure continual, high-performance of tenant-operated energy systems.

The design of new facility space must be based on the designated mandatory and prescriptive requirements of ASHRAE 90.1-2007 or USGBC-approved local code, whichever is more stringent. In addition, optimization of building energy performance beyond ASHRAE 90.1-2007 is required in EA Prerequisite 2, Minimum Energy Performance. Documenting the energy performance of the commercial interior can be accomplished through building energy simulation modeling or prescriptive options.

Commissioning begins with the development of the owner's project requirements, followed at a minimum by creation of a formal commissioning plan, verification of equipment installation, and submission of a final report. Enhanced commissioning includes additional tasks, such as design and contractor submittal reviews, creation of a formal systems manual, verification of staff training, and a follow-up review before the warranty period ends.

Commissioning identifies inefficiencies in building systems and provides a starting point for optimizing energy and water efficiency. Adjusting these systems for maximum efficiency, in turn, minimizes the environmental impacts associated with energy and water use. Properly executed commissioning can substantially reduce costs for maintenance, repairs, and resource consumption and improve indoor environmental quality, enhancing occupants' productivity. For example, studies conducted at the Lawrence Berkeley National Lab suggest that commissioning and improved operations could save 20% of the energy used by existing buildings.[5]

Monitoring the performance of building systems begins with establishing a measurement and verification plan based on the best practices developed by the International Performance Measurement and Verification Protocol (IPMVP). The plan must cover at least one year of postconstruction occupancy. Monitoring involves using appropriate measuring instruments and can include energy modeling.

Managing Refrigerants to Eliminate CFCs

The release of chlorofluorocarbons (CFCs) from refrigeration equipment destroys ozone molecules in the stratosphere and reduces the ozone layer's ability to block harmful ultraviolet light from penetrating Earth's atmosphere. CFCs in the stratosphere also absorb infrared radiation and create chlorine, a potent greenhouse gas, further harming the atmosphere. Banning the use of CFCs in refrigerants slows the depletion of the ozone layer and mitigates climate change.

Standard practice for commercial interiors is to install equipment that does not use CFC-based refrigerants.

Using Renewable Energy

Energy generation from renewable sources—such as solar, wind, and biomass—avoids air and water pollution and other environmental consequences associated with producing and consuming traditional fossil and nuclear fuels. Although hydropower is considered renewable, it can have harmful environmental effects, such as degrading water quality, altering fish and bird habitats, and endangering species. Low-impact hydropower, if available, is recommended.

Renewable energy minimizes acid rain, smog, climate change, and human health problems resulting from air contaminants. In addition, using renewable resources avoids the consumption of fossil fuels, the production of nuclear waste, and the environmentally damaging operation of hydropower dams.

LEED for Commercial Interiors Approach to Energy and Atmosphere

Because most commercial interiors projects occupy only a portion of a larger building, for which many energy-related decisions may have already been made, LEED for Commercial Interiors focuses on the individual tenant's options for energy efficiency, lighting, HVAC, appliances, and equipment. To support tenants' decisions to use renewable energy, LEED for Commercial Interiors offers incentive to purchase green power. Table 1 relates the timing of credit decisions and actions to the overall project schedule.

CREDIT	TITLE
EA Prerequisite 1	Fundamental Commissioning of Building Energy Systems
EA Prerequisite 2	Minimum Energy Performance
EA Prerequisite 3	Fundamental Refrigerant Management
EA Credit 1.1	Optimize Energy Performance—Lighting Power
EA Credit 1.2	Optimize Energy Performance—Lighting Controls
EA Credit 1.3	Optimize Energy Performance—HVAC
EA Credit 1.4	Optimize Energy Performance—Equipment and Appliances
EA Credit 2	Enhanced Commissioning
EA Credit 3	Measurement and Verification
EA Credit 4	Green Power

FUNDAMENTAL COMMISSIONING OF BUILDING ENERGY SYSTEMS

	CI
Prerequisite	EA Prerequisite 1
Points	Required

Intent

To verify that the project's energy-related systems are installed and calibrated to performing according to the owner's project requirements, basis of design and construction documents.

Benefits of commissioning include reduced energy use, lower operating costs, fewer contractor callbacks, better building documentation, improved occupant productivity, and verification that the systems perform in accordance with the owner's project requirements.

Requirements

The following commissioning process activities must be completed by the project team:

- Designate an individual as the commissioning authority (CxA) to lead, review and oversee the completion of the commissioning process activities.

  - The CxA must have documented commissioning authority experience in at least 2 building projects.

  - The individual serving as the CxA must be independent of the project's design and construction management, though the CxA may be an employee of any firms providing those services. The CxA may be a qualified employee or consultant of the owner.

  - The CxA must report results, findings and recommendations directly to the owner.

  - For projects smaller than 50,000 gross square feet, the CxA may be a qualified person on the design or construction teams who has the required experience.

- The owner must document the owner's project requirements. The design team must develop the basis of design. The CxA must review these documents for clarity and completeness. The owner and design team must be responsible for updates to their respective documents.

- Develop and incorporate commissioning requirements into the construction documents.

- Develop and implement a commissioning plan.

- Verify the installation and performance of the systems to be commissioned.

- Complete a summary commissioning report.

Commissioned Systems

Commissioning process activities must be completed for the following energy-related systems at a minimum:

- Heating, ventilating, air conditioning and refrigeration (HVAC&R) systems (mechanical and passive) and associated controls.

- Lighting and daylighting controls.

- Domestic hot water systems.

- Renewable energy systems (e.g. PV, wind, solar).

1. Benefits and Issues to Consider

Benefits of commissioning include reduced energy use, lower operating costs, fewer contractor callbacks, better building documentation, improved occupant productivity, and verification that the systems perform in accordance with the owner's project requirements.

Environmental Issues

Facilities that do not perform as intended may consume significantly more resources over their lifetimes. Commissioning can minimize the negative impacts buildings have on the environment by helping verify that buildings are designed and constructed to operate as intended and in accordance with the owner's project requirements.

Economic Issues

If commissioning has not been previously included as part of the project delivery process, the costs associated with commissioning may be met with initial resistance. When the long-term benefits are taken into consideration, however, commissioning can be seen as a cost-effective way to ensure that the building is functioning as designed and that the planned energy savings are realized.

Improved occupant well-being and productivity are other potential benefits when building systems function as intended. Proper commissioning of building systems can reduce employee illness, tenant turnover and vacancy, and liability related to indoor air quality, and it can avoid premature equipment replacement.

2. Related Credits

The commissioning effort can affect many performance-based features encouraged in the LEED for Commercial Interiors Rating System. Consider including the following features and systems in the commissioning effort: water efficiency and metering of plumbing fixtures, outdoor air delivery and monitoring, lighting, and thermal comfort systems. See Table 1 for a list of related credits.

3. Summary of Referenced Standards

There are no standards referenced for this prerequisite.

4. Implementation

Relationship between Fundamental and Enhanced Commissioning

LEED for Commercial Interiors addresses building commissioning in 2 places: EA Prerequisite 1, Fundamental Commissioning of Building Energy Systems, and EA Credit 2, Enhanced Commissioning.

For LEED design and construction projects, the scope of services for the commissioning authority (CxA) and project team should be based on the owner's project requirements. The commissioning process activities must address the commissioned systems noted in the EA Prerequisite 1 requirements. For commercial interior projects, the scope can vary tremendously. Some may include only lighting systems, whereas others may include all HVAC, service water, and lighting systems. EA Credit 2 requires that the commissioning authority be involved early in the process to help facilitate a commissioning design review and a commissioning documentation review. As the project nears completion, enhanced commissioning requires oversight of staff training, a walk-through 8 to 10 months after completion, and the completion of a systems manual.

Table 1. Potential Systems to Be Commissioned, as Applicable

Systems Prerequisites and Credits Potential Commissioning Activities
Heating, ventilating, air-conditioning, and refrigeration systems, both mechanical and passive, and associated controls
EA Prerequisite 2, Mandatory provisions and prescriptive requirements of ASHRAE 90.1-2007 have been met.
EA Prerequisite 3, No CFC in newly purchased equipment.
EA Credit 1.3, Option 1. HVAC equipment sized on actual loads; mechanical equipment meets enhanced efficiency standards; use of variable speed controls; appropriate zoning and controls.
EA Credit 1.3, Option 2. Same as EA Prerequisite 2.
IEQ Prerequisite 1, Ventilation is compliant with ANSI/ASHRAE 62.1–2007.
IEQ Prerequisite 2, Option 2. Designated smoking rooms verification requirements.
IEQ Prerequisite 2, Option 3. Residential facilities: test results of air leakage and air sampling.
IEQ Credit 1, Functioning outdoor air monitoring system.
IEQ Credit 2, Mechanical systems: air testing and balance confirm increased ventilation rates. Passive systems: minimum flow rates are set and met.
IEQ Credit 3.1, Filtration media replacement.
IEQ Credit 5, Exhaust system in areas where hazardous gases or chemicals are present, MERV 13 air filtration media.
IEQ Credit 6.2, Functioning controllability for temperature and ventilation.
IEQ Credit 7.1, HVAC system and control systems meet ANSI/ASHRAE 55–2004 requirements.
IEQ Credit 7.2, Monitoring system function.
ID Credit 1, If applicable.
Lighting controls, including daylighting
SS Credit 1, Option 6. Existing building, site, and project lighting designs comply with requirements.
EA Prerequisite 2, Mandatory provisions and prescriptive requirements of ASHRAE 90.1-2007 have been met.
EA Credit 1.1, ASHRAE 90.1-2007 compliance documentation.
EA Credit 1.2, Functioning daylight responsive controls.
IEQ Credit 8.1, Daylighting requirements are met.
ID Credit 1, If applicable.
Domestic hot water systems
IEQ Prerequisite 2, Mandatory provisions and prescriptive requirements of ASHRAE 90.1-2007 have been met.
ID Credit 1, If applicable.
Renewable energy systems (wind, solar, etc.)
SS Credit 1, Option 11. On-site renewable energy performance.

5. Timeline and Team

The commissioning process is a planned, systematic quality-control process that involves the owner, users, occupants, operations and maintenance staff, design professionals, and contractors. It is most effective when begun at project inception. All members of the project team are encouraged to participate in the commissioning activities as part of a larger commissioning team. The team approach to commissioning can speed the process and add a system of checks and balances.

The overall commissioning effort identified in both EA Prerequisite 1, Fundamental Commissioning of Building Energy Systems, and EA Credit 2, Enhanced Commissioning, is shown below in Table 2 as divided into 12 basic steps. The steps are presented in sequential order; however, some tasks can begin at various points in the project or be completed at various points in the project. For example, the development of the commissioning plan may begin in the design phase, have multiple updates during the project, and be considered completed at some point during the construction phase.

Some of the steps shown below are required for EA Prerequisite 1, Fundamental Commissioning of Building Energy Systems, and some are required for EA Credit 2, Enhanced Commissioning. Table 2 outlines the commissioning tasks, the team members primarily responsible for performing each project requirement, and the requirements common to EA Prerequisite 1 and EA Credit 2.

Table 2. Tasks and Responsibilities for EA Prerequisite 1 and EA Credit 2

Project Phases	Commissioning Tasks (Steps 1–12)	Rating System Tasks	Fundamental	Enhanced
Predesign, Design Phase				
Request for proposal Architect and engineer selection	1. Designate commissioning authority (CxA)	EA Prerequisite 1, Task 1 EA Credit 2, Task 1	Owner or project team	Owner or project team
Owners project requirements, basis of design	2. Document owner's project requirements; Develop basis of design	EA Prerequisite 1, Task 2	Owner or CxA* Design team	Owner or CxA* Design team
Schematic design	3. Review owner's project requirements and basis of design	EA Prerequisite 1, Task 2 EA Credit 2, Task 2	CxA**	CxA
Design development	4. Develop and implement Cx plan	EA Prerequisite 1, Task 4	Project team or CxA*	Project team or CxA
Construction documents	5. Incorporate commissioning requirements into the construction documents	EA Prerequisite 1, Task 3	Project team or CxA*	Project team or CxA
	6. Conduct commissioning design review prior to midconstruction documents	EA Credit 2, Task 2	N/A	CxA
Construction phase				
Equipment procurement Equipment installation	7. Review contractor submittals applicable to systems being commissioned	EA Credit 2, Task 3	N/A	CxA
Functional testing Test and balance Performance testing acceptance	8. Verify installation and performance of commissioned systems	EA Prerequisite 1, Task 5	CxA	CxA
Operations and maintenance (O&M) manuals	9. Develop systems manual for commissioned systems	EA Credit 2, Task 4	N/A	Project team or CxA
O&M training	10. Verify that requirements for training are completed	EA Credit 2, Task 2	N/A	Project team or CxA
Substantial completion	11. Complete a summary commissioning report	EA Prerequisite 1, Task 6	CxA	CxA
Occupancy				
Systems monitoring	12. Review building operation within 8 to 10 months after substantial completion	EA Credit 2, Task 6	N/A	CxA

*Although EA Prerequisite 1 does not require the CxA to be on the project team until just before the equipment installation phase, if brought in earlier, he or she can also help the owner develop the project requirements and assist with other important commissioning tasks.

**Some commissioning tasks can be performed by the owner or other project team members. However, the review of the owner's project requirements and basis of design must be performed by the CxA. For EA Prerequisite 1, Fundamental Commissioning, this may be performed at any time before verification of equipment installation and acceptance.

STEP 1

Designate an individual as the commissioning authority (CxA) to lead, review and oversee the completion of the commissioning process activities.

Ideally, the project team should designate an individual as the CxA as early as possible in the project timeline, preferably during predesign. The qualified individual designated as the CxA serves as an objective advocate for the owner and is responsible for the following:

- Directing the commissioning team and process in the completion of the commissioning requirements.

- Coordinating, overseeing, and/or performing the commissioning testing.

- Reviewing the results of the systems performance verification.

For LEED projects, a qualified CxA should have experience with 2 other projects of similar managerial and technical complexity.

The owner may want to specify additional qualifications for the CxA, depending on the scope and nature of the commissioning. CxA certification programs are administered by various industry groups.

For projects larger than 50,000 square feet, the individual serving as the CxA on a LEED project must be independent of the project's design and construction teams.

The CxA may be a qualified staff member of the owner, an owner's consultant to the project, or an employee of a firm providing design and/or construction management services. The CxA may not, however, have responsibility for design (e.g., be the engineer of record) or for construction. The CxA must report results, findings, and recommendations directly to the owner.

For projects smaller than 50,000 square feet, the CxA may be a qualified staff member of the owner, an owner's consultant to the project, or an individual on the design or construction team (such as the engineer of record) and may have additional project responsibilities beyond leading the commissioning services.

For projects pursuing EA Credit 3, Enhanced Commissioning, the CxA may not be an employee of the design firm but may be contracted through this firm.

Table 3. Commissioning Authority Qualifications

Party Acting as Commissioning Authority (CxA)	Fundamental Commissioning Prerequisite[2, 4, 5]		Enhanced Commissioning Credit[3, 4, 5]
	< 50,000 (sf)	≥ 50,000 (sf)	
Employee or subcontractor of general contractor with construction responsibilities	Yes		
Employee or subcontractor, with construction responsibilities, of construction manager who holds constructor contracts	Yes		
Employee or subcontractor, with project design responsibilities, of the architect or engineer of record	Yes		
Disinterested employee or subcontractor ofceneral contractor or construction manager[1]	Yes	Yes	
Disinterested employee of architect or engineer[1]	Yes	Yes	
Disinterested subcontractor to architect or engineer[1]	Yes	Yes	Yes
Construction manager not holding constructor contracts	Yes	Yes	Yes
Independent consultant contracted to Owner	Yes	Yes	Yes
Owner employee or staff	Yes	Yes	Yes

[1] "Disinterested" means an employee or subcontractor who has no project responsibilities other than commissioning.
[2] EA Prerequisite 1 requirements (see Table 1 above).
[3] EA Credit 3 requirements (the CxA must review the owner's project requirements, basis of design, and design documents prior to midconstruction documents phase and perform a back-check).
[4] The same CxA overseeing the enhanced commissioning tasks must also oversee the fundamental commissioning tasks.
[5] Regardless of who employs the CxA, he or she "shall have documented commissioning authority experience in at least two building projects" and ideally meet the minimum qualifications of having "a high level of experience in energy systems design, installation and operation, commissioning planning and process management, hands-on field experience with energy systems performance, interaction, startup, balancing, testing, troubleshooting, operation, and maintenance procedures and energy systems automation control knowledge."
(From "Who Can Be the Commissioning Authority?" 01/03/06 LEED 2.2 Commissioning Subcommittee, posted under LEED Reference Documents, http://www.usgbc.org.)

STEP 2

The owner must document the owner's project requirements for the fit-out project. The design team must develop the basis of design. The owner and design team are responsible for updates to their respective documents.

Clear and concise documentation of the owner's project requirements and the basis of design is a valuable part of any successful project delivery and commissioning process. These documents are used throughout the commissioning process to provide a baseline and focus for validating systems' energy and environmental performance.

Owner's Project Requirements

The owner's project requirements must be completed by the owner, CxA, and project team prior to the approval of contractor submittals of any commissioned equipment or systems. Updates during the design and construction process are the primary responsibility of the owner.

The owner's project requirements should detail the functional requirements of a project and the expectations of the building's use and operation as they relate to the systems to be commissioned. The owner's project requirements should address the following issues, as applicable to the project:

Owner and user requirements

Describe the primary purpose, program, and use of the proposed project (e.g., office building with data center, academic building addition and new gymnasium) and any pertinent project history. Provide any overarching goals relative to program needs, future expansion, flexibility, quality of materials, and construction and operational costs.

Environmental and sustainability goals

Describe any specific environmental or sustainability goals (e.g., LEED certification).

Energy efficiency goals

Describe overall project energy efficiency goals relative to the local energy code, ASHRAE standard, or LEED. Describe any goals or requirements for building orientation, landscaping, façade, fenestration, envelope and roof features that will affect energy use.

Indoor environmental quality requirements

For each program or area, describe the intended use, anticipated occupancy schedules, space environmental requirements (including lighting, temperature, humidity, acoustics, air quality, and ventilation), desired adjustability of system controls, and accommodations for after-hours use.

Equipment and system expectations

Describe the desired level of quality, reliability, type, automation, flexibility, and maintenance requirements for each of the systems to be commissioned. When known, provide specific efficiency targets, desired technologies, or preferred manufacturers for building systems.

Building occupant and O&M personnel requirements

Describe how the facility will be operated and by whom. Describe the desired level of training and orientation required for the building occupants to understand and use the building systems.

Basis of Design

The design team must document the basis of design for the systems to be commissioned prior to approval of contractor submittals of any commissioned equipment or systems. Updates to this document during the design and construction process are the responsibility of the design team.

The basis of design describes the systems to be commissioned and outlines any design assumptions that are not otherwise included in the design documents. It should be updated with each subsequent design submission, with increasing specificity as applicable.

The basis of design should include the following, as applicable:

Primary design assumptions

Include space use, redundancy, diversity, climatic design conditions, space zoning, occupancy, operations, and space environmental requirements.

Standards

Include applicable codes, guidelines, regulations, and other references that will be put into practice.

Narrative descriptions

Include performance criteria for the HVAC&R systems, lighting systems, hot water systems, on-site power systems, and other systems to be commissioned.

STEP 3

The CxA must review the owner's project requirements and the basis of design for clarity and completeness. The owner and design team are responsible for updates to their respective documents.

The CxA must ensure that the basis of design reflects the owner's project requirements. Both documents must be reviewed by the CxA for completeness prior to the approval of contractor submittals of any commissioned equipment or systems.

STEP 4

Develop and implement a commissioning plan.

Unique to a particular project, the commissioning plan is the reference document that identifies the strategies, aspects, and responsibilities within the commissioning process for each phase of a project, for all of the project team members. This document outlines the overall process, schedule, organization, responsibilities, and documentation requirements of the commissioning process.

The commissioning plan is developed at the start of the commissioning process, preferably during design development, and is updated during the course of a project to reflect any changes in planning, schedule, or other aspects.

The following list outlines required components of the commissioning plan.

- Commissioning Program Overview
  - Goals and objectives.
  - General project information.
  - Systems to be commissioned.
- Commissioning Team
  - Team members, roles, and responsibilities.
  - Communication protocol, coordination, meetings, and management.
- Commissioning Process Activities

- Documenting the owner's project requirements.
- Preparing the basis of design.
- Developing systems functional test procedures.
- Verifying systems performance.
- Reporting deficiencies and the resolution process.
- Accepting the building systems.

Project teams pursuing the enhanced commissioning credit (EA Credit 2) may need to expand the commissioning plan to include the following commissioning process activities:

- Documenting the commissioning review process
- Reviewing contractor submittals.
- Developing the systems manual.
- Verifying the training of operations personnel.
- Reviewing building operation after final acceptance.

Table 4. Required Commissioning Plan Components

Required Commissioning Plan Components
Brief overview of commissioning process.
List of all systems and assemblies included in commissioning authority's scope of work.
Identification of commissioning team and its responsibilities.
Description of management, communication, and reporting of commissioning process.
Overview of commissioning process activities for predesign, design, construction, and occupancy and operations phases, including development of owner's project requirements, review of basis of design, schematic design, construction documents and submittals, construction phase verification, functional performance test development and implementation, and 10-month warranty review.
List of expected work products.
List of commissioning process milestones.

STEP 5

Develop and incorporate commissioning requirements into the construction documents.

Typically, the project specifications are used to inform contractors of their responsibilities in the commissioning process. These specifications may describe the components listed in Table 5.

Often, all commissioning requirements are outlined in a section of the general conditions of the construction specifications. Placing all commissioning requirements in a single location gives responsibility for commissioning work to the general contractor, who can then assign responsibility to subcontractors. It is also valuable to refer to commissioning requirements on the drawings, in any bid forms, and in specification sections related to the systems to be commissioned.

Table 5. Commissioning Requirements for Construction Documents

Commissioning team involvement.
Contractors' responsibilities.
Submittal review procedures for commissioned systems.
Operations and maintenance documentation, system manuals.
Meetings.
Construction verification procedures.
Startup plan development and implementation.
Functional performance testing.
Acceptance and closeout.
Training.
Warranty review site visit.

STEP 6

The CxA should conduct at least 1 commissioning deign review of the owner's project requirements, basis of design, and design documents prior to midconstruction documents phase and back-check the review comments in the subsequent design submission.

This step is required by EA Credit 2, Enhanced Commissioning, but is not mandatory for achievement of EA Prerequisite 1, Fundamental Commissioning of Building Energy Systems.

The CxA should review the owner's project requirements, basis of design, and design documents to give the owner and design team an independent assessment of the state of the design for the commissioned systems. Typically, a design review performed by the CxA focuses on the following issues:

- Ensuring clarity, completeness, and adequacy of the owner's project requirements.

- Verifying that all issues discussed in the owner's project requirements are addressed adequately in basis of design.

- Reviewing design documents for achieving the owner's project requirements and basis of design and coordination of commissioned systems.

Additional reviews by the CxA throughout the design and construction process may be advisable and appropriate depending on the project duration, phasing, and complexity.

STEP 7

The CxA should review contractor submittals applicable to the systems being commissioned for compliance with the owner's project requirements and basis of design. This review must be concurrent with the architect's or engineer's reviews and submitted to the design team and the owner.

This step is required by EA Credit 2, Enhanced Commissioning, but is not mandatory for achievement of EA Prerequisite 1, Fundamental Commissioning of Building Energy Systems.

The CxA should review the contractor submittals and identify any issues that might otherwise result in rework or change orders. The CxA should specifically evaluate the submittals for the following:

- Conformance with the owner's project requirements and basis of design.

- Fulfilling operations and maintenance requirements.

- Facilitating performance testing.

The CxA review of contractor submittals does not typically replace or alter the scope or responsibility of the design team's role in approving submittals.

STEP 8

Verify the Installation andPerformance of the Systems to be Commissioned.

Commissioning is conducted to verify the performance of commissioned systems as installed to meet the owner's project requirements, basis of design, and contract documents.

Verification of the installation and performance of commissioned systems typically includes 3 steps for each commissioned system: installation inspection, performance testing, and the evaluation of results compared with owner's project requirements and the basis of design.

- Installation inspections (sometimes called prefunctional inspections) are a systematic set of procedures intended to identify whether individual system components have been installed properly. Often this process occurs at startup of individual units of equipment and may use "prefunctional checklists" or "startup and checkout forms" to ensure consistency in the inspections and document the process. Installation inspections may be performed by the CxA, the installing contractor, or others, depending on the procedures outlined in the commissioning plan. Installation inspections provide quality control to ensure that relatively minor issues (e.g., an improperly wired sensor, a control valve installed backward) are discovered and corrected prior to systems performance testing.

- Systems performance testing (sometimes called functional performance testing) occurs once all system components are installed, energized, programmed, balanced, and otherwise ready for operation under part- and full-load conditions. Testing should include each process in the sequence of operations under central and packaged equipment control, including startup, shutdown, capacity modulation, emergency and failure modes, alarms, and interlocks to other equipment.

Systems performance testing typically relies on testing procedures developed by the CxA specifically for the system to be tested. A wide variety of methods may be used to simulate and evaluate that the system being tested performs as expected (per the owner's project requirements, basis of design, and contract documents) in all modes of operation.

Systems performance testing may be performed by some combination of the CxA, the installing contractor, and others, depending on the procedures outlined in the commissioning specifications and the commissioning plan. It may reveal problems with the performance of the commissioned systems and may require significant follow-up and coordination among members of the project team.

- Evaluation of results is the final step. At each point in the process of installation inspections and systems performance testing the CxA should evaluate whether the installed systems meet the criteria for the project as set forth in the owner's project requirements and the basis of design documents.

Any discrepancies or deficiencies should be reported to the owner, and the team should work collaboratively to find an appropriate resolution.

STEP 9

Develop a systems manual that gives future operating staff the information needed to understand and optimally operate the commissioned systems.

This step is required by EA Credit 2, Enhanced Commissioning, but is not mandatory for achievement of EA Prerequisite 1, Fundamental Commissioning of Building Energy Systems.

Provide a systems manual in addition to the O&M manuals submitted by the contractor. The systems manual generally focuses on operating rather than maintaining the equipment, particularly the interactions.

The systems manual should include the following for each commissioned system:

- Final version of the basis of design.

- System single-line diagrams.

- As-built sequences of operations, control drawings, and original setpoints.

- Operating instructions for integrated building systems.

- Recommended schedule of maintenance requirements and frequency, if not already included in the project O&M manuals.

- Recommended schedule for retesting of commissioned systems with blank test forms from the original commissioning plan.

- Recommended schedule for calibrating sensors and actuators.

STEP 10

Verify that the requirements for training operating personnel and building occupants have been completed.

This step is required by EA Credit 2, Enhanced Commissioning, but is not mandatory for achievement of EA Prerequisite 1, Fundamental Commissioning of Building Energy Systems.

Establish and document training expectations and needs with the tenant. Many common training topics are listed in Table 6. Ensure that operations staff and occupants receive this training and orientation. Pay particular attention to new or uncommon sustainable design features that could be overridden or removed because of a lack of understanding. Document that the training was completed according to the contract documents.

Have a contract in place to review tenant space operation with O&M staff and occupants, including a plan for resolution of outstanding commissioning-related issues 8 to 10 months after substantial completion.

Table 6. Common Training Topics

Common Training Topics
General purpose of system (design intent).
Use of O&M manuals.
Review of control drawings and schematics.
Startup, normal operation, shutdown, unoccupied operation, seasonal changeover, manual operation, control setup and programming troubleshooting, and alarms.
Interactions with other systems.
Adjustments and optimizing methods for energy conservation.
Health and safety issues.
Special maintenance and replacement sources.
Occupant interaction issues.
System response to different operating conditions.

STEP 11

Complete a summary commissioning report.

After installation inspections and performance verification items have been completed, the results are tabulated and assembled into a commissioning report. Supporting information can be compiled as a Cx record but is not required in the summary.

The summary commissioning report should include the following:

- Executive summary of the process and the results of the commissioning program, including observations, conclusions, and any outstanding items.

- History of any system deficiencies identified and how they were resolved, including any outstanding issues or seasonal testing scheduled for a later date.

- Systems performance test results and evaluation.

- Confirmation from the CxA indicating whether individual systems meet the owner's project requirements, basis of design, and contract documents.

In addition, for projects pursuing EA Credit 2, Enhanced Commissioning, the summary commissioning report should include the following:

- Summary of the design review process.

- Summary of the submittal review process.

- Summary of the O&M documentation and training process.

Table 7. Commissioning Report Components

Commissioning Report Components
Owner's project requirements.
Project commissioning specifications.
Verification of installation (construction checklist).
Functional performance testing results and forms.
O&M documentation evaluation (EA Credit 2).
Training program evaluation (EA Credit 2).
Description of commissioning process benefits.
Outstanding issues.
Contract and plan for resolution within 8 to 10 months of substantial completion (EA Credit 2).

STEP 12

Ensure the involvement by the CxA in reviewing building operation within 10 months after substantial completion with O&M staff and occupants. Include a plan for resolving outstanding issues.

This step is required by EA Credit 2, Enhanced Commissioning, but is not mandatory for achievement of EA Prerequisite 1, Fundamental Commissioning of the Building Energy Systems.

The CxA should coordinate with the owner and the O&M staff to review the tenant space and its performance 8 to 10 months after substantial completion. All unresolved construction deficiencies as well as any deficiencies identified in this postoccupancy review should be documented and corrected under manufacturer or contractor warranties.

The CxA review of the building operation with operations staff and occupants should identify any problems in operating the building as originally intended. Any significant issues identified by the CxA that will not be corrected should be recorded in the systems manual.

6. Calculations

There are no calculations required for this prerequisite.

7. Documentation Guidance

As a first step in preparing to complete the LEED Online documentation requirements, work through the following measures. Refer to LEED Online for the complete descriptions of all required documentation.

- Update the commissioning plan at milestones throughout the project. This should happen, at a minimum, during the design development phase, the construction documents phase, and just prior to the kick-off meeting with the general contractor.

- Prepare a systems list that indicates which systems have been included within the scope of enhanced commissioning.

- Obtain confirmation that the commissioning authority has documented experience on at least 2 building projects.

- Retain copies of the owner's project requirements, basis of design, commissioning specifications, commissioning report, and systems manual.

8. Examples

EXAMPLE 1

The example below demonstrates the interconnectedness of the owner's project requirements, basis of design, construction documents, commissioning plan, commissioning report, and systems manual.

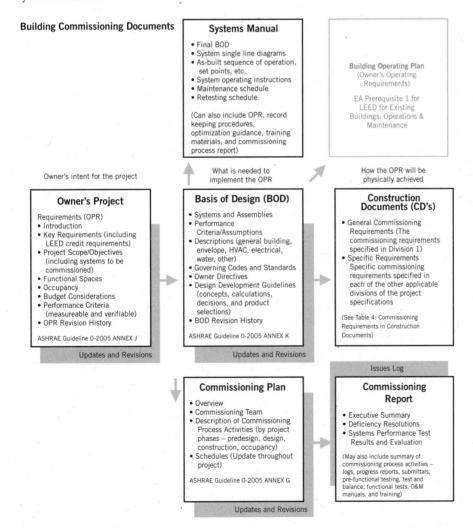

Building Commissioning Documents

Systems Manual
- Final BOD
- System single line diagrams
- As-built sequence of operation, set points, etc.
- System operating instructions
- Maintenance schedule
- Retesting schedule

(Can also include OPR, record keeping procedures, optimization guidance, training materials, and commissioning process report)

Building Operating Plan
(Owner's Operating Requirements)

EA Prerequisite 1 for LEED for Existing Buildings: Operations & Maintenance

Owner's intent for the project | What is needed to implement the OPR | How the OPR will be physically achieved

Owner's Project Requirements (OPR)
- Introduction
- Key Requirements (including LEED credit requirements)
- Project Scope/Objectives (including systems to be commissioned)
- Functional Spaces
- Occupancy
- Budget Considerations
- Performance Criteria (measureable and verifiable)
- OPR Revision History

ASHRAE Guideline 0-2005 ANNEX J

Updates and Revisions

Basis of Design (BOD)
- Systems and Assemblies
- Performance Criteria/Assumptions
- Descriptions (general building, envelope, HVAC, electrical, water, other)
- Governing Codes and Standards
- Owner Directives
- Design Development Guidelines (concepts, calculations, decisions, and product selections)
- BOD Revision History

ASHRAE Guideline 0-2005 ANNEX K

Updates and Revisions

Construction Documents (CD's)
- General Commissioning Requirements (The commissioning requirements specified in Division 1)
- Specific Requirements Specific commissioning requirements specified in each of the other applicable divisions of the project specifications

(See Table 4: Commissioning Requirements in Construction Documents)

Issues Log

Commissioning Plan
- Overview
- Commissioning Team
- Description of Commissioning Process Activities (by project phases – predesign, design, construction, occupancy)
- Schedules (Update throughout project)

ASHRAE Guideline 0-2005 ANNEX G

Updates and Revisions

Commissioning Report
- Executive Summary
- Deficiency Resolutions
- Systems Performance Test Results and Evaluation

(May also include summary of commissioning process activities – logs, progress reports, submittals, pre-functional testing, test and balance, functional tests, O&M manuals, and training)

EXAMPLE 2. Report Outline

The outline below is a guide for what can be included in the summary commissioning report. There is no required order of presentation, only that these primary report components (applicable to the commissioning scope) are included in the report.

The final report that goes to the owner should include copies of issue and testing logs, meeting minutes, and interim process reports.

Summary Commissioning Report

Executive Summary

Provide a brief description of project (size, space types, occupancy, etc.), highlighting commissioning goals.

Provide a brief narrative on the scope of commissioning, highlighting the systems to be commissioned, process activities, and examples of significant issues:

1. Predesign activities (if any)

2. Design activities (if any)

3. Construction activities

4. Postoccupancy activities (if any)

Highlight any significant systemic issues that were uncovered during the commissioning process.

Provide recommendations for future project commissioning activities.

Deficiency Resolution

Provide a more detailed summary of the types of issues uncovered and how they were resolved. These issues are best presented in order of project phases (e.g., during design, during construction). A copy of the issues log is typically included as an appendix.

Systems Performance Test Results and Evaluation

Summarize observations on test results and evaluations for prefunctional tests, test and balance, functional tests, and postoccupancy testing (if applicable).

---

9. Exemplary Performance

This prerequisite is not eligible for exemplary performance under the Innovation in Design section.

10. Regional Variations

The significance of commissioning tasks may vary with the climate. For example, in northern regions, the functioning of heating systems, such as boilers, is a critical issue. Suboptimal performance for heating systems in northern climates can result in high utility bills, wasted energy, and added emissions. In the Southeast, humidity is an important consideration. Here, the introduction of hot, humid outside air must be controlled, and suboptimal performance for cooling systems could raise utility bills. In other regions of the country, equipment such as economizers and evaporative cooling will be used for extended periods and must function correctly.

Regional climates tend to drive the selection of systems and the associated commissioning and maintenance decisions. For example, including the commissioning of the building envelope may be more important in certain regions than in others. Adding the commissioning of water systems may be important in arid regions.

Regardless of the types of equipment selected, each project can greatly benefit from a systematic approach to ensuring that the right equipment and systems are specified, ordered, installed, and tested to ensure proper operation and performance.

11. Operations and Maintenance Considerations

So that building systems operate effectively for the life of the building, use the commissioning process and outcomes to develop documents that will help facility managers run the building in a manner consistent with the design intent and equipment specifications. These documents should include the following:

- Building operating plan (owner's operating requirements). This plan defines the delivered conditions required by building management and occupants for the successful operation of a building. It identifies the spaces, uses, occupancy types, and required conditions. It includes the time-of-day schedules of every system, the mode of operation for each system when it is running, and the desired indoor conditions or setpoints for each schedule or mode. This information is initially developed in the basis of design.

- Systems narrative. The systems narrative is a summary description of each of the following types of base building systems installed in the project building: space heating, space cooling, ventilation, domestic water heating, humidification and/or dehumidification, and lighting. The description should include summaries of the central plant, distribution, and terminal units, as applicable, as well as the controls associated with these systems.

- Sequence of operations. The sequence of operations represents system-level documentation that defines what operational states are desired under what conditions. This can include which systems are running or idle; whether operations are full-load or part-load; staging or cycling of compressors, fans, or pumps; proper valve positions; desired system water temperatures and duct static air pressures, depending on other variables (e.g., outside air temperatures, room air temperatures, and/or relative humidity); and any reset schedules or occupancy schedules. The sequence of operations should include specific information on operating phases (warm-up, occupied, unoccupied), setpoints and controls, and feedback systems to monitor performance.

- Commissioning report. Ensure that the commissioning report adequately identifies problems that are likely to reemerge or merit particular attention on an ongoing basis.

Ensure that the commissioning report adequately identifies problems that are likely to reemerge or merit particular attention on an ongoing basis.

12. Resources

Please see USGBC's LEED Resources & Tools (http://www.usgbc.org/projecttools) for additional resources and technical information.

Websites

American Society of Heating, Refrigerating and Air-Conditioning Engineers

http://www.ashrae.org

ASHRAE advances the science of heating, ventilation, air conditioning, and refrigeration for the public's benefit through research, standards writing, continuing education, and publications. According to the ASHRAE website, "membership is open to any person associated with the field including indoor air quality, building design and operation, and environmental control for food processing and industry."

Building Commissioning Association

http://www.bcxa.org/resources/index.htm

BCxA promotes building commissioning practices that maintain high professional standards and fulfill building owners' expectations. The association offers a 5-day intensive course focused on how to implement the commissioning process and that is intended for commissioning authorities with at least 2 years of experience.

California Commissioning Collaborative

http://www.cacx.org

The California Commissioning Collaborative is a group of government, utility, and building services professionals committed to developing and promoting viable building commissioning practices in California. Its online library, available at http://resources.cacx.org/library/, has more than 300 resources, including articles, papers, guides, and sample commissioning documents.

California Department of General Services, Division of the State Architect, Adopting the Commissioning Process for the Successful Procurement of Schools

http://www.chps.net/links/pdfs/CommissioningProcessGuide.pdf

According to its publisher, this guide is "intended to be used by school districts, programmers, design professionals, contractors, operations and maintenance personnel, and commissioning authorities to understand the commissioning process and their role in it."

Energy Design Resources, Cx Assistant Commissioning Tool

http://www.ctg-net.com/edr2002/cx/

This web-based tool provides project-specific building commissioning information to design teams and enables users to evaluate probable commissioning cost, identify appropriate commissioning scope, and access project-related sample commissioning specifications.

Lawrence Berkeley National Laboratory, The Cost-Effectiveness of Commercial Buildings Commissioning: A Meta-Analysis of Existing Buildings and New Construction in the United States

http://eetd.lbl.gov/emills/PUBS/Cx-Costs-Benefits.html

Oregon Office of Energy, Commissioning for Better Buildings in Oregon

http://egov.oregon.gov/ENERGY/CONS/BUS/comm/bldgcx.shtml

This website and document of the same name contain a comprehensive introduction to the commissioning process, including research, financial benefits, and case studies.

Portland Energy Conservation Inc.

http://www.peci.org

PECI develops the field for commissioning services by helping building owners understand the value of commissioning and by producing process and technical information for commissioning providers. Their focus includes owners of private and public buildings and a range of building types. PECI manages the annual National Conference on Building Commissioning.

University of Wisconsin, Madison, Department of Engineering Professional Development

http://www.engr.wisc.edu

This program offers commissioning process training courses for building owners, architects, engineers, operations and maintenance staff, and other interested parties. The program also offers accreditation of commissioning process providers and managers.

Print Media

ASHRAE Guideline 0–2005: The Commissioning Process (American Society of Heating, Refrigerating and Air-Conditioning Engineers, 2005). http://www.ashrae.org.

ASHRAE Guideline 1–1996: The HVAC Commissioning Process, (American Society of Heating, Refrigerating and Air-Conditioning Engineers, 1996). http://www.ashrae.org.

ASHRAE Guideline 4–1993: Preparation of Operations & Maintenance Documentation for Building Systems (American Society of Heating, Refrigerating and Air-Conditioning Engineers, 1993). http://www.ashrae.org.

The Building Commissioning Handbook, second edition, by John A. Heinz and Rick Casault (Building Commissioning Association, 2004). http://www.bcxa.com.

Commissioning Fact Sheets (Collaborative of High Performance Schools). http://www.chps.net/manual/index.htm#com.
These fact sheets explore how can help school districts ensure their schools are built to high performance standards.

Model Commissioning Plan and Guide Specifications (Portland Energy Conservation Inc, 1998).

Building Commissioning Guide, Office of Energy Efficiency and Renewable Energy Federal Energy Management Program (U.S. Department of Energy). http://www.eere.energy.gov.

Commissioning for Better Buildings in Oregon (Oregon Office of Energy, 2007). http://egov.oregon.gov/ENERGY/CONS/BUS/comm/bldgcx.shtml.

PECI Model Building Commissioning Plan and Guide Specifications (Portland Energy Conservation Inc.). http://www.peci.org.

13. Definitions

Basis of design includes design information necessary to accomplish the owner's project requirements, including system descriptions, indoor environmental quality criteria, design assumptions, and references to applicable codes, standards, regulations, and guidelines.

Commissioning (Cx) is the process of verifying and documenting that a building and all of its systems and assemblies are planned, designed, installed, tested, operated, and maintained to meet the owner's project requirements.

The **commissioning authority (CxA)** is the individual designated to organize, lead, and review the completion of commissioning process activities. The CxA facilitates communication among the owner, designer, and contractor to ensure that complex systems are installed and function in accordance with the owner's project requirements.

The **commissioning plan** is a document that outlines the organization, schedule, allocation of resources, and documentation requirements of the commissioning process.

The **commissioning process** is a systematic quality-focused effort to ensure that building systems are designed, specified, procured, installed, and functioning in accordance with the owner's intent. The process uses planning, documentation, and verification of testing to review and oversee the activities of both designer and constructor.

The **commissioning report** documents the commissioning process, including a commissioning program overview, identification of the commissioning team, and description of the commissioning process activities.

Commissioning specification is the contract language used in the construction documents to detail the objective, scope, and implementation of the construction and acceptance phases of the commissioning process as developed in the design phase of the commissioning plan. This allows the construction contractor to ensure that these activities are considered in proposals for the construction work.

The **commissioning team** includes those people responsible for working together to carry out the commissioning process.

An **installation inspection** examines components of the building systems to determine whether they are installed properly and ready for systems performance testing.

Owner's project requirements is a written document that details the ideas, concepts, and criteria that are determined by the owner to be important to the success of the project.

Systems performance testing is the process of determining the ability of commissioned systems to perform in accordance with the owner's project requirements, the basis of design, and construction documents.

Tenant space is the area within the LEED project boundary. For more information on what can and must be in the LEED project boundary see the Minimum Program Requirements (MPRs) and LEED 2009 MPR Supplemental Guidance. Note: tenant space is the same as project space.

Verification is the range of checks and tests carried out to determine whether components, subsystems, systems, and interfaces between systems operate in accordance with the contract documents.

	CI
Prerequisite	EA Prerequisite 2
Points	Required

Intent

To establish the minimum level of energy efficiency for the tenant space systems to reduce environmental and economic impacts associated with excessive energy use.

Requirements

Design portions of the building as covered by the tenant's scope of work to comply with ANSI/ASHRAE/IESNA Standard 90.1-2007 (with errata but without addenda[1]), and complete the following:

- Comply with the mandatory provisions (Sections 5.4, 6.4, 7.4, 8.4, 9.4 and 10.4) of ANSI/ASHRAE/IESNA Standard 90.1-2007 (with errata but without addenda[1]).

- Achieve the prescriptive requirements (Sections 5.5 or 5.6, 6.5, 7.5 and 9.5 or 9.6) or performance requirements (Section 11) of ANSI/ASHRAE/IESNA Standard 90.1-2007 (with errata but without addenda[1]).

- Reduce connected lighting power density 10% below that allowed by ANSI/ASHRAE/IESNA Standard 90.1-2007 (with errata but without addenda[1]) using either the Space-by-Space Method or by applying the whole building lighting power allowance to the entire tenant space.

- Install ENERGY STAR® qualified equipment for 50% (by rated-power) of ENERGY STAR® eligible equipment[2] installed as part of the tenant's scope of work. This requirement includes appliances, office equipment, electronics, and commercial food service equipment. Excluded are heating, ventilating and air conditioning (HVAC), lighting, and building envelope products.

Projects in California may use Title 24-2005, Part 6 in place of ANSI/ASHRAE/IESNA Standard 90.1-2007.

---

1   Project teams wishing to use ASHRAE approved addenda for the purposes of this credit may do so at their discretion. Addenda must be applied consistently across all LEED credits.

1. Benefits and Issues to Consider

Environmental Issues

The process of extracting and consuming energy from fossil fuels causes many negative environmental impacts, including air and water pollution, land degradation, solid waste generation, and rising greenhouse gas emissions. Fossil fuel–based energy use causes climate change as well as serious risks to environmental and human health and safety. Given both the negative environmental impacts inherent in most traditional energy-production processes and our limited energy supplies, efficiency measures are an important strategy for managing the impacts of energy consumption. The commercial real estate industry's energy use accounts for approximately 18% of U.S. carbon dioxide emissions.[6] Additionally, data from the U.S. Energy Information Administration show that buildings are responsible for almost half (48%) of all energy consumed and greenhouse gases emitted annually.[7]

Economic Issues

Optimizing energy performance can reduce overall operating costs. Changing operational strategies to avoid energy use—for example, turning off lights and HVAC systems when the building is unoccupied—can often be done at zero or very low initial cost and rapid payback. Even seemingly small conservation measures can be significant; for instance, replacing a single incandescent lamp with a fluorescent lamp, which uses up to 75% less energy, can save more than $30 in energy costs over the lifetime of the lamp.[8]

2. Related Credits

LEED for Commercial Interiors addresses energy efficiency in 2 places: EA Prerequisite 2, Minimum Energy Performance, and EA Credit 1, Optimize Energy Performance. In addition to reducing energy use through efficiency, project teams can mitigate energy use impacts by using renewable energy generated off-site. Refer to these credits:

- EA Credit 1: Optimize Energy Performance
- EA Credit 4: Green Power

3. Summary of Referenced Standard

ANSI/ASHRAE/IESNA Standard 90.1–2007, Energy Standard for Buildings Except Low-Rise Residential Buildings

American National Standards Institute

American Society of Heating, Refrigerating and Air-Conditioning Engineers

Illuminating Engineering Society of North America

ANSI/ASHRAE/IESNA 90.1–2007 was formulated by ASHRAE under an ANSI consensus process. IESNA is a joint sponsor of the standard.

ANSI/ASHRAE/IESNA 90.1–2007 establishes minimum requirements for the energy-efficient design of buildings, with these exceptions: single-family houses; multifamily structures of 3 habitable stories or fewer above grade; manufactured houses (mobile and modular homes); buildings that do not use either electricity or fossil fuel; and equipment and portions of buildings systems that use energy primarily for industrial, manufacturing, or commercial processes. Building envelope requirements are provided for semiheated spaces, such as warehouses.

The standard provides criteria in the general categories shown in Table 1. Within each section are mandatory provisions and additional prescriptive requirements. Some sections also contain a performance alternative.

The energy cost budget method (Section 11) allows the project team to exceed some of the prescriptive requirements, provided energy cost savings are made in other areas. However, in all cases, the mandatory provisions must still be met.

Table 1. Energy Standard Requirements Addressed by ANSI/ASHRAE/IESNA Standard 90.1–2007

ANSI/ASHRAE/IESNA 90.1-2007 Components
Section 5. Building envelope (including semiheated spaces, such as warehouses)
Section 6. Heating, ventilation, and air-conditioning (including parking garage ventilation, freeze protection, exhaust air recovery, and condenser heat recovery for service water heating)
Section 7. Service water heating (including swimming pools)
Section 8. Power (including all building power distribution systems)
Section 9. Lighting (including exit signs, building exterior, grounds, and parking garages)
Section 10. Other equipment (including all permanently wired electrical motors)

4. Implementation

Design the tenant space so that it complies with ASHRAE 90.1-2007 or the local code, whichever is more stringent. Research the status of individual state energy codes compared with energy standards on the U.S. Department of Energy's Building Energy Codes website (see Resources).

If provisions of the base building are managed entirely by the landlord (and therefore cannot be changed by the building tenant) and do not meet the requirements of ASHRAE 90.1-2007, then only areas that are not part of the tenant scope of work and exclusively controlled by the landlord are exempt from the requirements of the standard.

More Stringent Local Code

ASHRAE 90.1-2007 is the baseline that registered projects must meet to satisfy the prerequisite requirement. Any local code (or provision in it) that is more stringent becomes part of the prerequisite requirement. In these cases, explain and document verification that the local code (or provision) is more stringent. California Title 24 is accepted as being more stringent with no further evaluation needed.

Less Stringent Local Code

In LEED for Commercial Interiors, the credit standards only to apply to the tenant's scope of work; this allows teams with projects in an existing core and shell building to certify their project without having to compel the building owner to make changes to existing systems. However, the intent of this prerequisite is to establish the minimum level of energy efficiency for the space systems; projects should still meet these standards.

If the local code is less stringent, follow ASHRAE 90.1-2007. Do not outline a tenant scope of work to avoid applying the standard. Whenever possible, work being done for the benefit of the tenant should meet the more stringent provisions of ASHRAE 90.1-2007.

Applying ASHRAE 90.1-2007

Section 2.1(a) of the standard specifies minimum energy efficiency requirements for the following 3 construction types:

- New buildings and their systems.
- New portions of buildings and their systems.
- New systems and equipment in existing buildings.

The third approach applies to most commercial interior projects and is addressed below. As stated in Section 4.2.1.3, existing building alterations must comply with the provisions of Sections

5, 6, 7, 8, 9, and 10, as long as compliance does not increase the building's energy consumption. Sections 5 through 10 (Table 1) explain when these provisions apply (e.g., definitions and the building elements), list the mandatory provisions, and give the applicable prescriptive criteria. EA Prerequisite 2, Minimum Energy Performance, recognizes exceptions for certain applications as outlined in the standard, such as those for historic buildings, 24-hour facilities, and equipment and portions of building systems that use energy primarily to provide for industrial, manufacturing, or commercial processes.

EA Prerequisite 2, Minimum Energy Performance, does not preclude using the exceptions provided for historic buildings or annual energy consumption comparison as long as compensating changes are made in more than 1 applicable requirement section.

Section 5. Building Envelope Requirements (ASHRAE 90.1-2007)

The mandatory provisions of Section 5.4 must be met if they may apply to a commercial interior project. Teams must use 1 of 3 compliance paths: Section 5.5, Prescriptive Path; Section 5.6, Building Envelope Trade-Off Option; or Section 11, Energy Cost Budget Method.

Section 6. Heating, Ventilating and Air Conditioning Requirements (ASHRAE 90.1-2007)

If the project involves altering or replacing HVAC systems in existing buildings, follow the requirements of Section 6.1.1.3. New HVAC equipment must meet the minimum efficiency requirements set by the standard. Note that project teams considering EA Credit 1.3, Optimize Energy Performance—HVAC, Option 1, should consult the New Buildings Institute publication *Advanced Buildings: Energy Benchmark for High Performance Buildings* (E-Benchmark) Prescriptive Criteria E 2.5 for more stringent minimum efficiency requirements.

Air-conditioning added for spaces previously not air-conditioned must meet the requirements of Section 6.2. Alterations to existing systems must not reduce economizer capability unless they meet the criteria set out in Section 6.5.1.

EA Prerequisite 2, Minimum Energy Performance, does not preclude using any of the exceptions in Section 6.1.1.3 that address equipment modifications and repairs, alterations involving extensive revisions to other systems, refrigerant change, relocation of existing equipment, or access limitations for ducts and pipes.

Section 6 provides 3 compliance paths, any of which meet the requirement of the prerequisite if justified and properly followed:

- Use the simplified approach option for HVAC Systems in Section 6.3, which addresses small buildings whose HVAC design meets certain criteria.
- Meet the mandatory and prescriptive provisions in Sections 6.4 and 6.5.
- Meet the mandatory provisions of Section 6.4 and the energy cost budget method in Section 11.

The mandatory provisions of Section 6.4 include minimum equipment efficiency requirements, controls, and HVAC system construction and insulation; they address ducts, plenums, and piping.

A project team not using the energy cost budget method must follow the prescriptive path in Section 6.5, which establishes the requirements for economizers, simultaneous heating and cooling limitations (significant to energy use reductions), humidification, air system design and control, hydronic system design and control, energy recovery, exhaust hoods, and radiant heating systems.

Project teams must meet he minimum efficiency requirements for system components listed in ASHRAE 90.1-2007, Tables 6.8.1A-G, even if using the energy cost budget method.

Section 7. Service Water Heating Requirements (ASHRAE 90.1-2007)

Section 7 addresses heating water for domestic or commercial purposes (restrooms, kitchens, etc.). When altering systems within existing buildings, follow the same requirements set out for new construction, unless there is insufficient space or a system is inaccessible. Project teams must meet the mandatory provisions of Section 7.4, and either the prescriptive path in Section 7.5 or the energy cost budget method in Section 11. The mandatory provisions of Section 7.5 delineate requirements for efficiency, controls, pools, and heat traps for storage tanks.

Section 8. Power Requirements (ASHRAE 90.1-2007, Section 8.4.1)

Section 8.4 describes mandatory provisions covering voltage drops in the power distribution system. There are no prescriptive provisions for this section.

Section 9. Lighting Requirements (ASHRAE 90.1-2007)

Section 9 outlines guidelines for replacement lighting systems and new systems. If the scope of the lighting work will replace less than half of the existing fixtures with new ones and will use no additional power, all other provisions of the section apply.

Section 9 specifies the same mandatory provisions and prescriptive requirements for either the building area method or space-by-space method.

Section 9.4 describes the mandatory provisions for controls (9.4.1), including automatic lighting shutoff, space controls, exterior lighting controls, task lighting, tandem wiring (9.4.2); exit signs (9.4.3); and exterior building and grounds lighting (9.4.4 and 9.4.5). Pay special attention to Section 9.4.1, Lighting Control. Buildings larger than 5,000 square feet must have an automatic control device to shut off all lighting in the building. The shut-off device may be a programmable control to schedule time-of-day control for areas no greater than 25,000 square feet but no less than every floor. The approach may use occupant sensors to turn lights off after 30 minutes of no activity or a signal from another control or alarm system that indicates the area is unoccupied. EA Prerequisite 2 does not preclude using any of the exceptions provided in Section 9.4.1.1 for 24-hour operations, patient care areas, and where automatic shutoff would endanger the safety or security of occupants.

A space control device must be provided in each area enclosed by ceiling-height partitions. Any device that must be turned on manually must be readily accessible and visible to users. Shared spaces (such as classrooms, conference and meeting rooms, and employee lunch and break rooms) must be equipped with a control that turns lights off within 30 minutes after occupants leave. In all other spaces, a device may be turned on manually or controlled by an occupancy sensor. Rooms smaller than 10,000 square feet must have at least 1 control for every 2,500 square feet, and rooms larger than 10,000 square feet must have least 1 every 10,000 square feet. If the control can override the time-of-day scheduled shutoff control, the override should be limited to 4 hours.

LEED for Commercial Interiors recognizes additional lighting controls in EA Credit 1.2, Optimize Energy Performance—Lighting, for daylight-responsive controls, and EQ Credit 6.1, Controllability of Systems—Lighting, for individual controls for task lighting and shared controls in multioccupant spaces. The function of these additional controls must comply with ASHRAE 90.1-2007.

The building area method of demonstrating compliance uses the building area types listed in Table 9.5.1 of ASHRAE 90.1-2007. The interior lighting power allowance is determined by multiplying the gross lighted floor area of the building type by the lighting power density value in the associated table. More than 1 building area type may be used; trade-offs among building area types are permitted provided the total installed interior lighting power does not exceed the interior lighting power allowance.

The space-by-space method is more flexible than the building area method and allows project teams to address each space individually. For each area, the lighting power density value in Table 9.6.1 is multiplied by the square footage. The interior lighting power allowance is the sum of those results. Trade-offs among spaces are allowed provided the total proposed lighting power density is less than the sum of the lighting power budget allowances for all individual occupancies. Additional interior lighting power may be added to the allowance for certain applications as described in Section 9.6.2.

The exterior lighting power allowance is calculated by multiplying the allowed lighting power for each exterior surface (found in ASHRAE 90.1-2007 Table 9.4.5) by the total area or length associated with that surface, summing the results, and then multiplying this number by 1.05. For exterior lighting surfaces, the allowed lighting power can be used only for the specific application; it cannot be traded among surfaces or with other exterior lighting.

Section 10. Other Equipment Requirements (ASHRAE 90.1-2007)
This section establishes mandatory efficiency standards for electric motors. There are no prescriptive provisions for this section.

Section 11. Energy Cost Budget Method (ASHRAE 90.1-2007)
The standard provides an alternative to the prescriptive approach, in which each section must be satisfied individually. The energy cost budget method requires the simulation of the proposed design and a baseline case that follows the prescriptive requirements of each section. The calculation usually requires computer modeling. The modeling must cover at least the segment of the building serviced by the same HVAC system supplying the project space. If the energy cost budget is used to demonstrate compliance with EA Prerequisite 2, note that the only permitted trade-offs are between regulated systems within the project space. Additional information about this method, as well as the performance rating method (Appendix G), is included in EA Credit 1.3, Optimize Energy Performance—HVAC.

5. Timeline and Team
The project team should start the energy simulation modeling early in the project design to gain insights for design decisions and an indication of how to achieve different levels of energy cost reductions.

The mechanical or electrical engineer must coordinate with the facility manager to ensure maximum energy efficiency in the tenant space. Facilitate energy-efficient operations by working with the facility manager when projecting energy loads, as well as implementing tools for tracking and analysis.

6. Calculations
For lighting power density, see the Calculations section in EA Credit 1.1.

For ENERGY STAR®–qualified equipment, see the Calculations section in EA Credit 1.4.

7. Documentation Guidance
As a first step in preparing to complete the LEED Online documentation requirements, work through the following measures. Refer to LEED Online for the complete descriptions of all required documentation.

- For ASHRAE compliance, list any addenda used, and retain copies of ASHRAE compliance forms.

- If the project is using the prescriptive compliance path, assemble documentation demonstrating that the project meets all applicable requirements.

- For lighting power density reduction, refer to the Documentation Guidance section in EA Credit 1.1.

- For ENERGY STAR® equipment, refer to the Documentation Guidance section in EA Credit 1.4.

8. Examples

Energy simulation software packages, such as DOE-2 or EnergyPlus, enable the creation of a representative model. Energy simulation software can be used to demonstrate compliance with the performance requirements of ASHRAE 90.1-2007, as an alternative to the prescriptive requirements. Figure 1 shows an example of a 3-D building model.

Figure 1. Screenshot from Building Simulation Software

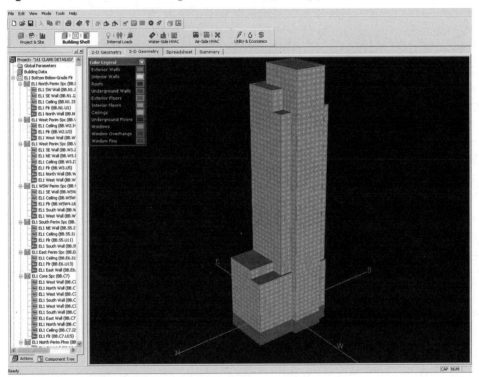

9. Exemplary Performance

This prerequisite is not eligible for exemplary performance under the Innovation in Design section.

10. Regional Variations

Savings achieved through energy efficiency improvements may qualify for state and local utility incentive programs. For instance, Washington State's Puget Sound Energy offers grants to customers that install efficiency upgrades to existing equipment or facilities. Grants range from several hundred dollars to more than $100,000 and typically pay for about 50% of a project's cost.[9] Ask local utility providers about the availability of incentives and rebate programs.

11. Operations and Maintenance Considerations

Provide the building operator with a breakdown of anticipated energy end uses based on any modeling results. The breakdown will provide a baseline to help operators evaluate ongoing energy consumption patterns for the project space and building. The facility manager should have an ongoing commissioning plan in place to catch any system inefficiencies.

Enable linkages with EPA's ENERGY STAR® software tools. Register the building with the ENERGY STAR® Portfolio Manager tool and input basic building data (e.g., location, square footage). Analyze anticipated building energy performance using the ENERGY STAR® Target Finder tool and make sure the facility owner or manager has access to this analysis.

12. Resources

Please see USGBC's LEED Registered Project (http://www.usgbc.org/projecttools) for additional resources and technical information.

Websites

Advanced Buildings Technologies and Practices

http://www.advancedbuildings.org

This online resource, supported by Natural Resources Canada, presents energy-efficient technologies, strategies for commercial buildings, and pertinent case studies.

American Council for an Energy-Efficient Economy

http://www.aceee.org

ACEEE is a nonprofit organization dedicated to advancing energy efficiency through technical and policy assessments; advising policymakers and program managers; collaborating with businesses, public interest groups, and other organizations; and providing education and outreach through conferences, workshops, and publications.

ENERGY STAR®, Buildings Upgrade Manual

http://www.energystar.gov/index.cfm?c=business.bus_upgrade_manual

This manual is a strategic guide for planning and implementing energy-saving building upgrades. It provides general methods for reviewing and adjusting system control settings, plus procedures for testing and correcting calibration and operation of system components such as sensors, actuators, and control devices.

New Buildings Institute, Inc.

http://www.newbuildings.org

The New Buildings Institute is a nonprofit, public-benefits corporation dedicated to making buildings better for people and the environment. Its mission is to promote energy efficiency in buildings through technology research, guidelines, and codes.

U.S. Department of Energy, Building Energy Codes Program

http://www.energycodes.gov

The Building Energy Codes program provides comprehensive resources for states and code users, including news, compliance software, code comparisons, and the Status of State Energy Codes database. The database includes state energy contacts, code status, code history, DOE grants awarded, and construction data. The program is also updating the COMcheck-EZ compliance tool to include ANSI/ASHRAE/IESNA 90.1–2007. This compliance tool includes the prescriptive path and trade-off compliance methods. The software generates appropriate compliance forms as well.

U.S. Department of Energy, Office of Energy Efficiency and Renewable Energy

http://www.eere.energy.gov

This website is a comprehensive resource for U.S. Department of Energy information on energy efficiency and renewable energy and provides access to energy links and downloadable documents.

Print Media

ANSI/ASHRAE/IESNA Standard 90.1–2007 User's Manual (ASHRAE, 2008).

The ANSI/ASHRAE/IESNA 90.1–2007 User's Manual was developed as a companion document to the ANSI/ASHRAE/IESNA 90.1–2007, Energy Standard for Buildings Except Low-Rise Residential

Buildings. The manual explains the new standard and includes sample calculations, useful reference material, and information on the intent and application of the standard. It is abundantly illustrated and contains numerous examples and tables of reference data. It also includes a complete set of compliance forms and worksheets that can be used to document compliance with the standard. The manual is helpful to architects and engineers applying the standard to the design of buildings, plan examiners and field inspectors who must enforce the standard in areas where it is adopted as code, and contractors who must construct buildings in compliance with the standard. A compact disk is included that contains electronic versions of the compliance forms found in the manual.

13. Definitions

Baseline building performance is the annual energy cost for a building design intended for use as a baseline for rating above standard design, as defined in ANSI/ASHRAE/IESNA 90.1–2007, Appendix G.

An **economizer** is a device used to make building systems more energy efficient. Examples include HVAC enthalpy controls, which are based on humidity and temperature.

An **energy simulation model**, or energy model, is a computer-generated representation of the anticipated energy consumption of a building. It permits a comparison of energy performance, given proposed energy efficiency measures, with the baseline.

Interior lighting power allowance is the maximum lighting power (in watts) allowed for the interior of a building.

Lighting power density is the installed lighting power, per unit area.

Proposed building performance is the annual energy cost calculated for a proposed design, as defined in ANSI/ASHRAE/IESNA 90.1–2007, Appendix G.

Tenant space is the area within the LEED project boundary. For more information on what can and must be in the LEED project boundary see the Minimum Program Requirements (MPRs) and LEED 2009 MPR Supplemental Guidance. Note: tenant space is the same as project space.

	CI
Prerequisite	EA Prerequisite 3
Points	Required

Intent

To reduce stratospheric ozone depletion.

Requirements

Zero use of chlorofluorocarbon (CFC)-based refrigerants in tenant heating, ventilating, air conditioning and refrigeration (HVAC&R) systems used within the LEED project scope of work.

1. Benefits and Issues to Consider

Environmental Issues

Chlorofluorocarbons (CFCs), used in refrigeration equipment, cause significant damage to Earth's protective ozone layer when they are released into the atmosphere. The reaction between CFC and ozone molecules in the stratosphere destroys the ozone and reduces the stratosphere's ability to absorb a portion of the sun's ultraviolet radiation.

As part of the U.S. commitment to implement the Montreal Protocol, EPA has established regulations for responsible management of ozone-depleting substances. In compliance with the Montreal Protocol, CFC production in the United States ended in 1995. Not using CFC refrigerants in new equipment and implementing a phase-out of CFC-based refrigerants in existing equipment have helped slow depletion of the ozone layer.

Economic Issues

The standard practice in new buildings is to install equipment that does not use CFCs. However, existing buildings may have CFC-based refrigeration equipment. Energy, demand, and maintenance savings realized from upgrading equipment may offset the cost of converting or replacing existing systems.

2. Related Credits

There are no related credits for this prerequisite.

3. Summary of Referenced Standards

There are no standards referenced for this prerequisite.

4. Implementation

Use only non-CFC-based refrigerants in all base building HVAC&R equipment built for the project; only HVAC systems built for the project are within the scope of work. HCFCs and CFCs are not part of this prerequisite. Consider the characteristics of various CFC substitutes.

Refrigerants have varying applications, lifetimes, ozone-depleting potentials (ODPs), and global-warming potentials (GWPs). Table 1 provides examples of environmental lifetimes, ODP values, and GWP values for a variety of refrigerants. Choose refrigerants that have short environmental lifetimes, small ODP values, and small GWP values.

No ideal alternative for CFCs has been developed, and some alternatives are not suitable for retrofits. See EPA's list of substitutes for ozone-depleting substances (http://www.epa.gov/ozone/snap).

Table 1. Ozone Depletion and Global Warming Potentials of Refrigerants (100-Year Values)

Chlorofluorocarbons	ODP	GWP	Common Building Applications
CFC-11	1.0	4,680	Centrifugal chillers
CFC-12	1.0	10,720	Refrigerators, chillers
CFC-114	0.94	9,800	Centrifugal chillers
CFC-500	0.605	7,900	Centrifugal chillers, humidifiers
CFC-502	0.221	4,600	Low-temperature refrigeration
Hydrochlorofluorocarbons			
HCFC-22	0.04	1,780	Air-conditioning, chillers
HCFC-123	0.02	76	CFC-11 replacement
Hydrofluorocarbons			
HFC-23	~ 0	12,240	Ultra-low-temperature refrigeration
HFC-134a	~ 0	1,320	CFC-12 or HCFC-22 replacement
HFC-245fa	~ 0	1,020	Insulation agent, centrifugal chillers
HFC-404A	~ 0	3,900	Low-temperature refrigeration
HFC-407C	~ 0	1,700	HCFC-22 replacement
HFC-410A	~ 0	1,890	Air conditioning
HFC-507A	~ 0	3,900	Low-temperature refrigeration
Natural Refrigerants			
Carbon dioxide (CO_2)	0	1.0	
Ammonia (NH_3)	0	0	
Propane	0	3	

District Energy Systems

For projects with district energy systems, specific technical guidance can be found on USGBC's Registered Project Tools (http://www.usgbc.org/projecttools). Follow the guidance in effect at the time of registration.

5. Timeline and Team

Consult with a mechanical engineer or HVAC&R specialist to confirm the presence of CFC-based refrigerants in the base building HVAC&R systems.

6. Calculations

There are no calculations associated with this prerequisite unless a third-party economic audit is conducted to determine feasibility of retrofitting existing equipment.

7. Documentation Guidance

As a first step in preparing to complete the LEED Online documentation requirements, work through the following measure. Refer to LEED Online for the complete descriptions of all required documentation.

- Assemble manufacturers' documentation demonstrating the type of refrigerant used by the HVAC&R systems installed within the scope of the LEED project.

8. Examples

There are no examples for this prerequisite.

9. Exemplary Performance

There is no exemplary performance available for this prerequisite.

10. Regional Variations
There are no regional variations associated with this prerequisite.

11. Operations and Maintenance Considerations
Provide facility operators with complete records (such as LEED application materials) for all refrigerant-containing systems, including fire suppression. Ensure that equipment labels are in place and accessible to building operators.

12. Resources
Please see USGBC's LEED Resources & Tools (http://www.usgbc.org/projecttools) for additional resources and technical information.

Websites
ASHRAE Service Life and Maintenance Cost Database
http://www.ashrae.org/database
This database provides current information on the service life and maintenance costs of typical HVAC equipment.

Facility Management, Coping with the CFC Phase-Out
http://www.facilitymanagement.com
This magazine's website provides various articles on the issues of CFC phase-out.

U.S. EPA, Benefits of CFC Phase-Out
http://www.epa.gov/ozone/geninfo/benefits.html
This document details the benefits of phasing out CFCs and includes brief case studies.

U.S. EPA, Building Owners Save Money, Save the Earth: Replace Your CFC Air Conditioning Chiller
http://www.epa.gov/ozone/title6/608/chiller1_07.pdf
This brochure documents the environmental and financial reasons to replace CFC chillers with new, energy-efficient equipment.

U.S. EPA, Ozone Layer Depletion
http://www.epa.gov/ozone/strathome.html
This website includes information about the science of ozone depletion, EPA's regulatory approach to protecting the ozone layer, and alternatives to ozone-depleting substances.

U.S. EPA, Significant New Alternatives Policy
http://www.epa.gov/ozone/snap/index.html
SNAP is an EPA program to identify alternatives to ozone-depleting substances. The program maintains up-to-date lists of environmentally-friendly substitutes for refrigeration and air-conditioning equipment, solvents, fire-suppression systems, adhesives, coatings, and other substances.

Print Media
Building Systems Analysis & Retrofit Manual (SMACNA, 1995).
CFCs, HCFC and Halons: Professional and Practical Guidance on Substances that Deplete the Ozone Layer (CIBSE, 2000).

The Refrigerant Manual: Managing the Phase Out of CFCs (BOMA International, 1993).

13. Definitions
Chlorofluorocarbons (CFCs) are hydrocarbons that are used as refrigerants and cause depletion of the stratospheric ozone layer.

Hydrochlorofluorocarbons (**HCFCs**) are refrigerants that cause significantly less depletion of the stratospheric ozone layer than chlorofluorocarbons.

Refrigerants are the working fluids of refrigeration cycles that absorb heat from a reservoir at low temperatures and reject heat at higher temperatures.

OPTIMIZE ENERGY PERFORMANCE—LIGHTING POWER

	CI
Credit	EA Credit 1.1
Points	1-5 points

Intent

To achieve increasing levels of energy conservation beyond the referenced standard to reduce environmental and economic impacts associated with excessive energy use.

Requirements

Reduce connected lighting power density below that allowed by ANSI/ASHRAE/IESNA Standard 90.1-2007 (with errata but without addenda[1]) using either the space-by-space method or by applying the whole building lighting power allowance to the entire tenant space.

The points earned for reducing lighting power density below the standard are as follows:

Lighting Power Density Reduction below the Standard	Points
15%	1
20%	2
25%	3
30%	4
35%	5

Project teams in California may use Title 24-2005, Part 6 in place of ANSI/ASHRAE/IESNA Standard 90.1-2007.

Potential Technologies & Strategies

Design the connected lighting power to maximize energy performance. If the project warrants, consider a computer simulation model to assess the performance and identify the most cost-effective energy efficiency measures.

---

1 Project teams wishing to use ASHRAE approved addenda for the purposes of this prerequisite may do so at their discretion. Addenda must be applied consistently across all LEED credits.

1. Benefits and Issues to Consider

Environmental Issues

Energy efficiency reduces the environmental burdens associated with producing and using energy. Fossil fuels, such as coal and oil, are the most common source of energy used in buildings. However, these fuels are also finite resources. The process of extracting and consuming energy from fossil fuels causes many environmental impacts, including air and water pollution, land degradation, solid waste generation, and greenhouse gas emissions. Mounting evidence connects fossil fuel–based energy use with climate change as well as serious risks to environmental and human health and safety. Data from the U.S. Energy Information Administration show that buildings are responsible for almost half (48%) of all energy consumed and greenhouse gases emitted annually.[10] EPA estimates that if the energy efficiency of commercial and industrial buildings improved by 10%, the resulting greenhouse gas reductions would be equivalent to taking about 30 million vehicles off the road.[11]

In addition to fossil fuels, other sources of energy also carry environmental costs. Hydropower activities, for example, can alter aquatic ecosystems and have significant impacts on endangered species. Nuclear power plants pose an environmental threat when they are decommissioned without appropriate storage sites for spent fuel. Given both the environmental impacts inherent in most energy-production processes and our limited energy supplies, efficiency measures are an important strategy for managing the impacts of energy consumption.

Economic Issues

Some energy-efficiency measures may not require additional first costs. Many measures that do result in higher capital costs may generate savings from lower energy use, smaller equipment, reduced space needs for mechanical and electrical equipment, and utility rebates. These savings may vastly exceed the incremental capital costs associated with the energy-efficiency measures over the life of the project.

Even seemingly small conservation measures can be significant; for instance, replacing 1 incandescent lamp with a fluorescent lamp will save over $30 in energy costs over the operating lifetime of the lamp.[12]

2. Related Credits

Optimal lighting systems will reduce lighting power through use of efficient systems, deliver appropriate target light levels, and incorporate daylighting to take advantage of natural light. Occupants' ability to control lighting systems can save even more energy while increasing occupants' satisfaction. Architectural strategies to increase daylighting can achieve greater energy savings through the use of daylight-responsive controls. Review the requirements in these credits:

- EA Prerequisite 2: Minimum Energy Performance

- EA Credit 1.2: Optimize Energy Performance—Lighting Controls

- IEQ Credit 6.1: Controllability of Systems—Lighting

- IEQ Credit 8.1: Daylight and Views—Daylight

Commissioning is required to ensure that lighting controls meet the design intent and are operating properly, as detailed in the following:

- EA Prerequisite 1: Fundamental Commissioning of the Building Energy Systems

- EA Credit 2: Enhanced Commissioning

3. Summary of Referenced Standards

	EA
CI	Credit 1.1

ANSI/ASHRAE/IESNA Standard 90.1–2007: Energy Standard for Buildings Except Low-Rise Residential

American National Standards Institute

American Society of Heating, Refrigerating and Air-Conditioning Engineers

Illuminating Engineering Society of North America

http://www.ashrae.org

ANSI/ASHRAE/IESNA 90.1–2007 was formulated by ASHRAE under an ANSI consensus process. IESNA is a joint sponsor of the standard.

ANSI/ASHRAE/IESNA 90.1–2007 establishes minimum requirements for the energy-efficient design of buildings with these exceptions: single-family houses; multifamily structures of 3 habitable stories or fewer above grade; manufactured houses (mobile and modular homes); buildings that do not use either electricity or fossil fuel; and equipment and portions of buildings systems that use energy primarily for industrial, manufacturing, or commercial processes. Building envelope requirements are provided for semiheated spaces such as warehouses.

4. Implementation

The connected lighting power should be designed to maximize energy performance. Consider using an energy simulation model to assess the performance of the tenant space or building.

General Guidance

- Although task lighting may be used to supplement general lighting, take care to balance the various illuminance requirements of the space.

- Lighting controls are not limited to on-off modes; continuous dimming can be implemented based on actual daylight levels.

- Use high-efficacy sources and high internal reflectances to reduce the lighting power density.

This credit compares the installed interior lighting power with the interior lighting power allowance. Use either the building area method or the space-by-space method in ASHRAE 90.1-2007. See the Calculations section for details.

5. Timeline and Team

Lighting requirements should be part of the owner's project requirements and may include the lighting technologies (LED, ceramic metal halide, T5-HO, etc.) to be considered for the intended uses of the space. The lighting designer should include in the basis of design specific footcandle target levels for each major space type. Once the lighting system has been designed, it can be helpful to complete a photometric floor plan to identify areas that will be over- or underlit and refine the lighting design.

6. Calculations

Installed Interior Lighting Power

The installed interior lighting power, calculated as shown by Equation 1, is the power in watts of all permanently installed general, task, and furniture lighting systems and luminaires. ASHRAE 90.1-2007, Section 9.2.2.3, lists lighting equipment that is exempted from consideration in determining the lighting power density and therefore does not need to be included in the calculation. Note that luminaire wattages must be determined in accordance with ASHRAE 90.1-2007, Section 9.1.4.

Equation 1. Installed Interior Lighting Power

Installed Interior Lighting Power (watts)	= Σ	Quantity by Type of Luminaires	X	Luminaire Wattage by Luminaire Type (watts)

Building Area Method

Use Equation 2 to determine the interior lighting power allowance according to the building area method described by ASHRAE 90.1-2007, Section 9.5. Begin by determining the appropriate building area types from the list in ASHRAE 90.1-2007, Table 9.5.1. For each building area type, there is a corresponding allowed lighting power density (watts per square foot). Determine the interior lighting power allowance (in watts) by multiplying the allowed lighting power density of each building area type by the gross lighted floor area of that building type. Sum the interior lighting power allowances to determine the total interior lighting power allowance.

Equation 2. Interior Lighting Power Allowance Using the Building Area Method

Installed Interior Lighting Power Allowance (watts)	= Σ	Gross Lighting Floor Area (sf)	X	Building Area Type Lighting Power Density (watts/sf)

Space-by-Space Method

In this alternative approach, defined by ASHRAE 90.1-2007, Section 9.6, the allowed lighting power density is determined for each space individually. Begin by determining the appropriate space area types from the list in ASHRAE 90.1-2007, Table 9.6.1. For each space type, there is a corresponding allowed lighting power density (watts per square foot). Determine the interior lighting power allowance (in watts) by multiplying the allowed lighting power density of each space area type by the gross lighted floor area of that space type. Space areas must be determined in accordance with ASHRAE 90.1-2007, Section 9.6.1.b. Finally, sum the individual space allowances per Equation 3 to determine the total interior lighting power allowance. See Table 1 for an example of a completed space-by-space method calculation.

Equation 3. Interior Lighting Power Allowance Using the Space-by-Space Method

Interior Lighting Power Allowance (watts)	= Σ	Gross Lighting Floor Area (sf)	X	Space Area Type Lighting Power Density (watts/sf)

For project teams using the space-by-space method, increases to the interior power allowance are permitted in 2 situations: for decorative appearance and for highlighting merchandise. See Section 9.6.2. Note that any additional allowances are provided only to the extent that they are actually used. For example, if an apparel retailer dedicates 1,000 square feet of floor area for the sale of clothing, the maximum additional allowance for the purposes of highlighting merchandise would be 3,600 watts (1,000 watts + 2.6 watts per square foot). However, if only 2,400 watts of merchandise display lighting is installed (and controlled separately from the general lighting), only 2,400 watts can be claimed as additional lighting power allowance for the purposes of highlighting merchandise. All additional lighting power allowances should be added to the interior lighting power allowance calculated per Equation 3 for the final determination of lighting power reduction. No increase to the lighting power allowance is permissible with the building area method.

Lighting Power Reduction

To determine the lighting power reduction, subtract the installed interior lighting power from the interior lighting power allowance, being sure to include any additional lighting power allowances if the space-by-space method was used. See Equation 4. Finally, determine the percentage reduction by dividing the lighting power reduction by the interior lighting power allowance (Equation 5).

Projects in California may use Title 24–2005, Part 6, in lieu of ASHRAE 90.1-2007 for calculating interior lighting power reduction.

Equation 4. Lighting Power Reduction

Lighting Power Reduction (watts)	=	Interior Lighting Power Allowance (watts)	−	Installed Interior Lighting Power (watts)

Equation 5. Lighting Power Density Percentage Reduction

$$\text{Percentage Reduction (\%)} = \frac{\text{Lighting Power Reduction (watts)}}{\text{Interior Lighting Power Allowance (watts)}}$$

7. Documentation Guidance

As a first step in preparing to complete the LEED Online documentation requirements, work through the following measures. Refer to LEED Online for the complete descriptions of all required documentation.

- For ASHRAE compliance, list any addenda used.
- Assemble lighting compliance documents from the ASHRAE 90.1-2007 user's manual.
- List the rated power of installed lighting systems.
- List building area types or space area types with their corresponding gross floor areas.
- Assemble information about additional lighting power allowances and document that the allowances apply only to lighting systems that are separate from general lighting.

8. Examples

The project team for a 20,000-square-foot office building uses the space-by-space method, in which the lighting power allowance varies for individual areas. Table 1 presents the calculation and indicates an overall lighting power allowance of 16,440 watts. Table 2 illustrates the same calculation using the building area method, in which the lighting power allowance is based on a single lighting power density applied across the entire lighted square footage.

Table 1. Interior Lighting Power Allowance, Space-by-Space Method

Space Type	Lighting Power Density (watts/sf)		Gross Area (sf)	Lighting Power Allowance (watts)
Office, enclosed	1.1	X	720	792
Office, open plan	1.1	X	16180	17798
Conference	1.3	X	850	1105
Training	1.4	X	1200	1680
Lobby	1.3	X	330	429
Corridor	0.5	X	720	360
Total floor area (sf)				20000
Interior lighting power allowance (watts)				22164
Installed interior lighting power (watts)				16440
Lighting power reduction (watts)				5724
Lighting power reduction achieved (5,724/22,164)				25.8%
			25.8% > 25%, 3 points earned	

Table 2. Interior Lighting Power Allowance, Building Area Method

Building Area Type	Lighting Power Density (watts/sf)		Gross Area (sf)	Lighting Power Allowance (watts)
Office	1.0	x	20000	20000
Total floor area (sf)				20000
Interior lighting power allowance (watts)				20000
Installed interior lighting power (watts)				16440
Lighting power reduction achieved (watts)				3560
Lighting power reduction achieved (3,560/20,000)				17.8%
				17.8% > 15%, 1 point earned

9. Exemplary Performance

Project teams may earn an exemplary performance point by reducing the lighting power density 40% or more below the standard.

10. Regional Variations

There are no regional variations associated with this credit.

11. Operations and Maintenance Considerations

Building operators should consider a group relamping policy. This can significantly reduce labor costs associated with conventional spot-relamping practices. It can also permit the use of lower-energy lighting equipment, since the system light output will be maintained at or close to the design condition.

12. Resources

Please see USGBC's LEED Resources & Tools (http://www.usgbc.org/projecttools) for additional resources and technical information.

Websites

U.S. Department of Energy, Building Energy Codes Program
http://www.energycodes.gov
The Building Energy Codes program provides comprehensive resources for states and code users, including news, compliance software, code comparisons, and the Status of State Energy Codes database. The database includes state energy contacts, code status, code history, DOE grants awarded, and construction data. The program is also updating the COMcheck-EZ compliance tool to include ASHRAE 90.1-2007. This compliance tool includes the prescriptive path and trade-off compliance methods. The software generates appropriate compliance forms as well.

Print Media

ANSI/ASHRAE/IESNA Standard 90.1–2007 User's Manual (ASHRAE, 2007).
The ANSI/ASHRAE/IESNA 90.1–2007 User's Manual was developed as a companion document to the ANSI/ASHRAE/IESNA 90.1–2007, Energy Standard for Buildings Except Low-Rise Residential Buildings. The manual explains the new standard and includes sample calculations, useful reference material, and information on the intent and application of the standard. It is abundantly illustrated and contains numerous examples and tables of reference data. It also includes a complete set of compliance forms and worksheets that can be used to document compliance with the standard. The manual is helpful to architects and engineers applying the standard to the design of buildings, plan examiners and field inspectors who must enforce the standard in areas where it is adopted as code, and contractors who must construct buildings in compliance with the standard. A compact disk is included that contains electronic versions of the compliance forms found in the manual.

IESNA Lighting Handbook, ninth edition (IESNA, 2000).

ANSI/IESNA RP.1.04, American National Standard Practice for Office Lighting (IESNA).

13. Definitions

Interior lighting power allowance is the maximum lighting power (in watts) allowed for the interior of a building.

Lighting power density is the installed lighting power, per unit area.

A **luminaire** is a complete lighting unit consisting of a lamp (or lamps) with the housing designed to distribute the light, position, and protect the lamp and connect it to the power supply.

Regularly occupied spaces in commercial buildings are areas where people sit or stand as they work.

Tenant space is the area within the LEED project boundary. For more information on what can and must be in the LEED project boundary see the Minimum Program Requirements (MPRs) and LEED 2009 MPR Supplemental Guidance. Note: tenant space is the same as project space.

OPTIMIZE ENERGY PERFORMANCE—LIGHTING CONTROLS

	CI
Credit	EA Credit 1.2
Points	1-3 points

Intent

To achieve increasing levels of energy conservation beyond the prerequisite standard to reduce environmental and economic impacts associated with excessive energy use.

Requirements

Design the project to include 1 or more of the following independent strategies:

- Daylight controls for daylit areas: (1 point)

  Install daylight responsive controls in all regularly occupied daylit spaces within 15 feet of windows and under skylights. Daylight controls must switch or dim electric lights in response to the presence or absence of daylight illumination in the space.[1]

- Daylight controls for 50% of the lighting load: (1 point)

  Install daylight responsive controls for 50% or more of the connected lighting load and demonstrate that 50% of the connected lighting load is daylight responsive. Daylight controls must switch or dim electric lights in response to the presence or absence of daylight illumination in the space.[2]

- Occupancy sensors: (1 point)

  Install occupancy sensors for 75% of the connected lighting load.

---

1 American Society of Heating, Refrigerating, and Air-Conditioning Engineers. ANSI/ASHRAE/IESNA Standard 90.1 – 2007 90.1 User's Manual. (Atlanta, 2008). P. 9-3
2 Ibid

1. Benefits and Issues to Consider

Daylighting improves the indoor environment. Using daylight to supplement or even eliminate the need for electric lighting is generally welcomed by occupants and reduces lighting energy consumption. Utilizing controls sensitive to daylight maximizes the efficiency and savings from daylighting. When planned in conjunction with heating and air conditioning requirements, the net cost of utilities can be reduced as well.

Refer to the Benefits and Issues section in EA Credit 1.1, Optimize Energy Performance—Lighting Power.

2. Related Credits

Refer to the Related Credits section in EA Credit 1.1.

3. Summary of Referenced Standards

There are no standards referenced for this credit.

4. Implementation

Ideally, the use of daylight-responsive controls should be part of a larger lighting strategy. The overall strategy should optimize natural daylighting, minimize electric lighting, provide appropriate task and ambient working conditions, and allow occupants to control the lighting of individual spaces. Consider using both daylight-responsive lighting controls and occupancy sensors. Daylighting controls typically include a photosensor that initiates a control response to increase or reduce the lighting power to the luminaires. A successful design should anticipate occupants' activities, avoid drastic changes in lighting levels, and minimize glare. Ideally, the system will employ continuous dimming, although on-off, bi-level, or step-dimming devices are acceptable for the purposes of this credit. All major commercial lamp types can now be dimmed, including incandescent, fluorescent, and HID.

When designing the lighting controls, consider how individual areas will be used, the relationship between luminaires and individual controls, and how the system works as a whole.

Establish control zones for the areas with daylight-responsive lighting. These areas should include all perimeter areas within a radius of at least 15 feet from windows and areas beneath skylights. Anticipate shading from neighboring buildings and trees, and indicate their effect on the control zones.

5. Timeline and Team

Consider developing a comprehensive lighting design intent during schematic design. This design intent should indicate the illuminance targets of each major space type, the overall level of daylight and occupancy responsiveness desired, and information on the type of luminaires being considered for the space. This will require coordination between the architect, electrical engineer, and lighting designer.

6. Calculations

See the Calculations section in EA Credit 1.1.

7. Documentation Guidance

As a first step in preparing to complete the LEED Online documentation requirements, work through the following measures. Refer to LEED Online for the complete descriptions of all required documentation.

- Highlight daylit zones on interior lighting plans; indicate which luminaries correspond to each controller.

- For more complex lighting designs, where the control logic cannot easily be discerned from the interior lighting plans, create a lighting control summary indicating the combined control logic for the project lighting.

8. Examples

There are no examples for this credit.

9. Exemplary Performance

Project teams may earn an exemplary performance point by implementing daylight-responsive controls for 75% of the connected lighting load or by installing occupancy-responsive controls for 95% of the connected lighting load.

10. Regional Variations

Refer to the Regional Variations section in EA Credit 1.1.

11. Operations and Maintenance Considerations

Refer to the Operations and Maintenance section in EA Credit 1.1.

12. Resources

Please see USGBC's LEED Resources & Tools (http://www.usgbc.org/projecttools) for additional resources and technical information.

International Energy Agency Solar Heating and Cooling Programme
http://www.iea-shc.org

Print Media

Design Brief—Lighting Controls, Southern California Edison (Energy Design Resources). http://www.energydesignresources.com.

Daylight in Buildings: A Source Book on Daylighting Systems and Components, Chapter 5, Daylight-Responsive Controls.

Advanced Lighting Guidelines, Chapter 8, Lighting Controls (New Buildings Institute, Inc., 2001). http://www.newbuildings.org/lighting.htm.

13. Definitions

Daylighting is the controlled admission of natural light into a space, used to reduce or eliminate electric lighting.

Daylight-responsive lighting controls are photosensors used in conjunction with other switching and dimming devices to control the amount of artificial lighting in relationship to the amount and quality of natural daylight.

OPTIMIZE ENERGY PERFORMANCE—HVAC

	CI
Credit	EA Credit 1.3
Points	5-10 points

Intent

To achieve increasing levels of energy conservation beyond the prerequisite standard to reduce environmental and economic impacts associated with excessive energy use.

Requirement

OPTION 1

Implement 1 or both of the following strategies:

- Equipment Efficiency—(5 points)

  Install heating, ventilation and air conditioning (HVAC) systems that comply with the efficiency requirements outlined in the New Building Institute's Advanced Buildings™ Core Performance™ Guide Sections 1.4: Mechanical System Design, 2.9: Mechanical Equipment Efficiency and 3.10: Variable Speed Control.

- Appropriate Zoning and Controls: (5 points)

  Zone tenant fit out of spaces to meet the following requirements:

  - Every solar exposure must have a separate control zone.
  - Interior spaces must be separately zoned.
  - Private offices and special occupancies (conference rooms, kitchens, etc.) must have active controls capable of sensing space use and modulating the HVAC system in response to space demand.

OR

OPTION 2

Reduce design energy cost compared with the energy cost budget for regulated energy components described in the requirements of ANSI/ASHRAE/IESNA Standard 90.1-2007 (with errata but without addenda[1])

AND

PATH 1 (5 points)

Demonstrate that HVAC system component performance criteria used for tenant space are 15% better than a system in minimum compliance with ANSI/ASHRAE/IESNA Standard 90.1-2007 (with errata but without addenda[1]).

OR

PATH 2 (10 points)

Demonstrate that HVAC system component performance criteria used for tenant space are 30% better than a system that is in minimum compliance with ANSI/ASHRAE/IESNA Standard 90.1-2007 (with errata but without addenda[1]).

1 Project teams wishing to use ASHRAE approved addenda for the purposes of this credit may do so at their discretion. Addenda must be applied consistently across all LEED credits.

1. Benefits and Issues to Consider

Environmental Issues

Conventional forms of energy production often have detrimental environmental effects. Producing electricity from fossil fuels pollutes air and water, hydroelectric plants can make waterways uninhabitable for indigenous fish, and nuclear power has safety concerns, as well as problems with disposal of spent fuel.

Using less energy reduces greenhouse gas emissions, limits the impact of natural resource extraction activities, and prevents water pollution, benefitting environmental and human health.

Economic Issues

Many energy efficiency measures do not require additional first costs. Those measures that do result in higher initial costs often create savings from lower energy use over the building's lifetime, downsized equipment, reduced mechanical space needs, and utility rebates. These savings can dwarf the increased first costs. Payback periods for off-the-shelf energy efficiency measures are generally short.

Even seemingly small conservation measures can be significant. Replacing 1 incandescent lamp with an ENERGY STAR®–qualified light avoids 450 pounds of greenhouse gas emissions over its lifetime or the combustion of more than 200 pounds of coal.[13] This substitution also saves more than $30 in energy costs over the operating lifetime of the lamp[14].

2. Related Credits

EA Credit 1.3, Optimize Energy Performance—HVAC, is related to several ventilation and thermal comfort credits because of the energy required to operate mechanically driven comfort systems. Additionally, system controllability should be incorporated with the HVAC system design to achieve a careful balance between comfort and energy performance. These topics are covered in the following credits:

- IEQ Prerequisite 1: Minimum Indoor Air Quality Performance
- IEQ Credit 1: Outdoor Air Delivery Monitoring
- IEQ Credit 2: Increased Ventilation
- IEQ Credit 6.2: Controllability of Systems—Thermal Comfort
- IEQ Credit 7.1: Thermal Comfort—Design
- IEQ Credit 7.2: Thermal Comfort—Verification

3. Summary of Referenced Standards

New Buildings Institute, **Advanced Buildings™ Core Performance™ Guide**

The Advanced Buildings program is a prescriptive plan for exceeding the energy performance requirements of ASHRAE 90.1–2004. It offers a predictable alternative to energy performance modeling and a simple set of criteria for significantly increasing building energy performance.

The program updates and replaces the Advanced Buildings Benchmarked program. Core Performance is calibrated to exceed the requirements of ASHRAE 90.1–2004 in all climate zones.

Information about the Core Performance program requirements and a range of additional reference material are available at http://www.advancedbuildings.net.

Several aspects of the Core Performance program overlap with other LEED credits and prerequisites. Following the Core Performance program is not an alternative path to achieving any LEED credits except EA Credit 1.3, Optimize Energy Performance—HVAC, but Core Performance may facilitate earning other LEED credits and prerequisites.

American National Standards Institute/ASHRAE/Illuminating Engineering Society of North America Standard 90.1–2007: Energy Standard for Buildings Except Low-Rise Residential
American National Standards Institute
American Society of Heating, Refrigerating and Air-Conditioning Engineers
Illuminating Engineering Society of North America
http://www.ashrae.org

ANSI/ASHRAE/IESNA Standard 90.1–2007 was formulated by ASHRAE under an ANSI consensus process. IESNA is a joint sponsor of the standard.

ANSI/ASHRAE/IESNA Standard 90.1–2007 establishes minimum requirements for the energy-efficient design of buildings, with these exceptions: single-family houses; multifamily structures of 3 habitable stories or fewer above grade; manufactured houses (mobile and modular homes); buildings that do not use either electricity or fossil fuel; and equipment and portions of buildings systems that use energy primarily for industrial, manufacturing, or commercial processes. Building envelope requirements are provided for semiheated spaces such as warehouses.

The energy cost budget method (Section 11) allows the project team to exceed some of the prescriptive requirements provided energy cost savings are made in other areas. However, in all cases, the mandatory provisions must still be met.

4. Implementation

OPTION 1. Equipment Efficiency and Zoning Controls

The equipment efficiency approach draws from Sections 1.4, 2.9, and 3.10 of the Advanced Buildings Core Performance Guide. Section 1.4 covers mechanical system design intended to closely match actual building loads and to meet ASHRAE 55; Section 2.9 covers Mechanical Equipment Efficiency Requirements; Section 3.10 covers Variable Frequency Drives.

Follow the requirements laid out in the Core Performance Guide to reduce operating costs, urban heat island effect, and energy use and to maximize occupants' comfort.

Small private spaces intended for single, temporary occupancy (e.g., for making confidential telephone calls) may be included as part of a larger thermal zone, since changes in occupancy will not cause large swings in the heating and cooling loads.

OPTION 2. Comparison with ASHRAE 90.1-2007

In this option, compare the design annual energy cost with the annual energy cost based on meeting the minimum ASHRAE 90.1-2007 requirements. Only energy costs for space heating, space cooling, and associated fans and pumps are considered; however, the performance of these systems is influenced by the performance of other building systems.

To determine the reduction in annual costs for the project area, consider the entire building area that is served by the HVAC plant for the project in the evaluation, since the building design and operations beyond the project space influence the design and operation of the HVAC plant.

Energy-Efficient Buildings

Landscaping protects a building from wind and provides shade, which helps reduce the heat island effect. Characteristically, buildings oriented along an east-west axis obtain the most effective exterior shading.

Confirm that the selected building is weather tight and meets code-minimum insulation levels.

Lighting accounts for a major portion of a commercial building's energy budget. Efficient lighting in common areas, inside and out, reduces costs. Confirm that the owner has established lighting density standards for all tenant spaces.

Consider the availability of natural light for daylighting and opportunities for natural ventilation. Windows high on walls, clerestories, and light shelves will maximize daylight penetration into a space. Light pipes or fiber optic devices can be used to introduce daylight in less accessible spaces.

Inspect the existing HVAC system. Discuss opportunities for specifying high efficiency HVAC equipment with the building owner. When included in the project scope, specify high-performance chillers and boilers with optimal part-load operation (e.g., variable-speed chillers and boilers with modulating burners). Specify high-efficiency motors for all applications and variable-speed drives for fans, chillers, and pumps.

Confirm that a building energy management system exists and is functional. If the project space is part of a larger building, determine whether the building controls interface with the functions within the project area. A good energy management system will facilitate smooth building startups and shutdowns and optimize efficiency and occupant comfort.

5. Timeline and Team

The owner and project team should thoroughly research the energy efficiency of potential tenant spaces. Review energy and water utility bills and develop, ideally, a 3-year history of use. Seek clarification on how utilities will be prorated in a multitenant building.

6. Calculations

OPTION 1. Equipment Efficiency and Zoning Controls

If the building has no separate method for modulating the HVAC system in response to space demand, such as demand-controlled ventilation or modulation of the HVAC system tied to occupant sensor controls, Meet the following criteria:

- The system must be capable of modulating air-handling units (AHUs) and zone minimum supply volume below 0.30 cubic feet per minute per square foot of supply volume for standard variable air volume (VAV) terminals, or below 22.5% of the peak design flow rate for fan-powered VAV boxes. For spaces where the minimum outdoor air flow exceeds the minimum supply volumes specified here, use occupant sensors or demand-controlled ventilation to achieve these minimum supply volumes.

- The building control system must include controls for fan static pressure reset.

- The mandatory requirements of ASHRAE 90.1-2007 and ASHRAE 62.1-2007 must be met.

OPTION 2. Comparison with ASHRAE 90.1-2007

Option 2 rewards reductions in the annual cost for electricity and fuel to drive the HVAC system. The project team compares the results from 2 simulation models, 1 based on the actual design and a second, similar model based on meeting all applicable mandatory and prescriptive provisions of ASHRAE 90.1-2007.

The standard has 2 energy comparison methods, both of which are appropriate for demonstrating energy cost savings to earn this credit. The energy cost budget method, found in Section 11 of the standard, allows projects to trade off energy performance between building systems as long as the calculated annual energy cost is no greater than that for the budget case. The performance rating method, found in Appendix G, was developed to rate the energy efficiency of buildings relative to a baseline that represents "typical" construction practices. The methods differ in the way they identify the budget or baseline HVAC system. Another important difference is that the energy cost budget does not recognize energy-efficient design of air distribution systems, and the performance rating method does.

Both methods include all end-use load components, including exhaust fans, parking garage ventilation, snow-melt and freeze-protection equipment, façade lighting, swimming pool heaters and pumps, elevators and escalators, refrigeration, and cooking. An end use that does not affect trade-offs between systems can be excluded from the energy cost budget. For a typical Commercial Interiors project, where the project space is only 1 of several tenants being served by a common HVAC system, the energy cost budget method is adequate and more direct. The performance rating method is considered more rigorous and comprehensive and is more appropriate for projects using unconventional HVAC systems.

Option 2 involves modifying the ASHRAE 90.1-2007 modeling requirements. The relationship of the energy end use to the calculations is shown in Table 1, and the modifications to the modeling requirements are listed in Table 2. The referenced sections and terminology in the tables and the following narrative are for the energy cost budget method.

Table 1. Energy End Uses for Option 2, Modeling Calculation Using ASHRAE 90.1-2007, Section 11

Energy End Uses	Design Case Design Energy Cost DEC	Baseline Case Energy Cost Budget ECB
Heating	Needed to model DEC Used in Option 2 calculation	Needed to model ECB Used in Option 2 calculation
Fans/Pumps	Needed to model DEC Used in Option 2 calculation	Needed to model ECB Used in Option 2 calculation
Lighting	Needed to model DEC But Costs are Not Included	Needed to model ECB But Costs are Not Included
Plug and Process loads	Needed to model DEC But Costs are Not Included	Needed to model ECB But Costs are Not Included
Service Water Heating	May be used to model DEC But Costs are Not Included	May be used to model ECB But Costs are Not Included
Miscellaneous Loads	Not required	Not required

STEP 1. Select a Modeler

The calculation will likely require energy simulation modeling. Sections 11.2 and G2.2 detail the requirements and software. Project teams may find that their logical first step is to identify an individual or firm with experience in energy modeling.

STEP 2. Determine the Building Segment

The simulation should generally involve more than just the project space and model the building segment that is served by the common HVAC system. For example, if the project area takes up the third floor of a 5-story building and the building has a single central plant, the entire building should be modeled.

STEP 3. Select a Modeling Method

Decide which modeling method to use. The energy cost budget (Section 11) is less demanding and may entail less cost. However, some host buildings (particularly those that are LEED certified) may already have been modeled using the performance rating method (Appendix G), and much of the work may be completed.

STEP 4. Obtain Building Information

Unless an earlier energy simulation modeling run and report are available, the modeler and the project mechanical engineer or architect should review the as-built drawings of the building and scout the premises to determine the existing conditions for at least the segment of the building with which the project area shares a common central HVAC system. The existing building envelope is used for the entire building segment being modeled, including the project area. Determine the existing conditions for operational schedules, lighting, HVAC systems and zones, and possibly service hot water systems for the rest of the building segment. Information should include the quantity of fenestration and its exposure, the thermal conductivity of all exterior walls, windows and doors, the type of HVAC system, and the size and efficiency of the HVAC components. For the occupied areas other than the project space, document the type of occupancy and operation schedule. Estimate the existing lighting and plug loads for these areas. Obtain other relevant information as necessary.

STEP 5. Model the Design Case

For the project area, use the existing building envelope, but for heating, cooling, fans and pump, lighting and plug loads, and (if needed) service water heating, use the project design. Any modifications to the HVAC central plant being made in conjunction with the project should be included in the design case. These changes do not have to be within the project area or part of the project's contractual scope of work if they are being done for the project occupants' benefit. Including these changes should improve the performance being measured under this credit.

If the project has attained SS Credit 1, Site Selection, Option 2, Path 10, Water Use Reduction—30%, or WE Credit 1, Water Use Reduction, the design case may reflect the reduced volumes of water for service hot water systems. The HVAC energy costs should not include the energy costs associated with service hot water systems.

For the rest of the building segment, use the existing conditions. Together, the results will generate the design energy cost (DEC). Follow Section 11 or Appendix G and the additional information in Table 2.

Table 2. Option 2 Procedure

ASHRAE/IENSA 90.1 Section	Design Energy Cost Model DEC	Energy Cost Budget Model ECB
1. Design Model	Follow Table 11.3.1, using the proposed design of the project space, and the existing conditions for the balance of the modeled building segment, as field verified (step 4 in the procedure) for the design case.	Baseline Case: Follow Table 11.3.1, using the mandatory and prescriptive requirements for the project space, but use the existing conditions for the balance of the modeled building segment. Alternative Baseline Case: Follow Table 11.3.1, using the mandatory and prescriptive requirements for both the project space and the balance of the modeled building segment.
2. Additions and Alterations	Follow Table 11.3.1. See (b) concerning the exclusion of HVAC systems not part of the modeled building segment.	Follow Table 11.3.1
3. Space Use Classification	Follow Table 11.3.1	Follow Table 11.3.1
4. Schedules	Follow Table 11.3.1 when field verification can not be attained.	Use the same schedule for DEC, ECB and A-ECB.
5. Building Envelope	Follow Table 11.3.1, using the proposed design of the project space, and the existing envelope conditions for the balance of the modeled building segment, as field verified (step 4 in the procedure) for the design case.	Baseline Case: Follow Table 11.3.1, using the proposed design of the project space, and the existing envelope conditions for the balance of the modeled building segment. Alternative Baseline Case: Follow Table 11.3.1, using the mandatory and prescriptive requirements, as described, for the baseline case.

6. Lighting	Follow Table 11.3.1, using the proposed design of the project space, and the field verified lighting for the balance of the modeled building segment.	Baseline Case: For the project space, use either 9.5 or 9.6; for the balance of the modeled building segment, use the same values used in the DEC model. Alternative Baseline Case: For both the project space and the balance of the modeled building segment, use either 9.5 or 9.6.
7. 8. 9. Thermal Blocks	Follow Table 11.3.1	Same as DEC model.
10. HVAC Systems	Follow Table 11.3.1, using the proposed design of the project space, and the field verified HVAC system information of the central plant when existing.	Follow Table 11.3.1, which references Figure 11.3.2, Table 11.3.2A
11. Service Hot Water Systems	Follow Table 11.3.1. If the project space has attained WE Credit 1, the model may reflect the reduced volumes. If the building has attained SS Credit 1 Option J, the model may reflect the reduced volumes.	Follow Table 11.3.1
12. Miscellaneous Loads	Follow Table 11.3.1. If the project space anticipates attaining EA Credit 1.4, the DEC may use a lower value reflecting the actual plug load planned for the project area. In the balance of the modeled building segment, use the field verified plug load (step 4 in the procedure). End-uses excluded in Section 13 and 14 of Table 11.3.1 may be excluded; these include exhaust fans, parking garage ventilation fans, exterior building lighting, swimming pool heaters and pumps, elevators and escalators, refrigeration equipment and cooking equipment.	Project Space: Follow Table 11.3.1. If the project space anticipates attaining EA Credit 1.4, the ECB shall use a higher plug load value reflecting the occupancy type. If EA Credit 1.4 is not being pursued, use the same plug value in both the DEC and ECB. Balance of the modeled building segment: ECB: Use existing plug load values; A-ECB: Use a higher plug load value reflecting the occupancy type. Both ECB and A-ECB: End-uses excluded in Section 13 and 14 of Table 11.3.1 may be excluded.

STEP 6. Model the Baseline Case

The baseline case is calculated by replacing the design conditions of the project area with the standard's mandatory and prescriptive requirements.

For lighting, use either the building area method (Table 9.5.1) in or the space-by-space method (Section 9.6) in ASHRAE 90.1-2007.

For the baseline HVAC model (no modifications to the central plant), change only those items within the project area to the mandatory and prescriptive requirements of the standard. Follow the requirements outlined in Table 11.3.1 of Section 11 or Table G.3.1 in Appendix G of the standard, and the additional notes in Table 2. Model the rest of the building segment using the same existing building conditions used in the design case.

If modifications to the central plant are included in the design case modeling, replace them in the baseline case with the mandatory and prescriptive equivalent. For example, if pumps were replaced with efficiencies higher than required, use the required equivalent in the baseline model. If extensive HVAC revisions have been made, follow the procedure outlined in Section 11 or Appendix G, using Figure 11.3.2 or Table G3.1.1 to determine the budget building design criteria. If using Section 11, the baseline budget building condenser cooling source may be defined as air, regardless of the proposed design, if the changed cooling equipment has less than 150 tons of cooling capacity. This exception is made to encourage the specification of more efficient water-based cooling systems over air-based cooling systems in smaller equipment sizes. Document the choices made in the narrative included with the submittal.

STEP 6A. Model an Alternative Baseline Case

In the above method, the differential between the DEC and energy cost budget increases as the energy efficiency of the building decreases. This could make it easier to reach the credit thresholds in a less efficient building. So as not to penalize project teams that have wisely located in a highly energy-efficient building—perhaps a building already LEED certified—an alternative baseline method is provided.

If the existing conditions are more energy efficient than the prescriptive requirements of ASHRAE 90.1-2007, replace the existing conditions in the baseline model with the ASHRAE 90.1-2007 requirements. Base the credit calculations on either baseline. Document the choice in the narrative included with the submittal; if results for both baselines were generated, consider submitting both.

STEP 7. Calculate the Energy Reduction

Because of the 2 possible baseline cases, there are 2 energy reduction calculations. The reduction for the model baseline case uses ASHRAE 90.1-2007 mandatory and prescriptive requirements in the project area and existing conditions in the balance of the modeled building segment, as shown in Equation 1. It corrects for the area relationship between the project space and the modeled building segment.

The reduction for the alternative baseline, potentially more generous if the building is highly efficient, is shown in Equation 2. No adjustment is made for the project-to-building segment area because the calculation evaluates the overall performance of the HVAC system.

Equation 1. Percent Annual HVAC Energy Cost Reduction

Baseline: Project Area - ANSI/ AHRAE/IESNA 90.1 mandatory and prescriptive requirements

Balance of modeled Building Segment - Existing Conditions

$$
\text{Reduction} = \frac{ECB_{HVAC} - DEC_{HVAC}}{ECB_{HVAC}} \times \frac{\text{Project Area}}{\text{Total Segment Area}}
$$

Equation 2. Percent Annual HVAC Energy Cost Reduction

Alternate Baseline: Both Project Area and Balance of Modeled Building Segment - ANSI/ AHRAE/IESNA 90.1 mandatory and prescriptive requirements

$$
\text{Reduction} = \frac{A\text{-}ECB_{HVAC} - DEC_{HVAC}}{A\text{-}ECB_{HVAC}}
$$

7. Documentation Guidance

As a first step in preparing to complete the LEED Online documentation requirements, work through the following measures. Refer to LEED Online for the complete descriptions of all required documentation.

- List locations and functions of HVAC system automatic controls or sensors.

- Document potential energy savings per control and reasons for zone distribution.

- For cost-budget compliance, list the proposed design energy by end use, associated peak demand, and cost. Additionally, list baseline costs by energy type.

8. Examples

Table 3 illustrates a calculation using Option 2 and the energy cost budget method. The baseline case and alternative baseline are both shown. Using the baseline case, the design case results in a 36.3% reduction. Using the alternative baseline, the design case has a 15.8% reduction.

Table 3. HVAC Energy Cost Reduction, Energy Cost Budget

HVAC Energy Uses Design Case	Energy Type	Electric (kWh)	Gas (CCF)	Energy Use (10 Btu)	Annual Cost ($)
Space Heating	Natural Gas		4,500	455,000	$3,223
Space Cooling	Electric	240,300		819,904	$16,800
Fans/Pumps	Electric	120,150		409,952	$8,400
Design Energy Cost HVAC (DEC$_{HVAC}$)					$28,421

Baseline Case Project Area - Code Balance - Existing Conditions					
Space Heating	Natural Gas		4,575	457,500	$3,239
Space Cooling	Electric	270,000		921,240	$18,876
Fans/Pumps	Electric	122,000		416,264	$8,529
Baseline Energy Cost Budget HVAC (ECB$_{HVAC}$)					$30,645

Reduction = (ECB$_{HVAC}$ − DEC$_{HVAC}$) / ECB$_{HVAC}$ x (Project Area / Total Segment Area)
Reduction = ($30,645 - $28,421) / ($30,645 x [20,000 ft / 100,000 ft])
Reduction = 36.3%

36.3% > 30% 2 Points Earned

Alternate Baseline Project Area - Code Balance - Code					
Space Heating	Natural Gas		5,200	520,000	$3,682
Space Cooling	Electric	295,000		1,006,540	$20,624
Fans/Pumps	Electric			460,620	$9,438
Alternate Baseline Energy Cost Budget HVAC (A-ECB$_{HVAC}$)					$33,744

Reduction = (A-ECB$_{HVAC}$ − DEC$_{HVAC}$) / A-ECB$_{HVAC}$
Reduction = ($33,744 − $28,421) / $33,744
Reduction = 15.8%

15.8% > 15% 1 Point Earned

9. Exemplary Performance

Projects that use Option 2 and demonstrate that HVAC system component performance for the tenant space is 33% more efficient than a system that is in minimum compliance with ASHRAE 90.1-2007 are eligible to earn 1 point under Innovation in Design.

10. Regional Variations

Regional variance is already incorporated in ASHRAE 90.1-2007, which accounts for 8 climate zones and 3 climate subzones and their minimum envelope and glazing property requirements.

11. Operations and Maintenance Considerations

See the Operations and Maintenance section in EA Credit 1.1.

12. Resources

Please see USGBC's LEED Resources & Tools (www.usgbc.org/projecttools) for additional resources and technical information.

Websites

DOE-2

http://www.doe2.com

This comprehensive energy analysis program predicts the hourly performance of a building's energy use and utility costs.

ENERGY STAR®

http://www.energystar.gov

ENERGY STAR® is a government-industry partnership managed by the U.S. Environmental Protection Agency and the U.S. Department of Energy. The program's website offers energy management strategies, benchmarking software tools for buildings, product procurement guidelines, and lists of ENERGY STAR®–qualified products and buildings.

National Renewable Energy Program, Energy-10

http://www.nrel.gov/buildings/energy10.html

ENERGY-10 is an award-winning software tool for designing low-energy buildings. ENERGY-10 integrates daylighting, passive solar heating, and low-energy cooling strategies with energy-efficient shell design and mechanical equipment. The program is applicable to commercial and residential buildings of 10,000 square feet or less.

U.S. Department of Energy Building Energy Codes Program

http://www.energycodes.gov

The Building Energy Codes program provides comprehensive resources for states and code users, including code comparisons, compliance software, news, and the Status of State Energy Codes database. The database includes state energy contacts, code status, code history, Department of Energy grants awarded, and construction data.

U.S. Department of Energy, Office of Energy Efficiency and Renewable Energy

http://www1.eere.energy.gov/buildings/

This extensive website for energy efficiency is linked to a number of DOE-funded sites that address buildings and energy. Of particular interest is the tools directory that includes the Commercial Buildings Energy Consumption Tool for estimating end-use consumption in commercial buildings. The tool allows the user to define a set of buildings by principal activity, size, vintage, region, climate zone, and fuels (main heat, secondary heat, cooling, and water heating), and to view the resulting energy consumption and expenditure estimates in tabular format.

Print Media

ANSI/ASHRAE/IESNA Standard 90.1–2007 User's Manual (ASHRAE, 2007).

The ANSI/ASHRAE/IESNA 90.1–2007 User's Manual was developed as a companion document to ANSI/ASHRAE/IESNA90.1–2007 (Energy Standard for Buildings Except Low-Rise Residential Buildings). The User's Manual explains the new standard and includes sample calculations, useful reference material, and information on the intent and application of the standard. It is abundantly illustrated and contains numerous examples and tables of reference data. It also includes a complete set of compliance forms and worksheets that can be used to document compliance with the standard. The manual is helpful to architects and engineers who must apply the standard to the design of the buildings, plan examiners and field inspectors who must enforce the standard in areas where it is adopted as code, and contractors who must construct buildings in compliance with the standard. A compact disk is included that contains the EnvStd 4.0 Computer Program for performing building envelope trade-offs plus electronic versions of the compliance forms found in the manual.

IESNA Lighting Handbook, ninth edition (IESNA, 2000).

Mechanical and Electrical Systems for Buildings, fourth edition, by Benjamin Stein and John S. Reynolds (John Wiley & Sons, 1992).

Sustainable Building Technical Manual (Public Technology, Inc., 1996). http://www.pti.org.

Advanced Buildings: Energy Benchmark for High Performance Buildings (E-Benchmark) (New Buildings Institute). http://www.buildinggreen.com/biblio/item.cfm?itemID=1290.

13. Definitions

An **economizer** is a device used to make building systems more energy efficient. Examples include HVAC enthalpy controls, which are based on humidity and temperature.

An **energy simulation model**, or energy model, is a computer-generated representation of the anticipated energy consumption of a building. It permits a comparison of energy performance, given proposed energy efficiency measures, with the baseline.

Tenant space is the area within the LEED project boundary. For more information on what can and must be in the LEED project boundary see the Minimum Program Requirements (MPRs) and LEED 2009 MPR Supplemental Guidance. Note: tenant space is the same as project space.

OPTIMIZE ENERGY PERFORMANCE—EQUIPMENT AND APPLIANCES

	CI
Credit	EA Credit 1.4
Points	1-4 points

Intent

To achieve increasing levels of energy conservation beyond the prerequisite standard to reduce environmental and economic impacts associated with excessive energy use.

Requirements

For all ENERGY STAR® eligible equipment and appliances installed as part of the tenant's scope of work, achieve one of the following percentages (by rated power):

Percent Installed ENERGY STAR® Qualified Equipment of ENERGY STAR® Eligible Equipment	Points
70%	1
77%	2
84%	3
90%	4

This requirement applies to appliances, office equipment, electronics, and commercial food service equipment. Excluded are HVAC, lighting, and building envelope products.

1. Benefits and Issues to Consider

Environmental Issues

According to the 2003 Commercial Building Energy Consumption Survey, conducted by the Energy Information Agency, plug loads, such as energy use for office equipment and computers, account for 9% of total office building energy consumption and 15% of total electricity consumption.[15] Because of the magnitude of plug loads in certain building types, encouraging their reduction is very important.

Plug loads, however, are hard to quantify and regulate. The few data that are available generally show that end-use consumption is quite variable—both across building types and within building types. ASHRAE 90.1-2007, addresses plug loads in a limited degree through the performance rating method in Appendix G.

Economic Issues

Using ENERGY STAR®–qualified products will reduce the energy used in the project space. ENERGY STAR® reports that qualified products use 30–75% less electricity than other products.[16] Although the initial purchase cost may be higher, the energy savings realized will translate directly into long-term cost savings. If every computer purchased by businesses this year met the new ENERGY STAR® requirements, firms would save more than $260 million over the lifetime of those models—equivalent to lighting 130 million square feet of U.S. commercial building space each year.[17]

2. Related Credits

Because thermal comfort can be affected by energy-using equipment, the equipment specifier and the HVAC designer need to coordinate their plans. Additionally, although not typically required by LEED, equipment and appliances can be included within the scope of commissioning. The following prerequisites and credits address these issues:

- EA Prerequisite 1: Fundamental Commissioning of Building Energy Systems
- EA Prerequisite 2: Minimum Energy Performance
- EA Credit 1.3: Optimize Energy Performance—HVAC
- EA Credit 2: Enhanced Commissioning
- IEQ Credit 7.1: Thermal Comfort—Design

3. Summary of Referenced Standard

ENERGY STAR®–Qualified Products
http://www.energystar.gov
Products in more than 50 categories are eligible for ENERGY STAR® certification. They use less energy, save money, and help protect the environment.

4. Implementation

Differing occupant densities and work schedules cause wide variations in plug loads and make it difficult to establish a constant metric. A few people in a big space with inefficient computers will use fewer watts per square foot than an office full of high-efficiency monitors, networked computers, laptops, and LCD displays. Similarly, fast food restaurants, where there is little or no sit-down dining, rate poorly when area is included in the plug load calculation. Using Btu per meal may be a more reliable metric for a fast food space. In retail stores, sales volume or the number of clients served potentially has a better correlation to process load. Using ENERGY STAR®–qualified products is the most straightforward way to optimize energy performance.

Appliances and equipment can have a large impact on the energy use within a space. Table 1 compares the regulated loads within offices with unregulated process loads. Table 2 lists values that represent average rated power figures for different office equipment types. Table 3 shows that the rated power of equipment is considerably higher than the actual average demand of the system.

Table 1. Regulated vs. Nonregulated Energy Consumption, by End Use

Load	kBtu (sf-yr)	watts (sf)
Heating	11.40	0.38
Cooling	7.46	0.25
Ventilation	3.63	0.12
Water heating	1.87	0.06
Lighting	22.15	0.74
Regulated Subtotal	46.51	1.56
Cooking	1.01	0.03
Refrigeration	0.37	0.01
Office Equipment	12.65	0.42
Misc.	3.45	0.12
Process Subtotal	17.48	0.59
Source: EIA, CBECS 1995		

Table 2. Energy Consumption and Rated Power, by Equipment Type

ENERGY STAR® Equipment	Rated Power (watts)	Total Number in Project	Number of ENERGY STAR®	Total Power in Project (watts)	Power that is ENERGY STAR® (watts)
Desktop Computer	120	10	8	1200	960
Notebook Computer	45	20	16	900	720
Display (CRT) 15"	100			0	0
Display (CRT) 17"	200	2	1	400	200
Display (CRT) 21"	300			0	0
Display (LCD) 15"	45	2	2	90	90
Display (LCD) 17"	75	6	4	450	300
Display (LCD) 21"	120			0	0
Desktop laser printer	120	1	0	120	0
Office laser printer	250	2	1	500	250
Desktop copier	225			0	0
Office copier	750	1	1	750	750
Fax machine	45	1	1	45	45
Scanner	45			0	0
Refrigerator	750	1	1	750	750
Dishwasher	1200	1	1	1200	1200
Televisions	100			0	0
Commercial refrigerator/freezer	1000			0	0
Commercial fryer	10000			0	0
Commercial hot food holding cabinet	1500			0	0
Commercial steam cooker	8000			0	0
Clothes washer	350			0	0
Clothes dryer	2000			0	0
Totals				6405	5265
Percent ENERGY STAR®					82.2%

Sources: ENERGY STAR® Website (www.energystar.gov)
DOE Energy Information Portal (http://www.eere.energy.gov) Lawrence Berkeley national Laboratory Website and Reports (http://enduse.lbl.gov/ESTAR.html)
Note: The values in this table represent average rated power figures for equipment based on a variety of government information sources. The values are applicable only for weighting the LEED calculation based on relative power draws of different equipment and are not meant to be accurate estimates of actual power in use.

Select energy-efficient equipment and appliances in the following categories:

- Appliances, such as dishwashers, refrigerators, and water coolers.
- Office equipment, such as computers, copiers, fax machines, digital duplicators, notebook computers, tablet PCs, mailing machines, external power adapters, monitors, printers, scanners, and all-in-ones.
- Electronics, such as battery charging systems, cordless phones, combination units, digital-to-analog converter boxes (DTAs), DVD players, external power adapters, home audio, televisions, and VCRs.
- Commercial food service equipment, such as dishwashers, fryers, hot food holding cabinets, ice machines, solid door refrigerators and freezers, and steam cookers.

HVAC, lighting systems, and building envelope products are outside the scope of EA Credit 1.4.

The credit applies to all installed equipment and appliances listed by the ENERGY STAR® program. Any categories added to the ENERGY STAR® list in the future may be used in the project team's calculation. Periodically review the ENERGY STAR® website for updates to product categories and models. Consult the interpretation rulings for this credit to find the rated power that must be used in the calculation.

Only new appliances and equipment purchased as part of the scope of work for the project need to be included in the credit for EA Prerequisite 2 and EA Credit 1.4. Equipment and appliances must meet the ENERGY STAR® criteria current at the time of purchase:

- Any items that are purchased after the item's category has become ENERGY STAR® eligible must meet the ENERGY STAR® rating.
- Any items already covered by the ENERGY STAR® program that are purchased after new criteria have been issued must meet the new criteria.
- Items purchased before the category is ENERGY STAR® eligible do not need to meet the ENERGY STAR® rating; similarly, items purchased before new criteria are issued do not need to meet the new criteria.

Upgraded Replacements

When appliances are replaced with ENERGY STAR®–qualified equipment from a different category and at a lower rated power, the higher rated power value corresponding to the new product category can be used for this credit. For example, if a desktop computer is replaced with a new, ENERGY STAR®–qualified notebook computer, the team may use 120 watts as the rated power for the desktop computer in place of 45 watts for the notebook computer. Similarly, when a CRT display unit is replaced with a new, more efficient ENERGY STAR®–qualified LCD display unit, the higher rated power value of the CRT display may be used in the credit calculation. The replacement must occur between the time of project registration and certification application.

The rated power of a piece of equipment is the maximum power it can draw under any conditions. The actual power used by office equipment and appliances is often less than half the rated power (Table 3). The actual power varies significantly based on factors such as frequency of use, number of simultaneous functions, resolution, and mode. The default power values used in this credit are not intended to be accurate estimates of the actual power draw of the equipment. Rather, the values weight the calculation based on the contribution of each piece of equipment or appliance to the overall plug load of the building.

Table 3. Comparison of Actual Power and Rated Power, by Equipment Type

Equipment Type	Actual power draw (as a % of rated power draw)	Source
PCs	25 – 50%	Norford et al., 1989
Impact and inkjet Printers	20 – 25%	
Computer network equipment	30%	Kunz, 1997
Computers	14 – 33%	Komor, 1997
Monitors	~28 – 85%	
Printers	~9 – 32%	
PCs	5 – 35%	Hosni, Jones, and X, 1999
Facsimile Machine	20 – 45%	
Network Server	50%	
Monitor	15 – 36%	

5. Timeline and Team

The office manager and project owner should institute a purchasing policy that specifies ENERGY STAR®–qualified equipment and appliances.

6. Calculations

At least 70% of the total power demand of all eligible equipment must be attributable to ENERGY STAR®–qualified products. The calculation is based on power demand rather than the number of appliances to normalize the anticipated energy savings to the consumption of each item.

Use the following calculation to determine percentage achievement:

STEP 1

Count the eligible appliances and pieces of equipment in the project and enter the number in column 3 of Table 2. Indicate how many of each equipment type are ENERGY STAR®–qualified products, and enter that number in column 4.

An upgrade should be shown in the same row as the item it replaced so that the team can count the higher wattage of the replaced equipment.

STEP 2

Multiply the total numbers and the ENERGY STAR® numbers by the rated power values in column 2 to calculate the total rated power installed and the total rated power that is attributable to ENERGY STAR®–qualified equipment.

STEP 3

Divide the rated power of ENERGY STAR® equipment by the project's total equipment rated power to determine the percentage; refer to the Requirements section to determine the number of points achieved.

7. Documentation Guidance

As a first step in preparing to complete the LEED Online documentation requirements, work through the following measure. Refer to LEED Online for the complete descriptions of all required documentation.

- List generic and ENERGY STAR®–qualified equipment, associated rated power (watts), and energy use per day for the project space.

8. Examples

A small office has 20 computers and 1 refrigerator; all the computers are ENERGY STAR®–qualified models but the refrigerator is not. The office is using ENERGY STAR®–qualified equipment for more than 90% of its equipment by quantity but must calculate the percentage of rated power attributable to ENERGY-STAR products; the rated input wattage is 75%. This example qualifies for 1 point under this credit. The team would need to achieve a rated power of 77% to reach the threshold for a second point.

9. Exemplary Performance

Projects may earn an exemplary performance credit under Innovation and Design by achieving a rated power of 97% attributable to ENERGY STAR®–qualified equipment and appliances.

10. Regional Variations

There are no regional variations associated with this credit.

11. Operations and Maintenance Considerations

To facilitate continued purchase of qualifying equipment, provide information to the tenant's operations team, including cutsheets and purchase orders, for all ENERGY STAR®–qualified equipment installed within the space.

12. Resources

Please see USGBC's LEED Resources & Tools (http://www.usgbc.org/projectools) for additional resources and technical information.

Websites

http://www.energystar.gov
ENERGY STAR® is a government-industry partnership managed by the U.S. Environmental Protection Agency and the U.S. Department of Energy. The program's website offers energy management strategies, benchmarking software tools for buildings, product procurement guidelines, and lists of ENERGY STAR®–qualified products and buildings.

EPA provides an innovative energy performance rating system that organizations have already used to rate more than 70,000 buildings across the country. EPA recognizes top performing buildings with the ENERGY STAR®.

Department of Energy, Energy Information Agency
http://www.eia.doe.gov
This website links to EIA's Commercial Building Energy Consumption Survey.

Print Media

Electricity Used by Office Equipment and Network Equipment in the U.S.: Detailed Report and Appendices, by Kawamoto, Kaoru, et al. (Lawrence Berkeley National Laboratory, February 2001). http://enduse.lbl.gov/Projects/InfoTech.html and http://eetd.lbl.gov/BEA/SF/GuideR.pdf.

13. Definitions

Rated power is the nameplate power on a piece of equipment. It represents the capacity of the unit and is the maximum that it will draw.

Receptacle (or plug) load is the current drawn by all equipment that is plugged into the electrical system.

ENHANCED COMMISSIONING

	CI
Credit	EA Credit 2
Points	5 points

Intent

To verify and ensure that the tenant space is designed, constructed and calibrated to operate as intended.

Requirements

Implement, or have a contract in place to implement, the following additional commissioning process activities in addition to the requirements of EA Prerequisite 1: Fundamental Commissioning of Building Energy Systems:

- Prior to the start of the construction documents phase, designate an independent commissioning authority (CxA) to lead, review and oversee the completion of all commissioning process activities.

  - The CxA must have documented commissioning authority experience in at least 2 building projects.

  - The individual serving as the CxA:

    - Must be independent of the work of design and construction;

    - Must not be an employee of the design firm, though he or she may be contracted through them;

    - Must not be an employee of, or contracted through, a contractor or construction manager holding construction contracts;

    - May be a qualified employee or consultant of the owner.

  - The CxA must report results, findings and recommendations directly to the owner.

- The CxA must conduct, at a minimum, 1 commissioning design review of the owner's project requirements, basis of design and design documents prior to the mid-construction documents phase and must back-check the review comments in the subsequent design submission.

- The CxA must review contractor submittals applicable to systems being commissioned for compliance with the owner's project requirements and basis of design. This review must be concurrent with the reviews of the architect or engineer of record and submitted to the design team and the owner.

- The CxA or other project team members must develop a systems manual that gives future operating staff the information needed to understand and optimally operate the project's commissioned systems.

- The CxA or other project team members must verify that the requirements for training operating personnel and building occupants have been completed.

- The CxA must be involved in reviewing the operation of the tenant space with operations and maintenance (O&M) staff and occupants within 8 to 10 months after substantial completion. A plan for resolving outstanding commissioning-related issues must be included.

1. Benefits and Issues to Consider

Environmental Issues

Facilities that do not perform as intended will consume significantly more resources over their lifetimes. Enhanced commissioning is a best practice in the building industry; it ensures that building performance requirements have been clearly and completely identified early in the project's construction, and it verifies that designed systems have been installed in compliance with those requirements.

Economic Issues

An effective commissioning process typically increases soft costs and may require additional scheduling for commissioning activities. This investment is generally recouped in improved design and construction coordination, fewer change orders, and reduced operating costs.

Indoor air quality and building occupants' comfort may have tremendous impact on their productivity, health, and well-being, as well as the cost of ownership. Commissioning can significantly reduce repairs, construction change orders, energy costs, and operations and maintenance (O&M) costs.

2. Related Credits

The commissioning effort can affect many performance-based features encouraged in the LEED for Commercial Interiors Rating System. Consider including the following features and systems in the commissioning effort: water efficiency and metering of plumbing fixtures, outdoor air delivery and monitoring, lighting, and thermal comfort systems. See Table 1 in EA Prerequisite 1 for a list of related credits.

3. Summary of Referenced Standards

There are no standards referenced for this credit.

4. Implementation

Relationship between Fundamental and Enhanced Commissioning

LEED for Commercial Interiors addresses building commissioning in 2 places, EA Prerequisite 1, Fundamental Commissioning of Building Energy Systems, and EA Credit 2, Enhanced Commissioning.

For LEED design and construction projects, the scope of services for the commissioning authority (CxA) and project team should be based on the owner's project requirements. The commissioning process activities must address the commissioned systems noted in the EA Prerequisite 1 requirements. For commercial interior projects, the scope can vary greatly. Some may include only lighting systems; others may include all HVAC and service water systems as well. EA Credit 2 requires that the commissioning authority be involved early in the process to help facilitate a commissioning design review and then a commissioning documentation review. As the project nears completion, enhanced commissioning requires oversight of staff training, a walk-through 8 to 10 months after completion, and the completion of a systems manual.

5. Timeline and Team

See the Timeline and Team section in EA Prerequisite 1.

6. Calculations

There are no calculations required for this credit.

7. Documentation Guidance

As a first step in preparing to complete the LEED Online documentation requirements, work through the following measures. Refer to LEED Online for the complete descriptions of all required documentation.

- Update the commissioning plan at milestones throughout the project. This should happen, at a minimum, during the design development phase, the construction documents phase, and just prior to the kick-off meeting with the general contractor.

- Prepare a systems list that indicates which systems have been included within the scope of enhanced commissioning.

- Confirm that the commissioning authority has documented experience on at least 2 building projects.

- Create a written schedule of building operator trainings.

- Retain a copy of the commissioning authority's design review, any designer responses to this review, and confirmation of the back-check.

- Retain copies of the owner's project requirements, basis of design, commissioning specifications, commissioning report, and systems manual.

8. Examples

There are no examples for this credit.

9. Exemplary Performance

This credit is not eligible for exemplary performance under the Innovation in Design section.

10. Regional Variations

Refer to the Regional Variations section in EA Prerequisite 1.

11. Operations and Maintenance Considerations

Refer to the Operations and Maintenance section in EA Prerequisite 1.

12. Resources

Please see USGBC's LEED Resources & Tools (http://www.usgbc.org/projecttools) for additional resources and technical information.

See the Resources section of EA Prerequisite 1 for a list of specific commissioning resources.

13. Definitions

Basis of design includes design information necessary to accomplish the owner's project requirements, including system descriptions, indoor environmental quality criteria, design assumptions, and references to applicable codes, standards, regulations, and guidelines.

Commissioning (Cx) is the process of verifying and documenting that the facility and all of its systems and assemblies are planned, designed, installed, tested, operated, and maintained to meet the *owner's project requirements*.

The **commissioning plan** is a document that outlines the organization, schedule, allocation of resources, and documentation requirements of the commissioning process.

The **commissioning process** is a systematic quality-focused effort to ensure that building systems are designed, specified, procured, installed, and functioning in accordance with the owner's intent.

The process uses planning, documentation, and verification of testing to review and oversee the activities of both designer and constructor.

The **commissioning report** documents the commissioning process, including a commissioning program overview, identification of the commissioning team, and description of the commissioning process activities.

Commissioning specification is the contract language used in the construction documents to detail the objective, scope, and implementation of the construction and acceptance phases of the commissioning process as developed in the design phase of the commissioning plan. This allows the construction contractor to ensure that these activities are considered in proposals for the construction work.

The **commissioning team** includes those people responsible for working together to carry out the commissioning process.

An **installation inspection** examines components of the building systems to determine whether they are installed properly and ready for systems performance testing.

Owner's project requirements is a written document that details the ideas, concepts, and criteria that are determined by the owner to be important to the success of the project.

Systems performance testing is the process of determining the ability of commissioned systems to perform in accordance with the owner's project requirements, the basis of design, and construction documents.

Tenant space is the area within the LEED project boundary. For more information on what can and must be in the LEED project boundary see the Minimum Program Requirements (MPRs) and LEED 2009 MPR Supplemental Guidance. Note: tenant space is the same as project space.

Verification is the range of checks and tests carried out to determine whether components, subsystems, systems, and interfaces between systems operate in accordance with the contract documents.

	CI
Credit	EA Credit 3
Points	2-5 points

Intent

To provide for the ongoing accountability and optimization of tenant energy and water consumption performance over time.

Requirements

CASE 1. Projects Less Than 75% of the Total Building Area

Complete 1 or more of the following:

- Install submetering equipment to measure and record energy use within the tenant space. (2 points)

- Negotiate a lease whereby energy costs are paid by the tenant and not included in the base rent. (3 points)

OR

CASE 2. Projects 75% or More of the Total Building Area

Install continuous metering equipment for the following end uses: (5 points)

- Lighting systems and controls.
- Constant and variable motor loads.
- Variable frequency drive operation.
- Chiller efficiency at variable loads (kW/ton).
- Cooling load.
- Air and water economizer and heat recovery cycles.
- Air distribution static pressures and ventilation air volumes.
- Boiler efficiencies.
- Building-related process energy systems and equipment.
- Indoor water riser and outdoor irrigation systems.

Develop and implement a measurement and verification (M&V) plan that incorporates the monitoring information from the above end uses and is consistent with Option B, C or D of the 2001 International Performance Measurement & Verification Protocol (IPMVP) Volume I: Concepts and Options for Determining Energy and Water Savings.

Provide a process for corrective action if the results of the M&V plan indicate that energy savings are not being achieved.

1. Benefits and Issues to Consider

Environmental Issues

Measurement and verification of a building's ongoing energy use optimize performance and minimize the economic and environmental impacts associated with its energy-using systems.

Economic Issues

The benefits of optimal tenant space operation, especially in terms of energy performance, are substantial. The lifetime of many buildings is longer than 50 years, and so even minor energy savings are significant when considered in aggregate. Potential long-term benefits often go unrealized because of maintenance personnel changes, aging of building equipment, and changing utility rate structures. Therefore, it is important to institute M&V procedures and continuous monitoring to achieve and maintain optimal performance over the lifetime of tenant spaces. The goal of M&V activities is to provide building owners and tenants with the tools and data necessary to identify systems that are not functioning as expected and thus optimize system performance.

Buildings that institute effective M&V practices report energy savings that are, on average, greater than similar buildings that do not. The added cost to institute a rigorous M&V program when retrofitting buildings with energy and water equipment is typically a very small percentage of the total retrofit cost. These additional first costs can be recouped within a few months of operation because of energy and water utility savings as well as reduced operations and maintenance costs.

2. Related Credits

Implementation of a measurement and verification plan can help ensure accountability and contribute to realizing optimal energy performance. If system performance is the basis for the funding of the project (such as with energy performance contracts), the international protocol (see the Referenced Standards section) will likely be used for verification. M&V can also help establish a baseline for ongoing green power purchases. Refer to the following:

- EA Prerequisite 2: Minimum Energy Performance

- EA Credit 1: Optimize Energy Performance

- EA Credit 4: Green Power

Commissioning often employs measurement devices and capabilities to track building performance. These same devices can also serve as the basis for a measurement and verification plan, especially if ongoing commissioning programs have been adopted by the tenant. See the following prerequisite and credit:

- EA Prerequisite 1: Fundamental Commissioning of Building Energy Systems

- EA Credit 2: Enhanced Commissioning

3. Summary of Referenced Standards

International Performance Measurement and Verification Protocol Volume I, Concepts and Options for Determining Energy and Water Savings, effective 2001
http://www.evo-world.org
The Efficiency Valuation Organization is a nonprofit organization whose vision is a global marketplace that properly values energy and water efficiency.

IPMVP Volume I defines basic terminology used in the measurement and verification field. It defines general procedures for achieving reliable and cost-effective determination of savings. Verification of actual savings is specific to each project. Volume I is written for general application in measuring and verifying the performance of projects that improve energy or water efficiency in buildings and industrial plants.

4. Implementation

First consider how to approach the measurement and verification tasks. Consult IPMVP Volume I, Options B, C, and D, and consider the specific characteristics of the project to determine which approach is most suitable. All M&V plans compliant with Options B, C, or D must meet the requirements identified in Table 1.

Table 1. Measurement and Verification Plan Requirements

Use standard IPMVP language and terminology.
State which option and method from the document will be used.
Indicate who will conduct the M&V.
State assumptions about significant variables or unknowns.
Create an accurate baseline using techniques appropriate to the project.
Describe the method of ensuring accurate energy savings determination.
Define a postinstallation inspection plan.
Specify criteria for equipment metering, calibration, and measurement period.
Define the level of accuracy to be achieved for all major components.
Indicate quality assurance measures.
Describe the contents of reports to be prepared, along with a schedule.

The steps to create an M&V plan are as follows:

STEP 1. List All Measures to be Monitored and Verified

Summarize any whole building or system-specific energy or water conservation measures that will be implemented in the project.

STEP 2. Define the Baseline

First, develop and define a baseline case. This baseline can range from the stipulation of specific baseline equipment to specifying whole-building compliance with energy codes or standards.

Then, use analytical tools to estimate the associated performance of the baseline. It is sometimes appropriate to develop a baseline by deleting specific energy conservation measures or features from the energy-efficient building. This approach can be particularly useful for whole-building M&V, with computer simulation methods (Option C). For retrofits, the baseline is the existing systems in place. Incorporating assumptions about energy and water unit costs, weather, utility distribution, system schedule, occupancy, or other factors.

STEP 3. Estimate Projected Savings

Computer-aided tools are used to estimate performance of the final design, which is subtracted from the baseline performance to find projected savings. Estimate energy consumption and associated cost reductions to be achieved on a monthly, measure-specific basis. The estimation process should also identify and, if possible, quantify factors that could affect the performance of both the baseline case and the design case.

STEP 4. Define the General Approach

Identify the specific IPMVP option for the project.

Option B, directed at end-use measures, prescribes the minimum level of precision. Option C addresses whole-building M&V methods. The trend toward holistic building design is making Option C more common, but the relative suitability of each approach depends on the following:

- M&V objectives and requirements of any related performance contracts.

- Energy conservation measures and the degree of interaction among them and with other systems.

- Practicality of measuring and verifying the energy conservation measures.

STEP 5. Prepare a Project-Specific M&V Plan

Developing an effective and efficient M&V plan for new buildings tends to be more involved than for retrofit projects because performance strategies are usually more complex and the technical issues more challenging.

Technical analyses performed in support of design decisions during the building design process provide a starting point in defining the M&V objectives and approach. The major elements of energy analyses are also usually the important factors in M&V. Energy analyses and projections should therefore be well documented and organized. M&V considerations should influence certain design decisions, such as instrumentation and building systems organization. Identify any applicable data sources (utility bills, control system points and trending periods, portable metering), the method of data collection (including equipment calibration requirements, other quality assurance practices) and the identity of monitoring personnel.

STEP 6. Verify Installation and Commissioning of Energy Conservation Measures and Strategies

Installation and proper operation are verified through site inspections and a review of reports, such as the commissioning report and fluid or air test and balance reports. Any deviations should be noted and addressed.

STEP 7. Determine Savings Under Actual Postinstallation Conditions

Virtually all performance projections are predicated on certain assumptions regarding operational conditions, such as occupancy and weather, that affect the baseline and design estimations. Work with the facility manager to make accurate projections. Deviations from the operational assumptions must be tracked by an appropriate mechanism (e.g., site survey or short- and/or long-term metering), and the baseline and design projections must be modified accordingly.

The mechanical engineer or responsible party should describe any engineering calculations and/or software tools that will be used to process the data and project savings. This includes any stipulated variables or values to be used in the calculations, as well as baseline adjustment factors and regression analysis tools.

STEP 8. Re-evaluate at Appropriate Intervals

Ongoing performance of energy conservation measures and strategies and the associated savings must be reevaluated and verified at intervals so that significant deviations from projected performance can be corrected. The timeframe should be specified by the M&V plan and related performance contract requirements.

It is important to link the contractor's final payments to documented M&V system performance. Make sure that the contractor provides all documentation in the final report. The contractor must also provide an ongoing M&V system maintenance and operating plan in the building operations and maintenance manuals.

STEP 9. Corrective Action Process

The plan must specify a process for corrective action if the results of the M&V plan indicate that energy savings are not being achieved.

CASE 1. Projects Less Than 75% of Total Building Area

The intent is to encourage efficient operation of leased spaces through measurement and financial responsibility for the energy being used.

Submetering

Submetering measures a mechanical end use within a building. In a commercial office building that has a master electric meter, submeters enable individual tenant systems to know their actual consumption. For electrical service, the equipment and installation of submeters is not a major expense. In tests of commercial and residential situations, paying based on submetered use has resulted in conservation.

The electricity used for lighting, plug loads, and HVAC equipment may be measured on a single meter and reported together. Natural gas, which may be used for both space heating and service water heating, can also be submetered. Fuel oil, district or distributed energy sources, steam, chilled water, other fuels, and process water must be submetered. Water used for the convenience of occupants does not need to be submetered. This includes restrooms, changing facilities, water fountains, break rooms, and janitorial uses (see Table 2).

Table 2. Submetering Requirements for Projects Less Than 75% of Total Building Area

Function	Typical Energy Sources	Submetering Requirements
Lighting	Electric	Yes
Plug loads	Electric	Yes
Heating	Fuels Electric Steam Hot Water	Submetering is required unless included in prorated building payment for a central plant serving multiple tenants.
Cooling	Electric Fuels Chilled Water	
Service water	Water	No
Process uses	Water Electric Fuels	Yes

Payment

Projects can qualify for points under this credit by negotiating a lease whereby energy costs are paid by the tenant and not included in the base rent. The lease cannot be a "gross" lease, in which 1 payment covers everything. The most direct way to satisfy both requirements for the credit is separate metering and payments to the utility.

The tenant's payment must be based on actual consumption, even if costs have been prorated by the size of the tenant space or occupancy count.

The typical approach, in which the landlord prorates the utilities based on the tenant's portion of the total leasable area, meets the credit requirement. Flat rates set by the landlord at the time of lease negotiation do not satisfy the requirement. The tenant's payments must be a proration of the true quantities used, and the landlord needs to give the tenant this information and keep a written record. Periodic adjustments to tenant payments and rates are acceptable as long as the adjustments reflect true consumption.

CASE 2. Projects 75% or More of Total Building Area

This credit requires development and implementation of a measurement and verification plan that incorporates the monitoring information from various end uses and is consistent with Option B, C, or D of IPMVP Volume I, Concepts and Options for Determining Energy and Water Saving, 2001. For projects pursuing Case 2, the following end uses must be monitored:

- Lighting systems and controls.

- Constant and variable motor loads.

- Variable frequency drive operation.

- Chiller efficiency at variable loads (kW/ton).

- Cooling load.

- Air and water economizer and heat recovery cycles.

- Air distribution static pressures and ventilation air volumes.

- Boiler efficiencies.

- Building-related process energy systems and equipment.

- Indoor water riser and outdoor irrigation system.

The referenced standard describes a methodology to ensure that the design team consistently addresses the basic aspects of energy and water efficiency performance:

- Accurate cataloging of baseline conditions.

- Verification of the complete installation and proper operation of new equipment and systems specified in the contract documents.

- Confirmation of the quantity of energy and water savings, as well as energy and water cost savings, that occur during the period of analysis.

The 3 M&V options that projects can use to satisfy the credit requirements are listed in Table 3, in order of increasing rigor. The appropriate level for a particular project depends on such project specifics as scope, the building owner's interest in M&V, and contractual relationships of the design team.

IPMVP's Option A does not satisfy the credit. Options B, C, and D satisfy the credit requirements when implemented correctly. Compliance with the credit requirements can be demonstrated through engineering calculations, operational estimates, and utility meter billing analysis, or through more rigorous statistical sampling, metering and monitoring, and computer simulations.

All the options in the referenced standard require the design team to specify equipment for installation in the building systems to allow for comparison, management, and optimization of actual versus estimated energy and water performance. The mechanical engineer in particular should take advantage of the building automation systems to perform M&V functions where applicable. Elements of the M&V plan that are required to comply with the requirements of this credit are listed in Table 1.

Retrofits

Use of Option B in retrofits is appropriate when the end-use capacity, demand, or power level of the baseline can be measured and the energy or water consumption of the equipment or subsystem will be measured over time. This option can involve continuous measurement of energy or water use (both before and after the retrofit for the specific equipment), or it can involve measurements for a limited period of time necessary to determine the retrofit savings. Portable monitoring equipment may be installed for a period of time or continuously to measure in situ, baseline, and postinstallation consumption. Periodic inspection of the equipment is recommended. Energy or water consumption is then calculated by developing statistical models of the end-use capacity.

Table 3. M&V Options for New and Renovation Construction Projects

M & V Option	Option Description	Savings Calculations	Cost
B	Savings are determined after project completion by short-term or continuous measurements taken throughout term of the contract at the device or system level. Both performance and operations factors are monitored.	Engineering calculations using metered data.	Typically 3-10% of project construction cost, dependent on number and type of systems measured an the term of analysis/metering
C	After project completion, savings are determined at "whole-building" or facility level using current-year and historical utility meter (gas or electricity) or submeter data.	Analysis of utility meter (or submeter) data using techniques from simple comparison with multivariate (hourly or monthly) regression analysis.	Typically 1-10% of project construction cost, dependent on number and complexity of parameters in analysis
D	Savings are determined through simulation of facility components and/or the whole facility.	Calibrate energy simulation and modeling; calibrated with hourly or monthly utility billing data and/or end-use metering.	Typically 3-10% of project construction cost, dependent on number and complexity of systems evaluated.

5. Timeline and Team

The owner should decide whether to pursue M&V as early as possible in the project. Successful implementation of M&V requires careful coordination between design team members (architect, mechanical engineer, electrical engineer, and lighting designer, among others) and is greatly assisted by early identification of the systems that will be monitored so that appropriate metering equipment can be included in the initial designs and does not have to be added in later, at greater cost.

During the design phase, the project team should incorporate the necessary metering equipment into their designs. Also at this time, the M&V plan should developed and, at a minimum, identify the party or parties responsible for implementation.

6. Calculations

IPMVP, Volume I, provides fundamental calculation formulas as well as quantitative guidelines for error estimation and tolerance for various M&V options.

7. Documentation Guidance

As a first step in preparing to complete the LEED Online documentation requirements, work through the following measures. Refer to LEED Online for the complete descriptions of all required documentation.

- Develop an IPMVP-compliant measurement and verification plan, conforming to Option B, C, or D.

- For projects with an area less than 75% of the total building area, assemble documentation (e.g., lease agreements, utility bills) demonstrating that the tenant energy costs are paid by the tenant.

- Summarize the installed monitoring systems in the tenant space, demonstrating that, at a minimum, the required systems are monitored.

8. Examples
There are no examples for this credit.

9. Exemplary Performance
This credit is not eligible for exemplary performance under the Innovation in Design section.

10. Regional Variations
There are no regional variations in the M&V methods, but the type of energy conservation measures employed does depend on climate. For example, optimization of heating systems optimization will be more critical in northern regions, and optimization of air-conditioning systems will be more important in the South. Various M&V techniques may become more popular in a given region because of the typical projects employing them. However, IPMVP is based on industry best practices, and the fundamentals of M&V apply to all projects.

11. Operations and Maintenance Considerations
Consider submetering major energy end uses in tenant spaces to help operators identify any deviations from expected consumption. Ensure that building operators are given the original and recalibrated energy use models so that they can identify unusual or unexpected consumption patterns.

12. Resources
Please see USGBC's LEED Resources & Tools (http://www.usgbc.org/projecttools) for additional resources and technical information.

Websites
ENERGY STAR®
http://www.energystar.gov
ENERGY STAR® is a government-industry partnership managed by the U.S. Environmental Protection Agency and the U.S. Department of Energy. The program's website offers energy management strategies, benchmarking software tools for buildings, product procurement guidelines, and lists of ENERGY STAR®-qualified products and buildings.

International Performance Measurement and Verification Protocol
http://www.evo-world.org
The IPMVP presents internationally developed best-practice techniques for verifying results of energy efficiency, water efficiency, and renewable energy projects in commercial and industrial facilities.

Lawrence Berkeley National Laboratory, Measurement and Verification Documents
http://http://ateam.lbl.gov/mv
This website provides list of resources ranging from implementation guidelines to hands-on checklists.

13. Definitions

Energy conservation measures are installations or modifications of equipment or systems intended to reduce energy use and costs.

Submetering is used to determine the proportion of energy use within a building attributable to specific end uses or subsystems (e.g., the heating subsystem of an HVAC system).

Tenant space is the area within the LEED project boundary. For more information on what can and must be in the LEED project boundary see the Minimum Program Requirements (MPRs) and LEED 2009 MPR Supplemental Guidance. Note: tenant space is the same as project space.

GREEN POWER

	CI
Credit	EA Credit 4
Points	5 points

Intent

To encourage the development and use of grid-source, renewable energy technologies on a net zero pollution basis.

Requirements

OPTION 1

Engage in at least a 2-year renewable energy contract to provide at least 50% of the tenant's electricity from renewable sources, as defined by the Center for Resource Solutions' Green-e energy product certification requirements.

All purchases of green power must be based on the quantity of energy consumed, not the cost, as determined by the annual electricity consumption results of EA Credit 1, Optimize Energy Performance.

OR

OPTION 2

Engage in at least a 2-year renewable energy contract to purchase at least 8 kilowatt hours per square foot per year from renewable electricity sources as defined by the Center for Resource Solutions (CRS) Green-e Energy's product certification requirements.

All purchases of green power must be based on the quantity of energy consumed, not the cost.

1. Benefits and Issues to Consider

Environmental Issues

Energy production from traditional sources (such as coal, natural gas, and other fossil fuels) is a significant contributor to air pollution in the United States, releasing such pollutants as sulfur dioxide, nitrogen oxide, and carbon dioxide. These pollutants are primary contributors to acid rain, smog, and climate change. Along with other associated pollutants, they have widespread and adverse effects on human health, especially respiratory health.

Green electricity products reduce the air pollution impacts of electricity generation by relying on renewable energy sources such as solar, water, wind, biomass, and geothermal sources. In addition, the use of ecologically responsive energy sources avoids reliance on nuclear power and large-scale hydropower, which have their own drawbacks—security and environmental issues related to nuclear waste reprocessing, transportation, and storage, and alteration of aquatic habitats in the case of hydroelectric dams. Deregulated energy markets have enabled hydroelectric generators to market their electricity in areas unaffected by the dams' regional impacts.

The overall environmental benefit of renewable energy depends on the source of energy and the process by which it is extracted. For example, using biomass can reduce the estimated 136 million tons of woody construction, demolition, and land clearing waste sent annually to landfills,[18] but if these wastes are not processed properly, their combustion could result in harmful air quality. Although green electricity is not entirely benign, it significantly lessens the negative environmental impacts of power generation. Using renewable energy generated either on-site or off-site is an excellent way for owners to reduce the negative environmental impacts on air and water associated with a building's energy requirements.

While acknowledging the difficulty of identifying the exact source of green energy in every region, this credit requires that the renewable energy used for the building and its site be certified as green by the Green-e program or its equivalent. The program was established by the Center for Resource Solutions to promote green electricity and provide consumers with a rigorous and nationally recognized method to identify green electricity products.

Economic Issues

Green power products may cost somewhat more than conventional energy products but are derived, in part, from renewable energy sources with stable energy costs. As the green power market matures and environmental costs are factored into the pricing of conventional fuels, renewable energy is expected to become less expensive. Typically, programs are structured such that utility customers can choose the portion of their electricity delivered from renewable sources. In these cases, a premium may be added to the monthly utility bill. Although the source of the green power is different from traditional sources, it reaches end users via the established grid distribution system, and thus project teams can implement green power programs, even in the postdesign phase, with very few design changes and, consequently, fewer maintenance costs. Find out whether the local government sponsors any incentive program or tax benefit for using renewable energy, particularly for the type of renewable energy planned for a project. The Database for State Incentives for Renewables and Efficiency (DSIRE: http://www.dsireusa.org/) is good source of information on federal and state programs supporting the use of renewable energy.

2. Related Credits

Replacing conventional energy sources with renewable energy sources works synergistically with efforts to reduce energy costs. Refer to the following credit:

- EA Credit 1: Optimize Energy Performance

3. Summary of Referenced Standards

Center for Resource Solutions, Green-e Renewable Electricity Certification Program

http://www.green-e.org

(888) 634-7336

Green-e Energy is a voluntary certification and verification program for renewable energy products. Green-e certifies products that meet environmental and consumer protection standards developed in conjunction with environmental, energy, and policy organizations. Sellers of Green-e–certified energy must disclose clear and useful information to customers. Three types of renewable energy options are eligible for Green-e certification: renewable energy certificates, utility green-pricing programs, and competitive electricity products. The Green-e standard that went into effect on January 1, 2007, supersedes previous regional and product-specific criteria.

Products exhibiting the Green-e logo are greener and cleaner than the average retail electricity product sold in that particular region. To be eligible for the Green-e logo, companies must meet certain criteria. The first criterion is the inclusion of qualified sources of renewable energy content such as solar electric, wind, geothermal, biomass, and small or certified low-impact hydro facilities. Other criteria are the inclusion of new renewable energy content (to support new generation capacity); compliance with emissions regulations for the nonrenewable portion of the energy product; and the absence of nuclear power. Companies must also meet other criteria regarding renewable portfolio standards. Criteria are often specific to a state or region of the United States. Refer to the standard for more details.

4. Implementation

Renewable energy calculated for this credit must be Green-e certified or equivalent. This means that eligible renewable energy sources must meet the requirements detailed in the current version of the Green-e standard and come from a supplier that has undergone an independent, third-party verification that the standard has been met. The third-party verification process must be as rigorous as that used in the Green-e certification process, and it must be performed annually.

There are 3 approaches for achieving this credit.

1. In a state with an open electricity market, tenants may be able to select a Green-e–certified power provider. Investigate green power and power markets licensed to provide power in the state and secure a 2-year contract for the credit-required green power purchase from a Green-e–certified provider.

2. In a state with a closed electricity market, the governing utility company may have a Green-e–accredited utility program. In this case, enroll the project in the renewable power program for the credit required green power purchase. Typically, programs are structured such that utility customers can choose how much of their electricity will be delivered from renewable sources; a premium may be added to the monthly utility bill. Commit to a 2-year enrollment period or use other strategies to accumulate 2 years' worth of renewable energy for the desired portion of total annual energy use. If the utility does not offer 2-year enrollment options, submit a letter of commitment to stay enrolled in the program for the required period.

3. The tenant and project team can purchase Green-e–accredited renewable energy certificates (RECs). In this case, purchase a quantity of RECs equal to the credit required green power purchase over a 2-year period, either all at once or in contracted installments. These RECs, or "green-tags," compensate Green-e generators for the premium of production over the market rate they sell to the grid. Purchasing Green-e RECs will not affect the cost or procurement of the electricity from the local electrical utility.

Establishing Green-e Equivalency

If renewable energy is not Green-e certified, establish that it is equivalent for the 2 major criteria for Green-e certification: (1) the energy source meets the requirements for renewable resources detailed in the current version of the Green-e standard, and (2) the renewable energy supplier has undergone an independent, third-party verification that the standard has been met. The current version of the standard is available on the Green-e website (http://www.green-e.org). The third-party verification process must be as rigorous as that used in the Green-e certification process, and it must be performed annually.

Retention of Renewable Energy Environmental Attributes

For renewable energy coming from both on-site and off-site sources, the associated environmental attributes must be retained or retired; they cannot be sold.

Centralized Approach (When Tenant Purchases Electricity from Building Owner)

A campus facility that produces renewable power to Green-e standards may supply other buildings on the same or a different campus through a private agreement. Renewable power may be purchased or produced on a centralized basis, and credit can be allocated to a specific project. For example, if RECs are purchased at the office park level, the owner of the RECs can apportion any part of that purchase to the project interior. To prevent double-counting, this same renewable energy must be retained on behalf of the project currently pursuing LEED certification.

5. Timeline and Team

Green power can be incorporated into the project at any time prior to submission for certification review. Once the annual energy use of the project is known (based on actual consumption), has been estimated (through tenant space energy simulation), or calculated using the default values, purchase green power in the qualifying amounts.

6. Calculations

Use 1 of 3 methods to calculate the amount of electrical energy that must be obtained from qualifying providers to achieve compliance with this credit.

1. Design Energy Cost

The first method is based on the design case annual electricity consumption, which the project team may have calculated as part of compliance with EA Credit 1.3. See EA Credit 1.3 for information regarding calculation of the design energy cost.

Sample Calculation Based on Design Energy Cost

The annual electricity consumption of a project has been determined to be 100,000 kWh. The minimum green power purchase (measured in kWh) is calculated in Equation 1.

Equation 1. Required Green Power Quantity

Project Electricity Consumption	X	Required Threshold	X	Required Duration	=	100,000 (kWh/yr)	X	50%	X	2 yrs	=	100,000 kWh Minimum Green Power Purchase

2. Actual Consumption

Project teams with a record of a full year's electricity consumption may use 50% of the actual electricity use (in kWh) from the utility bills. If the separation of regulated and nonregulated electricity loads is impractical or impossible, use the default electricity consumption calculation methodology, described below.

3. Default Electricity Consumption

If an energy model was not performed in EA Credit 1, use 8 kilowatt-hours per square foot per year times the area of the project. In the example, 16 kilowatt-hours per square foot would have to be purchased over 2 years. This default is based on Department of Energy's Commercial Buildings Energy Consumption Survey data.

Sample Calculation Based on Default Electricity Consumption

The annual electricity consumption of a project area is 10,000 square feet. The minimum green power purchase is calculated in Equation 2.

Equation 2. Green Power Amount Using Default Electricity Consumption

$$
\text{Project Area} \times \text{Required Threshold} \times \text{Required Duration} = 10{,}000 \text{ (sf)} \times 8 \text{ (kWh/sf/yr)} \times 2 \text{ yrs} = 160{,}000 \text{ kWh Minimum Green Power Purchase}
$$

7. Documentation Guidance

As a first step in preparing to complete the LEED Online documentation requirements, work through the following measures. Refer to LEED Online for the complete descriptions of all required documentation.

- Maintain contractual documentation of the purchase of Green-e (or equivalent) certified renewable energy.

- If the certified renewable energy is purchased for the project by others, maintain documentation indicating that the renewable energy was retained on behalf of the project.

8. Examples

The project area is the third floor of a 100,000-square-foot commercial office building and measures 20,000 square feet. The tenant space is served by a single, common HVAC system supplying the entire building, certified LEED for Core & Shell Gold, and the design team modeled energy use with a DOE-2 simulation. The owner also has installed an on-site renewable energy source that will reduce the minimum amount of Green-e power that must be purchased. The values in Table 1 are from the modeling.

Table 1. Regulated Electrical Use in 100,000 sf Modeled Building Segment

Regulated Electrical End Uses	Design Energy Not Costs (kWh)
Lighting	160,200
Space Cooling	240,300
Fans/Pumps	120,150
Other "regulated" electrical compoenents	20,000
(DEC')	540,650
Renewable Energy Equivalent	– 65,641
Net Regulated Electrical Useage (DEC")	475,009

Equation 1: Determination of Annual Green Power Contract Amount Using Design Energy Cost

$$\text{Annual Green Power Contract} = 50\% \times \left(\frac{\text{Tenant Area}}{\text{Building Area}} \right) \times \text{DEC}''$$

$$= 50\% \times \left(\frac{20{,}000 \text{ ft}^2}{100{,}000 \text{ ft}^2} \right) \times 475{,}009 \text{ kWh}$$

$$\text{Annual Green Power Contract} = 47{,}501 \text{ kWh}$$

Equation 2: Determination of Annual Green Power Contract Amount Using Office Occupancy Default

$$\text{Annual Green Power Contract} = \text{Tenant Area} \times 8 \text{ kWh/yr-ft}^2$$

$$= 20{,}000 \text{ ft}^2 \times 8 \text{ kWh/yr-ft}^2$$

$$\text{Annual Green Power Contract} = 160{,}000 \text{ kWh}$$

9. Exemplary Performance

Project teams may earn an Innovation in Design point for exemplary performance by meeting 100% of the calculated annual use (or a default of 16 kWh per square foot per year) through contracted green power.

10. Regional Variations

An off-site energy source that is close to the building site is likely to be more cost-effective because its proximity avoids losses in energy over the grid. Information on availability of green power in each state is available at U.S. Department of Energy's Energy Efficiency and Renewable Energy website.

Although energy efficiency is universally important, it is crucial in regions where coal is used to generate electricity. It is also particularly important to reduce peak energy use because units brought online to meet peak demand tend to be the greatest contributors to greenhouse gas emissions. Replacing fossil fuel with renewable energy for generating electricity during peak periods delivers the greatest benefits in reducing the marginal emissions.

Currently, some states do not subsidize renewable energy; others do not offer tax rebates for investing in energy efficiency. However, these policies may change as states adopt programs and new measures are put into place, making research to determine the regional importance of credits in the context of local policy very complex. The fact that green power can be sourced from a region where incentives are provided but used in a region where it is not supported by local policy makes the issue even more complicated. The Database for State Incentives for Renewables and Efficiency (DSIRE: http://www.dsireusa.org/) is a good source of information on federal and state programs supporting the use of renewable energy.

11. Operations and Maintenance Considerations

To facilitate the continued purchase of green power beyond the 2-year contract period, give building operators the details of the original green power contract.

12. Resources

Please see USGBC's LEED Resources & Tools (http://www.usgbc.org/projecttools) for additional resources and technical information.

Websites

Center for Resource Solutions, Green-e Program

http://www.green-e.org

See the Referenced Standards section for more information.

North Carolina Solar Center, Database of State Incentives for Renewable Energy

http://www.dsireusa.org

This database collects information on state financial and regulatory incentives (e.g., tax credits, grants, and special utility rates) to promote the application of renewable energy technologies. The database details the incentives on a state-by-state basis.

Union of Concerned Scientists, Clean Energy

http://www.ucsusa.org/clean_energy

This independent nonprofit analyzes and advocates energy solutions that are environmentally and economically sustainable. The site provides news and information on research and public policy.

U.S. Department of Energy, Green Power Network

http://www.eere.energy.gov/greenpower

The Green Power Network provides news and information on green power markets and related activities. It contains up-to-date information on green power providers, product offerings, consumer issues, and in-depth analyses of issues and policies affecting green power markets. The website is maintained by the National Renewable Energy Laboratory for the Department of Energy.

U.S. Department of Energy, Energy Efficiency and Renewable Energy—Green Power

http://apps3.eere.energy.gov/greenpower/buying/buying_power.shtml

This website offers information on the availability of green power in the United States in each state. The results include green utility pricing programs, retail green power products offered in competitive electricity markets, and renewable energy certificate products sold separately from electricity.

U.S. EPA, Green Power Partnership

http://www.epa.gov/greenpower

EPA's Green Power Partnership provides assistance and recognition to organizations that demonstrate environmental leadership by choosing green power. It includes a buyer's guide with lists of providers of green power in each state.

13. Definitions

Biofuel-based systems are power systems that run on renewable fuels derived from organic materials, such as wood by-products and agricultural waste. Examples of biofuels include untreated wood waste, agricultural crops and residues, animal waste, other organic waste, and landfill gas.

Biomass is plant material from trees, grasses, or crops that can be converted to heat energy to produce electricity.

Geothermal energy is electricity generated by converting hot water or steam from within the earth into electrical power.

Geothermal heating systems use pipes to transfer heat from underground steam or hot water for heating, cooling, and hot water. The system retrieves heat during cool months and returns heat in summer months.

Green power is synonymous with **renewable energy.**

Hydropower is electricity produced from the downhill flow of water from rivers or lakes.

Photovoltaic (PV) energy is electricity from photovoltaic cells that convert the energy in sunlight into electricity.

Renewable energy comes from sources that are not depleted by use. Examples include energy from the sun, wind, and small (low-impact) hydropower, plus geothermal energy and wave and tidal systems. Ways to capture energy from the sun include photovoltaic, solar thermal, and bioenergy systems based on wood waste, agricultural crops or residue, animal and other organic waste, or landfill gas.

Renewable energy certificates (**RECs**) are tradable commodities representing proof that a unit of electricity was generated from a renewable energy resource. RECs are sold separately from electricity itself and thus allow the purchase of green power by a user of conventionally generated electricity.

Solar thermal systems collect or absorb sunlight via solar collectors to heat water that is then circulated to the building's hot water tank. Solar thermal systems can be used to warm swimming pools or heat water for residential and commercial use.

Tenant space is the area within the LEED project boundary. For more information on what can and must be in the LEED project boundary see the Minimum Program Requirements (MPRs) and LEED 2009 MPR Supplemental Guidance. Note: tenant space is the same as project space.

Wave and tidal power systems capture energy from waves and the diurnal flux of tidal power, respectively. The captured energy is commonly used for desalination, water pumping, and electricity generation.

Wind energy is electricity generated by wind turbines.

Endnotes

[1] U.S. Department of Energy, Office of Energy Efficiency and Renewable Energy. "Table 1.1.1 U.S. Residential and Commercial Buildings Total Primary Energy Consumption (Quadrillion Btu and Percent of Total), 2006." *2008 Buildings Energy Data Book*. 2008. http://buildingsdatabook.eren. doe.gov (accessed November 2008).

[2] Ibid.

[3] U.S. Environmental Protection Agency. "Clean Energy: Air Emissions." http://www.epa.gov/ cleanenergy/energy-and-you/affect/air-emissions.html (accessed November 2008).

[4] U.S. Environmental Protection Agency, Office of Air and Radiation. "Six Common Air Pollutants: SO2: What is it? Where does it come from?". http://www.epa.gov/air/urbanair/so2/what1.html (accessed November 2008).

[5] Chen, Allan. "New Commercial Buildings Energy Efficiency Program Launched." Berkeley Lab, (August 24, 2000). http://www.lbl.gov/Science-Articles/Archive/combldg-energy.html.

[6] BOMA International. "BEEP's Quick Facts." BOMA Energy Efficiency Program. http://www.boma. org/TrainingAndEducation/BEEP/ (accessed November 2008).

[7] Architecture 2030. "The Building Sector: A Hidden Culprit." http://www.architecture2030.org/ current_situation/building_sector.html (accessed November 2008).

[8] U.S. Environmental Protection Agency, "ENERGY STAR® Home Improvement Tips." http://www. energystar.gov/index.cfm?c=home_improvement.hi_tips (accessed November 2008).

[9] Puget Sound Energy. Efficiency Programs and Rebates. Retrieved May 2008. http://www.pse.com/ solutions/forbusiness/pages/customGrants.aspx?tab=1&chapter=2.

[10] Architecture 2030. "The Building Sector: A Hidden Culprit." http://www.architecture2030.org/ current_situation/building_sector.html (accessed November 2008).

[11] U.S. Environmental Protection Agency. "Facts About Energy Use in Commercial and Industrial Facilities." http://www.energystar.gov/index.cfm?c=learn_more.fast_facts (accessed November 2008).

12   Ibid.

13   ENERGY STAR® Factoid Worksheet for 2008.

14   U.S. Environmental Protection Agency. "ENERGY STAR® Compact Fluorescent Light Bulbs." http://www.energystar.gov/index.cfm?c=cfls.pr_cfls (accessed November 2008).

15   Energy Information Administration. 2003. "2003 CBECS Detailed Tables." http://www. eia.doe.gov/emeu/cbecs/cbecs2003/detailed_tables_2003/detailed_tables_2003. html?featureclicked=1&#enduse03

16   U.S. Environmental Protection Agency. "ENERGY STAR® Office Equipment." http://www. energystar.gov/index.cfm?c=ofc_equip.pr_office_equipment

17   2007 CCAP update for Factoid Workbook and ENERGY STAR® Factoid Worksheet for 2008.

18   U.S. Environmental Protection Agency, Office of Solid Waste. "Wastes—Resource Conservation—Reduce, Reuse, Recycle—Construction and Demolition Materials." http://www. epa.gov/osw/conserve/rrr/imr/cdm/ (accessed November 13, 2008).

Overview

Building operations generate a large amount of waste on a daily basis. Meeting the LEED Materials and Resources (MR) credits can reduce the quantity of waste while improving the building environment through the use of sustainable materials. The credits in this section focus on 2 main issues: the environmental impact of materials brought into the project building, and the minimization of landfill and incinerator disposal for materials that leave the project building.

This credit category addresses the environmental concerns related to materials selection, waste disposal, and waste reduction. The Commercial Interiors Materials and Resources prerequisites and credits promote the following measures:

Selecting Sustainable Materials

Materials selection plays a significant role in sustainable building design and construction. During the life cycle of a material, its extraction, processing, transportation, use, and disposal can have negative environmental consequences, polluting water and air, destroying native habitats, and depleting natural resources. Environmentally responsible materials selection can significantly reduce these impacts. Project teams should consider the relative environmental, social, and health benefits of the available choices when specifying materials and furniture. For example, the purchase of products containing recycled content expands markets for recycled materials, slows the consumption of raw materials, and reduces the amount of waste entering landfills.

When selecting materials, evaluate new and different sources. Salvaged materials can be substituted for new materials, saving costs and adding character to the building. Recycled-content materials reuse waste products that would otherwise be deposited in landfills. Using local materials supports the local economy while reducing transportation costs and emissions. The use of rapidly renewable materials minimizes natural resource consumption. Using third-party-certified wood improves the stewardship of forests and related ecosystems. Because materials, particularly furniture and furnishings, are such a major portion of a commercial interior project, there is considerable opportunity to make a positive impact.

Practicing Waste Reduction

In 2006, U.S. residents, businesses, and institutions produced more than 251 million tons of solid waste, a 65% increase since 1980. That amount is roughly equivalent to 4.6 pounds per person per day, a 25% increase since 1980.[1]

A long-term lease reduces redundant development and the associated environmental impact of producing and delivering new materials. Construction waste disposal through landfilling or incineration contributes significantly to the negative environmental impacts of a build-out. Construction and demolition wastes constitute about 40% of the total solid waste stream in the United States. In its solid waste management hierarchy, the U.S. Environmental Protection Agency (EPA) ranks source reduction, reuse, and recycling as the 3 preferred strategies for reducing waste.[2] Source reduction appears at the top of EPA's hierarchy because it reduces environmental impacts throughout the material's life cycle, from the supply chain and use to recycling and waste disposal. Reuse of materials is ranked second because the reused materials are diverted from the waste stream and substitute for other materials with greater environmental impacts. Recycling does not have all the same benefits as source reduction and reuse, but it diverts waste from landfills and incinerators, and reduces the need for virgin materials.

MR OVERVIEW

Reducing the amount of waste disposed in landfills or incinerators is an important component of a sustainable construction waste management plan. A plan for managing construction waste requires contractors to establish a system for tracking waste generation and disposal during construction.

Reusing components from existing buildings, versus building new interior components, is one of the most effective strategies for minimizing environmental damage. When rehabilitating components from existing buildings is included in the strategy, waste can be reduced and diverted from landfills.

An effective way to use salvaged interior components is to specify them in the construction documents.

Recycling construction, demolition, and land-clearing debris reduces demand for virgin resources. Recycling this material has the potential to reduce the environmental and health burdens associated with resource extraction, processing, and transportation. Debris recycling also reduces dependence on landfills, which may contaminate groundwater and encroach upon valuable open space. In addition, it lessens disposal in incinerators, which may contaminate groundwater and pollute the air. Effective construction waste management can extend the life of existing landfills, which in turn reduces the need to expand or develop new landfill sites.

Many public and private waste management operations have reduced construction debris volumes through recycling. Recovery typically begins on the job site, with separation of debris into bins or disposal areas. Some regions have access to mixed-waste processing facilities. EPA reports that in 2007 in the United States, there were 34 mixed-waste processing facilities handling about 43 millions tons of waste per day.[3]

Over the past few decades, recycling has increased in the United States. In 1960, only 6.4% of U.S. waste was recycled. By 2006, the amount had climbed to 32.5%.[4] Curbside recycling is now standard in many communities, and recycling facilities are available throughout the nation. In addition, many businesses, nonprofit organizations, and manufacturers have successful recycling programs that divert a wide range of materials from the waste stream.

Recycling diverts items from the waste stream and provides materials for new products that would otherwise be manufactured from virgin materials. It avoids the extraction of raw materials and preserves landfill space. Recycling certain products, such as batteries and fluorescent lights, prevents toxic materials from polluting the air and groundwater.

Recycling and reuse can also save money. Effective waste management benefits organizations by reducing the cost of waste disposal and generating revenue from recycling or resale proceeds.

Division 12, Furniture

Regardless of who specifies or provides them, all furniture and furnishings in the project should be included in calculations for LEED for Commercial Interiors. Unlike in other LEED rating systems, project teams do not have the option to exclude certain materials (exception: MR Credit 3.1). For Materials and Resources credits, furniture and furnishings are defined as those materials included in CSI MasterFormat™ Division 12. See Table 1 for the specific credits where they are included. Because the value of these materials can be significant, the design and construction team should work closely with the facility manager, interior designer, furniture dealership, and installers from the outset.

No Default Value

Because of the variability of project scopes, the LEED for Commercial Interiors Rating System does not have an automatic default relationship between materials costs and the total construction cost.

Summary

A sustainable commercial interiors project requires strategies for construction, materials selection, and waste management. The Materials and Resources prerequisites and credits set the foundation for effective materials selection strategies. Construction waste management, in conjunction with materials selection that reduces waste and specifies less harmful materials and furniture, can effectively reduce a building's overall impact on the environment.

Credit Timing

Design team members make most of the decisions needed to successfully earn LEED for Commercial Interiors credits. Contractors and suppliers should participate in determining the actual values and ensuring compliance.

Only in 1 credit, MR Credit 1.1, Tenant Space—Long-Term Commitment, has the decision already been made before the start of the design. The configuration of the space selected has a major influence on earning MR Credits 1.2: Building Reuse—Maintain 40% or 60% of Interior Nonstructural Components. To improve the possibilities for earning credits, select a space that closely matches the design intent with minimal construction.

Table 1. Units of Measurement for Materials and Resources Credits

Material	MRc1.2 Building Reuse	MRc2 Construction Waste Management[1]	MRc3.1 Material Reuse	MRc3.2 Material Reuse—Furniture	MRc4 Recycled Content	MRc5 Regional Materials	MRc5 Extracted and Manufactured Regionally	MRc6 Rapidly Renewable Materials	MRc7 Certified Wood
Mechanical	N/A		N/A	N/A	N/A	N/A	N/A	N/A	
Electrical	N/A		N/A	N/A	N/A	N/A	N/A	N/A	
Plumbing	N/A	Either Pounds or Cubic Feet but Consistent Throughout	N/A	N/A	N/A	N/A	N/A	N/A	
Ceiling	SF			N/A					Cost New ($) - Identify all wood-based materials, then exclude salvaged and refurbished material and postconsumer recycled wood fiber or portion of any products
Floors	SF			N/A	Cost New ($) - Excludes Salvaged and Refurbished Materials counted in MRc3				
Walls	SF		Replacement Value ($)	N/A					
Doors	SF			N/A		Cost New ($)			
Case Goods	SF			N/A			Cost New ($)	Cost New ($)	
Windows	SF			N/A					
All Other Construction Materials	N/A			N/A					
Furniture and Furnishings (CSI Division 12)	N/A	N/A	N/A	Replacement Value ($)					

1 Do not include hazardous waste and excavated soil in MRc2 calculations.

Calculating Materials Costs to Achieve MR Credits

Project teams are encouraged to determine the actual total materials cost (excluding labor and equipment) from Construction Specification Institute (CSI) MasterFormat™ Divisions 3–10, 31 (section 31.60.00 Foundations) and 32 (sections 32.10.00 Paving, 32.30.00 Site Improvements, and 32.90.00 Planting). Table 1 contains guidance regarding specification sections included in the cost calculation.

CREDIT	TITLE
MR Prerequisite 1	Storage and Collection of Recyclables
MR Credit 1.1	Tenant Space—Long-Term Commitment
MR Credit 1.2	Building Reuse—Maintain Interior Nonstructural Components
MR Credit 2	Construction Waste Management
MR Credit 3.1	Materials Reuse
MR Credit 3.2	Materials Reuse—Furniture and Furnishings
MR Credit 4	Recycled Content
MR Credit 5	Regional Materials
MR Credit 6	Rapidly Renewable Materials
MR Credit 7	Certified Wood

	CI
Prerequisite	MR Prerequisite 1
Points	Required

Intent

To facilitate the reduction of waste generated by building occupants that is hauled to and disposed of in landfills.

Requirements

Provide an easily accessible dedicated area or areas for the collection and storage of materials for recycling for the tenant space. Materials must include at a minimum paper, corrugated cardboard, glass, plastics, and metals.

MR	
CI	Prerequisite 1

1. Benefits and Issues to Consider

Environmental Issues

By creating convenient recycling opportunities for all building occupants, a significant portion of the solid waste stream can be diverted from landfills. Recycling of paper, metals, glass, cardboard, and plastics reduces the need to extract virgin natural resources. For example, recycling 1 ton of paper prevents the processing of 17 trees and saves 3 cubic yards of landfill space.[5] Recycled aluminum requires only 5% of the energy required to produce virgin aluminum from bauxite, its raw material form.[6] Diverting waste from landfills can help minimize land, water, and air pollution. An occupant education program that addresses the environmental and financial benefits of recycling can encourage occupants to participate in preserving the environment.

Economic Issues

Recycling infrastructure, such as storage areas and bins, may add to project costs and take up floor area needed for other purposes. However, recycling offers significant savings on landfill disposal costs or tipping fees. In larger projects, processing equipment (can crushers, cardboard balers) can minimize the space required for recycling activities. Some recyclables can generate revenue that offsets collection and processing costs.

Many communities sponsor and promote recycling programs to reduce the amount of waste sent to landfills. Community recycling efforts return valuable resources to local production processes and may spur increases in employment in the recycling industry. Community-wide participation results in higher recycling rates and, in turn, more stable markets for recycled materials.

2. Related Credits

Selecting a location within a LEED-certified building can help projects achieve certification under LEED for Commercial Interiors because a LEED-certified building will have committed to establishing a building recycling program and centralized collection and storage areas.

Project teams seeking an Innovation in Design credit for educational outreach can create signage and displays to inform building occupants and visitors about on-site recycling.

3. Summary of Referenced Standards

There are no standards referenced for this prerequisite.

4. Implementation

When selecting a building, determine what recycling and reuse services are available in the region. Identify local waste handlers to determine the extent of services available; often these handlers will help set up the recycling program. The Resources section includes helpful links to local and regional recycling opportunities. For a project located within a leased facility, determine what services are offered by the building owner. If there is a building-wide recycling program, confirm that the program meets the requirements of this prerequisite.

Identify easily accessible collection and storage areas within the building that meet the recycling needs of the occupants. Recycling collection points should be appropriately sized and conveniently located and should include signage to discourage contamination. If the building's common collection area is not large enough to handle the full building occupancy, tenants will need to have their own dedicated and secure spaces. Projects that occupy less than a full building do not need to provide an outdoor collection area if a common collection area exists or if the materials hauler or landlord makes pickups within the tenant space.

In dense urban areas, finding additional space for collection and storage may be costly or even increase the project footprint. For a commercial interior project in a LEED-certified building, adequate storage and collection of recyclables should already be available, and the team may need to provide only additional interior recycling collection points.

Encourage activities to reduce and reuse materials to decrease the amount of recyclable volumes handled. For instance, building occupants can reduce the solid waste stream by using reusable bottles, bags, and other containers. Maintenance personnel can reduce waste by purchasing cleaners in bulk or concentrated form. Consider employing cardboard balers, aluminum can crushers, recycling chutes, on-site compost bins, and other waste management technologies to further improve the recycling program.

If recycling collection and storage space is not available, another option is to conduct a waste stream audit of existing materials. The waste stream audit should categorize all waste consistently (by either weight or volume), identify which waste streams are recyclable, and list the 3 waste streams that will be collected and stored for recycling. If no information is available on typical waste streams for the project, make projections based on the types of waste the operations will produce. Provide an easily accessible area that serves the project and is dedicated to the separation, collection, and storage of at least 3 recyclable materials as identified by the waste stream audit. Once the volume of waste is calculated, this information will help identify which occupants are disposing of, instead of recycling, eligible materials, and where improvements can be made.

Researching local recycling efforts will help identify the best method of diverting recyclable materials from the waste stream. Potential recyclable waste streams include plastic film, plastics, hanger metals, paper, cardboard, food waste, glass, or special waste as defined by local code.

5. Timeline and Team

Early in the design phase, to ensure that adequate space is allocated for a centralized collection point, seek input from the local hauler who will be providing waste management services to the site. Attention should be given to the accessibility and convenience of the waste and recycling collection locations. Prior to occupancy, the owner or owner's representative should ensure that sufficient recycling bins are in place. Postoccupancy, the project team should educate occupants on the benefits of recycling, as well as the location of facilities.

During the design phase, the project team and the designer should designate well-marked collection and storage areas for recyclable office paper, cardboard, glass, plastic, and metals. Locate a central collection and storage area in the basement or on the ground level with easy access for collection vehicles. Within the tenant spaces, establish a collection area convenient to a freight elevator for custodial pickup. Collection and storage space should be sized to accommodate the anticipated recyclables.

6. Calculations

There are no calculations required for this prerequisite. However, project teams should refer to Table 1 for sizing recycling areas. The values in this table were developed by the City of Seattle in support of an ordinance requiring minimum areas for recycling and storage of recyclables in commercial buildings. The ordinance is based on the total square footage of the building. Minimum areas for residential buildings are also specified.

Table 1 provides a recycling area guideline, by commercial square foot, to help size space needs. LEED for Commercial Interiors does not require adherence to these guidelines; the intent is for the design team to size the facilities appropriately for the specific building operations. In determining the building's square footage, include corridors, elevators, stairwells, and shaft spaces.

Table 1. Recycling Area Guidelines

Building Size (sf)	Minimum Recycling Area (sf)
0 to 5,000	82
5,001 to 15,000	125
15,001 to 50,000	175
50,001 to 100,000	225
100,001 to 200,000	275
200,001 or greater	500

Another source of sizing guidelines for recycling areas is the California Integrated Waste Management Board's (CIWMB) 2004 Statewide Waste Characterization Study,[7] which gives quantity and composition estimates for commercial, residential, and self-hauled waste streams. The study examines material disposal rates of rigid plastic packaging containers and California redemption value containers in more detail beyond the 1999 report (see the References section).

7. Documentation Guidance

As a first step in preparing to complete the LEED Online documentation requirements, work through the following measures. Refer to LEED Online for the complete descriptions of all required documentation.

- Prepare documentation such as floor plans and site plans that highlight all recycling storage areas.

- Obtain a letter from the landlord outlining the building's recycling program.

8. Examples

Figure 1 shows a typical breakdown of waste stream materials. The 5 materials required for collection— paper, glass, plastics, cardboard, and metals—make up 59% of the waste stream.

Figure 1. Municipal Solid Waste Generation

Data from U.S. Environmental Protection Agency, 2006.

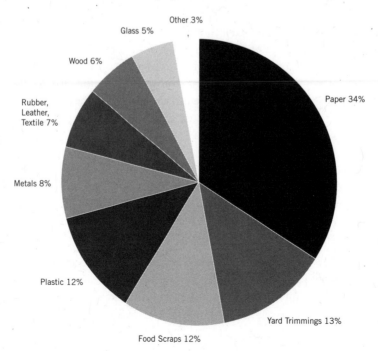

9. Exemplary Performance

This prerequisite is not eligible for exemplary performance under the Innovation in Design section.

10. Regional Variations

Dense urban areas typically have recycling infrastructure in place, but some less populated areas may not. Research local recycling programs to find the best method of diverting recyclable materials from the waste stream for the particular location. Space needs can vary depending on collection strategies used by the hauler, and whether recyclables are commingled or separated at the source. For example, if the local hauler accepts commingled recyclables, it may be possible to reduce the area needed for separate collection bins.

Commingled collection will be useful to offices in urban areas, where there is little room for outdoor collection locations.

11. Operations and Maintenance Considerations

Establish a sustainable waste management plan with building operators or management. Engage with these parties early enough in the design phase so that storage and collection facilities reflect the actual operating needs and waste flows of the new space.

Consider developing a commercial waste and recycling policy and education program for occupants. The policy should outline the protocol for collection and processing that the facility staff will follow and detail the signage for collection areas. The education component should explain the environmental and financial benefits of recycling to all building occupants.

Postoccupancy, tenant space operations managers should implement a waste tracking system to determine the success of the recycling program; as issues arise, the recycling program should be reviewed and updated accordingly. Have a system in place to adjust the number and size of recycling bins, find additional on-site recycling resources, or provide occupant training if needed. Periodic waste stream audits will help identify the types and amounts of building occupant waste.

12. Resources

Please see USGBC's LEED Resources & Tools (http://www.usgbc.org/projecttools) for additional resources and technical information.

Websites
California Integrated Waste Management Board
http://www.ciwmb.ca.gov/
The California Integrated Waste Management Board (CIWMB) offers information about waste reduction, recycling and solid waste characterization, as well as generation rates for offices, schools, and residences.

Earth 911
http://www.earth911.com/
This group provides information and education programs on recycling as well as links to regional recyclers.

U.S. Conference of Mayors, Recycling at Work
http://www.usmayors.org/recycle/
This program that provides information on workplace recycling efforts.

Waste at Work: Prevention Strategies for the Bottom Line
http://www.informinc.org/wasteatwork.php
This report from Inform, Inc., and the New York City Council on the Environment offers strategies and case studies for reducing workplace waste generation.

Print Media

Composting and Recycling Municipal Solid Waste, by Luis Diaz, et al. (CRC Press, 1993).

McGraw-Hill Recycling Handbook, by Herbert F. Lund (McGraw-Hill, 2000).

13. Definitions

Landfills are waste disposal sites for solid waste from human activities.

Occupants in a commercial building are workers who either have a permanent office or workstation in the building or typically spend a minimum of 10 hours per week in the building. In a residential building, occupants also include all persons who live in the building.

Recycling is the collection, reprocessing, marketing, and use of materials that were diverted or recovered from the solid waste stream.

A **recycling collection area** is located in regularly occupied space in the building for the collection of occupants' recyclables. A building may have numerous collection areas from which recyclable materials are typically removed to a central collection and storage area.

Reuse returns materials to active use in the same or a related capacity as their original use, thus extending the lifetime of materials that would otherwise be discarded.

Source reduction reduces the amount of unnecessary material brought into a building. Examples include purchasing products with less packaging.

Tenant space is the area within the LEED project boundary. For more information on what can and must be in the LEED project boundary see the Minimum Program Requirements (MPRs) and LEED 2009 MPR Supplemental Guidance. Note: tenant space is the same as project space.

Tipping fees are charged by a landfill for disposal of waste, typically quoted per ton.

Waste comprises all materials that flow from the building to final disposal. Examples include paper, grass trimmings, food scraps, and plastics. In LEED, waste refers to all materials that are capable of being diverted from the building's waste stream through waste reduction.

Waste disposal eliminates waste by means of burial in a landfill, combustion in an incinerator, dumping at sea, or any other way that is not recycling or reuse.

Waste diversion is a management activity that disposes of waste other than through incineration or the use of landfills. Examples include reuse and recycling.

Waste reduction includes both source reduction and waste diversion through reuse or recycling.

The **waste stream** is the overall flow of waste from the building to a landfill, incinerator, or other disposal site.

	CI
Credit	MR Credit 1.1
Points	1 point

Intent

To encourage choices that will conserve resources, reduce waste and reduce the environmental impacts of tenancy as they relate to materials, manufacturing and transport.

Requirements

The occupant or tenant must commit to remain in the same location for a minimum of 10 years.

1. Benefits and Issues to Consider

Environmental Issues

Ownership and long-term leases reduce the frequency of relocation and associated construction activities. With longer-term commitments, there is greater return on energy efficiency and improvements that benefit occupants' well-being. Many decisions go into the selection of the project location, including issues of employee convenience and quality of life, such as where workers reside and shop and the length of their commutes. Community improvements, from mass transit to cultural amenities, take time to develop. Longer and more stable tenancy improves the entire community.

Economic Issues

Relocation—including employee down time, labor and moving equipment, and assimilation time to a new location—entails significant costs. These costs can be avoided simply by remaining in 1 location. Long-term leases help ensure that the space will remain available for the tenant.

2. Related Credits

Additional credits that will enhance the project's sustainability include locating in a LEED-certified building close to alternative transportation, investing in energy efficiency and renewable energy technologies, and selecting sustainable materials; see the following credits:

- SS Credit 1: Site Selection
- SS Credit 3.1: Alternative Transportation—Public Transportation Access
- EA Credit 1: Optimize Energy Performance
- MR Credit 3: Materials Reuse
- MR Credit 4: Recycled Content
- MR Credit 5: Regional Materials
- MR Credit 6: Rapidly Renewable Materials
- MR Credit 7: Certified Wood
- IEQ Credit 1: Outdoor Air Delivery Monitoring
- IEQ Credit 2: Increased Ventilation
- IEQ Credit 3: Construction Indoor Air Quality Management Plan
- IEQ Credit 4: Low-Emitting Materials
- IEQ Credit 5: Indoor Chemical and Pollutant Source Control
- IEQ Credit 6: Controllability of Systems
- IEQ Credit 7: Thermal Comfort
- IEQ Credit 8: Daylight and Views

3. Summary of Referenced Standards

There are no standards referenced for this credit.

4. Implementation

The credit requirements are satisfied when the project area is either owned by the occupant or is currently included in a lease with a term of no less than 10 years. Tenant lease agreements with an option to renew the lease after less than 10 years do not meet the requirements of this credit.

Condominium ownerships satisfy the credit requirement.

The requirement does not stipulate a relationship between the start of the lease period and the project construction activities.

Though it may be necessary to displace occupants during the construction, there are no stipulations concerning temporary relocations.

5. Timeline and Team

Discussions regarding the duration of the lease are often most productive at the project concept phase. Depending on the nature of the project, this may entail discussions with building owners and zoning and civic officials and could include community and neighborhood organizations.

Projects planning for long-term leases will benefit if this option is considered during the predesign and design development phases. Decisions may be influenced regarding project site location selection, investment in energy efficient technologies, and the design and specification of durable, long-lasting finish materials—all of which may affect project costs and budgets, as well as other credits being pursued for LEED certification.

The tenant should select a site that provides the space necessary for growth. Once the site is selected, the tenant must agree to sign a lease of 10 years or longer.

6. Calculations

There are no calculations associated with this credit.

7. Documentation Guidance

As a first step in preparing to complete the LEED Online documentation requirements, work through the following measures. Refer to LEED Online for the complete descriptions of all required documentation.

- Retain a copy of the signed tenant lease agreement for the space that stipulates no less than a 10-year commitment.

8. Examples

There are no examples for this credit.

9. Exemplary Performance

This credit is not eligible for exemplary performance under the Innovation in Design section.

10. Regional Variations

There are no regional variations for this credit. Investment in a long-term lease benefits community development and has an inherent environmental benefit (see the Benefits and Issues section).

11. Operations and Maintenance Considerations

There are no operations and maintenance considerations applicable to this credit.

12. Resources

Please see USGBC's LEED Resources & Tools (http://www.usgbc.org/projecttools) for additional resources and technical information.

Websites

CoreNet Global Corporate Real Estate Network
http://www.corenetglobal.org
CoreNet Global is an organization of corporate real estate executives.

Congress for the New Urbanism

http://www.cnu.org

This organization of planners and designers identifies and applies principles that foster community spirit.

Print Media

How Buildings Learn: What Happens after They're Built, by Stewart Brand (Viking Penguin, 1995).

13. Definitions

Occupants in a commercial building are workers who either have a permanent office or workstation in the building or typically spend a minimum of 10 hours per week in the building. In a residential building, occupants also include all persons who live in the building.

The **owner** is the person directly employed by the organization holding title to the project building and recognized by law as having rights, responsibilities, and ultimate control over the building.

A **tenant** is a person or entity that pays to occupy land or space that is owned by someone else.

Tenant space is the area within the LEED project boundary. For more information on what can and must be in the LEED project boundary see the Minimum Program Requirements (MPRs) and LEED 2009 MPR Supplemental Guidance. Note: tenant space is the same as project space.

BUILDING REUSE—MAINTAIN INTERIOR NONSTRUCTURAL COMPONENTS

	CI
Credit	MR Credit 1.2
Points	1-2 points

Intent

To extend the life cycle of existing building stock, conserve resources, retain cultural resources, reduce waste and reduce environmental impacts of new buildings as they relate to materials manufacturing and transport.

Requirements

Maintain at least 40% or 60% by area of the existing non-shell, nonstructural components (e.g., walls, flooring and ceiling systems). The minimum percentage interior component reuse for each point threshold is as follows:

Interior Reuse	Points
40%	1
60%	2

1. Benefits and Issues to Consider

Environmental Issues

Building reuse is a very effective strategy in reducing the overall environmental impact of construction. Reusing existing buildings significantly reduces the energy use associated with the demolition process as well as construction waste and the environmental impacts associated with raw material extraction, manufacturing, and transportation. In addition, the character of the neighborhood environment is often defined by historic buildings. Building reuse maintains the vital link between neighborhoods of the past and present, reduces emissions and waste, and preserves open space. Commercial interior projects that reuse a high percentage of the nonstructural components serve as an example for future tenants in their building and for others in the community.

Economic Issues

Although retrofitting an existing building to accommodate new programmatic and LEED requirements may add to the complexity of design and construction—reflected in the project's soft costs—reuse of existing components can reduce overall construction costs by reducing costs associated with demolition, hauling fees, purchase of new construction materials, and labor.

2. Related Credits

When working on an adaptive reuse project, assess the site early on to determine which areas and materials would be valuable to reincorporate into the new development. Inventory the areas and square footage of the existing site, and incorporate a reuse strategy into the initial design charrettes. Review these 2 credits:

- MR Credit 2: Construction Waste Management

- MR Credit 3: Materials Reuse

The development of a comprehensive reuse management plan that evaluates the anticipated materials saved will determine whether the project meets the requirements of MR Credit 1, Building Reuse. If reuse is not enough to achieve credit compliance, the materials can still contribute toward MR Credit 2, Construction Waste Management, if the material has not been applied to MR Credit 1.

3. Summary of Referenced Standards

There are no standards referenced for this credit.

4. Implementation

If the project will reuse part of an existing building, inventory the existing conditions. The architect should develop a floor plan showing the location of finished ceilings and flooring, interior wall partitions, doors within the interior walls, exterior and party walls, and exterior windows and doors. If existing built-in case goods will be reused, they should be documented as well. The drawings should be detailed enough to determine the surface area of all elements to be reused.

Confirm that the items designated for reuse can be reused and take the necessary steps to retain and maintain them. Fixed items, such as nonstructural walls and doors, are included in this credit and count toward the percentage of reuse when they perform the same function (e.g., doors reused as doors). If materials are used for another purpose (e.g., doors made into tables), they can contribute toward the achievement of MR Credit 3.1, Materials Reuse.

Projects that incorporate part of an existing building but do not meet the requirements for MR Credit 1.2 may apply the reused portion toward the achievement of MR Credit 2, Construction Waste Management. To do so, determine an approximate weight or volume for existing building elements.

Include full-height wall systems in MR Credit 1.2, Building Reuse. Division 12 items, including furniture and furnishings, are addressed in MR Credit 3.2, Materials Reuse—30% Furniture and Furnishings.

Moving the demolition out of the project scope by making it the building owner's responsibility defeats the objective of this credit.

5. Timeline and Team

As a design strategy, building reuse has significant impact on all phases of a project, from schematic design through bidding and construction.

During the schematic design phase, the architect and owner should identify nonstructural building elements that can be retained and reused. The specifications for bid, developed by the architect in consultation with the owner, should outline measures to preserve the building during the construction process, and these should be implemented with project team oversight.

6. Calculations

Figure 1: Sample Comparison of Floor

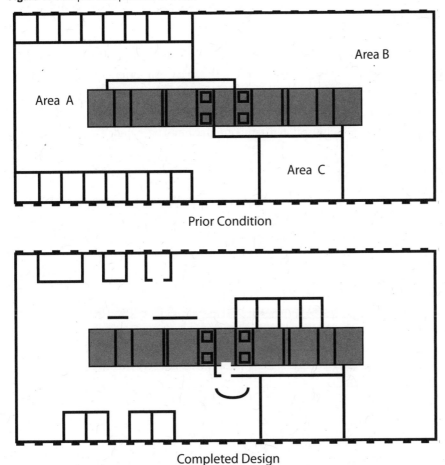

Prior Condition

Completed Design

Quantity of Finished Area

This credit is based on surface areas. The components included in the calculation are finished ceilings, walls, doors, flooring, and built-in case goods. Take measurements as if preparing a bid for flooring, ceiling, or painting:

- Finished ceilings and flooring areas. Use square footage.

- Walls. Determine the finished area between floor and ceiling.

- Interior wall partitions and doors. Count the area of both sides.

- Exterior and party walls. Count only 1 side, even if the drywall has been reused and new interior finishes applied.

- Exterior windows and exterior doors. Subtract their area from both the prior condition and the completed design tallies.

- Built-in case goods. Determine the finished area, as would a painter.

Prior Condition

Determine the total finished area that existed before the project and any demolition began. If the ceiling is exposed, both prior to construction and in the final design, include this area for both. If there was a lay-in ceiling prior to construction and none after, include the ceiling area in the prior condition and completed design areas but not in the retained components area.

Completed Design

Determine the total finished area in the completed design, including all new and retained elements.

Retained Components Area

In determining the retained components area, include only the surface areas of ceilings, walls, interior doors, floors, and built-in case goods that were in the space both prior to construction and in the completed design.

Include items that have been saved but may have been relocated, such as full-height demountable walls and doors that were rehung. Items counted in this credit cannot be included in MR Credits 3.1, Materials Reuse—5% and 10%.

Percentage Maintained

Complete a table similar to the example shown in Table 1. In determining the interior nonstructural component reuse, divide the total retained components area by the larger of either the total prior condition area or total completed design area (Equation 1).

Table 1. Sample Finished Surface Area Calculation

Finished Surface Areas			
Element	Prior Condition Area (ft²)	Completed Design Area (ft²)	Retained Components Area (ft²)
Finished Ceiling	20,000	20,000	12,610
Finished Flooring	10,200	20,000	1,800
Interior Wall Partitions	8,640	8,380	5,520
Doors within Interior Walls	1,400	800	500
Built-in case goods	500	800	400
Exterior and Party Walls	13,820	13,820	13,820
Less Exterior Windows and doors	-2,280	-2,280	-2,280
Totals	52,280	61,520	32,370
Determine the Larger Completed Design Area > Prior Condition Area		61,520 > 52,280	
Interior Non-Structural Component Reuse (32,370/61,520)		53%	
		40% < 53% < 60% earns 1 point but not 2	

Equation 1. Determination of Maintained Area

$$\text{Interior Nonstructural Component Reuse (\%)} = \frac{\text{Total Retained Components Area (sf)}}{\text{Larger of Prior Condition OR Completed Design Area (sf)}} \times 100$$

By using the larger of the 2 values in the denominator, this equation puts projects that have minimized materials use in the completed design on a level playing field with projects that have optimized reuse of components from the prior condition.

7. Documentation Guidance

As a first step in preparing to complete the LEED Online documentation requirements, work through the following measure. Refer to LEED Online for the complete descriptions of all required documentation.

- List shell attributes of existing building elements, the corresponding element IDs, the total area of new and existing elements, and the area of reused interior nonstructural elements.

8. Examples

Evaluate the interior nonstructural components to determine what can be salvaged. Figure 2 illustrates the applicable components.

Figure 2. Components Eligible for MR Credit 1.2

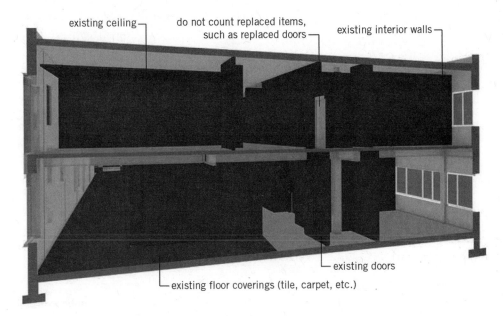

surfaces that can be counted toward area for this credit

Prior Condition

In Calculations, Figure 1, the tenant has taken the entire 20,000-square-foot floor in an existing commercial office building that has 6-foot-wide floor-to-ceiling windows at 12-foot centers on the 2 sides. Area A was previously built out with a 2-by-2-foot lay-in ceiling at 10 feet above the carpeted floor. Drywall partitions enclosed 16 private offices. Area B had never been occupied, but the building owner had completed the ceiling system and the exterior and common area walls. Area C was built as a training facility with floating acoustic panels and a mix of reclaimed wood and recycled rubber flooring. The corridors to the stairs had the same ceiling system as Area A, in addition to carpet tiles.

Completed Design

The design team opened up the space by eliminating a hallway and a party wall. They saved several private offices in Area A. In Area B, the new occupants kept the ceiling and added 4 enclosed sections for copying, recycling, storage, and conferencing. The training facility, Area C, needed only a fresh coat of paint.

The quantities shown in Table 1 are from this example.

9. Exemplary Performance

Project teams may earn an Innovation in Design credit for exemplary performance by reusing 80% or more of the existing walls, flooring, and ceiling systems.

10. Regional Variations

This credit may have particular importance in areas with historic structures where reuse of components can preserve the history and character of a building and its region. When deciding which interior structures to preserve, the project team should consider not only the nature of the building and whether the materials will enhance the project's character, but also the local historical context. Reuse of interior materials as a strategy to divert material from landfills may be particularly important in areas with constrained landfill space.

11. Operations and Maintenance Considerations

The project team should communicate to building operators any special maintenance practices required by the reused materials, or any differences in life expectancy or durability compared with new materials.

12. Resources

Please see USGBC's LEED Resources & Tools (http://www.usgbc.org/projecttools) for additional resources and technical information.

Print Media

How Buildings Learn: What Happens after They're Built, by Stewart Brand (Viking Penguin, 1994).

13. Definitions

Adaptive reuse is the renovation of a space for a purpose different from the original.

Completed design area is the total area of finished ceilings, floors, full-height walls and demountable partitions, interior doors, and built-in case goods in the completed project. It does not include exterior windows and doors.

Interior nonstructural components reuse is determined by dividing the area of retained components by the larger of (1) the area of the prior condition or (2) the area of the completed design.

Prior condition is the state of the project space at the time it was selected.

Prior condition area is the total area of finished ceilings, floors, and full-height walls that existed when the project area was selected. It does not include exterior windows and doors.

Retained components are portions of the finished ceilings, finished floors, full-height walls and demountable partitions, interior doors, and built-in case goods that existed in the prior condition area and remain in the completed design.

Soft costs are expense items that are not considered direct construction costs. Examples include architectural, engineering, financing, and legal fees.

CONSTRUCTION WASTE MANAGEMENT

	CI
Credit	MR Credit 2
Points	1-2 points

Intent

To divert construction and demolition debris from disposal in landfills and incineration facilities. Redirect recyclable recovered resources back to the manufacturing process and reusable materials to appropriate sites.

Requirements

Recycle and/or salvage nonhazardous construction and demolition debris. Develop and implement a construction waste management plan that, at a minimum, identifies the materials to be diverted from disposal and whether the materials will be sorted on-site or comingled. Excavated soil and land-clearing debris do not contribute to this credit. Calculations can be done by weight or volume, but must be consistent throughout. The minimum percentage debris to be recycled or salvaged for each point threshold is as follows:

Recycled or Salvaged	Points
50%	1
75%	2

1. Benefits and Issues to Consider

Environmental Issues

Construction and demolition generate enormous quantities of solid waste. EPA estimates that 136 million tons of such debris was generated in 1996, 57% of it from nonresidential sources.[8] Commercial construction generates between 2 and 2.5 pounds of solid waste per square foot; the majority of this waste could be recycled.[9]

The greatest environmental benefit is achieved through source control—reducing the total waste generated. Use design strategies that minimize waste, such as shop fabrication of component parts, modular construction, and the ordering of materials cut to size. Work with manufacturers to minimize unnecessary packaging and make arrangements for pallets to be reclaimed after use to reduce waste volumes and waste management costs. Extending the lifetime of existing landfills through effective construction waste management can avoid the need for expansion or new landfill sites.

Recycling of construction and demolition debris reduces demand for virgin resources and, in turn, reduces the environmental impacts associated with resource extraction, processing, and in many cases, transportation.

Economic Issues

In the past, when landfill capacity was readily available and disposal fees were low, recycling or reuse of construction waste was not economically feasible. Construction materials were less expensive than labor, and construction site managers focused on worker productivity rather than on materials conservation. In addition, recycling infrastructure and recycled-materials marketplaces that process and resell construction debris did not exist. The economics of recycling has improved in recent years, particularly with the advent of international competition for both raw and recycled materials, and disposal costs have increased. More stringent waste disposal regulations coupled with ever-decreasing landfill capacity have changed the waste management equation.

Waste management plans require time and money to draft and implement; in the long term, however, they provide guidance to achieve substantial savings throughout the construction process.

Recyclable materials have differing market values, depending on the presence of local recycling facilities, reprocessing costs, and the availability of virgin materials on the market. In general, it is economically beneficial to recycle metals, concrete, asphalt, and cardboard. Market values for recyclables fluctuate from month to month, so track the values and project different cost-recapturing scenarios. When no revenue is received for materials, as is often the case for scrap wood and gypsum wallboard, it is still possible to benefit from recycling by avoiding landfill tipping fees.

2. Related Credits

Projects that reuse existing buildings but do not meet the threshold requirements for the following credit may apply the reused building portions toward achievement of MR Credit 2, Construction Waste Management:

- MR Credit 1.2: Building Reuse—Maintain Interior Nonstructural Components

If an existing building is found to contain contaminated substances, such as lead or asbestos, these materials should be remediated as required by EPA; see the following credit:

- SS Credit 1, Path 1: Brownfield Redevelopment

3. Summary of Referenced Standards

There are no standards referenced for this credit.

4. Implementation

This credit addresses how much waste material leaving the site is diverted from landfills. The percentage requirement represents the amount of waste diverted through recycling and salvage divided by the total waste generated by the construction project.

Identify construction haulers and recyclers to handle designated materials; they often serve as valuable partners in this effort. Make sure that job-site personnel understand and participate in construction debris recycling, and ask them to provide updates throughout the construction process. Obtain and retain verification records (e.g., waste haul receipts, waste management reports, and spreadsheets) to confirm that the diverted materials have been recycled or salvaged as intended. Diversion may include salvaged materials such as furniture, computers and other electronic equipment, white boards, lockers, doors, lighting, and plumbing fixtures. Salvaged material can be donated to charitable organizations such as Habitat for Humanity, reuse centers, other nonprofit organizations, or other buildings. Materials sold to the community can also be counted.

A project may choose to separate construction waste on-site or have commingled construction waste sorted at an off-site facility. On-site separation provides immediate feedback of the ongoing waste diversion efforts but may require additional labor for implementation. Although commingled recycling can increase recycling costs, it could also simplify the waste management effort on-site and ensure that diversion rates will be high. This option is especially useful for projects with tight space constraints and no room for multiple collection bins.

5. Timeline and Team

After researching regional recycling options, the project team must create a construction waste management plan during the design phase. The general contractor should identify on-site recycling locations and review recycling requirements with all subcontractors to ensure that the plan is implemented. During construction, the general contractor should remind subcontractors of the plan requirements and confirm that the plan is implemented. The general contractor will continually track construction waste and report to the project team. At the end of construction the contractor should complete the documentation and submit detailed records to the project team.

6. Calculations

Calculations for this credit are based on the amount of waste diverted from landfills or incineration compared with the total amount of waste generated on-site. Convert all materials to either weight or volume to calculate the percentage. Projects that crush and reuse existing concrete, masonry, or asphalt on-site should include the weight or volume of these materials in the calculations. Any construction debris processed into a recycled content commodity that has an open-market value (e.g., alternative daily cover material) may be applied to the construction waste calculation. Projects that use commingled recycling rather than on-site separation should obtain summaries of diversion rates from the recycler. Typically, the recycler should provide monthly reports.

Hazardous waste should be excluded from calculations and should be disposed of according to relevant regulations.

Table 1 provides an example of a summary calculation for waste diversion. If exact material weights are not available, use the conversion factors from Table 2 or another defensible conversion metric to estimate the weight of construction waste.

Table 1. Sample Waste Diversion Calculation

Material Diverted	Method of Diversion	Diverted Material, in: tons or cubic yards
Carpet Tiles	Donation to Salvation Army	25
Cardboard Packaging	Recycler	10
Ceiling Tiles	Returned to Manufacturer	32
Steel Studs	Recycler	8
Drywall	Recycler	12
Total quantity of diverted waste		87
Material sent to landfill		63
Total quantity of waste		150
Percentage of waste diverted (87/150)		58%
	1 point (50%) earned, but the second point (75%) was not earned	

Table 2. Solid Waste Conversion Factors

Materials	Density (lbs/cy)
Cardboard	100
Gypsum Walboard	500
Mixed Waste	350
Rubble	1,400
Steel	1,000
Wood	300

7. Documentation Guidance

As a first step in preparing to complete the LEED Online documentation requirements, work through the following measures. Refer to LEED Online for the complete descriptions of all required documentation.

- Track and keep a summary log of all construction waste generated by type, the quantities of each type that were diverted and landfilled, and the total percentage of waste diverted from landfill disposal.

- A project's construction waste management plan should, at a minimum, identify the diversion goals, relevant construction debris and materials to be diverted, implementation protocols, and parties responsible for implementing the plan.

8. Examples

A contractor is preparing for partial demolition of 5,400-square-foot urban structure built in 1918. The new tenant intends to keep the structural components of the building but remove the existing interior walls and floors. The contractor, prior to construction, developed a construction waste management plan to aid in the demolition and construction process. The plan outlines the staging of waste materials during demolition to be sorted within the building before being delivered to local recycling facilities.

- Existing wood will be treated with care as it is removed from the building so that it can be reused by another local contractor or donated to a reuse store.
- Gypsum board from a previous building remodel will be composted.
- Existing doors will be removed, restored, and stored off-site before being reinstalled during construction.
- The construction waste will be commingled and sorted off-site because the site does not have enough room for sorting materials.
- All cardboard, wood, plastic, and metals will be placed in the same bins.
- The construction waste management plan outlines the responsibility of each subcontractor to recycle lunch waste in a separate, smaller container, to prevent contaminating the construction waste.
- The construction office is instructed to sort paper, plastic, cans, and bottles within the office.
- The contractor takes responsibility for enforcing the plan throughout the construction process.

Because most of the construction waste is sorted off-site, the contractor can document a construction waste diversion rate of 96%.

9. Exemplary Performance

Project teams may earn an Innovation in Design credit for exemplary performance by diverting 95% or more of total construction waste.

10. Regional Variations

Recycling opportunities are expanding rapidly in many communities. Vegetation, metal, concrete, and asphalt recycling has long been available and affordable in most communities. Paper, corrugated cardboard, plastics, and clean wood markets vary with regional and local recycling infrastructure. Some materials, such as gypsum wallboard, can be recycled only in communities that have reprocessing plants or where soil can handle the material as a stabilizing agent. The recyclability of a demolished material often depends on the extent of contamination. Demolished wood, for instance, is often not reusable or recyclable unless it is taken apart and the nails removed.

In urban areas, recycling resources are frequently more developed, and project managers can decide whether to separate waste on-site or hire a commingled waste recycler. In more rural and remote areas, recyclers may be harder to find. The environmental benefits of recycling in these cases need to be balanced against the environmental impacts of transporting waste long distances to recycling centers.

Other regional variances that affect the treatment of construction waste include landfill space, waste diversion options, and tipping fees.

11. Operations and Maintenance Considerations

A challenging aspect of managing and diverting construction waste is identifying appropriate entities to receive the diverse waste types generated. Tenants should develop waste management plans for facility alterations and additions, with specific construction waste recycling targets and end sources.

12. Resources

Please see USGBC's LEED Resources & Tools (http://www.usgbc.org/projecttools) for additional resources and other technical information.

Websites
California Integrated Waste Management Board, Construction and Demolition Debris Recycling Information
http://www.ciwmb.ca.gov/ConDemo

The CIWMB offers case studies, fact sheets, and links to additional resources for construction *and* demolition debris recycling.

Construction Materials Recycling Association
http://www.cdrecycling.org
The Construction Materials Recycling Association is a nonprofit organization dedicated to information exchange within the North American construction waste and demolition debris processing and recycling industries.

Smart Growth Online, Construction Waste Management Handbook
http://www.smartgrowth.org/library/articles.asp?art=15
This report by the National Association of Home Builders Research Center discusses residential construction waste management for a housing development in Homestead, Florida.

Business and Industry Resource Venture, Construction Waste Management Guide
http://www.resourceventure.org/free-resources/get-started/green-building-publications/CWM%20Guide.pdf/view?searchterm=construction%20waste%20prevention
This is a guidebook on waste prevention during construction.

Government Resources
Check with the solid waste authority or natural resources departments in your city or county. Many local governments provide information about regional recycling opportunities.

King County, Washington, Recycling and Waste Management during Construction
http://www.metrokc.gov/procure/green/wastemgt.htm
View specification language from the cities of Seattle and Portland metro projects on construction waste management.

A Sourcebook for Green and Sustainable Building, Construction Waste
http://www.greenbuilder.com/sourcebook/ConstructionWaste.html
This website offers a guide to construction waste management during construction.

U.S. EPA, Environmental Specifications for Research Triangle Park
http://www.epa.gov/rtp/campus/environmental/specs.htm
Learn about waste management and other specifications from EPA.

Triangle J Council of Governments, Waste Spec: Model Specifications for Construction Waste Reduction, Reuse, and Recycling
ftp://ftp.tjcog.org/pub/tjcog/regplan/solidwst/wastspec.pdf
This organization has developed model specifications for North Carolina. Ten case studies show the results of using the specifications.

13. Definitions
Alternative daily cover is material (other than earthen material) that is placed on the surface of the active face of a municipal solid waste landfill at the end of each operating day to control vectors, fires, odors, blowing litter, and scavenging.

Construction and demolition debris includes waste and recyclables generated from construction and from the renovation, demolition, or deconstruction of preexisting structures. It does not include land-clearing debris, such as soil, vegetation, and rocks.

Recycling is the collection, reprocessing, marketing, and use of materials that were diverted or recovered from the solid waste stream.

Reuse returns materials to active use in the same or a related capacity as their original use, thus extending the lifetime of materials that would otherwise be discarded.

Tipping fees are charged by a landfill for disposal of waste, typically quoted per ton.

MATERIALS REUSE

	CI
Credit	MR Credit 3.1
Points	1-2 points

Intent

To reuse building materials and products to reduce demand for virgin materials and reduce waste, thereby lessening impacts associated with the extraction and processing of virgin resources.

Requirements

Use salvaged, refurbished or reused materials, the sum of which constitutes at least 5% or 10%, based on cost, of building (construction) materials, excluding furniture and furnishings The minimum percentage materials reused for each point threshold is as follows:

Reused Materials	Points
5%	1
10%	2

1. Benefits and Issues to Consider

Environmental Issues

Many existing materials can be salvaged, refurbished, or reused. Reuse strategies divert material from the construction waste stream, reducing the need for landfill space and environmental impacts from associated water and air contamination. Use of salvaged materials also avoids the environmental impacts of producing new construction products and materials. These impacts are significant because buildings account for a large portion of natural resource consumption, including 40% of raw stone, gravel, and sand as well as 25% of virgin wood.[10]

Economic Issues

Although some salvaged materials are more costly than new materials because of the high cost of labor involved in recovering and refurbishing processes, local demolition companies or buildings undergoing a remodel may be willing to sell materials recovered from existing buildings to avoid landfill tipping fees and to generate income. In some areas, municipalities and waste management companies have established facilities for selling salvaged building materials at landfill sites. Sometimes, salvaged materials are offered at prices that appear to be cost-effective but may include hidden costs, such as reprocessing fees, excessive transportation costs, or liabilities associated with toxic contamination. Conversely, certain salvaged materials may be impossible to duplicate (e.g., turn-of-the century lumber and casework) and may be worth the higher cost compared with new materials.

2. Related Credits

The development of a comprehensive reuse management plan that evaluates the anticipated materials saved will help determine whether the project meets the requirements of the following credits:

- MR Credit 1: Building Reuse
- MR Credit 2: Construction Waste Management
- MR Credit 3.2: Materials Reuse—Furniture and Furnishings

Remanufactured materials are not considered a reuse of the material and do not contribute toward this credit. However, these materials can contribute toward the following credits:

- MR Credit 2: Construction Waste Management
- MR Credit 4: Recycled Materials

3. Summary of Referenced Standards

There are no standards referenced for this credit.

4. Implementation

Consider using salvaged and refurbished materials to reduce overall initial costs. Using salvaged materials as architectural details can also add character to the building. Identify and reuse existing materials found both on-site and off. Furniture and furnishings (CSI Division 12 components) are excluded from the calculations for this credit, but are covered by MR Credit 3.2.

Refurbished materials, such as a door that has been converted into a table, can count toward this credit or toward MR Credit 3.2, Materials Reuse—30% Furniture and Furnishings, but not both.

Table 1 clarifies materials considered within the scope of this credit.

Table 1. Materials Covered by MR Credit 3.1

Used Materials Found on Site		Used Materials Found Off Site
Fixed Items	Modified + New Use	Purchased from Others Same or New Use
Example: Door converted to table Excluded: Items included in MRc1.2 and 3.2 including demountable full-height walls; mechanical, electrical and plumbing fixtures; reused appliances and equipment		· Example: Demountable full-height walls Excluded: Items covered in MRc3.2; mechanical, electrical and plumbing fixtures; appliances and equipment
Finish Items	Refurbished + Reused Same or New Use	Owned Same or New Use
Examples: Door hardware refinished and reused. Excluded: Items covered in MRc1.2 and 3.2, including demountable full-height walls		Example: Portable signage Excluded: Items covered in MRc3.2: mechancial, electrical and plumbing fixtures; appliances and equipment.

Reused Materials Found On-site

Items that were "fixed" components on-site before construction began. To qualify as reused for this credit, these items must no longer be able to serve their original functions and must then be installed for a different use or in a different location. An example would be a door removed and modified to serve as the countertop for the receptionist station.

Walls, ceilings, and flooring. If such items continue to serve their original functions in the new building, they are excluded from this credit but are covered by MR Credit 1.2, Building Reuse—Maintain Interior Nonstructural Components.

Other reused materials found on-site. Components that are retained and continue to serve their original function, such as door hardware, are eligible for this credit.

Reused Materials Found Off-site

Reusable materials eligible for this credit are not limited to items found within the project building. Materials obtained off-site qualify as reused if they have been previously used. These materials may be purchased as salvaged, similar to any other project material, or they may be relocated from another facility, including ones previously used by the occupant. The salvaged materials from both on-site and off-site can be applied to MR Credit 5, Regional Materials, if they comply with the requirements of that credit. Materials qualifying as reused for MR Credit 3 cannot be applied to MR Credits 1, 2, 4, 6, or 7.

This credit applies primarily to CSI MasterFormat™ 2004 Edition Divisions 3–10, 31 (Section 31.60.00 Foundations) and 32 (Sections 32.10.00 Paving, 32.30.00 Site Improvements, and 32.90.00 Planting). Do not include mechanical, electrical, and plumbing components or appliances and equipment in the calculations for this credit. This exclusion is consistent with MR Credits 4 and 6. Exclude furniture and furnishings (CSI Division 12 components).

Generally, opportunities to reuse building materials may be limited. Core materials that may be eligible include salvaged brick, structural timbers, stone, and pavers. While considering the potential to reuse salvaged materials, confirm that they do not contain toxic substances, such as lead or asbestos.

5. Timeline and Team

The incorporation of materials reuse as a design strategy affects cost estimates, the demolition phase (if salvaging from the project site), and the ultimate design development of the project. Coordination among the owner, architect or design team, and contractor should begin early in the predesign phase and continue through design development so that knowledge of the site and building areas to be salvaged and reused can be creatively and efficiently worked into the basis of design, and opportunities to bring in salvaged materials from off-site can be incorporated into the project. Documentation should likewise begin early.

During predesign, the project team should assess opportunities for materials reuse and the extent of site demolition involved, and set goals accordingly. In the design phase, the architect should incorporate salvaged or reused materials into the design and then, during the construction documents and specifications development phase, identify sources and outline measures for their use. The contractor should locate sources for these materials and document and track their cost and quantity during construction. This recordkeeping will aid the project team in the credit submittal process.

6. Calculations

List the reused or salvaged materials used and their cost. Table 2 provides an example of a salvaged materials tracking log. For items that were formerly fixed items found on-site, indicate both the former and the new uses (e.g., wall paneling made from wood flooring) and how it was modified or refurbished. If the item is from off-site, indicate where it was acquired. The project owner is an acceptable source of off-site reusable materials.

The replacement value can be determined by pricing a comparable material in the local market; exclude labor and shipping. If a project team receives a discount from a vendor, the replacement value should reflect the discounted price as opposed to the list value. When the actual cost paid for the reused or salvaged material is below the cost of an equivalent new item, use the higher value in the calculations. When the cost to reclaim an item found on-site is less than the cost of an equivalent new item, use the cost of the new item (or replacement cost).

Do not include mechanical, electrical, and plumbing components or appliances and equipment in the calculations for this credit. In determining the net construction material value, subtract the costs of all such materials. The net construction material value is divided into the total salvaged material value to determine the percentage salvaged.

Table 2. Sample Spreadsheet for Salvaged Construction Materials

Salvaged Material	On- or Off- site	Modification made to On-site Materials or Source of Off-site Salvaged Materials	Replacement Value ($)
Wall paneling from wood flooring	On	Salvaged, re-milled	4,000
Stone flooring	Off	Alpha Architectural Resuse	3,640
Ceiling Tiles	Off	Project owner's inventory	2,000
Door Hardware	On	Finish item refurbished	1,750
Used demountable full-height walls	Off	Xi Walls, salvaged	2,200
Used demountable full-height walls	Off	Project owner's inventory	1,100
Total salvaged material value			$14,400
Total construction material cost			$341,214
Less MEP material value			-158,180
Net construction material value			$183,034
Percentage salvaged (14,490/183,034)			7.9%
		1 point (5%) earned, but the 2nd point (10%) was not earned	

7. Documentation Guidance

As a first step in preparing to complete the LEED Online documentation requirements, work through the following measures. Refer to LEED Online for the complete descriptions of all required documentation.

- Track costs according to CSI MasterFormat™ 2004 Edition Divisions 3–10, 31 (Section 31.60.00 Foundations), and 32 (Sections 32.10.00 Paving, 32.30.00 Site Improvements, and 32.90.00 Planting).

8. Examples

There are no examples for this credit.

9. Exemplary Performance

Project teams may earn an Innovation in Design credit for exemplary performance if the value of salvaged or reused materials used on the project is 15% or more of the total materials cost.

10. Regional Variations

This credit may have particular importance in areas with historic structures and neighborhoods, in renovating a historic building, or in offering the benefits of a nonvirgin source of building material. New England, the Pacific Northwest, and California have well-developed markets for salvaged materials. Project teams should research rebuilding centers in their region using the resources listed in this section. Where salvage markets are not as readily available, consider using deconstruction techniques. By increasing the demand for used materials, teams might encourage the development of a regional salvage market that would expand economic opportunities while diverting waste Building reuse can encourage development while preserving the history and character of an area, and materials reuse can work in tandem with this strategy.

11. Operations and Maintenance Considerations

There are no operations and maintenance considerations specific to reused or refurbished materials.

12. Resources

Please see USGBC's LEED Resources & Tools (http://www.usgbc.org/projecttools) for additional resources and technical information.

Government Resources

Check with the solid waste authority and natural resources departments in your city or county. Many local governments provide information about regional materials exchanges and other sources.

Websites

Builders' Guide to Reuse and Recycling

http://www.mwcog.org/buildersrecyclingguide/

The Builders' Guide to Reuse and Recycling is a directory for construction and demolition materials in the Metropolitan Washington, D.C., region, produced by the Metropolitan Washington Council of Governments. The website includes a searchable database for sources of salvaged materials.

California Integrated Waste Management Board, California Materials Exchange

http://www.ciwmb.ca.gov/CalMAX

The California Materials Exchange is a program of the CIWMB. This site enables users to exchange nonhazardous materials online.

Materials Exchanges on the Web

King County, Washington, Industrial Materials Exchange (IMEX) Local Hazardous Waste Management Program

http://www.govlink.org/hazwaste

The Local Hazardous Waste Management Program is a regional program of local governments working together to protect public health and environmental quality by reducing the threat posed by the production, use, storage, and disposal of hazardous materials.

Reuse Development Organization

http://www.redo.org

ReDO is a national nonprofit in Baltimore that promotes reuse as an environmentally sound, socially beneficial, and economical means of managing surplus and discarded materials. See the list of ReDO subscribers for contacts around the United States.

Green Building Resource Guide, Salvaged Building Materials Exchange

http://www.greenguide.com/exchange/search.html

The Green Building Resource Guide is a database of more than 600 green building materials and products selected specifically for their usefulness to the design and building professions.

Building Materials Reuse Association (formerly Used Building Materials Association)

http://www.bmra.org

The Building Materials Reuse Association is a nonprofit, membership-based organization that represents companies and organizations involved in the acquisition and/or redistribution of used building materials.

Used Building Materials Exchange

http://www.build.recycle.net

The Used Building Materials Exchange is a free marketplace for buying and selling recyclables and salvaged materials.

The Greater Vancouver Regional District, Old to New: Design Guide, Salvaged Building Materials in New Construction

http://www.lifecyclebuilding.org/files/Old%20to%20New%20Design%20Guide.pdf

This useful and detailed guidebook reviews the use of salvaged materials in real-life case studies.

13. Definitions

Market value, presumed to be less than replacement value, is the amount that either was paid or would have been paid for a used product.

Refurbished materials are products that could have been disposed of as solid waste. These products have completed their life cycle as consumer items and are then refurbished for reuse without substantial alteration of their form. Refurbishing includes renovating, repairing, restoring, or generally improving the appearance, performance, quality, functionality, or value of a product.

Remanufactured materials are items that are made into other products. One example is concrete that is crushed and used as subbase.

Replacement value is the estimated cost of replacing a used product. This value may be equal to the cost of a similar new product or based on a new product with comparable features.

Salvaged materials or **reused materials** are construction materials recovered from existing buildings or construction sites and reused. Common salvaged materials include structural beams and posts, flooring, doors, cabinetry, brick, and decorative items.

MATERIALS REUSE—FURNITURE AND FURNISHINGS

MR CREDIT 3.2

	CI
Credit	MR Credit 3.2
Points	1 point

Intent

To reuse building materials and products to reduce demand for virgin materials and reduce waste, thereby reducing impacts associated with the extraction and processing of virgin resources.

Requirements

Use salvaged, refurbished or used furniture and furnishings for 30% of the total furniture and furnishings budget.

1. Benefits and Issues to Consider

Environmental Issues

Reusing furniture and furnishings can reduce the environmental impacts associated with the manufacturing and disposal of materials. Further, some reused furnishings may be of historical value. For more environmental Issues, see the Benefits and Issues section in MR Credit 3.1.

Economic Issues

For commercial interiors projects, furniture often is the largest single purchase. Furniture reuse is thus a strategy for considerable savings. Office systems furniture is a particular cost focus for many commercial projects, and its reuse could help in the achievement of this credit.

2. Related Credits

The development of a comprehensive reuse management plan that evaluates the anticipated materials saved will help determine whether the project meets the requirements of the following credits:

- MR Credit 2: Construction Waste Management
- MR Credit 3.1: Materials Reuse—5% and 10%

3. Summary of Referenced Standards

There are no standards referenced for this credit.

4. Implementation

The objective of this credit is to recognize the environmental benefits of reusing furniture and furnishings, with other reused materials itemized in the Construction Specification Institute MasterFormat™ Division 12. The percentage is based on calculations for only the furniture and furnishing materials in Division 12, using replacement values. See Equation 1.

Identify opportunities to reuse furniture from the occupant's existing inventory. Also consider obtaining used furniture from materials suppliers.

Research and identify opportunities to reuse furniture and consider salvaging and reusing systems furniture and furnishings, such as case pieces, seating, filing systems, decorative lighting, and accessories.

5. Timeline and Team

The reuse of furniture should be part of a larger plan for materials reuse. Although this planning can happen at any stage of the design process, project teams may assume that there will be enough potential savings to free up the construction budget for other priorities.

Inventory the furnishings, identify likely items for reuse, tally the potential savings, and identify potential materials suppliers. The ideal time for this is during the design development phase of work, when the projected cost benefits of reuse can have the greatest impact on the project's finances.

If the furnishings are on-site at the beginning of the construction process, the contractor should plan to store and conserve them. This is an opportunity in the project timeline for any necessary repair and refurbishment.

6. Calculations

Calculate the percentage of reused furniture and furnishings used on a project. Include only furniture and furnishings, components typically found in CSI MasterFormat™ Division 12 (Figure 1). Exclude artwork, interior plants, and musical instruments.

Equation 1. Salvage Rate for Furniture and Furnishings

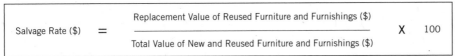

$$\text{Salvage Rate (\$)} = \frac{\text{Replacement Value of Reused Furniture and Furnishings (\$)}}{\text{Total Value of New and Reused Furniture and Furnishings (\$)}} \times 100$$

The items covered by this credit must have been previously used but can come from anywhere on or off the site. There is no requirement that they be modified or refurbished.

Figure 1. Sample Division 12 Items

Construction Acitivity
Fabrics
Artwork (exclude from calculation)
Key cabinets
Hospital casework
Display casework
Window treatment
Panels and dividers
Furniture
Furniture systems
Furniture accessories
Floor mats and framees
Multiple seating
Chairs
Interior plants (exclude from calculation)
Planters

Calculations are based upon the replacement value of the reused furniture and furnishings. Replacement value is presumed to be greater than the market value (what would be paid for the reused product in the marketplace). With justification, the project team may use replacement values greater than the amount paid for newly acquired refurbished product. When basing the determinations on comparable new products, consider using the discounted contract prices as opposed to the published list price.

The replacement values used in MR Credit 3.2 are part of the total Division 12 material value, which is also used in the calculations for MR Credit 5. Materials qualifying as reused for MR Credit 3 cannot be applied to MR Credits 1, 2, 4, 6, or 7.

7. Documentation Guidance

As a first step in preparing to complete the LEED Online documentation requirements, work through the following measure. Refer to LEED Online for the complete descriptions of all required documentation.

- Track actual costs for salvaged, reused, or refurbished furniture and furnishings.

8. Examples

Figure 1. Sample Spreadsheet for Salvaged Furniture and Furnishings

Product name	Source	Replacement Value ($)
Reused Workstation	Owner's former site	103,300
Reused File Cabinets	Zeta Old to New	100,400
Total Salvaged Material Value		$203,700
Total Division 12 Material Value		$598,722
% Salvaged (203,700 f 598,722)		34.0%
		34.0% > 30.0% MR 3 earned

9. Exemplary Performance

Project teams may earn an Innovation in Design credit for exemplary performance by using at least 60% salvaged, refurbished, or reused furniture and furnishings.

10. Regional Variations

In urban areas, project teams can shop reused furniture and thrift stores, which will provide the greatest opportunities for reused furnishing finds. If the project owner is looking for a unique touch for the office space, consider antiques shops, many of which are in rural areas. Research vendors in the region and consult contractors for sources.

11. Operations and Maintenance Considerations

Project teams should, if possible, obtain the records detailing the maintenance needs of the reused furnishings. Office managers may have records of the furniture specifications.

12. Resources

Refer to the Resources section in MR Credit 3.1.

13. Definitions

Market value, presumed to be less than replacement value, is the amount that either was paid or would have been paid for a used product.

Refurbished materials are products that could have been disposed of as solid waste. These products have completed their life cycle as consumer items and are then refurbished for reuse without substantial alteration of their form. Refurbishing includes renovating, repairing, restoring, or generally improving the appearance, performance, quality, functionality, or value of a product.

Remanufactured materials are items that are made into other products. One example is concrete that is crushed and used as subbase.

Replacement value is the estimated cost of replacing a used product. This value may be equal to the cost of a similar new product or based on a new product with comparable features.

Salvaged materials or **reused materials** are construction materials recovered from existing buildings or construction sites and reused. Common salvaged materials include structural beams and posts, flooring, doors, cabinetry, brick, and decorative items.

RECYCLED CONTENT

	CI
Credit	MR Credit 4
Points	1-2 points

Intent

To increase demand for building products that incorporate recycled content materials, thereby reducing impacts resulting from extraction and processing of virgin materials.

Requirements

Use materials, including furniture and furnishings, with recycled content[1] such that the sum of postconsumer[2] recycled content plus 1/2 of the preconsumer[3] content constitutes at least 10% or 20% based on cost of the total value of the materials in the project. The minimum percentage materials recycled for each point threshold is as follows:

Recycled Content	Points
10%	1
20%	2

The recycled content value of a material or furnishing is determined by weight. The recycled fraction of the assembly is then multiplied by the cost of assembly to determine the recycled content value.

Mechanical, electrical and plumbing components cannot be included in this calculation.

---

1 Recycled content is defined in accordance with the International Organization of Standards document, ISO 14021 — Environmental labels and declarations — Self-declared environmental claims (Type II environmental labeling).
2 Postconsumer material is defined as waste material generated by households or by commercial, industrial and institutional facilities in their role as end-users of the product, which can no longer be used for its intended purpose.
3 Preconsumer material is defined as material diverted from the waste stream during the manufacturing process. Reutilization of materials (i.e., rework, regrind or scrap generated in a process and capable of being reclaimed within the same process that generated it) is excluded.

1. Benefits and Issues to Consider

Environmental Issues

Products with recycled content reduce virgin materials use and solid waste volumes. As the number of building products containing recycled content grows, the marketplace for recycled materials develops.

Postconsumer recycled content is derived from materials that can no longer be used for their original purpose, and preconsumer recycled content consists of raw material diverted from the waste stream during the manufacturing process. Although the use of both types of recycled content is encouraged, postconsumer recycled content is accorded greater value because of its increased environmental benefit over the life cycle of the product.

Economic Issues

Many commonly used products are now available with recycled content, including metals, concrete, masonry, gypsum wallboard, acoustic tile, carpet, ceramic tile, rubber flooring and wall base, and insulation. Research all recycled-content materials for environmental pros and cons; if the product with recycled content is not as durable as its conventional counterpart, the environmental benefits may be compromised by the need for more frequent replacement. Most recycled-content products, however, exhibit performance similar to products containing only virgin materials and can be incorporated into building projects with ease and little to no cost premium.

2. Related Credits

Coordinate recycled material procurement with a construction waste management plan to make use of on-site salvaged deconstruction and demolition waste. There are opportunities for synergies with the following credits:

- MR Credit 2: Construction Waste Management
- MR Credit 3: Materials Reuse

When purchasing new materials, look for recycled-content materials that use local waste products and are remanufactured locally to take advantage of synergies with MR Credit 5, Regional Materials.

Check recycled-content materials for problematic air emissions, especially with synthetic products such as plastic, rubber, or polyester. Make sure that any recycled-content materials are considered in the planning and execution of IEQ Credit 4, Low-Emitting Materials.

The project materials costs used here need to be consistent with those used in the following credits:

- MR Credit 3.1: Materials Reuse
- MR Credit 5: Regional Materials
- MR Credit 6: Rapidly Renewable Materials

3. Summary of Referenced Standard

International Standard ISO 14021–1999, Environmental Labels and Declarations, Self-Declared Environmental Claims (Type II Environmental Labeling)
International Organization for Standardization (ISO)
http://www.iso.org
This International Standard specifies requirements for self-declared environmental claims, regarding products, including statements, symbols and graphics for products. It further describes selected terms commonly used in environmental claims and gives qualifications for their use. It also

describes a general evaluation and verification methodology for self-declared environmental claims and specific evaluation and verification methods for the selected claims.

4. Implementation

Establish goals for recycled content during the design phase and include them in the project specifications. Doing so is not a LEED requirement, but it can help in achieving the credit. To establish recycled-content goals, first add a LEED general requirements section to Division 01 to allow for writing LEED performance requirements for elements overlapping work sections (such as building envelope and structure). Then, specify products and materials according to CSI MasterFormat 2004 classifications for Division 01 recycled-content requirements. Careful research may be required to determine the percentages of recycled content that can realistically be expected in specific products and materials.

Many standard materials contain recycled content because of how they are manufactured; examples are steel, gypsum board and acoustical ceiling tile. Design and construction teams may need to research which materials contain high levels of recycled content or verify which models of a certain product line feature the desired recycled content; examples are carpet and ceramic tile.

Work with subcontractors and suppliers to make sure that materials containing recycled content are available. The contractor should run preliminary calculations based on the construction budget or schedule of values during the preconstruction phase. This will allow the construction team to focus on those materials with the greatest contribution to the project's recycled content value during the buy-out phase.

Reusing materials reclaimed from the same process in which they are generated—though good practice—does not contribute toward the recycled content of the material. In other words, putting waste back into the same manufacturing process from which it came is not considered recycling because it was not diverted from the waste stream. Reuse of materials includes rework, regrind, or scrap product (Source ISO 14021); examples are glass culls, which are often reused in the making of new glass, as well as planer shavings, plytrim, sawdust, chips, bagasse, sunflower seed hulls, walnut shells, culls, trimmed materials, print overruns, over-issue publications, and obsolete inventories.

Distinguish between postconsumer and preconsumer recycled content when tracking materials for the purpose of credit calculations (see the Definitions section).

5. Timeline and Team

Run preliminary calculations during the design phase, as soon as a project budget is available, to set appropriate recycled-content targets. Identification of materials that contain recycled content should begin during the preconstruction phase. All project team members, including the general contractor and subcontractors, should consult with suppliers prior to the buy-out phase to determine the availability of materials and the specific amount of postconsumer and preconsumer content within each type of material. Careful planning before construction can minimize capital expenses and allow the project team to verify whether the procured building materials contain the desired amount of recycled content.

The architect should identify and then specify products with recycled content. The contractor is responsible for ensuring the appropriate installation of these materials, documenting and tracking the cost and quantity of recycled materials, and providing this documentation to the project team.

6. Calculations

Materials costs include all expenses to deliver the material to the project site. Materials cost should account for all taxes and transportation costs incurred by the contractor but exclude any cost for labor and equipment once the material has been delivered to the site.

List all recycled-content materials and products and their costs. For each product, identify the percentage of postconsumer and/or preconsumer recycled content by weight, and list the recycled content information source. LEED requires that the information come from a reliable, verifiable source.

Postconsumer Recycled Content

Postconsumer recycled content is consumer waste, much of which comes from residential curbside recycling programs for aluminum, glass, plastic, and paper. To be a feedstock, the raw materials must have served a useful purpose in the consumer market before being used again. Other postconsumer feedstock is generated when construction and demolition debris is recycled.

Preconsumer Recycled Content

Preconsumer (or postindustrial) recycled content comes from process waste that an industry has sold or traded with another through the marketplace. For instance, a composite board manufacturer may obtain sawdust from a lumber mill or waste straw from a wheat farm. This definition does not include in-house industrial scrap or trimmings, which are normally fed back into the same manufacturing process.

Calculate the recycled-content value of each material according to Equation 1.

Equation 1

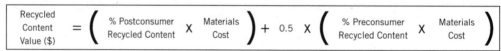

Calculate the project's percentage recycled content according to Equation 2.

Equation 2

Default Recycled Content

For steel products where no recycled content information is available, assume the recycled content to be 25% postconsumer. No other material has been recognized as having a similarly consistent minimum recycled content. Many steel products contain 90% or higher recycled content if manufactured by the electric arc furnace process, so it may be beneficial to obtain actual information from the manufacturer rather than relying on the default value.

Calculating Assembly Recycled Content

An assembly can be either a product formulated from multiple materials (e.g., concrete) or a product made up of subcomponents (e.g., a workstation). For assembly recycled contents, determine the percentage by weight of the postconsumer recycled content and the preconsumer recycled content. For subcomponents, determine the percentage by using the weights of the component elements. No consideration is given to relative costs of the materials or the subcomponents. For example, a pound of steel in a storage unit is of equal significance as a pound of fabric on a panel.

To incorporate assembly recycled content into Equation 2, use Equation 3 and add the resulting value to Equations 2's total recycled content value:

Equation 3

$$\text{Assembly Recycled Content Value (\$)} = \frac{\text{\% Postconsumer Recycled Content}}{\text{Total Assembly Weight}} \times \text{Assembly Cost} + \frac{\text{\% Preconsumer Recycled Content}}{\text{Total Assembly Weight}} \times 0.5 \times \text{Assembly Cost}$$

Table 1 shows a sample calculation of the assembly recycled contents for a hypothetical concrete mix. The cement type includes a small amount of preconsumer content. The fly ash is a by-product of coal-fired electrical generation, and slag is a by-product of steel production. The aggregate comes from concrete demolition that has been recycled, ground, and washed. Unfortunately, even though the batch plant recaptures the water it uses in cleaning the trucks and bins, this environmentally responsible practice cannot be counted as being preconsumer.

Table 1. Sample Assembly Recycled Content Calculation for Concrete

Components	Weight (lbs)	Postconsumer %	Postconsumer Weight (lbs)	Preconsumer %	Preconsumer Weight (lbs)
Cement	282			10%	28
Fly Ash	282			100%	282
Water	275				
Slag	750			100%	750
Recycled Concrete Aggregate	1000	100%	1000		
Sand	1200				
Sample Totals	3,789		1000		1060
Postconsumer Content (1000/3789)					26.4%
Preconsumer Content (1060/3789)					28.0%

Table 2. Sample Assembly Recycled Content for BIFMA Typical Workstation Configuration

Manufacturer	Lambda Furniture				
Product Line	High End Workstations				
BIFMA Typical Configuration	Workstation Configuration 0010				
Component	Weight (lbs)	Postconsumer %	Postconsumer Weight (lbs)	Preconsumer %	Preconsumer Weight (lbs)
Aluminum	25.0	53%	13.3	47%	11.8
Wood	35.0	3%	1.1	87%	30.5
Steel	650.0	22%	143.0	5%	32.5
Textile	20.0	100%	20.0	0%	0.0
Other	23.0	0%	0.0	0%	0.0
Sample Totals	753.0		177.4		74.7
Postconsumer Content (177.4/753.0)					23.4%
Preconsumer Content (74.7/753.0)					9.9%

Systems Furniture

Materials listed in CSI MasterFormat™ Division 12 (Furniture) should be included in the calculation of MR Credit 4, Recycled Content. This category includes systems furniture. Teams may use the percentages of postconsumer and preconsumer recycled content determined by the product manufacturer for the typical workstation configuration that best represents their project installation.

This approach also may be used in calculating MR Credit 6, Rapidly Renewable Materials, and MR Credit 7, Certified Wood.

The Business and Institutional Furniture Manufacturers Association (BIFMA) International has defined typical workstation configurations for both open plans and private offices, available at http://www.bifma.org. Using these typical configurations, manufacturers have determined the recycled content percentages for their individual product lines. Table 2 illustrates a manufacturer's calculation. Project teams should obtain this documentation from the manufacturer.

Project teams, most likely in conjunction with their furniture supplier, must separate their total new furniture costs according to the industry-typical configurations for each manufacturer and product line. Multiply these segmented values by the manufacturer's recycled-content percentages (Table 3).

Table 3. Sample Spreadsheet for Recycled Content

Product	Company	Product Cost ($)	% Postconsumer	Postconsumer Value ($)	% Preconsumer	Preconsumer Value ($)	Recycled Content Information Source
Steel lintel	Alpha Steel	400	25.0%	100	0%	0	25% LEED default
Wheatboard shelving	Beta Mills	1,950	0%	0	100.0%	1,950	Cut sheet
Fireproofing	Gamma insulation	3,300	25.0%	825	0%	0	Product brochure
Metal doors and frames	Delta doors	920	59.0%	543	31.9%	293	Product brochure
Rolling service door	Epsilon Specials	2,100	55.0%	1,155	27.9%	586	Product brochure
Glass side lights	Zeta Glaze	4,500	10.0%	450	5.8%	261	Cut sheet
Gypsum wall board	Eta Wall	9,900	20.0%	1,980	0%	0	Letter from factory
Acoustic ceilings	Theta Tiles	3,680	42.4%	1,560	20.6%	758	Product brochure
Acoustic insulation	Iota Insulates	2,340	0%	0	75.0%	1,755	Letter from factory
Carpet tile	Kappa Karpet	63,293	45.0%	24,051	6.8%	4,304	Product brochure
Systems furniture, new	Lambda Furniture	288,366	23.6%	68,054	9.9%	28,548	Manufacturer's typical
Seating	Lambda Furniture	59,253	26.0%	15,406	11.7%	6,933	Manufacturer's detail
Conference tables	Mu Mills	19,751	2.8%	553	81.0%	15,998	Product brochure
File cabinets	Mu Mills	27,652	22.0%	6,083	5.0%	1,383	Product brochure
Subtotals				$120,760		$62.769	

Total Construction Material Value	$341,214
Less MR 3.1 Value	-12,640
Net Construction Material Value	$170,394
Division 12 Material Value	598,722
Less MR 3.2 Value	-203,700
Net Project Material Value	$565,466
% Postconsumer + 1/2 Preconsumer ((120,760 + 0.5 x 62,769) / 565,466)	26.9%
	MRc4, 2 points earned 26.9% > 20%

This approach was developed so that project teams would not have to build the credit values starting from individual workstation component counts, costs, and recycled-content percentages. However, if a project team has purchased components that have rapidly renewable contents outside a 5% range of those used in the manufacturer's published percentages for the typical configurations, project-specific detail will be required. In this case, request that the manufacturer prepare an assembly recycled-content calculation, similar to Table 2, for the actual products purchased.

Other products, such as seating, storage units, and conference tables, are not included in typical configurations. For some of these items, there are consistent attributes across a product line; the percentage of recycled content of a steel 3-drawer file will be the same as that in a 5-drawer file. When this is the case, identify the dollar amount for all products used on the project within the product line and multiply by the recycled-content percentages. Products without consistent attributes must be addressed separately. Table 3 shows examples of both situations.

Exclusions

Excluded from the credit calculation is the salvaged and refurbished material value of reused materials as defined in MR Credit 3.1, Materials Reuse and MRc3.2, Materials reuse—Furniture and Furnishings.

Default Materials Value

The LEED for Commercial Interiors Rating System has no default relationship between the value (in dollars) of materials and total construction costs.

7. Documentation Guidance

As a first step in preparing to complete the LEED Online documentation requirements, work through the following measures. Refer to LEED Online for the complete descriptions of all required documentation.

- Record product names, manufacturers' names, costs, percentage postconsumer content, and percentage preconsumer content.

- Retain cutsheets to document the listed products' recycled content.

8. Examples

The total materials cost (excluding labor and equipment) for Sparting & Company's tenant improvement project is $270,000. Table 4 lists recycled-content products purchased for the project, the product cost, and the percentage postconsumer or preconsumer content for each. For this example, the total combined value of postconsumer content plus half the preconsumer content of the total cost of all materials is 11.31%. The project earns 1 point under MR Credit 4.

Table 4. Sample Calculations for Recycled Content

Total Construction Cost						$600,000
Default Total Materials Cost (45% of Total Construction Cost)						$270,000
Product Name	**Vendor**	**Product Cost ($)**	**% Postconumer**	**% Preconsumer**	**Recycled Content Value (Equation 1) ($)**	**Recycled Content Information Source**
Structural steel	Multi Steel	40,000	10.00%	85.00%	21,000	Structural manufacturer
Underlay aggregate	ABC Foundation	21,000	20.00%		4,200	Concrete manufacturer
Particleboard	Sol's Big Boards	4,000		100.00%	2,000	Manufacturer
Gypsum board	Gypsum R Us	8,550		78.00%	3,335	Manufacturer
Combined Value of Postconsumer + 1/2 Preconsumer Content (Total Recycled Content Value)						$30,535
Combined Value of Postconsumer + 1/2 Preconsumer Content, as a Percentage of Default Total Materials Cost (Total Percent Recycled Content) (Equation 2)						11.31%
Total Points Documented						1

Figure 1. Preconsumer versus Postconsumer Recycled Content

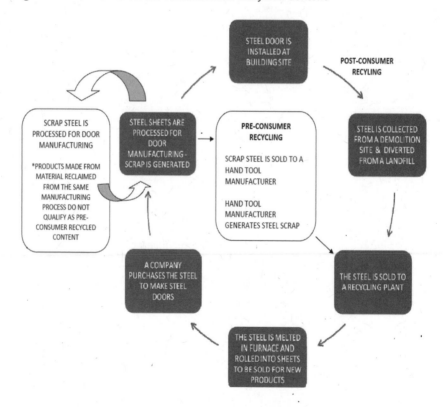

9. Exemplary Performance

Project teams may earn an Innovation in Design credit for exemplary performance by achieving a total recycled-content value of 30% or more.

10. Regional Variations

The location of the project site affects the availability of locally sourced materials. Availability of building materials containing recycled content may vary by region based on the proximity of suppliers. Some materials, such as structural steel, will be readily available for any project site; others may be manufactured or distributed in specific regions only. A project team may need to decide whether it is more sustainable to use a local material containing virgin content or to import a material containing recycled content from a long distance.

11. Operations and Maintenance Considerations

Recycled-content materials may require different maintenance practices than conventional products. When sourcing recycled products, request maintenance recommendations from the manufacturer and give this information to the operations team.

The duplication, replacement, and repair of recycled-content materials will be easier if information about the installed products has been maintained. Encourage the creation of a sustainable purchasing plan and provide building operators with lists of the installed products and their manufacturers, such as the documentation used in the LEED application.

12. Resources

Please see USGBC's LEED Resources & Tools (http://www.usgbc.org/projecttools) for additional resources and technical information.

Government Resources

Check with the solid waste authority or natural resources departments in your city or county. Many local governments provide information on recyclers and recycled content product manufacturers within their region.

Websites

U.S. Federal Trade City Guides for the Use of Environmental Marketing Claims, 16 CFR 260.7 (e)
http://www.ftc.gov/bcp/grnrule/guides980427.htm
The guides provided on this site represent administrative interpretation of Section 5 of the FTC Act to environmental advertising and marketing practices.

BuildingGreen, Inc., GreenSpec
http://www.buildinggreen.com/menus/index.cfm
GreenSpec contains detailed listings for more than 2,000 green building products, and each entry includes environmental data, manufacturer information, and links to additional resources.

California Integrated Waste Management Board, Recycled Content Product Directory
http://www.ciwmb.ca.gov/rcp
Developed by the CIWMB, the Recycled Content Product Directory is a searchable database for recycled content products.

Center for Resourceful Building Technology, Guide to Resource-Efficient Building Elements
http://crbt.ncat.org/
The directory of environmentally responsible building products is a resource that provides introductory discussions for each topic and contact information for specific products, including salvaged materials. (The CRBT project is no longer active, and the CRBT website is no longer updated. The National Center for Appropriate Technology is providing this website for archival purposes only.)

Oikos

http://www.oikos.com/

Oikos is a searchable directory of efficient building products and sustainable design resources.

Recycled Content: What Is It and What Is It Worth?

Environmental Building News, February 2005.

http://www.buildinggreen.com/auth/article.cfm?filename=140201a.xml

U.S. EPA Comprehensive Procurement Guidelines Program

http://www.epa.gov/cpg/products.htm

The Comprehensive Procurement Guidelines Program contains EPA information on recycled-content materials with guidelines for recycled percentages. It also includes a searchable database of suppliers.

Construction Specifications Institute, Green Format

http://www.greenformat.com

This database from the features standardized reporting format for manufacturers to report recycled content as well as certifications of recycled content, and other environmental and sustainable attributes. The website is based on principles of ISO 14021 - Environmental labels and declarations — Self-declared environmental claims (Type II Environmental Labelling) and ASTM E 2129 Standard Practice for Data Collection for Sustainability Assessment of Building Products.

13. Definitions

Assembly recycled content is the percentage of material in a product that is either postconsumer or preconsumer recycled content. It is determined by dividing the weight of the recycled content by the overall weight of the assembly.

Fly ash is the solid residue derived from incineration processes. Fly ash can be used as a substitute for Portland cement in concrete.

Net project material value includes the construction material value and the CSI Division 12 (Furniture and Furnishings) material value, the lesser of material values for mechanical and electric components, and the salvage value identified in the MR credits.

Postconsumer recycled content is the percentage of material in a product that was consumer waste. The recycled material was generated by household, commercial, industrial, or institutional end-users and can no longer be used for its intended purpose. It includes returns of materials from the distribution chain (ISO 14021). Examples include construction and demolition debris, materials collected through recycling programs, discarded products (e.g., furniture, cabinetry, decking), and landscaping waste (e.g., leaves, grass clippings, tree trimmings).

Preconsumer recycled content, formerly known as postindustrial content, is the percentage of material in a product that is recycled from manufacturing waste. Examples include planer shavings, sawdust, bagasse, walnut shells, culls, trimmed materials, overissue publications, and obsolete inventories. Excluded are rework, regrind, or scrap materials capable of being reclaimed within the same process that generated them (ISO 14021).

Recycled content is the proportion, by mass, of preconsumer or postconsumer recycled material in a product (ISO 14021).

REGIONAL MATERIALS

	CI
Credit	MR Credit 5
Points	1-2 points

Intent

To increase demand for building materials and products that are extracted and manufactured within the region, thereby supporting the regional economy and reducing the environmental impacts resulting from transportation.

Requirements

OPTION 1 (1 point)

Use a minimum of 20% of the combined value of construction and Division 12 (Furniture) materials and products that are manufactured[1] regionally within a radius of 500 miles.

OR

OPTION 2 (2 points)

Meet the requirements for Option 1.

Use a minimum of 10% of the combined value of construction and Division 12 (furniture) materials and products extracted, harvested or recovered, as well as manufactured, within 500 miles of the project.

---

1 Manufacturing refers to the final assembly of components into the building product that is furnished and installed by the tradesmen. For example, if the hardware comes from Dallas, Texas, the lumber from Vancouver, British Columbia, and the joist is assembled in Kent, Washington, then the location of the final assembly is Kent, Washington

1. Benefits and Issues to Consider

Environmental Issues

The use of regional building materials reduces transportation activities and associated pollution. Trucks, trains, ships, and other vehicles deplete finite reserves of fossil fuels and generate air pollution. It also is important to address the source of raw materials used to manufacture building products; some are harvested or extracted far from the point of manufacture, also contributing to air and water pollution associated with transportation.

Economic Issues

The availability of regionally manufactured building materials depends on the project location. In some areas, the majority of products needed for the project can be obtained within a 500-mile radius. In other areas, only a small portion or no building materials can be sourced locally. However, the purchase of regional building materials is generally more cost-effective because of reduced transportation costs. Also, the support of regional manufacturers and labor forces retains capital in the community, contributing to a more stable tax base and a healthier local economy, as well as showcases the resources and skills of the region.

2. Related Credits

Specifying regional materials to achieve this credit may affect the levels of achievement for the following credits:

- MR Credit 3: Materials Reuse
- MR Credit 4: Recycled Content
- MR Credit 6: Rapidly Renewable Materials

Set goals early for materials use; assess the availability of regional materials and determine the best available products to minimize the project's environmental impact. The use of life-cycle assessment tools may be employed in the decision-making process.

The project materials costs used in this credit need to be consistent with those used in the following credits:

- MR Credit 3.1: Materials Reuse
- MR Credit 4: Recycled Content
- MR Credit 6: Rapidly Renewable Materials

3. Summary of Referenced Standards

There are no standards referenced for this credit.

4. Implementation

It may require careful research to determine what local products are available, so evaluate this credit early in the design process. This credit is achieved by summing the cost of all materials that are sourced, extracted, and manufactured within 500 miles of the construction site. If the material contains components that were sourced from a place within 500 miles but the final assembly was farther away, the product cannot be counted toward the credit. In cases where products and construction components are assembled on-site, the individual components that are extracted within 500 miles of the site will be counted toward this credit.

The general contractor should work with subcontractors and suppliers to verify availability of materials that are extracted, harvested, or recovered and manufactured locally. The contractor should run preliminary calculations based on the construction budget or schedule of values during the preconstruction phase. This will allow the construction team to focus on those materials with the greatest contribution to this credit as early as possible.

5. Timeline and Team

Run preliminary calculations, as soon as a project budget is available, to set appropriate regional materials targets. Architects should specify in the construction documents products that are extracted, harvested, recovered, and manufactured within 500 miles and work with the general contractor on approved alternatives that meet the requirements of this credit. During construction, the general contractor is typically responsible for documenting the amounts and values of regionally harvested and manufactured materials used on the project. The general contractor must track the materials cost of each locally harvested and manufactured product that will be applied to this credit.

6. Calculations

List products that were extracted, harvested, or recovered and manufactured within 500 miles of the project site. Indicate the manufacturer, the product cost, the distance between the project site and the manufacturer, and the distance between the project site and the extraction site for each raw material contained within each product.

Materials costs include all expenses to deliver the materials to the project site. Materials costs should account for all taxes and transportation costs incurred by the contractor but exclude any cost for labor and equipment once the material has been delivered to the site.

Calculate the percentage of local materials using Equation 1.

Equation 1

$$\text{Percentage Local Materials} = \frac{\text{Total Cost of Local Materials (\$)}}{\text{Total Materials Cost (\$)}} \times 100$$

No Default Materials Value

The LEED for Commercial Interiors Rating System has no default relationship between the value (in dollars) of materials and total construction costs.

Reused and Salvaged Materials

Reused and salvaged materials that satisfy the requirements of MR Credit 3 may also contribute to MR Credit 5. Use the location from which they were salvaged as the point of extraction, and use the location of the salvaged goods vendor as the point of manufacture.

For materials with more than 1 point of manufacture or extraction, all within the 500-mile radius, list the component with the greatest distance. If a portion of the material was either manufactured or extracted beyond the 500-mile radius, list only that portion and associated cost satisfying the credit requirement.

For assemblies or products manufactured within the 500-mile radius that contain some components extracted farther away, use multiple lines when listing purchases. Base the proportionality of such products' costs on the weight of their various components (see the example for concrete in Tables 1 and 2.)

Table 1. Sample Assembly Percentage Regionally Extracted Calculation for Concrete

Components	Weight (lbs)	Distance between Project & Extraction Site (miles)	Weight Contributing to Regional Extraction (lbs)
Cement	282	1,250	0
Fly Ash	282	125	282
Water	275	1	275
Slag	750	370	750
Recycled Concrete & Aggregate	1,000	8	1,000
Sand	1,200	18	1,200
Component Totals	3,789	NA	3,507
Percent Regionally Extracted Materials (3,507/3,789)			92.6%

Table 2. Sample Spreadsheet for Regional Materials

Product	Manufacturer	Distance Between Project & Manufacturer (miles)	Product Cost ($)	Distance Between Project & Extraction site (miles)	Product Cost ($)	Regional Content Information Source
Concrete (manufactured and extracted)	Omega Mix	5	926	370	926	Letter from supplier
Concrete (just manufactured)	Omega Mix	5	74			
Wood Paneling	Zeta Panels	25	6,000			Contractor submittal
Casework	Chi Casework	20	30,000			Letter from fabricator
Gypsum wall	Nu Gyps	320	9,900	312	9,900	Letter from fabricator
Wood flooring, salvaged	Xi Floors	20	2,640			Cut sheet
Furniture, reused	Pi Works	45	203,700			Letter from prior owner
Component Totals			$274,240		$10,826	
Total Construction Material Value						$341,214
Division 12 Material Value						$598,722
Total Project Material Value						$939,986
Percent Manufactured Regionally (274,240/939,986)						29.2%
				29.2% > 20% MR 5, 1 point earned		
Percent Both Manufactured Regionally & Extracted Regionally (10,826/939,986)						1.2%
				1.1% < 10.0% MR 5, 2nd point not earned		

Exclusions

Do not include mechanical, electrical, and plumbing system components in the calculations for this credit. Compared with structural and finish materials, mechanical and electrical equipment tends to have a high dollar value relative to the amount of material it contain and that high dollar value would skew the results of the calculation.

7. Documentation Guidance

As a first step in preparing to complete the LEED Online documentation requirements, work through the following measures. Refer to LEED Online for the complete descriptions of all required documentation.

- Compile a list of product purchases manufactured, extracted, or harvested regionally.

- Record manufacturers' names, product costs, distances between the project and manufacturer, and distances between the project and the extraction site.

- Retain cutsheets that document product manufacture locality within a 500-mile radius of the project site.

- In addition, for Option 2, prepare cutsheets to document extraction within a 500-mile radius of the project site.

8. Examples

EXAMPLE 1

Figure 2 illustrates an example for a hypothetical slag concrete material that is extracted, processed, and manufactured within 500 miles of a project site.

Figure 2. Extraction and Manufacturing Location of Fly Ash Concrete

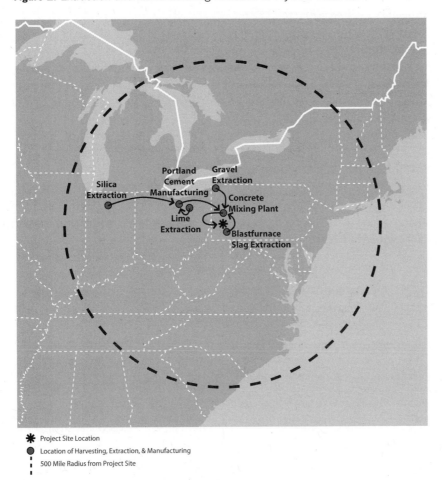

✳ Project Site Location
⬤ Location of Harvesting, Extraction, & Manufacturing
⦙ 500 Mile Radius from Project Site

EXAMPLE 2

Tenant X is evaluating material purchases to meet the requirements of MR Credit 5. Table 3 lists materials and components that comply with this credit.

Table 3. Sample Material for MR Credit 5, Options 1 and 2

Distance of project from point of harvest or extraction	Distance of project from point of manufacture or assembly	Product Included for Option 1?	Product Included for Option 2?
Flooring: Lumber harvested 450 miles	Flooring mill 400 miles	Yes	Yes
I Beams: Steel extraction 1000 miles	Steel mill 300 miles	Yes	No
Concrete: Cement 650 miles Aggregate: 150 miles	Cement plant 600 miles Aggregate and sand 100 miles	No for cement Yes for aggregate and sand	No for cement Yes for aggregate
Drywall: Gypsum factory 200 miles	Drywall supplier 600 miles	No	No

9. Exemplary Performance

Project teams may earn an Innovation in Design credit for exemplary performance by achieving a total value of regionally harvested, extracted, and manufactured materials of 20% or more.

10. Regional Variations

Local availability of materials will vary by region. Regional building materials are often consistent with regional design aesthetics and may be more stable in the local climate than materials from other regions. Consider the local vernacular architecture and adopt a design that incorporates locally produced materials wherever possible. Those project sites near sources for material origin and manufacture will have an advantage in the achievement of this credit.

11. Operations and Maintenance Considerations

The duplication, replacement, and repair of regional materials will be easier if information about the installed products has been maintained. Encourage the creation of a sustainable purchasing plan and provide building operators with lists of the installed products and their manufacturers, such as the documentation used in the LEED application.

12. Resources

Please see USGBC's LEED Resources & Tools (http://www.usgbc.org/projecttools) for additional resources and technical information.

Government Resources

Check with the local chamber of commerce and regional and state economic development agencies for building materials manufacturers in the region.

13. Definitions

An **assembly** can be either a product formulated from multiple materials (e.g., concrete) or a product made up of subcomponents (e.g., a workstation).

Extraction, harvest or recovery point refers to the location of raw materials prior to manufacturing of the building material or product that is furnished and installed in the project building.

Regionally extracted materials are raw materials taken from within a 500-mile radius of the project site.

Regionally manufactured materials are assembled as finished products within a 500-mile radius of the project site. Assembly does not include on-site assembly, erection, or installation of finished components.

RAPIDLY RENEWABLE MATERIALS

	CI
Credit	MR Credit 6
Points	1 point

Intent

To reduce the use and depletion of finite raw materials and long-cycle renewable materials by replacing them with rapidly renewable materials.

Requirements

Use rapidly renewable construction and Division 12 (Furniture and Furnishings) materials and products for 5% of the total value of all materials and products used in the project, based on cost. Rapidly renewable building materials and products are made from plants that are typically harvested within a 10-year or shorter cycle.

1. Benefits and Issues to Consider

Environmental Issues

Many conventional building materials require large inputs of land, natural resources, capital, and time to produce. Conversely, rapidly renewable materials generally require fewer of these inputs and are likely to have fewer environmental impacts. Rapidly renewable resources are replenished faster than traditional materials—they are planted and harvested in a cycle of 10 years or less.

Sourcing rapidly renewable materials reduces the use of raw materials whose extraction and processing have greater environmental impacts. A common example is the use of agricultural fiber such as wheat in composite panels as a substitute for wood products, reducing the overall consumption of wood. Irresponsible forestry practices cause ecosystem and habitat destruction, soil erosion, and stream sedimentation; replacing wood products with rapidly renewable resources reduces a product's overall environmental impact. Because of their intensive production and shorter growing cycles, rapidly renewable crops also require significantly less land to produce the same amount of end product; some are byproducts that are otherwise considered waste. Bio-based plastics (e.g., from corn starch) and other rapidly renewable resources are beginning to provide alternatives to some petroleum-based plastics.

Many products made from rapidly renewable materials have interesting visual or tactile qualities. Using these materials in a visually prominent way provides opportunities for learning about manufacturing processes, economics, environmental impacts, and embodied energy.

Economic Issues

Land saved by the use of rapidly renewable materials will be available for a variety of other uses, including open space and food crops. Because rapidly renewable resources can be harvested more quickly, they tend to give faster payback on investment for producers. Although rapidly renewable materials can carry a price premium over their conventional counterparts, as demand increases, they are expected to become cost-competitive with conventional materials.

2. Related Credits

Rapidly renewable materials like cork or bamboo plywood may come from distant sources and may affect achievement of the following credit:

- MR Credit 5: Regional Materials

To reduce the detrimental effects some materials have on indoor air quality, project teams should follow the guidelines of the prerequisites and credits below and specify materials and furnishings that do not release harmful or irritating chemicals, such as volatile organic compounds (VOCs), from paints and solvents.

- MR Credit 3.1: Materials Reuse

- IEQ Credit 4.1: Low-Emitting Materials—Adhesives and Sealants

- IEQ Credit 4.2: Low-Emitting Materials—Paints and Coatings

- IEQ Credit 4.3: Low-Emitting Materials—Flooring Systems

- IEQ Credit 4.4: Low-Emitting Materials—Composite Wood and Agrifiber Products

- IEQ Credit 4.5: Low-Emitting Materials—Systems Furniture and Seating

The project materials costs used in this credit need to be consistent with those used in the following credits:

- MR Credit 4: Recycled Content

- MR Credit 5: Regional Materials

Reused furniture that qualifies for MR Credit 3.2, Materials Reuse—Furniture and Furnishings, and building materials qualifying for MR Credit 3.1—Materials Reuse should be excluded from the credit calculations (numerator and denominator) for this credit.

3. Summary of Referenced Standards

There are no standards referenced for this credit.

4. Implementation

Establish a goal for the use of rapidly renewable materials early in the design phase, identify possible building materials that may be substituted with rapidly renewable products, and find vendors that can achieve this goal. Table 1 provides examples of common rapidly renewable materials, and Figure 1 illustrates the typical harvest rate of sample materials. Identify products and vendors in the project specifications and plans, and work with the general contractor to source acceptable alternatives. During construction, make sure that the specified rapidly renewable materials are installed.

Examples of rapidly renewable materials include bamboo flooring and plywood, cotton batt insulation, linoleum flooring, sunflower seed board panels, wheatboard cabinetry, wool carpeting, cork flooring, bio-based paints, geotextile fabrics such as coir and jute, soy-based insulation and form-release agent, and straw bales.

Figure 1. Harvest Rates of Sample Materials

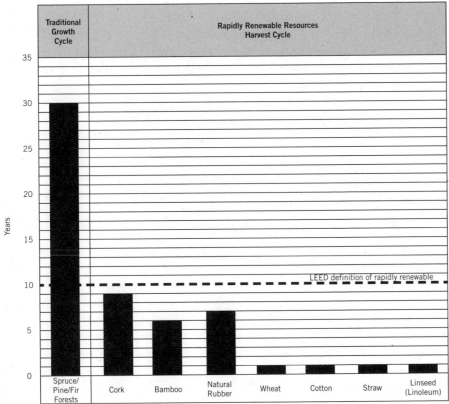

5. Timeline and Team

Run preliminary calculations during the early design phase, as soon as a project budget is available, to determine the feasibility of achieving this credit and identify the quantity of material (by cost) that must be purchased to meet the 5% threshold (refer to the Examples and Calculations sections). Research the availability and cost of rapidly renewable materials. The architect should specify these materials. During construction, the general contractor should ensure that the specified rapidly renewable materials are properly installed and collect product documentation from manufacturers to give to the project team.

6. Calculations

Identify those products and materials that are considered rapidly renewable and sum the cost. Materials costs include all expenses to deliver the material to the project site. Materials costs should account for all taxes and transportation costs incurred by the contractor but exclude any cost for labor and equipment once the material has been delivered to the site. Do not include reused furniture that qualifies for MR Credit 3.

Divide that sum by the total project material value (in dollars), as shown in Equation 1.

Equation 1

$$\text{Percent of Rapidly Renewable Materials} = \frac{\text{Total Cost of Rapidly Renewable Material (\$)}}{\text{Total Materials Cost (\$)}} \times 100$$

Assembly Rapidly Renewable Content

Assemblies are products made of multiple materials, either in their formulation (e.g., particle board) or in their manufacture (e.g., workstation components). The determination of the rapidly renewable content of an assembly should not be confused with the calculation shown in Equation 1, where the final value is expressed in dollars. For assembly rapidly renewable content, determine the fraction of the assembly that is considered rapidly renewable, by weight. Table 1 illustrates a manufacturer's workstation product lines for a Business and Institutional Furniture Manufacturer's Association (BIFMA) International typical workstation configuration.

Table 1. Sample Assembly Rapidly Renewable Content for BIFMA Typical Configuration

Manufacturer		Lambda Furniture	
Product Line		High End Workstations	
BIFMA Typical Configuration		Workstation Configuration 0010	
Component	Weight (lbs)	Percent Rapidly Renewable	Weight Contributing to Rapidly Renewable Content (lbs)
Wheat Board	28.0	100%	28.0
Top Veneer, Bamboo	4.0	75%	3.0
Other	721.0	0%	0.0
Totals	753.0		31.0
Percent Rapidly Renewable (31.0/753.0)			4.1%

For subcomponents, determine the percentage by using the weights of the component elements. No consideration is given to relative costs of the subcomponents. In the example in Table 2, the top veneer is 75% bamboo by weight, and thus 75% of 3 pounds counts toward the rapidly renewable content.

Systems Furniture

In LEED for Commercial Interiors, those materials listed in Construction Specification Institute (CSI) MasterFormat™ 2004 Division 12 (Furnishings) must be included in the calculation of MR Credit 6. This CSI category includes systems furniture. A team may use the percentages of rapidly renewable content determined by the product manufacturer for the typical workstation configuration that best represents the project installation. This approach also may be used in calculating MR Credits 4 and 7.

BIFMA International has defined typical workstation configurations for both open plans and private offices, available at http://www.bifma.org. Using these typical configurations, manufacturers have determined the rapidly renewable content percentages for their individual product lines. Table 1 shows an example of a manufacturer's calculation. Project teams should have this documentation from the manufacturer available for reference during the certification review process.

Project teams, most likely in conjunction with their furniture supplier, will need to separate their total new furniture costs to correspond to the industry-typical configurations for each manufacturer and product line. These segmented values are then multiplied by the manufacturer's rapidly renewable content percentages for the credit calculation. See Table 2.

Table 2. Sample Spreadsheet for Rapidly Renewable Materials

Product Name	Company	Product ($)	% Renewable	Renewable Value ($)	Rapidly renewable content information source
Countertops - wheatboard	Rho Tops	6,700	30.0%	2,010	Letter
Casework	Sigma Mills	30,000	50.0%	15,000	Letter
Linoleum flooring	Tau Floors	882	60.0%	529	Cut sheet
Bamboo window blinds	Upsilon Shades	14,079	75.0%	10,559	Product Literature
Systems Furniture, new	Lambda Cubicles	228,366	4.1%	9,363	Manufacturer's typical
Tables, new	Mu Mills	19,751	88.4%	17,460	Manufacturer's detail
Rapidly Renewable Materials Subtotal				$54,921	
Total Construction Material Value					$341,214
Division 12 Material Value					$598,772
Total Project Material Value					$939,986
Percent Rapidly Renewable Value (54,921/939,986)					5.8%
				5.8% > 5.0% MR 6 earned	

This approach was developed so that project teams would not have to build the credit values starting from individual workstation component counts, costs, and rapidly renewable content percentages. However, if a project team has purchased components that have rapidly renewable contents outside a 5% range of those used in the manufacturer's published percentages for the typical configurations, project-specific detail will be required. This may occur when certain green materials have been specified. In this case, request that the manufacturer prepare an assembly rapidly renewable content calculation for the actual products purchased.

Other products, such as seating, storage units, and conference tables, are not included in typical configurations. For some of these items, there are consistent attributes across a product line; the percentage of rapidly renewable content of a 36-inch-diameter table will be the same as that in a 72-inch-diameter table. When this is the case, identify the dollar amount for all products used on the project within the product line and multiply by the rapidly renewable percentages. Products without consistent attributes must be addressed separately. Table 2 shows examples of both situations.

Exclusions
Do not include mechanical, electrical, and plumbing components in the calculations for this credit. Also exclude reused furniture that qualifies for MR Credit 3.1, Materials Reuse and MR Credit 3.2, Materials Reuse—Furniture and Furnishings.

No Default Materials Value
The LEED for Commercial Interiors Rating System has no default relationship between the value of materials and total construction cost.

7. Documentation Guidance

As a first step in preparing to complete the LEED Online documentation requirements, work through the following measures. Refer to LEED Online for the complete descriptions of all required documentation.

- Compile a list of rapidly renewable product purchases.
- Record manufacturers' names, materials costs, the percentage of each product that is rapidly renewable criteria (by weight), and each compliant value.
- Retain cutsheets that document rapidly renewable criteria.

8. Examples

The total materials costs for the tenant improvement for Fry Industries is $270,000. Table 3 lists rapidly renewable products purchased for this project, the assembly cost, and the percentage of rapidly renewable content as part of assembly components. The total cost of rapidly renewable content equals 12.15% of Fry's total cost of all materials, and the project earns 1 point.

Table 3. Sample Calculations for Rapidly Renewable Material

Provide total materials cost (exclude labor, equipment)					$270,000
Product name	Countertop wheatboard	Bamboo window blinds	Cork panels	Linoleum flooring	Totals
Vendor name	Rho Company	Upsilion shades	Garcias cork	Tau floors	
Assembly product cost	$6,700	$14,079	$22,000	$882	$43,661
Percentage rapidly renewable content (if part of assembly)*	30.00%	75.00%	90.00%	50.00%	
Value of rapidly renewable content	$2,010.00	$10,559.25	$19,800.00	$441.00	$32,810
Rapidly renewable content information source	Vendor	Website	Vendor	Manufacturer letter	
Value of rapidly renewable content					$32,810
Percentage cost of rapidly renewable content total cost of all materials					12.15%
Points documented					1 points
MR Credit 6 (1 point): Combined value of rapidly renewable content≥5%					

9. Exemplary Performance

Project teams may earn an Innovation in Design credit for exemplary performance by achieving a rapidly renewable materials content of 10% or more.

10. Regional Variations

Assess the availability of rapidly renewable materials that also contribute to MR Credit 5, Regional Materials, and select products manufactured from rapidly renewable resources within 500 miles of the project site.

11. Operations and Maintenance Considerations

Some rapidly renewable materials may require different maintenance practices. For example, bamboo and cork generally should not be exposed to excessive moisture from damp mopping and other common janitorial or maintenance activities. When sourcing rapidly renewable products, request maintenance recommendations from the manufacturer and give this information to the operations team.

The duplication, replacement, and repair of rapidly renewable materials will be easier if information about the installed products has been maintained. Encourage the creation of a sustainable purchasing plan and provide building operators with lists of the installed products and their manufacturers, such as the documentation used in the LEED application.

12. Resources

Please see USGBC's LEED Resources & Tools (http://www.usgbc.org/projecttools) for additional resources and technical information.

Websites

BuildingGreen, Inc., Environmental Building News

http://www.buildinggreen.com/products/bamboo.html

Read an article in *Environmental Building News* on bamboo flooring that includes a listing of bamboo flooring suppliers.

Environmental Design + Construction, Highlights of Environmental Flooring

http://www.edcmag.com

Read an *Environmental Design + Construction* article with information on bamboo flooring, linoleum, and wool carpeting.

BuildingGreen, Inc., GreenSpec

http://www.buildinggreen.com/menus/index.cfm

GreenSpec contains detailed listings for more than 2,000 green building products that include environmental data, manufacturer information, and links to additional resources.

Oikos

http://www.oikos.com

Oikos is a searchable directory of efficient building products and sustainable design resources.

13. Definitions

An **assembly** can be either a product formulated from multiple materials (e.g., concrete) or a product made up of subcomponents (e.g., a workstation).

Embodied energy is the energy used during the entire life cycle of a product, including its manufacture, transportation, and disposal, as well as the inherent energy captured within the product itself.

Life cycle assessment is an analysis of the environmental aspects and potential impacts associated with a product, process, or service.

Rapidly renewable materials are agricultural products, both fiber and animal, that take 10 years or less to grow or raise and can be harvested in a sustainable fashion.

CERTIFIED WOOD

	CI
Credit	MR Credit 7
Points	1 point

Intent

To encourage environmentally responsible forest management.

Requirements

When using new wood-based products and materials, use a minimum of 50% that are certified in accordance with the Forest Stewardship Council's principles and criteria. Division 12 (Furniture) material value is included in the determination of the certified wood content.

1. Benefits and Issues to Consider

Environmental Issues

The negative environmental impacts of irresponsible forest practices can include forest destruction, wildlife habitat loss, soil erosion and stream sedimentation, water and air pollution, and waste generation. The Forest Stewardship Council (FSC) standard incorporates many criteria that contribute to the long-term health and integrity of forest ecosystems. From an environmental perspective, the elements of responsible FSC-certified forestry include harvesting timber sustainably (i.e., not removing more timber volume than replaces itself over the cutting interval, or rotation), preserving wildlife habitat and biodiversity, maintaining soil and water quality, minimizing the use of harmful chemicals, and conserving forests of high conservation value (e.g., endangered and old-growth forests).

Economic Issues

As more developing countries enter world forest product markets and their growing economies drive domestic consumption, the protection of forests will become a critical issue. As of 2007, FSC-certified forests represent the equivalent of 7% of the world's productive forests.[11] Currently, the costs of FSC-certified wood products are equal to or higher than conventional wood products, and availability varies by region. The price of FSC-certified wood products is expected to become more competitive with conventional wood products as the world's forest resources are depleted and the forest industry adopts more sustainable business principles.

Because irresponsible logging practices can have harmful social as well as environmental impacts, the socioeconomic and political components of FSC certification include respecting indigenous people's rights and adhering to all applicable laws and treaties. Certification also involves forest workers and forest-dependent communities as stakeholders and beneficiaries of responsible forest management. Responsible forest practices help stabilize economies and preserve forestland for future generations.

2. Related Credits

Project teams pursuing this credit may find opportunities to achieve other MR credits. An FSC strategy should be developed early to determine whether certified wood can be sourced and manufactured within 500 miles of the site. Additionally, when specifying mixed FSC materials and pursuing IEQ Credit 4.4, determine whether the finished product will be free of urea-formaldehyde. Refer to the following credits:

- MR Credit 5: Regional Materials

- IEQ Credit 4.4: Low-Emitting Materials—Composite Wood and Agrifiber Products

3. Summary of Referenced Standard

Forest Stewardship Council's Principles and Criteria

http://www.fscus.org

Certification by the Forest Stewardship Council (FSC) is a seal of approval awarded to forest managers who adopt environmentally and socially responsible forest management practices, and to companies that manufacture and sell products made from certified wood. This seal enables consumers, including architects and specifiers, to identify and procure wood products from well-managed sources and thereby use their purchasing power to influence and reward improved forest management activities around the world.

LEED accepts certification according to the comprehensive system established by the internationally recognized Forest Stewardship Council. FSC was created in 1993 to establish international forest management standards, known as the FSC principles and criteria, to ensure that forestry practices are environmentally responsible, socially beneficial, and economically viable. These principles and criteria are also intended to ensure the long-term health and productivity of forests for timber production, wildlife habitat, clean air and water supplies, climate stabilization, spiritual renewal, and social benefit, such as lasting community employment derived from stable forestry operations. These global principles and criteria are translated into meaningful standards at a local level through region-specific standard-setting processes.

FSC also accredits and monitors certification organizations. The certifiers are independent, third-party auditors that are qualified to annually evaluate compliance with FSC standards on the ground and to award certifications. There are 2 types of certification:

- Forest management certification is awarded to responsible forest managers after their operations successfully complete audits of forestry practices and plans.

- Chain-of-custody (COC) certification is awarded to companies that process, manufacture, and/or sell products made of certified wood and who successfully complete audits to ensure proper use of the FSC name and logo, segregation of certified and noncertified materials in manufacturing and distribution systems, and observation of other relevant FSC rules (e.g., meeting minimum requirements for FSC fiber content in assembled and composite wood products).

The majority of FSC certification audits performed in North America are conducted by SmartWood and Scientific Certification Systems (SCS), which are based in the United States. A limited number are performed by SGS, which is based in Europe.

4. Implementation

Establish a project goal for FSC-certified wood products and identify suppliers that can achieve this goal. Research the availability of the wood species and products that they want to use, and make sure that they are available from FSC-certified sources. Another method for lowering the impact of wood resources is to research and specify quality grades that are most readily available from well-managed forests. Using lower grades of wood (e.g., Architectural Woodwork Institute Grades 2 or 3 for lumber or veneer rather than Grade 1) can dramatically reduce pressure on forests, which produce only limited quantities of top-grade timber.

Contact local vendors, suppliers, and manufacturers that provide FSC-certified products as early as possible in the design phase. Design teams should provide project bidders with a list of certified vendors and encourage them to make contact early in the project to establish product availability and pricing. Consult the Resources section for information about product databases and boilerplate forms. Since the availability of certain certified wood products may vary over the life of a project, teams should consider having the owner prepurchase, store, and supply particular items to the contractor ("furnished by the owner, installed by the contractor," or FOIC). Finding a storage location that matches the final ambient moisture of the space will ensure proper installation. Because ambient moisture is usually higher during construction, a job site is not the best location to store wood.

The design team should specify in contract documents that wood products must come from forests that are certified as well-managed according to the rules of the FSC, and the team should require chain-of-custody documentation. Wherever possible, use a line-item strategy based on the current availability of specific products rather than a blanket approach.

Figure 1 is based on information from FSC's website at http://www.fsc.org/ and outlines the FSC process when chain-of-custody documentation is required, and what types of information a project should collect.

Figure 1. FSC Certification Process and FSC Certification Categories

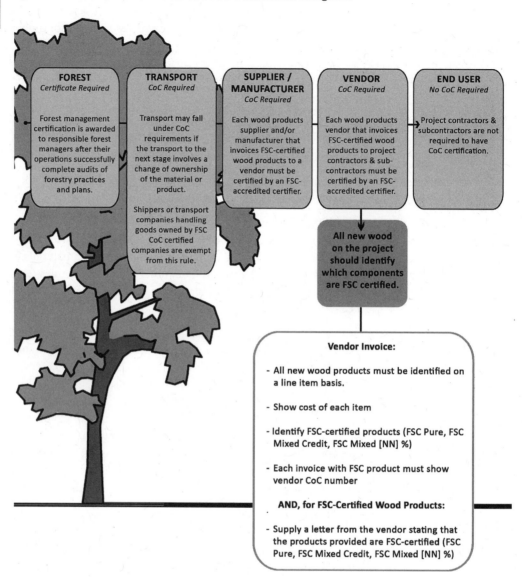

Chain-of-Custody Requirements

Collect all vendor invoices for permanently installed wood products, FSC certified or not, purchased by the project contractor and subcontractors. Vendors are defined as those companies that sell products to the project contractor or subcontractors. Entities that install an FSC-certified product on the project building/site (typically project contractors or subcontractors, but also furniture installers and the like), do not require COC certification as long as they do not modify the product's packaging or form except as is required for installation. Contractors and sub-contractors that temporarily possess FSC-certified material prior to installation should be careful not mix or contaminate the FSC-certified material with non-FSC-certified material.

Each vendor invoice must conform to the following requirements (except as noted below):

    a. Each wood product must be identified on a line-item basis.

    b. FSC products must be identified as such on a line-item basis.

    c. The dollar value of each line item must be shown.

d. The vendor's COC certificate number must be shown on any invoice that includes FSC products.

Each wood products vendor that invoices FSC-certified products must be COC certified by an FSC-accredited certifier.

Exceptions: In some rare instances, it may not be practical for a vendor to invoice wood products on a line-item basis because the invoice would be dozens of pages long. In such cases, the invoice should indicate the aggregate value of wood products sold by the vendor. If the wood products are FSC certified, comply with the following requirements:

a. The vendor's COC number must be shown on the invoice.

b. The invoice must be supplemented by a letter from the vendor stating that the products invoiced are FSC certified.

c. The invoice or the letter must state whether the products are FSC Pure, FSC Mixed Credit, or FSC Mixed (NN)%.

5. Timeline and Team

Consider the FSC-certified wood content of construction materials, furniture, and furnishings in the selection and purchasing process. During the design phase, the architect should incorporate certified wood products into the project plans and specifications. During construction, the contractor should review the project cost to verify that 50% of wood costs are FSC-certified. As materials are purchased during construction, the general contractor must obtain and retain COC certificates. At the end of construction, the general contractor should provide the documentation needed for the LEED certification application.

6. Calculations

List all new wood products (not reclaimed, salvaged, or recycled) on the project and identify which components are FSC certified. The cost of all new wood products, both FSC certified and not, must be tallied. Develop a spreadsheet to calculate the amount of new wood and the amount of FSC certified wood permanently installed on the project. Wood products that are not FSC certified and those that are identified on invoices as FSC Pure and FSC Mixed Credit should be valued at 100% of the product cost unless the product is an assembly in which case only the new wood portion of the product counts for credit, see the guidance for assemblies in this credit. Wood products identified as FSC Mixed (NN)% should be valued at the indicated percentage of their cost. For example, a product identified as FSC Mixed 75% should be valued at 75% of the cost. Entities that install an FSC-certified product on the project building/site (typically project contractors or subcontractors, but also furniture installers and the like), do not require COC certification as long as they do not modify the product's packaging or form except as is required for installation. Contractors and sub-contractors that temporarily possess FSC-certified material prior to installation should be careful not mix or contaminate the FSC-certified material with non-FSC-certified material.

Wood products identified as FSC Recycled or FSC Recycled Credit do not count toward MR Credit 7, Certified Wood. They qualify instead as recycled-content products that may contribute to MR Credit 4, Recycled Content.

Using Equation 1, determine the percentage of FSC-certified wood.

Equation 1

$$\text{Certified Wood Material Percentage} = \frac{\text{FSC-certified Wood Material Value (\$)}}{\text{Total New Wood Material Value (\$)}} \times 100$$

Table 1. Sample Assembly Percentage Wood-Based Content for BIFMA Typical Configuration.

Manufacturer		Lambda Furniture		
Product Line		High End Workstations		
BIFMA Typical Configuration		Workstation Configuration 0010		
Component	Weight (lbs)	Less Postconsumer Weight (lbs)	Wood-based Component Weight (lbs)	FSC Certified Wood Weight (lbs)
Wheat Board	28.0		28.0	28.0
Top Veneer	4.0		4.0	0.0
Other Wood	3.0	-1.1	1.9	1.5
Non-wood content	718.0		0.0	0.0
Totals	753.0		33.9	29.5
Percent Wood (33.9/753.0)				4.5%
Percent FSC Certified Wood (29.5/753.0)				3.9%

Assemblies

In the case of manufactured products, such as windows and some furniture systems that combine wood and nonwood materials, only the new wood portion can be applied toward the credit. To determine the value of the wood component(s), calculate the amount of new wood as a percentage of the total weight or volume and the amount of FSCcertified wood as a percentage of the total weight or volume. Multiply these figures by the total value of the product as invoiced to project contractors, subcontractors, or buying agents.

Develop a separate spreadsheet for each assembly to calculate the amount of new wood and amount of FSC-certified wood for assemblies and enter the summary data as a line item on the comprehensive spreadsheet used to calculate the percentage of certified wood used in the project.

To incorporate assembly FSC-certified and new wood content into Equation 1, use Equations 2 and 3 and add the resulting value to the appropriate category:

Equation 2

$$\text{Assembly FSC Certified Wood Material Value} = \frac{\text{Weight of FSC-certified Wood in Assembly}}{\text{Weight of Assembly}} \times \text{Assembly Value (\$)}$$

Equation 3

$$\text{Assembly New Wood Material Value} = \frac{\text{Weight of New Wood in Assembly}}{\text{Weight of Assembly}} \times \text{Assembly Value (\$)}$$

Furniture and Furnishings

Include the wood content of newly purchased furniture and furnishings in this calculation. Furniture and furnishings are not limited to what is supplied by the contractor; owner purchases must also be included.

Systems Furniture

Use the percentages of wood content and FSC-certified wood content determined by the product manufacturer for the typical workstation configuration that best represents the project installation.

For use in this credit, BIFMA International has defined typical workstation configurations for both open plan and private offices; they are available at http://www.bifma.org. Using these typical configurations, manufacturers have determined the wood content and the FSC-certified wood content percentages for their individual product lines. Table 1 is an example of a manufacturer's calculation.

Project teams, most likely in conjunction with their furniture supplier, will need to segregate their total new furniture costs to correspond to the industry-typical configurations for each manufacturer and product line. These segmented values are then multiplied by the manufacturer's wood content and FSC-certified wood content percentages for the credit calculation. See Table 2.

Table 2. MR Credit 7 Percentage Certified Wood Example

Wood Product	Vendor	Materal Value ($)	Percent Wood (by weight)	Value of Wood ($)	Percent Certified Wood (by weight)	Value of Certified Wood ($)	Forest Stewardship Council chain-of-custody certificate number
Carpentry	Phi Woods	19,800	92.1%	18,240	92.1%	18,240	SW-COC-013
Door bucks	Chi Bucks	720	100%	720	46.0%	331	SCS-COC-00067
Moldings	Psi Trim	1,710	100%	1,710	100.0%	1,710	SCS-COC-00094
Selving	Psi Trim	2,407	77%	1,753	0.0%	0	n/a
Countertops	Beta Mills	6,347	95%	6,030	0.0%	0	n/a
Casework	Beta Mills	34,875	80%	27,900	58.50%	20,402	SW-COC-675
Wood doors and frames	Beta Mills	383	100%	383	100.0%	383	SCS-COC-00122
Furniture systems, new	Lambda Cubicles	288,366	4.5%	12,976	3.9%	11,297	Manufacturer's detail
Tables, new	Mu Mills	19,751	93.0%	18,974	11.0%	2,173	Manufacturer's detail
Subtotal				$88,786		$54,536	
% Certified Wood (54,536/88,786)							61.4%
						61.4% > 50.0% MR 7 earned	

This approach was developed so that project teams would not have to build the credit values starting from individual workstation component counts, costs, and wood content percentages. However, when a project team has purchased components that have certified-wood content outside a 5% range of that used in the manufacturer's published percentages for the typical configurations, project-specific detail will be required. This may occur when FSC-certified materials have been specified. In this case, request that the manufacturer prepare an assembly content calculation, similar to Table 1, for the actual products purchased.

Other products, such as seating, storage units, and conference tables, are not included in the typical configurations. For some of these items, there are consistent attributes across a product line: the percentage of wood content and FSC-certified wood content of a 36-inch-diameter table will be the same as that in a 72-inch-diameter table. When this is the case, identify the dollar amount for all those products used on the project within the product line and multiply by the wood content and FSC-certified wood content percentages. When this is not the case, individual products must be addressed separately.

7. Documentation Guidance

As a first step in preparing to complete the LEED Online documentation requirements, work through the following measures. Refer to LEED Online for the complete descriptions of all required documentation.

- Prepare the CSI MasterFormat™ 2004 Divisions 3–10 cost to determine the net construction materials cost.

- Prepare the CSI MasterFormat™ 2004 Division 12 (Furniture and Furnishings) cost to determine the net construction materials cost.

- Track certified wood purchases and retain associated COC documentation.

- Collect copies of vendor invoices for each certified wood product.

- Maintain a list that identifies the percentage of certified wood in each purchase.

8. Examples

See Table 1 for a sample calculation of wood-based content for a BIFMA typical configuration.

9. Exemplary Performance

Project teams may earn an Innovation in Design credit for exemplary performance by achieving an FSC-certified wood content of 95% or more of the project's total new wood.

10. Regional Variations

This credit may have particular importance in areas with poor forestry practices or high forest conversion rates. Encouraging the development of local FSC markets and assigning economic value to responsible forestry practices will promote the retention of local, indigenous animal and plant species, the preservation of open space, the improvement of local air quality, and the reduction of heat-island effects for areas of developed infrastructure.

11. Operations and Maintenance Considerations

The duplication, replacement, and repair of certified wood products will be easier if information about the installed products has been maintained. Encourage the creation of a sustainable purchasing plan and provide building operators with lists of the installed products, their manufacturers, and COC certificates, such as the documentation used in the LEED application.

12. Resources

Please see USGBC's LEED Resources & Tools (http://www.usgbc.org/projecttools) for additional resources and other technical information.

Websites

Forest Stewardship Council, United States
http://www.fscus.org/green_building
For information and practical tools such as databases of certified product suppliers, referral service, specification language, and the Designing & Building with FSC guide and forms.

Print Media

Sustainable Forestry: Philosophy, Science, and Economics, by Chris Maser (DelRay Beach, St. Lucie Press, 1994).

The Business of Sustainable Forestry: Strategies for an Industry in Transition, by Michael B. Jenkins and Emily T. Smith (Island Press, 1999).

Governing through Markets: Forest Certification and the Emergence of Non-State Authority, by Deanna Newsom, Benjamin Cashore, and Graeme Auld (Yale University Press, 2004).

Tapping the Green Market: Certification and Management of Non-Timber Forest Products, edited by Patricia Shanley, Alan R. Pierce, Sarah A. Laird, and Abraham Guillén (Earthscan Publications, 2002).

13. Definitions

Chain-of-custody (COC) is a tracking procedure for a product from the point of harvest or extraction to its end use, including all successive stages of processing, transformation, manufacturing, and distribution.

Chain-of-custody certification is awarded to companies that produce, sell, promote, or trade forest products after audits verify proper accounting of material flows and proper use of the Forest Stewardship Council name and logo. The COC certificate number is listed on invoices for nonlabeled products to document that an entity has followed FSC guidelines for product accounting.

Sustainable forestry is the practice of managing forest resources to meet the long-term forest product needs of humans while maintaining the biodiversity of forested landscapes. The primary goal is to restore, enhance, and sustain a full range of forest values, including economic, social, and ecological considerations.

A **vendor** of certified wood is the company that supplies wood products to contractors or subcontractors for on-site installation. A vendor needs a chain-of-custody number if it is selling FSC-certified products that are not individually labeled; this includes most lumber.

Endnotes

[1] U.S. Environmental Protection Agency, Office of Solid Waste. *Municipal Solid Waste Generation, Recycling, and Disposal in the United States: Facts and Figures for 2005.* 2006. http://www.epa.gov/osw/rcc/resources/msw-2005.pdf (accessed May 2008).

[2] U.S. Environmental Protection Agency, Office of Solid Waste. *Municipal Solid Waste Generation, Recycling, and Disposal in the United States: Facts and Figures for 2005.* 2006. http://www.epa.gov/osw/rcc/resources/msw-2005.pdf (accessed November 2008).

[3] U.S. Environmental Protection Agency, Office of Solid Waste. *Municipal Solid Waste: 2007 Facts and Figures.* 2008. http://www.epa.gov/osw/nonhaz/municipal/pubs/msw07-rpt.pdf (accessed November 2008).

[4] Ibid.

[5] Oberlin College Recycling Program. "Recycling Facts." http://www.oberlin.edu/recycle/facts.html (accessed November 2008).

[6] The Aluminum Association. "Aluminum Industry Vision." http://www1.eere.energy.gov/industry/aluminum/pdfs/alum_vision.pdf (accessed November 2008).

[7] Contractor's Report to the Board: Statewide Waste Characterization Study, December 2004. http://www.ciwmb.ca.gov/Publications/LocalAsst/34004005.pdf (accessed December 2008)

[8] U.S Environmental Protection Agency, Office of Solid Waste. *Characterization of Building-Related Construction and Demolition Debris in the United States.* http://www.epa.gov/epawaste/hazard/generation/sqg/c&d-rpt.pdf (accessed January 2009).

[9] Department of Natural Resources, Northeast Region. "Building Green at DNR — Northeast Region Headquarters Construction Waste & Recycling." http://dnr.wi.gov/org/land/facilities/greenbldg/gbhqwaste.html (accessed November 2008).

10 County of San Mateo, California. *San Mateo Countywide Guide Sustainable Buildings.* 2004. http://www.recycleworks.org/pdf/GB-guide-2-23.pdf (accessed November 2008).

11 Forest Stewardship Council. "FSC: Facts & Figures." http://www.fsc.org/facts-figures.html (accessed November 2008).

Overview

Americans spend an average of 90% of their time indoors, and the quality of the indoor environment therefore has a significant influence on their well-being, productivity, and quality of life. The U.S. Environmental Protection Agency (the EPA) reports that pollutant levels of indoor environments may run 2 to 5 times—and occasionally more than 100 times—higher than outdoor levels.[1] Correspondingly, the World Health Organization (WHO) reported in its "Air Quality Guidelines for Europe, 2nd edition," that most of an individual's exposure to air pollutants comes through inhalation of indoor air. Following the release in 1987[2] and in 1990[3] of the EPA reports that designated indoor air pollution as a top environmental risk to public health, assessing and managing indoor pollutants have become the focus of integrated governmental and private efforts. Recent increases in building-related illnesses and "sick building syndrome," as well as increasing numbers of related legal cases, have further heightened awareness of indoor air quality (IAQ) among building owners and occupants.[4] Strategies to improve indoor environmental quality have the potential to reduce liability for building owners, increase the resale value of the building, and improve the health of building occupants.

In addition to health and liability concerns, productivity gains also drive indoor environmental quality improvements. With employees' salaries a significant cost in any commercial building, it makes good business sense to keep staff healthy and productive by improving and maintaining the quality of the indoor environment. The potential annual savings and productivity gains from improved indoor environmental quality in the United States are estimated at $6 billion to $14 billion from reduced respiratory disease, $1 billion to $4 billion from reduced allergies and asthma, $10 billion to $30 billion from reduced sick building syndrome symptoms, and $20 billion to $160 billion from direct improvements in worker performance that are unrelated to health.[5]

Over the past 20 years, research and experience have improved our understanding of what is involved in attaining high indoor environmental quality and revealed manufacturing and construction practices that can prevent many indoor environmental quality problems. The use of better products and practices has reduced potential liability for design team members and building owners, increased market value for buildings with exemplary indoor environmental quality, and resulted in greater productivity for building occupants. In a case study included in the 1994 publication, "Greening the Building and the Bottom Line," the Rocky Mountain Institute highlighted how improved indoor environmental quality increased worker productivity by 16%, netting a rapid payback on the capital investment.[6]

This credit category addresses environmental concerns relating to indoor environmental quality; occupants' health, safety, and comfort; energy consumption; air change effectiveness; and air contaminant management. The following are important strategies for addressing these concerns and improving indoor environmental quality:

Improving Ventilation

Actions that affect employee attendance and productivity will affect an organization's operating bottom line. One study estimates a 283% return on investment associated with increased ventilation in less than 6 months.[7]

Specify building systems that will provide a high level of indoor air quality. Increased ventilation in buildings may require additional energy use, but the need for additional energy can be mitigated by using heat-recovery ventilation and/or economizing strategies. Indoor air quality design can help take advantage of regional climate characteristics and reduce energy costs. In regions with significant heating and/or cooling loads, for example, using exhaust air to heat or cool the incoming air can significantly reduce energy use and operating costs.

Managing Air Contaminants

Protecting indoor environments from contaminants is essential for maintaining a healthy space for building occupants. Several indoor air contaminants should be reduced to optimize tenants' comfort and health. There are 3 basic contaminants:

Environmental tobacco smoke (ETS), or secondhand smoke, is both the smoke given off by ignited tobacco products and the smoke exhaled by smokers. Environmental tobacco smoke contains thousands of chemicals, more than 50 of which are carcinogenic.[8] Exposure to environmental tobacco smoke is linked to an increased risk of lung cancer and heart disease in nonsmoking adults[9] and associated with increased risk of sudden infant death syndrome and asthma, bronchitis, and pneumonia in children.[10] Smoking should be eliminated in all indoor spaces and limited to designated outdoor areas.

Carbon dioxide (CO_2) concentrations can be measured to determine and maintain adequate outdoor air ventilation rates in buildings. CO_2 concentrations are an indicator of air change effectiveness, where elevated levels indicate inadequate ventilation and possible buildup of indoor air pollutants. CO_2 levels should be measured to validate indications that ventilation rates need to be adjusted. Although relatively high concentrations of CO_2 alone are not known to cause serious health problems, they can lead to drowsiness and lethargy in building occupants.[11]

Particulate matter in the air degrades the indoor environment. Airborne particles in indoor environments include lint, dirt, carpet fibers, dust, dust mites, mold, bacteria, pollen, and animal dander. These particles can exacerbate respiratory problems such as allergies, asthma, emphysema, and chronic lung disease.[12] Air filtration reduces the exposure of building occupants to these airborne contaminants, and high-efficiency filters greatly improve indoor air quality. Protecting air handling systems during construction and flushing the building before occupancy further reduce the potential for problems to arise once the building is occupied.

Specifying Less Harmful Materials

Preventing indoor environmental quality problems is generally more effective and less expensive than identifying and solving them after they occur. One practical way to prevent indoor environmental quality problems is to specify materials that release fewer and less harmful chemical compounds. Adhesives, paints, carpets, composite wood products, and furniture with low levels of potentially irritating off-gassing can reduce occupant exposure and harm. Appropriate scheduling of deliveries and sequencing of construction activities can reduce material exposure to moisture and absorption of off-gassed contaminants.

Allowing Occupants to Control Desired Settings

Working with building occupants to assess their needs will help improve building efficiencies. Providing individual lighting controls and area thermostats can improve occupants' comfort and productivity and save energy. Individual controls enable occupants to set light levels appropriate to tasks, time of day, personal preferences, and individual variations in visual acuity. Individual thermostats enable them to more accurately meet their heating and cooling needs during different seasons.

Providing Daylighting and Views

Daylighting reduces the need for electric lighting, which lowers energy use and thereby decreases the environmental effects of energy production and consumption. Natural daylight also improves occupants' productivity and reduces absenteeism and illness. Courtyards, atria, clerestory windows, skylights, interior light shelves, exterior fins, louvers, and adjustable blinds, used alone or in combination, are effective strategies to achieve deep daylight penetration. The desired amount of daylight depends on the tasks in a given space. Daylit buildings often have several daylight zones with differing target light levels. In addition to light levels, daylighting strategies address interior color schemes, direct beam penetration, and integration with the electric lighting system.

Building occupants with access to outside views have an increased sense of well-being, leading to higher productivity and increased job satisfaction. Important considerations for providing views include building orientation, window size and spacing, glass selection, and locations of interior walls.

Summary

Ensuring excellent indoor environmental quality requires the joint efforts of the building owner, design team, contractors, subcontractors, and suppliers. To provide optimal indoor environmental quality, automatic sensors and individual controls can be integrated with the building systems to adjust temperature, humidity, and ventilation. Sensors can measure building CO_2 levels and indicate the need for increased outdoor airflow to eliminate high levels of volatile organic compounds (VOCs) and other air contaminants. Other indoor environmental quality issues addressed by the LEED for Commercial Interiors Rating System include daylighting and lighting quality, thermal comfort, acoustics, and access to views. All of these issues have the potential to enhance the indoor environment and optimize interior spaces for building occupants.

CREDIT	TITLE
IEQ Prerequisite 1	Minimum Indoor Air Quality Performance
IEQ Prerequisite 2	Environmental Tobacco Smoke (ETS) Control
IEQ Credit 1	Outdoor Air Delivery Monitoring
IEQ Credit 2	Increased Ventilation
IEQ Credit 3.1	Construction Indoor Air Quality Management Plan—During Construction
IEQ Credit 3.2	Construction Indoor Air Quality Management Plan—Before Occupancy
IEQ Credit 4.1	Low-Emitting Materials—Adhesives and Sealants
IEQ Credit 4.2	Low-Emitting Materials—Paints and Coatings
IEQ Credit 4.3	Low-Emitting Materials—Flooring Systems
IEQ Credit 4.4	Low-Emitting Materials—Composite Wood and Agrifiber Products
IEQ Credit 4.5	Low-Emitting Materials—Systems Furniture and Seating
IEQ Credit 5	Indoor Chemical and Pollutant Source Control
IEQ Credit 6.1	Controllability of Systems—Lighting
IEQ Credit 6.2	Controllability of Systems—Thermal Comfort
IEQ Credit 7.1	Thermal Comfort—Design
IEQ Credit 7.2	Thermal Comfort—Verification
IEQ Credit 8.1	Daylight and Views—Daylight
IEQ Credit 8.2	Daylight and Views—Views for Seated Spaces

MINIMUM INDOOR AIR QUALITY PERFORMANCE

	CI
Prerequisite	IEQ Prerequisite 1
Points	Required

Intent

To establish minimum indoor air quality (IAQ) performance to enhance indoor air quality in buildings, thus contributing to the comfort and well-being of the occupants.

Requirements

Meet the minimum requirements of Section 4 through 7 of ASHRAE Standard 62.1-2007, Ventilation for Acceptable Indoor Air Quality (with errata but without addenda[1]).

AND

CASE 1. Mechanically Ventilated Spaces

Mechanical ventilation systems must perform according to the ventilation rate procedure.

Modify or maintain existing building outside-air ventilation distribution system to supply at least the outdoor air ventilation rate required by ASHRAE Standard 62.1-2007 (with errata but without addenda[1]).

If the project team cannot meet the outside air requirements of ASHRAE Standard 62.1-2007 (with errata but without addenda[1]) document the space and system constraints that make it not possible, complete an engineering assessment of the system's maximum cubic feet per minute (cfm) capability toward meeting the requirements of ASHRAE Standard 62.1-2007 (with errata but without addenda[1]), and achieve those levels, with a minimum of 10 cfm per person. All other requirements must be met.

CASE 2. Naturally Ventilated Projects

Naturally ventilated buildings must comply with ASHRAE Standard 62.1-2007 Section 5.1 (with errata but without addenda[1]).

---

1   Project teams wishing to use ASHRAE approved addenda for the purposes of this prerequisite may do so at their discretion. Addenda must be applied consistently across all LEED credits

1. Benefits and Issues to Consider

Minimum indoor air quality (IAQ) performance in buildings improves occupant comfort, well-being, and productivity compared with buildings with poor IAQ performance. Key strategies for maintaining minimum IAQ include limiting potential indoor contaminant sources, limiting the introduction of contaminants from potential outdoor sources, and—most importantly—determining and maintaining at least the minimum zone outdoor airflow and the minimum outdoor air intake flow required by the ventilation rate procedure of Standard 62.1–2007.

Environmental Issues

Providing minimum IAQ performance improves IAQ generally. Doing so can require higher energy use to operate compliant HVAC systems compared with systems that do not meet the ventilation guidelines of ASHRAE 62.1–2007. Compared with personnel costs, any premium associated with ensuring IAQ is insignificant. Poor IAQ can cause illness, and the additional energy cost of ensuring IAQ may be offset by improved occupant productivity and lower absentee rates. The USGBC website (http://www.usgbc.org) provides links to recent studies on this issue.

Economic Issues

Because ASHRAE 62.1–2007 is the required standard for ventilation design for many areas, no additional design effort or cost will be incurred to meet this prerequisite in general. If there are added energy costs related to increasing ventilation because of a remodel, strategies to mitigate these costs include energy recovery ventilation, economizers and controls, CO_2 monitors, and demand-controlled ventilation. The successful implementation of ASHRAE 62.1–2007 reduces potential liability regarding IAQ issues for architects, builders, owners, building operators, and occupants.[13]

2. Related Credits

Providing minimum IAQ performance can solve some IAQ problems by diluting contaminant concentration, but this strategy may affect indoor thermal comfort and increase energy use. The building commissioning and measurement and verification processes are tools that can improve IAQ while minimizing energy efficiency losses, as described in the following:

- EA Prerequisite 1: Fundamental Commissioning of Building Energy Systems
- EA Credit 2: Enhanced Commissioning
- EA Credit 3: Measurement and Verification

Dense neighborhoods and heavy traffic as well as existing site contamination can adversely affect the quality of outside air available for ventilation purposes. Refer to these 2 credits

- SS Credit 4: Alternative Transportation
- SS Credit 1: Option 1, Brownfield Redevelopment

To reduce the detrimental effects some materials have on IAQ, follow the guidelines of the prerequisites and credits below and specify materials and furnishings that do not release harmful or irritating chemicals, such as volatile organic compounds (VOCs) from paints and solvents. Occupants' activities such as chemical handling and smoking can also affect air quality.

- IEQ Credits 4.1–4.5: Low-Emitting Materials
- IEQ Credit 5: Indoor Chemical and Pollutant Source Control
- IEQ Prerequisite 2: Environmental Tobacco Smoke

3. Summary of Referenced Standard

American National Standards Institute (ANSI)/ASHRAE Standard 62.1–2007, Ventilation for Acceptable Indoor Air Quality

American Society of Heating, Refrigerating, and Air-Conditioning Engineers

http://www.ashrae.org

This standard specifies minimum ventilation rates and IAQ levels so as to reduce the potential for adverse health effects. The standard specifies that ventilation systems be designed to prevent uptake of contaminants, minimize growth and dissemination of microorganisms, and if necessary, filter particulates.

The standard outlines a ventilation rate procedure and an IAQ procedure for compliance. The ventilation rate procedure prescribes outdoor air quality levels acceptable for ventilation; treatment measures for contaminated outdoor air; and ventilation rates for residential, commercial, institutional, vehicular, and industrial spaces. The IAQ procedure is a performance-based design approach in which the building and its ventilation system maintain concentrations of specific contaminants at or below certain determined limits to achieve an indoor air quality acceptable to building occupants and/or visitors. For the purposes of this procedure, acceptable perceived indoor air quality means there is no dissatisfaction related to thermal comfort, noise and vibration, lighting, and psychological stressors. The IAQ procedure also includes criteria for the following situations: reducing outdoor air quantities when recirculated air is treated by contaminant-removal equipment, and ventilating when a space's air volume is used as a reservoir to dilute contaminants. The IAQ procedure incorporates quantitative and subjective evaluation and restricts contaminant concentrations to acceptable levels.

ASHRAE updated the standard in 2007 to include requirements for buildings that allow smoking in designated areas to separate areas with environmental tobacco smoke (ETS) from those without ETS. The standard now also clarifies how designers must analyze mechanical cooling systems to limit indoor relative humidity that would cause dampness-related problems such as mold and microbial growth.

4. Implementation

Local code can be used in lieu of ASHRAE when the local code is more stringent. For the purposes of this credit, the code that requires providing more outside air is considered more stringent. Mechanical and natural ventilation systems should ensure that building occupants receive adequate fresh air. Underventilated buildings may be stuffy, odorous, uncomfortable, and/or unhealthful for occupants. ASHRAE 62.1–2007 establishes minimum requirements for ventilation air rates in various occupied zones and building ventilation systems. The standard takes into account an area's square footage, number of occupants and their activities, and the ventilation system.

This prerequisite requires project teams to verify that the building HVAC system can supply enough ventilation to provide acceptable IAQ. Many other credits in LEED for Commercial Interiors require the project space to meet the minimum outdoor air flow rates that are determined in the referenced standard. For this reason, this prerequisite is not limited to the project scope of work. Many of the provisions of ASHRAE 62.1–2007, such as the location of air intakes, apply to functional aspects of the HVAC system that are most commonly located in parts of the building outside the project space. When a project space is to be served by a central HVAC system (or existing system), the project team should confirm as early as possible that the system will adequately function in the project space and meet the standard's provisions.

Prior to leasing or acquisition, evaluate the planned location of the project; this can be combined with the evaluation confirming compliance with IEQ Prerequisite 2, Environmental Tobacco Smoke (ETS) Control.

When determining outside air quality, heavy traffic, nearby industrial sites, or neighboring waste management sites may pose problems. In the evaluation, consider possible future uses of nearby sites that may affect outdoor air quality. Obtain ambient air quality data and local wind patterns from the EPA or local entities to determine whether sources of pollution will affect the site.

After the building has been chosen, identify site activities that may have a negative impact on air quality, such as construction activities, materials installed in the building, and chemical handling activities during occupancy.

If possible, design the outdoor air intakes away from possible sources of contamination or confirm that the existing outdoor air intakes are at least 25 feet from sources of contamination. Possible sources of contamination include loading areas, building exhaust fans, cooling towers, street traffic, idling vehicles, standing water, parking garages, sanitary vents, waste bins, and outside smoking areas.

The outside air capacity for the ventilation system should meet the requirements of the referenced standard in all modes of operation. Consider the potential occupancy load when calculating outside air needs in all spaces. Assess changes in occupant loads for renovation or retrofit projects and, where possible, allow flexibility to accommodate future changes in occupant loads. It is important to avoid over- or underdesign of the ventilation systems and to plan for future retrofits when possible.

Operational testing should be included in the building commissioning report. Implement an operations and maintenance plan based on the ASHRAE 62.1–2007, Section 8, to maintain an uncontaminated HVAC system.

Strategies

There are 3 basic methods for ventilating buildings:

- mechanical ventilation (i.e., active ventilation);
- natural ventilation (i.e., passive ventilation); and
- mixed-mode ventilation (i.e., both mechanical and natural ventilation).

Mechanically Ventilated Spaces: Ventilation Rate Procedure

For mechanical ventilation systems, ASHRAE 62.1–2007, Section 6, explains how to determine the minimum required ventilation rates for various applications, using either the ventilation rate procedure or the indoor air quality procedure. The ventilation rate procedure is easier to apply and used more frequently and is the prescribed approach for this prerequisite.

The ventilation rate procedure methodology is found in Section 6.2 of ASHRAE 62.1–2007. The standard's Table 6-1, Minimum Ventilation Rates in Breathing Zone, provides information by occupancy category to determine the amount of outdoor air needed to ventilate both people-related source contaminants and area-related source contaminants. The outdoor air rate for people-related source contaminants takes into account the number of occupants and their activities. The outdoor air rate for area-related sources contaminants accounts for background off-gassing from building materials, furniture, and materials typically found in that particular occupancy. Finally, the required zone outdoor airflow is the breathing zone outdoor airflow adjusted to reflect the "zone air distribution effectiveness" using adjustment factors in Table 6-2 of the standard. For multiple-zone systems, outdoor air intake flow is adjusted to reflect the "system ventilation efficiency" of the air distribution configuration, using adjustment factors in Table 6-3 of the standard.

If an occupancy category is not included in ASHRAE 62.1–2007, it is up to the the designer to choose 1 that best corresponds to the usage of the space. Explain the rationale for the selection in the submission. Spaces that do not qualify as occupiable spaces are not necessarily excluded from ventilation rate procedure calculations. Additional ventilation and odor or pollutant control might be necessary to fulfill this prerequisite.

Naturally Ventilated Spaces

ASHRAE 62.1–2007, Section 5.1, provides requirements on the location and size of ventilation openings for naturally ventilated buildings. All naturally ventilated spaces must within 25 feet of (and permanently open to) an operable wall or roof opening to the outdoors; the operable area also must be at least 4% of the space's net occupiable floor area. Interior spaces without direct openings to the outdoors can be ventilated through adjoining rooms if the openings between rooms are unobstructed and at least 8% or 25 square feet of the area is free. As appropriate, all other nonventilation-related requirements (e.g., exhaust for combustion appliances, outdoor air assessment, and outdoor air intakes) in the standard must be met.

An engineered natural ventilation system can show compliance with acceptable engineering calculations or multinodal bulk airflow simulation.

Mixed-Mode Ventilated Spaces

For mixed-mode ventilated spaces and hybrid ventilation systems, meet the minimum ventilation rates required by Chapter 6 of ASHRAE 62.1–2007, regardless of ventilation mode (natural ventilation, mechanical ventilation, or both mechanical and natural ventilation). Project teams can use any acceptable engineering calculation methodology to demonstrate compliance.

5. Timeline and Team

Early in the design process, the architect and mechanical engineer teams determine and design the most appropriate ventilation system for the project building. The design team may include the building owner, tenants, facility manager, and maintenance personnel as applicable; these team members should be present in the design meetings to share ideas on the building owner's needs, special requirement areas, zone categories, occupant density, and occupant needs.

Air quality standards should also be established early in the design process and be clearly stated in plans and specifications as design criteria.

6. Calculations

For mechanically ventilated spaces, calculations pertaining to the ventilation rate procedure methodology are found in Section 6.2 of ASHRAE 62.1–2007. The breathing zone outdoor airflow is equal to the sum of the outdoor airflow rate required per person times the zone population, plus the outdoor airflow rate required per unit area times the zone floor area.

Breathing zone outdoor airflow is the design outdoor airflow required in the breathing zone of the occupiable space or spaces in a zone and is calculated as follows:

$$V_{bz} = R_p \times P_z + R_a \times A_z$$

Where:

R_p = outdoor airflow rate required per person as determined from Table 6-1 in ASHRAE 62.1–2007;

P_z = zone population, the largest number of people expected to occupy the zone during typical use;

R_a = outdoor airflow rate required per unit area as determined from Table 6-1 in ASHRAE 62.1–2007; and

A_z = zone floor area, the net occupiable floor area of the zone.

Zone outdoor airflow is the outdoor airflow that must be provided to the zone by the supply air distribution system and is calculated as follows:

$$Voz = \frac{Vbz}{Ez}$$

Where:

Ez = Zone air distribution effectiveness as determined from Table 6-2 in ASHRAE 62.1–2007.

For **single-zone systems,** in which 1 air handler supplies a mixture of outdoor air and recirculated air to only 1 zone, the **outdoor air intake flow** is (Vot) = Voz.

For **100% outdoor air systems,** in which 1 air handler supplies only outdoor air to 1 or more zones, Vot = $\sum$all zones x Voz.

For **multiple-zone recirculating systems,** in which 1 air handler supplies a mixture of outdoor air and recirculated return air to more than 1 zone, calculate the **outdoor air intake flow** (Vot) as follows:

- Determine the **zone primary outdoor air fraction,** (Zp) = Voz/Vpz, where **Vpz** is the **zone primary airflow** (i.e., the primary airflow to the zone from the air handler including outdoor air and recirculated air). For VAV systems, Vpz is the minimum expected primary airflow for design purposes.

- Determine the **system ventilation efficiency (Ev)** from Table 6-3 in in ASHRAE 62.1–2007.

- Determine the **uncorrected outdoor air intake (Vou)** = D $\sum$all zones (Rp)(Pz) + $\sum$all zones RaAz, where the **occupant diversity (D)** may be used to account for variations in occupancy within zones served by the same system: D = Ps / $\sum$all zones Pz, and where Ps is the **system population,** the total population in the area served by the system.

The outdoor air intake flow for a multiple-zone recirculating system may then be determined by this calculation:

$$Vot = \frac{Vou}{Ev}$$

7. Documentation Guidance

As a first step in preparing to complete the LEED Online documentation requirements, work through the following measures. Refer to LEED Online for the complete descriptions of all required documentation.

- Develop ventilation calculations demonstrating compliance with the applicable sections of Section 4 through 7 of ASHRAE 62.1–2007, Ventilation for Acceptable Indoor Air Quality.

8. Examples

The following are examples of the ASHRAE 62.1–2007 ventilation rate procedure calculations. Refer to the ASHRAE standard for project specific applications.

Table 1. Sample Summary Calculations for Determining Outdoor Air Ventilation Rates

Zone	Occupancy Category	Outdoor Airflow Rate Required per Person (Rp)	Zone Population (Pz)	Outdoor Airflow Rate Required per Unit Area (Ra)	Zone Floor Area (Az)	Zone Air Distribution Effectiveness (Ez)	Breathing Zone Outdoor Airflow (Voz)
VAV-1	Office space	5	8	0.06	310	1.0	59
VAV-2	Conference room	5	10	0.06	270	1.0	66

Table 2. Ventilation Rate Procedure for Multiple-Zone, Variable-Volume System

Inputs for Potentially Critical Zones			Corner Open Office	North Conference Room
Zone Name	Zone title turns purple italic for critical zones(s)			
Zone Tag			VAV-1	VAV-2
Space type	Select from pull-down list		Office space	Conference/ meeting
Floor Area of zone	Az	sf	310	270
Design population of zone	Pz	P (default value listed; may be overridden)	8	7
Design discharge airflow to zone (total primary plus local recirculated)	Vdzd	cfm	590	30
Induction Terminal Unit, Dual Fan Dual Duct or Transfer Fan?	Select from pull-down list or leave blank if N/A		ITU	ITU
Local recirc. air fraction representative of ave system return air	Er		0.50	0.5
Inputs for Operating Condition Analyzed				
Percent of total design airflow rate at conditioned analyzed	Ds	% 100%	100%	100%
Air distribution type at conditioned anlayzed	Select from pull-down list		CS	CS
Zone air distribution effectiveness at conditioned analyzed	Ez		1.00	1.00
Primary air fraction of supply air at conditioned analyzed	Ep		.95	.95

Potentially Critical Zones											
North Conference Room	North Private Office	Corner Open Office	South Private Office	Reception	West Open Office	East Private Office	Interior Private Office	Interior Private Office	Interior Conference Room	Server Room
VAV-2	VAV-3	VAV-4	VAV-5	VAV-6	VAV-7	VAV-8	VAV-9	VAV-10	VAV-11	VAV12
Conference/ meeting	Office Space	Office Space	Office Space	Reception areas	Office Space	Office Space	Office Space	Office Space	Conference/ meeting	Computer (not printing)
270	107	310	165	258	347	140	65	65	220	140
10	1	8	1	3.5	5	1	1	1	8	0
300	120	465	215	250	450	155	50	50	200	50
ITU	ITU	ITU	ITU	ITU	ITU	ITU	ITU	ITU	ITU	ITU
.50	.50	.50	.50	.50	.50	.50	.50	.50	.50	.50
100%	100%	100%	100%	100%	100%	100%	100%	100%	100%	100%
CS	CS	CS	CS	CS	CS	CS	CS	CS	CS	CS
1.00	1.00	1.00	1.00	1.00	1.00	1.00	1.00	1.00	1.00	1.00
0.90	0.90	0.90	0.90	0.90	0.90	0.80	0.70	0.70	0.75	0.80

Table 3. Results from Ventilation Rate Procedure

Results		
System Ventilation Efficiency	Ev.	0.78
Outdoor air intake airflow rate required at condition analyzed	Vot	331 cfm
Outdoor air intake rate per unit floor area	Vot/As	0.14 cfm/sf
Outdoor air intake rate per person served by system (including diversity)	Vot/Ps	14.4 cfm/p
Outdoor air intake rate as a % of design primary supply air	Vot/Vpsd	13%
Uncorrected outdoor air intake airflow rate	Vou	259 cfm

Table 4. Sample Summary Calculations for Naturally Ventilated Spaces

Zone	Floor Area (sf)	Natural Ventilation Opening Area (sf)	Opening Areas as Percentage of Floor Area	Is Distance to Opening 25 Feet or Less?
General office	8,000	336	4.20	Yes
Training room	750	32	4.30	Yes
Break room	216	12	5.60	Yes

9. Exemplary Performance

This prerequisite is not eligible for exemplary performance under the Innovation in Design section.

10. Regional Variations

There are no regional variations associated with this prerequisite.

11. Operations and Maintenance Considerations

For mechanically ventilated systems, provide the building operator with copies of the ventilation rate procedure calculations for each zone used to show compliance with ASHRAE 62.1–2007. Over the building's life, these can be updated with actual occupancy values to adjust delivered ventilation rates as appropriate.

Provide maintenance personnel with the information needed to understand, maintain, and adjust the ventilation system, and retain mechanical design documents showing zone configurations. Include appropriate setpoints and control sequences in the facility's building operating plan, a sequence of operations document, and recommendations for typical corrective actions. Establish procedures and schedules for testing and maintaining exhaust systems and include them in the building's preventive maintenance plan.

12. Resources

Please see USGBC's LEED Resources & Tools (http://www.usgbc.org/projecttools) for additional resources and technical information.

Websites
American Society of Heating, Refrigerating, and Air-Conditioning Engineers (ASHRAE)
http://www.ashrae.org
(404) 636-8400
ASHRAE advances the science of heating, ventilation, air conditioning, and refrigeration for the public's benefit through research, standards writing, continuing education, and publications.

U.S. EPA's Indoor Air Quality website
http://www.epa.gov/iaq
(800) 438-4318
The EPA's IAQ website includes a variety of tools, publications, and links to address IAQ concerns in schools and large buildings. A software program available for download, IAQ Building Education and Assessment Model (I-BEAM) provides comprehensive IAQ management guidance and calculates the cost, revenue, and productivity impacts of planned IAQ activities. Publications include these titles: *Energy Cost and IAQ Performance of Ventilation Systems and Controls Modeling Study*; *Building Assessment, Survey, and Evaluation Study*; and *Building Air Quality Action Plan*.

13. Definitions

Active ventilation is synonymous with mechanical ventilation.

Air-conditioning is the process of treating air to meet the requirements of a conditioned space by controlling its temperature, humidity, cleanliness, and distribution. (ASHRAE 62.1–2007)

Breathing zone is the region within an occupied space between 3 and 6 feet above the floor. Note that this definition varies from that of ASHRAE 62.1-2007, which states that the breathing zone is between 3 inches and 6 feet from the floor, and 2 feet from the walls as well as fixed air conditioning equipment.

Contaminants are unwanted airborne constituents that may reduce air quality (ASHRAE 62.1–2007).

Indoor air quality (IAQ) is the nature of air inside the space that affects the health and well-being of building occupants. It is considered acceptable when there are no known contaminants at harmful concentrations as determined by cognizant authorities and with which a substantial majority (80% or more) of the people exposed do not express dissatisfaction. (ASHRAE 62.1–2007)

Mechanical ventilation, or active ventilation, is provided by mechanical powered equipment, such as motor-driven fans and blowers, but not by devices such as wind-driven turbine ventilators and mechanically operated windows. (ASHRAE 62.1–2007)

Mixed-mode ventilation combines mechanical and natural ventilation methods.

Natural ventilation, or passive ventilation, is provided by thermal, wind or diffusion effects through doors, windows or other intentional openings in the building. (ASHRAE 62.1–2007)

Passive, or natural, ventilation uses the building layout, fabric, and form to provide ventilation to a conditioned space using nonmechanical forms of heat transfer and air movement, such as stack effect and cross ventilation.

Off-gassing is the emission of volatile organic compounds (VOCs) from synthetic and natural products.

Outdoor air is the ambient air that enters a building through a ventilation system, either through intentional openings for natural ventilation or by infiltration. (ASHRAE 62.1–2007)

Thermal comfort exists when building occupants express satisfaction with the thermal environment.

Ventilation is the process of supplying air to or removing air from a space for the purpose of controlling air contaminant levels, humidity, or temperature within the space. (ASHRAE 62.1-2007).

ENVIRONMENTAL TOBACCO SMOKE (ETS) CONTROL

	CI
Prerequisite	IEQ Prerequisite 2
Points	Required

Intent

To prevent or minimize exposure of building occupants, indoor surfaces and ventilation air distribution systems to environmental tobacco smoke (ETS).

Requirements

OPTION 1

Locate tenant space in a building that prohibits smoking by all occupants and users, within 25 feet of entries, outdoor air intakes and operable windows.

OR

OPTION 2

CASE 1. Non-Residential Projects

Confirm that smoking is prohibited in the portions of the tenant space not designated as a smoking space, all other building areas served by the same HVAC system, and the common areas used by occupants. Ensure that ETS cannot migrate by either mechanical or natural ventilation from other areas of the building.

If the occupants are permitted to smoke, provide one or more designated smoking rooms designed to contain, capture and remove ETS from the building. At a minimum, each smoking room must be directly exhausted to the outdoors, with no recirculation of ETS-containing air to nonsmoking areas, enclosed with impermeable deck-to-deck partitions, and operated at a negative pressure compared with surrounding spaces of at least an average of 5 Pa (0.02 inches of water gauge) and with a minimum of 1 Pa (0.004 inches of water gauge) when the doors to the smoking rooms are closed.

Verify performance of the smoking rooms differential air pressure by conducting 15 minutes of measurement, with a minimum of 1 measurement every 10 seconds, of the differential pressure in the smoking room with respect to each adjacent area and in each adjacent vertical chase with the doors to the smoking rooms closed. Conduct the testing with each space configured for worst case conditions of transport of air from the smoking rooms (with doors closed) to adjacent spaces.

CASE 2. Multi-Unit Residential Buildings

Minimize uncontrolled pathways for ETS transfer between individual residential units by sealing penetrations in walls, ceilings, and floors in the residential units and by sealing vertical chases adjacent to the units.

Weather-strip all doors in the residential units leading to common hallways to minimize air leakage into the hallway[1].

---

1   If the common hallways are pressurized with respect to the residential units then doors in the residential units leading to the common hallways need not be weather-stripped provided that the positive differential pressure is demonstrated as in Option 2, Case 1 above, considering the residential unit as the smoking room.

Demonstrate acceptable sealing of residential units by conducting a blower door test in accordance with ANSI/ASTM-779-99, Standard Test Method for Determining Air Leakage Rate by Fan Pressurization.

Use the progressive sampling methodology defined in Chapter 7 (Home Energy Rating Systems (HERS) Required Verification and Diagnostic Testing) of the California Low Rise Residential Alternative Calculation Method Approval Manual. Residential units must demonstrate less than 1.25 square inches of leakage area per 100 square feet of enclosure area (i.e., sum of all wall, ceiling and floor areas).

1. Benefits and Issues to Consider

The purpose of this prerequisite is to limit the exposure of building occupants to Environmental Tobacco Smoke (ETS), or secondhand smoke. ETS is produced by burning cigarettes, pipes, or cigars. It contains thousands of different compounds, many of which are known carcinogens. [14] The relationship between smoking and various health risks, including lung disease, cancer, and heart disease, is well documented. A strong link between ETS and similar health risks has also been demonstrated.

The most effective way to avoid health problems associated with ETS is to prohibit smoking indoors. If this cannot be accomplished, indoor smoking areas must be isolated from nonsmoking areas and have separate ventilation systems to prevent the introduction of tobacco smoke contaminants to nonsmoking areas.

Environmental Issues

Separate indoor smoking areas occupy additional space and may result in a larger building, greater material use, and increased energy for ventilation. However, these environmental impacts can be offset by the gains in health and well-being of building occupants who are more comfortable, have higher productivity rates. lower absenteeism, and less illness.

Economic Issues

For a LEED for Commercial Interiors project, the economic impacts of a nonsmoking policy may be positive or negative and also affect the long-term value of the building. Providing separate smoking areas adds to the design and construction costs of most projects, and maintaining designated smoking areas also adds to lease and operating costs. Prohibiting indoor smoking can increase the useful life of interior fixtures and furnishings.

Smoking within a building contaminates indoor air and can cause occupant reactions, including irritation, illness, and decreased productivity. These problems increase expenses and liability for building owners, tenants, operators, and insurance companies. Strict no-smoking policies will result in lower health care and insurance costs.

2. Related Credits

The use of separate ventilation systems to isolate smoking areas from the rest of the building requires additional energy and commissioning, as well as measurement and verification efforts. This prerequisite is related to the following prerequisites and credits:

- EA Prerequisite 1: Fundamental Commissioning of Building Energy Systems
- EA Credit 1: Optimize Energy Performance
- EA Credit 2: Enhanced Commissioning
- EA Credit 3: Measurement and Verification

Because smoking, both indoors and outdoors, affects the IAQ performance of the building, this prerequisite is also related to the following prerequisites and credits:

- IEQ Prerequisite 1: Minimum Indoor Air Quality Performance
- IEQ Credit 1: Outdoor Air Delivery Monitoring
- IEQ Credit 2: Increased Ventilation

Project teams may wish to address smoking-related contaminants in the building in conjunction with other sources of air pollutants, as outlined in the following credits:

- IEQ Credit 4: Low-Emitting Materials
- IEQ Credit 5: Indoor Chemical and Pollutant Source Control

3. Summary of Referenced Standards

American National Standards Institute ANSI-E779-03, Standard Test Method for Determining Air Leakage Rate by Fan Pressurization

To purchase this standard, go to http://www.astm.org.

This test method covers a standardized technique for measuring air leakage rates through a building envelope under controlled pressurization and depressurization; it should produce a measurement of the air tightness of a building envelope.

California Low Rise Residential Alternative Calculation Method Approval Manual, Home Energy Rating Systems (HERS) Required Verification and Diagnostic Testing,
California Energy Commission
http://www.energy.ca.gov/HERS/%20
http://www.energy.ca.gov/title24/2005standards/residential_acm/index.html

4. Implementation

Choose a building in which smoking is prohibited. Provide appropriately located designated smoking areas outside the building—away from building entrances, operable windows, and ventilation system fresh air intakes—and post information on the nonsmoking policy for occupants to read.

If interior smoking areas are incorporated within the building, install separate ventilation systems and test their effectiveness to ensure that they are isolated from the nonsmoking portions of the building.

5. Timeline and Team

The tenant space, building, and site smoking policies should be drafted by the facility manager and signed by the occupant, facility manager, and property manager or owner. These policies should be in place over the tenant's occupancy. Enforcing the tenant space policy is the responsibility of the tenant. Enforcing the building and site policy is the responsibility of the facility manager or owner, and groundskeeper. Any building modifications made to accommodate new smoking rooms should be coordinated by the facility manager in consultation with the building owner.

6. Calculations

There are no calculations required for this prerequisite.

7. Documentation Guidance

As a first step in preparing to complete the LEED Online documentation requirements, work through the following measures. Refer to LEED Online for the complete descriptions of all required documentation.

- Develop an environmental tobacco smoke policy that details areas where smoking is prohibited.

- Maintain documentation (e.g., site plans and renderings) that visually indicates how the smoking policy has been implemented on-site.

- Track and record testing data for any interior smoking rooms to verify that there is no cross contamination to adjacent spaces.

8. Examples

Figure 1. Compliant Smoking Room

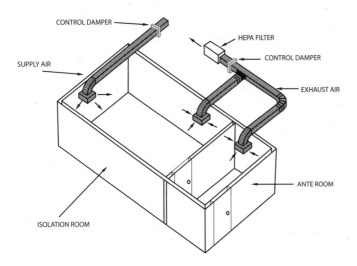

Figure 1 illustrates the degree of isolation required to comply with this prerequisite. The anteroom helps prevent pollutants from entering the rest of the building. Air enters and exits the designated smoking room through control dampers, maintaining a constant flow. Upon exiting, the air may or may not be filtered before exiting the building. Air recirculated into the room is filtered.

9. Exemplary Performance

This credit is not eligible for exemplary performance under the Innovation in Design section.

10. Regional Variations

Figure 2. Smoking Bans, by State[15]

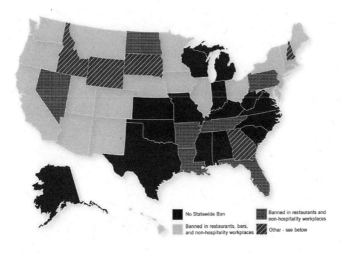

Figure 2 shows how the U.S. states regulate smoking. Idaho has a statewide ban on smoking in restaurants, as does Georgia. South Dakota has a statewide ban on smoking in nonhospitality workplaces. New Hampshire bans smoking in restaurants and bars. Individual cities, counties, or towns may have their own laws on smoking. Consult local ordinances before establishing a smoking policy for the project building.

11. Operations and Maintenance Considerations

Communicate the building's smoking policy to all occupants, establish a plan for enforcement, and designate the person responsible for implementing the policy. This person should verify the effectiveness of ETS control measures in the designated areas, track the dates of each performance test, make sure that the air sealing of designated smoking areas (including any residential units) is not damaged, and investigate smoke odor complaints.

12. Resources

Please see USGBC's LEED Resources & Tools (http://www.usgbc.org/projecttools) for additional resources and technical information.

Websites

Isolation Rooms and Pressurization Control
http://www.engr.psu.edu/AE/iec/abe/control/isolation.asp
This document describes the engineering involved in negative pressure rooms.

Secondhand Smoke: What You Can Do about Secondhand Smoke as Parents, Decision Makers, and Building Occupants
The EPA
http://www.ehso.com/ehshome/SmokingEPAFacts.htmhttp://www.ehso.com/ehshome/SmokingEPAF
This EPA document (reprinted by Environment, Health, and Safety Online) describes the effects of ETS and measures for reducing human exposure to it.

Setting the Record Straight: Secondhand Smoke Is a Preventable Health Risk
The EPA
http://www.epa.gov/smokefree/pubs/strsfs.html
This EPA document reviews laboratory research on ETS and federal legislation aimed at curbing ETS-related problems.

Smoke-Free Lists, Maps, and Data
http://www.no-smoke.org/goingsmokefree.php?id=519
These publications from the American Nonsmokers' Rights Foundation describe all of the tobacco control ordinances, by-laws, and board of health regulations.

Print Media

The Chemistry of Environmental Tobacco Smoke: Composition and Measurement, 2nd edition, by R.A. Jenkins, B.A. Tomkins, et al. (CRC Press & Lewis Publishers, 2000).

The Smoke-Free Guide: How to Eliminate Tobacco Smoke from Your Environment, by Arlene Galloway (Gordon Soules Book Publishers, 1988).

13. Definitions

Environmental tobacco smoke (ETS), or secondhand smoke, consists of airborne particles emitted from the burning end of cigarettes, pipes, and cigars, and exhaled by smokers. These particles contain about 4,000 compounds, up to 50 of which are known to cause cancer.

Tenant space is the area within the LEED project boundary. For more information on what can and must be in the LEED project boundary see the Minimum Program Requirements (MPRs) and LEED 2009 MPR Supplemental Guidance. Note: tenant space is the same as project space.

Ventilation is the provision and removal of air to control air contaminant levels, humidity, or temperature within an indoor space. Ventilation is measured in air changes per hour—the quantity of infiltration air in cubic feet per minute (cfm) divided by the volume of the room.

	CI
Credit	IEQ Credit 1
Points	1 point

Intent

To provide capacity for ventilation system monitoring to promote occupant comfort and well-being.

Requirements

Install permanent monitoring systems to ensure that ventilation systems maintain design minimum requirements. Configure all monitoring equipment to generate an alarm when the airflow values or carbon dioxide(CO_2) levels vary by 10% or more from the design values, via either a building automation system alarm to the building operator or a visual or audible alert to the building occupants.

AND

CASE 1. Mechanically Ventilated Spaces

Monitor CO_2 concentrations within all densely occupied spaces (those with a design occupant density of 25 people or more per 1,000 square feet). CO_2 monitors must be between 3 and 6 feet above the floor.[1]

Provide a direct outdoor airflow measurement device capable of measuring the minimum outdoor air intake flow with an accuracy of plus or minus 15% of the design minimum outdoor air rate, as defined by ASHRAE 62.1-2007 (with errata but without addenda[2]) for mechanical ventilation systems where 20% or more of the design supply airflow serves nondensely occupied spaces.

CASE 2. Naturally Ventilated Spaces

Monitor CO_2 concentrations within all naturally ventilated spaces. CO_2 monitors must be between 3 feet and 6 feet above the floor. One CO_2 sensor may be used to monitor multiple nondensely occupied spaces if the natural ventilation design uses passive stack(s) or other means to induce airflow through those spaces equally and simultaneously without intervention by building occupants.

---

1   CO_2 monitoring is required in densely occupied spaces, in addition to outdoor air intake flow measurement.
2   Project teams wishing to use ASHRAE approved addenda for the purposes of this credit may do so at their discretion. Addenda must be applied consistently across all LEED credits.

1. Benefits and Issues to Consider

Environmental Issues

Measuring CO_2 concentrations to determine and maintain adequate outdoor air ventilation rates in buildings is 1 recommended method for achieving better indoor air quality (IAQ). Increasing ventilation rates may require additional energy inputs, which generate additional air and water pollution.

CO_2 concentrations are an indicator of ventilation effectiveness, with elevated levels suggesting inadequate ventilation and possible buildup of indoor air pollutants. Although CO_2 alone is not harmful, high concentrations of CO_2 in indoor environments displace oxygen and therefore can lead to headaches, dizziness, and increased heart rate.[16]

Economic Issues

Installing CO_2 and ventilation rate monitoring systems requires an investment in equipment, installation, annual calibration, and maintenance. However, these systems enable building owners, maintenance personnel, and occupants to detect air quality problems quickly so that corrective action can be taken. Reduced absenteeism and increased occupant productivity, though difficult to quantify, are important factors in the valuation on investment for these systems. Effective air quality monitoring can also extend the life of a building's HVAC system and reduce building energy use by ensuring that the amount of makeup air provided accurately reflects building occupancy loads.

CO_2 and ventilation rate monitoring systems increase initial construction costs. Capital costs and annual costs for air-flow monitoring equipment maintenance and calibration procedures may be offset by reduced absenteeism, increased occupant productivity, and reduced HVAC energy use.

2. Related Credits

The indoor air quality (IAQ) of the project building is important to occupants' productivity, health, and satisfaction. In addition, it is related to daily building activities. The monitors can help inform the commissioning agents and the measurement and verification process and thereby improve IAQ while minimizing energy losses. The following prerequisites and credits are related to this credit:

- IEQ Credit 2: Increased Ventilation

- EA Prerequisite 1: Fundamental Building Commissioning

- EA Credit 2: Enhanced Commissioning

- EA Credit 3: Measurement and Verification

Dense neighborhoods, heavy traffic, and existing site contamination can adversely affect CO_2 levels and the quality of outside air available for ventilation purposes. Consider also these credits:

- SS Credit 3: Alternative Transportation

- SS Credit 1: Option 1, Brownfield Redevelopment

3. Summary of Referenced Standards

American National Standards Institute (ANSI)/ASHRAE Standard 62.1–2007, Ventilation for Acceptable Indoor Air Quality
American Society of Heating, Refrigerating, and Air-Conditioning Engineers (ASHRAE)
http://www.ashrae.org
This standard specifies minimum ventilation rates and IAQ levels so as to reduce the potential for adverse health effects. The standard specifies that ventilation systems be designed to prevent uptake of contaminants, minimize growth and dissemination of microorganisms, and, if necessary, filter particulates.

The standard outlines a ventilation rate procedure and an IAQ procedure for compliance. The ventilation rate procedure prescribes outdoor air quality levels acceptable for ventilation; treatment measures for contaminated outdoor air; and ventilation rates for residential, commercial, institutional, vehicular, and industrial spaces. The IAQ Procedure is a performance-based design approach in which the building and its ventilation system maintain concentrations of specific contaminants at or below certain previously determined limits in order to achieve an indoor air quality acceptable to building occupants and/or visitors. For the purposes of this procedure, acceptable perceived indoor air quality excludes dissatisfaction related to thermal comfort, noise and vibration, lighting, and psychological stressors. The IAQ procedure also includes criteria for the following situations: reducing outdoor air quantities when recirculated air is treated by contaminant-removal equipment and ventilating when a space's air volume is used as a reservoir to dilute contaminants. The IAQ procedure incorporates quantitative and subjective evaluation and restricts contaminant concentrations to acceptable levels.

ASHRAE updated the standard in 2007 to include requirements for buildings that allow smoking in designated areas to separate areas with environmental tobacco smoke (ETS) from those without ETS . The standard now also clarifies how designers must analyze mechanical cooling systems to limit indoor relative humidity that would cause dampness-related problems such as mold and microbial growth.

Project teams wishing to use ASHRAE-approved addenda for the purposes of this credit may do so at their own discretion. Apply addenda consistently across all LEED credits.

4. Implementation

Building HVAC systems are designed to flush out indoor airborne contaminants by exhausting old air and replacing it with outdoor air. The rate of ventilation air exchange is generally determined in the design phase based on space density and type of occupancy. Many conventional ventilation systems do not directly measure the how much outdoor air is delivered. Implementation of the following strategies is recommended to achieve this credit.

Outdoor Air Flow Monitoring

Monitoring the outdoor air flow rate confirms that the HVAC equipment is providing the required ventilation rate. Air balance control methodologies such as fan-tracking and measuring building-pressurization do not directly prove that appropriate ventilation air is being provided and do not satisfy the credit requirement. The ventilation rate can be measured at the outdoor air intake of an air distribution system using a variety of airflow devices, including Pitot tubes, Venturi meters, rotating vane anemometers, and mass air flow sensors. These sensors must be installed according to the manufacturer's best practices guidelines. The ventilation rate for a particular HVAC system also can be determined from a mass balance calculation if both supply air flow and return air flow are directly measured with air flow monitoring devices. To satisfy the requirements of this credit, the measurement device must be capable of measuring the minimum outdoor air intake flow with an accuracy of plus or minus 15% when the system is providing the design minimum outdoor air rate. When the measurement device generates a measurement of outdoor air intake flow that is more than 10% below the design outdoor air minimum values, the monitoring system should be configured to deliver a visible or audible alert to the system operator to indicate that operational adjustments may be necessary.

The minimum outdoor air rate might change based on the design and modes of the HVAC system. Constant volume systems with steady-state design occupancy conditions usually have different outdoor air rates for weekdays and nighttime or off-peak conditions. In variable air volume (VAV) systems, the rate of outdoor air needs to stay above the design minimum, even when the supply air flow is decreased because of reduced thermal load conditions.

CO_2 Monitoring

Carbon dioxide (CO_2) monitors can also measure the effectiveness of the ventilation system in delivering outdoor air. Properly placed CO_2 monitors can confirm that a ventilation system is functioning properly. There are 2 typical system configurations that generally meet the requirements of this credit.

The first approach involves CO_2 sensors that use measured concentration to provide an alert. An indoor concentration of 1000 ppm was commonly used in the past as the set point for the alarm, but a higher alarm concentration may be appropriate when the design complies with Standard 62.1–2007 because the effective ventilation rate per person has been reduced significantly for some zones. ASHRAE 62.1–2007 Users Manual Appendix A provides a further discussion on CO_2 sensors, including demand control ventilation (DCV).

Locate CO_2 monitors so that they provide accurate representative readings of the CO_2 concentrations in occupied spaces. Multiple CO_2 monitoring stations throughout occupied spaces provide better information and control than a single CO_2 monitor for the entire system. A single CO_2 monitor, typically installed in the return air duct, is less expensive and easier to use than providing multiple sensors, but it may be able to identify underventilated areas in the building.

The second approach for buildings with HVAC systems that have limited airflow monitoring capabilities (small capacity air handling units or split systems) is to use differential CO_2 monitoring to satisfy the requirements of the credit. This approach requires CO_2 monitors in all occupied spaces, an outdoor CO_2 monitor, and a means by which the air handling units can provide a greater amount of outside air if the CO_2 delta between the spaces reaches or exceeds 530 ppm,

CO_2 Monitoring in Densely Occupied Spaces

The CO_2 level for each densely occupied space in a mechanically ventilated building needs to be monitored to satisfy the credit requirements. The density factor is 25 people per 1,000 square feet; for example, a 240-square-foot conference room that accommodates six or more people would need a CO_2 monitor. CO_2 monitors in densely occupied spaces should be mounted within the space's vertical breathing zone (between 3 and 6 feet above the floor).

CO_2 Monitoring in Naturally Ventilated Spaces

Monitoring CO_2 levels in the occupied spaces in naturally ventilated buildings provides feedback to building occupants and operators so that they can adjust the ventilation by, for example, opening windows.

CO_2 monitoring requires additional commissioning, maintenance attention, and the installation of additional equipment.

Monitoring Existing HVAC Systems

For new outdoor air monitoring systems added to an existing building HVAC system, make sure that the design strategy is compatible with the existing HVAC and automation systems. This is especially important for commercial interior projects where a tenant space will likely share a central HVAC system with the rest of the building. If the building owner does not allow modulation of the outside air based on feedback from CO_2 monitors located in 1 tenant space, consider including monitoring in the building selection criteria.

Prior to Occupancy

Before air balancing and commissioning, the project team should make sure that the monitoring system is calibrated and that the set points and control sequences meet project specifications. The team should provide the building owner, maintenance personnel, and occupants with the information and training needed to understand, maintain, and respond to the monitoring system. Sensors should be recalibrated based on the manufacturer's requirements. CO_2 sensors that require recalibration intervals of at least 5 years are recommended. If a CO_2 monitor is allowed to fall out of calibration, it may indicate that indoor CO_2 concentrations are lower or higher than they actually are, leading to under- or over-ventilation of the space. A permanent ventilation monitoring system assists in detecting IAQ problems quickly so that any problems can be corrected. Under-ventilation of a space can lead to unsatisfactory indoor environmental conditions and occupant discomfort. Overventilation of a space may needlessly increase utility costs and pose a challenge to maintaining indoor comfort.

5. Timeline and Team

The placement of outdoor air sensors and intakes should be coordinated with the design team before construction documents are prepared. Engage a mechanical engineer on the issues of outdoor air delivery monitoring no later than the design development phase.

6. Calculations

There are no calculations required for this credit.

7. Documentation Guidance

As a first step in preparing to complete the LEED Online documentation requirements, work through the following measures. Refer to LEED Online for the complete descriptions of all required documentation.

- Incorporate air flow monitors and CO_2 sensors into floor plans, schematics, elevations (where applicable), and mechanical schedules

- Commission ventilation systems to monitor for excess energy use

- Check alarm systems to make sure settings are in accordance with ASHRAE 62.1–2007 for mechanical ventilation systems

- Calibrate all building automation systems according to the manufacturer's recommendations and routinely check the function of the alarm systems

8. Examples

There are no examples for this credit.

9. Exemplary Performance

This credit is not eligible for exemplary performance under the Innovation in Design section.

10. Regional Variations

Ambient outdoor CO_2 concentrations may fluctuate between approximately 300 and 500 *ppm* based on local and regional factors. Time-of-day fluctuations near major congested highways and annual fluctuations, if any, should also be considered. High ambient CO_2 concentrations typically indicate combustion or other *contaminant* sources. Lower ventilation rates may yield a sense of stuffiness or general dissatisfaction with IAQ.

11. Operations and Maintenance Considerations

Provide the building owner, maintenance personnel, and occupants with the information and training needed to understand, maintain, and use the monitoring system. Maintenance personnel should make inspection of CO_2 monitors part of routine operations and maintenance and preventive maintenance activities. In the facility's operating plan and sequence of operations document, include appropriate setpoints and control sequences as well as recommendations for typical corrective actions.

Establish procedures and schedules for inspecting CO_2 monitors and airflow monitoring stations, recalibrating sensors based on the manufacturer's requirements, and testing and maintain the exhaust systems, and include them in the building's preventive maintenance plan.

Use CO_2 sensors that require recalibration no less than every 5 years. A CO_2 monitor that has fallen out of calibration may indicate that indoor CO_2 concentrations are lower or higher than they actually are, leading to underventilation or overventilation of the space.

12. Resources

Please see USGBC's LEED Resources & Tools (http://www.usgbc.org/projecttools) for additional resources and technical information.

Websites

American Society of Heating, Refrigerating, and Air-Conditioning Engineers (ASHRAE)
http://www.ashrae.org
ASHRAE advances the science of heating, ventilation, air conditioning, and refrigeration for the public's benefit through research, standards writing, continuing education, and publications.

Building Air Quality: A Guide for Building Owners and Facility Managers
http://www.epa.gov/iaq/largebldgs
This EPA publication details IAQ sources in buildings and methods to prevent and resolve IAQ problems.

Print Media

Air Handling Systems Design, by Tseng-Yao Sun. (McGraw Hill, 1992).

Efficient Building Design Series, Volume 2: Heating, Ventilating, and Air Conditioning, by J. Trost and Frederick Trost (Prentice Hall, 1998).

ASHRAE 55–2004: Thermal Environmental Conditions for Human Occupancy (ASHRAE, 2004).

ASHRAE 62.1–2007: Ventilation for Acceptable Indoor Air Quality (ASHRAE, 2007).

ASTM D 6245–1998: Standard Guide for Using Indoor Carbon Dioxide Concentrations to Evaluate Indoor Air Quality and Ventilation (ASTM, 1998).

13. Definitions

Breathing zone is the region within an occupied space between 3 and 6 feet above the floor. Note that this definition varies from that of ASHRAE 62.1-2007, which states that the breathing zone is between 3 inches and 6 feet from the floor, and 2 feet from the walls as well as fixed air conditioning equipment.

CO_2 is carbon dioxide.

Densely occupied space is an area with a design occupant density of 25 people or more per 1,000 square feet (40 square feet or less per person).

HVAC systems are equipment, distribution systems, and terminals that provide the processes of heating, ventilating, or air-conditioning. (ASHRAE 90.1–2007)

Indoor air quality (IAQ) is the nature of air inside a building that affects the health and well-being of building occupants. It is considered acceptable when there are no known contaminants at harmful concentrations as determined by cognizant authorities and with which a substantial majority (80% or more) of the people exposed do not express dissatisfaction. (ASHRAE 62.1–2007)

Mechanical ventilation is provided by mechanically powered equipment, such as motor-driven fans and blowers, but not by devices such as wind-driven turbine ventilators and mechanically operated windows. (ASHRAE 62.1–2007)

Natural ventilation is provided by thermal, wind or diffusion effects through doors, windows, or other intentional openings in the building. (ASHRAE 62.1–2007)

Occupants in a commercial building are workers who either have a permanent office or workstation or typically spend a minimum of 10 hours per week in the project building; in a residential building, regular occupants also include all persons who live in the building.

Outdoor air is the ambient air that enters a building through a ventilation system, either through intentional openings for natural ventilation or by infiltration. (ASHRAE 62.1–2007)

ppm is parts per million.

Return air is removed from a space and then recirculated or exhausted. (ASHRAE 62.1–2007)

Tenant space is the area within the LEED project boundary. For more information on what can and must be in the LEED project boundary see the Minimum Program Requirements (MPRs) and LEED 2009 MPR Supplemental Guidance. Note: tenant space is the same as project space.

Ventilation is the process of supplying air to or removing air from a space for the purpose of controlling air contaminant levels, humidity or temperature within the space. (ASHRAE 62.1–2007)

Volatile organic compounds (**VOCs**) are carbon compounds (excluding carbon monoxide, carbon dioxide, carbonic acid, metallic carbides and carbonates, and ammonium carbonate) that participate in atmospheric photochemical reactions. The compounds vaporize (become a gas) at normal room temperatures.

INCREASED VENTILATION

	CI
Credit	IEQ Credit 2
Points	1 point

Intent

To provide additional air ventilation to improve indoor air quality for improved occupant comfort, well-being and productivity.

Requirements

CASE 1. Mechanically Ventilated Spaces

Increase breathing zone outdoor air ventilation rates to all occupied spaces by at least 30% above the minimum rates required by ASHRAE 62.1-2007 (with errata but without addenda[1]) as determined by IEQ Prerequisite 1: Minimum Indoor Air Quality Performance.

CASE 2. Naturally Ventilated Spaces

Determine that natural ventilation is an effective strategy for the project by following the flow diagram process shown in Figure 2.8 of the Chartered Institution of Building Services Engineers (CIBSE) Applications Manual 10: 2005, Natural Ventilation in Non-domestic Buildings

AND

OPTION 1

Show that the natural ventilation systems design meets the recommendations set forth in the CIBSE manuals appropriate to the project space.

PATH 1. CIBSE Applications Manual 10: 2005, Natural Ventilation in Non-domestic Buildings.

PATH 2. CIBSE AM 13:2000, Mixed Mode Ventilation.

OR

OPTION 2

Use a macroscopic, multizone, analytic model to predict that room-by-room airflows will effectively naturally ventilate, defined as providing minimum ventilation rates required by ASHRAE 62.1-2007 Chapter 6 (with errata but without addenda[1]), for at least 90% of occupied spaces.

---

1 Project teams wishing to use ASHRAE approved addenda for the purposes of this credit may do so at their discretion. Addenda must be applied consistently across all LEED credits

1. Benefits and Issues to Consider

Environmental Issues

Americans spend about 90% of their time indoors, where concentrations of pollutants are often much higher than those outside. Of the thousands of chemicals and biological pollutants found indoors, many are known to have significant health impacts. Risks include asthma, cancer, and reproductive and developmental problems.[17] Increasing ventilation above minimum standards improves the indoor air quality (IAQ) of a building's occupied spaces and directly benefits occupants' health and well-being.

Economic Issues

Depending on the climate, increasing ventilation rates by 30% beyond ASHRAE 62.1–2007 can yield higher HVAC energy costs and potentially greater HVAC capacity needs than associated with the minimum ventilation rates established in the standard. This increase in HVAC capacity and energy use will be more pronounced in extreme climates than in mild, temperate climates. Some organizations increase the outdoor air intake rate because they have found the resulting IAQ is associated with improved employee health, welfare, well-being and productivity. The use of heat transfer equipment, like heat recovery wheels, can precondition intake air and minimize the extent to which increased ventilation requires additional energy to heat and cool intake air. Although a naturally ventilated building may have less invested in equipment, it may have higher quality windows and increased thermal mass. Power, fuel, and maintenance costs of naturally ventilated buildings tend to be lower.

2. Related Credits

Ventilation strategies influence the overall energy performance of the building and require commissioning as well as measurement and verification. Increased ventilation, particularly when delivered by mechanical systems, can increase energy consumption. Installing a permanent ventilation performance monitoring system can facilitate the achievement and maintenance of increased ventilation. For these reasons, increased ventilation is related to the following other credits:

- EA Prerequisite 1: Fundamental Commissioning of Building Energy Systems
- EA Prerequisite 2: Minimum Energy Performance
- EA Credit 1: Optimize Energy Performance
- EA Credit 2: Enhanced Commissioning
- EA Credit 3: Measurement and Verification
- IEQ Credit 1: Outdoor Air Delivery Monitoring

3. Summary of Referenced Standards

American National Standards Institute (ANSI)/ASHRAE Standard 62.1–2007, Ventilation for Acceptable Indoor Air Quality (Ventilation Rate Procedure), American Society of Heating, Refrigerating, and Air-Conditioning Engineers (ASHRAE)
http://www.ashrae.org

This standard specifies minimum ventilation rates and IAQ levels so as to reduce the potential for adverse health effects. The standard specifies that ventilation systems be designed to prevent uptake of contaminants, minimize growth and dissemination of microorganisms, and, if necessary, filter particulates.

The standard outlines a ventilation rate procedure and an IAQ procedure for compliance. The ventilation rate procedure prescribes outdoor air quality levels acceptable for ventilation; treatment measures for contaminated outdoor air; and ventilation rates for residential, commercial, institutional, vehicular, and industrial spaces. The IAQ Procedure is a performance-based design approach in which the building and its ventilation system maintain concentrations of specific contaminants at or below certain previously determined limits in order to achieve an indoor air quality acceptable to building occupants and/or visitors. For the purposes of this procedure, acceptable perceived indoor air quality excludes dissatisfaction related to thermal comfort, noise and vibration, lighting, and psychological stressors. The IAQ procedure also includes criteria for the following situations: reducing outdoor air quantities when recirculated air is treated by contaminant-removal equipment and ventilating when a space's air volume is used as a reservoir to dilute contaminants. The IAQ procedure incorporates quantitative and subjective evaluation and restricts contaminant concentrations to acceptable levels.

ASHRAE updated the standard in 2007 to include requirements for buildings that allow smoking in designated areas to separate areas with environmental tobacco smoke (ETS) from those without ETS . The standard now also clarifies how designers must analyze mechanical cooling systems to limit indoor relative humidity that would cause dampness-related problems such as mold and microbial growth.

Project teams wishing to use ASHRAE-approved addenda for the purposes of this credit may do so at their own discretion. Apply addenda consistently across all LEED credits.

Chartered Institute of Building Services Engineers (CIBSE) Applications Manual 10, Natural Ventilation in Non-Domestic Buildings, 2005
Chartered Institute of Building Services Engineers (CIBSE)
http://www.cibse.org/
CIBSE Applications Manual 10 provides guidance for implementing natural ventilation in nonresidential buildings. It provides detailed information on how to adopt natural ventilation as the sole servicing strategy for a building or as an element in a mixed mode design. According to the publisher, this manual "is a major revision of the Applications Manual (AM) first published in 1997. At the time, there was a significant expansion of interest in the application of engineered natural ventilation to the design of non-domestic buildings. The original AM10 sought to capture the state of knowledge as it existed in the mid-90s and present it in a form suited to the needs of every member of the design team. Some 10 years on from the time when the initial manual was conceived, the state of knowledge has increased, and experience in the design and operation of naturally ventilated buildings has grown. This revision of AM10 is therefore a timely opportunity to update and enhance the guidance offered to designers and users of naturally ventilated buildings."

4. Implementation
A green building should provide its occupants with superior indoor air quality (IAQ) to support their productivity and well-being. Providing adequate ventilation rates is key to maintaining superior IAQ. Underventilated buildings may be stuffy, odorous, uncomfortable and/or unhealthy for occupants.

Building ventilation systems, including both active HVAC systems and natural ventilation systems, are designed and installed to introduce outside air into the building while exhausting an equal amount of building air. HVAC systems typically serve other functions as well, including providing thermal comfort for occupants. Building conditioning systems that provide enhanced ventilation air as efficiently and effectively as possible will help maintain a high standard of IAQ in the building.

There are 3 basic methods for ventilating buildings:

- mechanical ventilation (i.e., active ventilation)

- natural ventilation (i.e., passive ventilation)

- mixed-mode ventilation (i.e., both mechanical and natural ventilation)

ASHRAE 62.1–2007 provides ventilation rate standards for different types of buildings and building uses. Projects that exceed the standards for mechanically ventilated buildings by 30% will meet the requirements for the LEED for Commercial Interiors credit. The Applications Manual 10–2005, "Natural Ventilation in Non-Domestic Buildings," provides guidance on appropriate natural ventilation design for adequate outdoor air exchange in a building. Naturally ventilated spaces should follow these guidelines to meet the credit requirements. Projects using mixed-mode ventilation need to comply with ASHRAE 62.1–2007 for the mechanically ventilated portion and CIBSE AM10 for the naturally ventilated portion.

In addition to designing the HVAC systems properly and selecting appropriate building materials, increasing ventilation rates beyond standard practice is 1 way to provide superior IAQ. Managing IAQ concerns during construction and operations is also appropriate for many green building projects. For mechanically ventilated and air-conditioned buildings, increasing ventilation rates will likely mean greater HVAC system capacity and energy use. Natural ventilation systems can provide increased ventilation rates, good IAQ, and occupant control over thermal comfort and ventilation via operable windows.

Mechanically Ventilated Spaces: Ventilation Rate Procedure

Section 6 of ASHRAE 62.1–2007 outlines guidelines for determining ventilation rates for various applications, using either the ventilation rate procedure or the IAQ procedure. The ventilation rate procedure is easier to apply and used more frequently than the IAQ procedure. It is the recommended approach used in IEQ Prerequisite 1, Minimum Indoor Air Quality Performance.

When following the ventilation rate procedure, use the methodology found in Section 6.2 of ASHRAE 62.1–2007. The breathing zone outdoor airflow is equal to the sum of the outdoor airflow rate required per person times the zone population, plus the outdoor airflow rate required per unit area times the zone floor area:

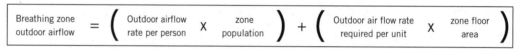

The standard's Table 6-1, Minimum Ventilation Rates in Breathing Zone, provides information by occupancy category to determine both the amount of outdoor air needed to ventilate people-related source contaminants and area-related source contaminants. The people-related sources figure of the outdoor air rate addresses actual occupancy density and activity. The area-related sources figure accounts for background off-gassing from building materials, furniture and materials typically found in that particular occupancy. Finally, the required zone outdoor airflow is the breathing zone outdoor airflow adjusted to reflect the efficiency of the actual air distribution configuration.

This LEED for Green Interior Design and Construction credit requires that applicants demonstrate that the delivered zone outdoor airflow is at least 30% more than what is required by ASHRAE 62.1–2007 for each zone. Table 1 shows how the sample space used in IEQ Prerequisite 1: Minimum Indoor Air Quality Performance, has reached the 30% increase.

Table 1. ASHRAE 62.1–2007 Ventilation Rate Procedure

Zone		Standard Case: ASHRAE 62.1–2007 Verification Rate Procedure										Design Case		
			Table 6-1				Table 6-2		Table 6-3					
Zone	Occupancy Category	Area (sf)	People Outdoor Air Rate (cfm/person)	Area Outdoor Air Rate (cfm/sf)	Occupant Density (#/1000 sf)	Breathing Zone Outdoor Air Flow Vbz (cfm)	Zone Air Distribution Effectiveness Ez	Zone Outdoor Air Flow Voz (cfm)	System Ventilation Efficiency Ev	Minimum Outdoor Air Intake Flow Vot (cfm)	Design Outdoor Air Intake Flow (cfm)	Zone Primary Air Flow Faction Vpz (cfm)	Primary Outdoor Air Fraction Zp = Voz/Vpz	% Increase Over Standard
General Office	Office Space	8000	5	0.06	5	680	1.0	680	1.0	680	900	8000	0.09	32%
Training Room	Lecture Classroom	750	7.5	0.06	65	411	1.2	342	0.9	380	500	1400	0.24	32%
Break Room	Conference Meeting	250	5	0.06	50	63	1.0	63	1.0	63	85	500	0.13	36%
Total		9000				1154		1085		1123	1485	9900		32%
Notes:	For the general office space, air distribution is overhead, hence Ez = 1. Outdoor air fraction, Zp, < 0.15, hence system ventilation efficiency is 1.0. For the training room, air distribution is underfloor, hence Ez = 1.2. Outdoor air fraction, Zp < 0.25, hence system ventilation efficiency is 0.9. For the break room, air distribution is overhead, hence Ez = 1. Outdoor air fraction, Zp, < 0.15, hence system ventilation efficiency is 1.0.													

Naturally Ventilated Spaces

There are 2 ways to demonstration compliance when using natural ventilation: 1 is the compliance path found in Chapter 2 of the CIBSE Applications Manual 10 (AM10); the other is to provide documentation using a macroscopic, multizone, analytic model that predicts room-by-room air flow rates.

When using AM10 (see Figure 1), should begin by establishing the required flow rates through each space. There is an acceptable average rate needed for IAQ and thermal comfort; exceeding this rate results in wasted energy during the heating seasons. Additional ventilation is needed for the summer cooling requirements. There are several ways to determine the acceptable average rate needed for IAQ and thermal comfort such as using a separate manual or simulation software listed in AM10. Project teams should explain their choice. Submittals must include a narrative with information on the building, its orientation, and the glazing ratios. Include a summary of the internal heat gains and weather conditions; explain the ventilation strategy, including the airflow paths, rates planned for different operational periods during the day and night, peak internal temperatures, and means of shading for summer solar gains; provide sample calculations on how the opening size for operable windows, trickle vents and louvers was determined; and include the calculations for the driving pressure, showing the effects of both wind and stack-induced pressure differentials.

When using a macroscopic, multizone, analytic model that predicts room-by-room air flow rates, prepare a narrative with the same information listed above and demonstrate that 90% of the occupied areas meet the room-by-room airflow rates. Indicate the source of the standard being used, such as Volume A of the CIBSE Guide, ASHRAE 62.1–2007, Section 6.2.

5. Timeline and Team

Most project teams decide early on whether to have a mechanical ventilation system, a passive ventilation system, or a combination. This decision might be influenced by the building size and type, as well as climatic, economic, and organizational considerations. Figure 1, from CIBSE AM10, provides a decision diagram to help teams make an informed evaluation. In addition, project teams considering natural ventilation should evaluate site conditions and building design. Potential IAQ problems might arise from traffic exhaust, nearby polluting industries, and neighboring waste management sites. This credit requires that applicants demonstrate the required increased ventilation rate for the project during the performance period. Critical team members during this phase include the design team, mechanical engineers, the facility manager, and building owner.

Figure 1. Selecting Natural Ventilation for Nondomestic Buildings

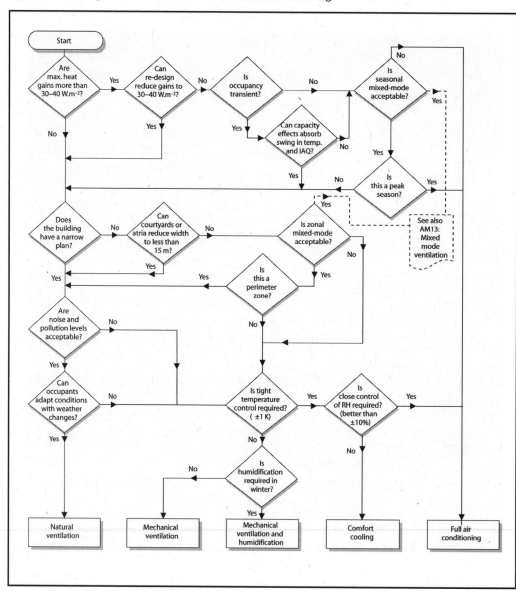

From CIBSE Applications Manual AM10–2005.

6. Calculations

Mechanically Ventilated Spaces

To show compliance in mechanically ventilated spaces, use the calculations in the ASHRAE User Manual and the calculators for IEQ Prerequisite 1, Minimum Indoor Air Quality Performance, available for free download on the LEED Resources & Tools page of the USGBC website. The same calculations are used to document IEQ Prerequisite 1.

Naturally Ventilated Spaces

Determine the opening sizes for operable windows, trickle vents, and louvers in accordance with CIBSE Applications Manual 10. Alternatively, for project teams using a macroscopic, multizone, analytic model that predicts room-by-room airflow rates, provide the room-by-room outdoor airflow rates predicted by the analysis and a comparison with minimum ventilation rates required by ASHRAE 62.1–2007, Section 6.

7. Documentation Guidance

As a first step in preparing to complete the LEED Online documentation requirements, work through the following measures. Refer to LEED Online for the complete descriptions of all required documentation.

- Perform calculations and size mechanical equipment to accommodate increased ventilation rates.

- For naturally ventilated projects, maintain appropriate visual documentation (e.g., plans) of open areas within the project.

8. Examples

Ventilation rates as specified by ASHRAE must be determined for each space. The example in Table 2 calculates the percentage increase in ventilation for 3 sample spaces, each of which provides increased ventilation sufficient to meet the credit requirements.

Table 2. Sample Summary Calculations for Increased Mechanical Ventilation

Zone	Occupancy	Area (sf)	Standard Zone Outdoor Airflow Voz (cfm/sf)	Design Zone Outdoor Airflow (cfm/sf)	Percentage Increase
General office	Office space	8,000	0.088	0.115	30.7
Training room	Lecture hall	750	0.460	0.600	32.6
Break room	Conference, meeting	216	0.338	0.440	30.2

9. Exemplary Performance

This credit is not eligible for exemplary performance under the Innovation in Design section.

10. Regional Variations

Additional ventilation is more practical for mild climates, where increasing ventilation rates beyond standard practice will not have as great an impact on HVAC systems' capacity and energy consumption as in extremely hot, humid, or cold climates. Natural ventilation and passive conditioning approaches are also more typical in mild and temperate climates, although there are precedents for passively conditioned buildings in all climates.

11. Operations and Maintenance Considerations

See the Operations and Maintenance Considerations section in IEQ Prerequisite 1.

12. Resources

Please see USGBC's LEED Resources & Tools (http://www.usgbc.org/projecttools) for additional resources and technical information.

Websites

American Society of Heating, Refrigerating, and Air-Conditioning Engineers (ASHRAE)
http://www.ashrae.org
ASHRAE advances the science of heating, ventilation, air conditioning, and refrigeration for the public's benefit through research, standards writing, continuing education, and publications. To purchase ASHRAE standards and guidelines, visit the bookstore on the ASHRAE website.

Energy Cost and Indoor Air Quality Performance of Ventilation Systems and Controls Modeling Study
The EPA
http://www.epa.gov/iaq/largebldgs/energy_cost_and_iaq/executive_summary.pdf

Building Assessment, Survey, and Evaluation Study
The EPA
http://www.epa.gov/iaq/base/index.html

Building Air Quality Action Plan
The EPA
http://www.epa.gov/iaq/largebldgs/pdf_files/baqactionplan.pdf

The Chartered Institution of Building Services Engineers (CIBSE)
http://www.cibse.org/
Located in London, this organization, publishes a series of guides on ventilation, including natural ventilation, on its own and in collaboration with other entities.

13. Definitions

Air-conditioning is the process of treating air to meet the requirements of a conditioned space by controlling its temperature, humidity, cleanliness and distribution. (ASHRAE 62.1–2007)

Breathing zone is the region within an occupied space between 3 and 6 feet above the floor. Note that this definition varies from that of ASHRAE 62.1-2007, which states that the breathing zone is between 3 inches and 6 feet from the floor, and 2 feet from the walls as well as fixed air conditioning equipment.

Conditioned space is the part of a building that is heated or cooled, or both, for the comfort of occupants. (ASHRAE 62.1–2007)

Contaminants are unwanted airborne constituents that may reduce air quality. (ASHRAE 62.1–2007)

Exfiltration is air leakage through cracks and interstices and through the ceilings, floors, and walls.

Exhaust air is removed from a space and discharged to outside the building by means of mechanical or natural ventilation systems.

HVAC system is equipment, distribution systems, and terminals that provide the processes of heating, ventilating, or air-conditioning. (ASHRAE 90.1–2007)

Indoor air quality (**IAQ**) is the nature of air inside a building that affects the health and well-being of building occupants. It is considered acceptable when there are no known contaminants at harmful concentrations as determined by cognizant authorities and with which a substantial majority (80% or more) of the people exposed do not express dissatisfaction. (ASHRAE 62.1–2007)

Infiltration is air leakage into conditioned spaces through cracks and interstices and through ceilings, floors, and walls.

Mechanical ventilation is ventilation provided by mechanically powered equipment, such as motor-driven fans and blowers, but not by devices such as wind-driven turbine ventilators and mechanically operated windows.

Mixed-mode ventilation combines natural ventilation with mechanical systems; the latter are only when necessary. Mixed-mode ventilation strategies include 3 distinct approaches; contingency, complementary, and zoned. (CIBSE Guide F–2008)

Natural ventilation is ventilation provided by thermal, wind or diffusion effects through doors, windows or other intentional openings in the building.

Outdoor air is the ambient air that enters a building through a ventilation system, either through intentional openings for natural ventilation or by infiltration. (ASHRAE 62.1–2007)

Recirculated air is removed from a space and reused as supply air. (ASHRAE 62.1–2007)

Supply air is delivered by mechanical or natural ventilation to a space, composed of any combination of outdoor air, recirculated air or transfer air. (ASHRAE 62.1–2007)

Ventilation is the process of supplying air to and removing air from a space for the purpose of controlling air contaminant levels, humidity or temperature within the space. (ASHRAE 62.1–2007)

CONSTRUCTION INDOOR AIR QUALITY MANAGEMENT PLAN—DURING CONSTRUCTION

	CI
Credit	IEQ Credit 3.1
Points	1 point

Intent

To reduce indoor air quality (IAQ) problems resulting from construction or renovation and promote the comfort and well-being of construction workers and building occupants.

Requirements

Develop and implement an IAQ management plan for the construction and preoccupancy phases of the tenant space as follows:

- During construction, meet or exceed the recommended design approaches of the Sheet Metal and Air Conditioning National Contractors Association (SMACNA) IAQ Guidelines for Occupied Buildings Under Construction, 2nd Edition 2007, ANSI/SMACNA 008-2008 (Chapter 3).

- Protect stored on-site and installed absorptive materials from moisture damage.

- If permanently installed air handlers are used during construction, filtration media with a minimum efficiency reporting value (MERV) of 8 must be used at each return air grille, as determined by ASHRAE 52.2-1999. (with errata but without addenda[1]). Replace all filtration media immediately prior to occupancy.

---

1   Project teams wishing to use ASHRAE approved addenda for the purposes of this credit may do so at their discretion. Addenda must be applied consistently across all LEED credits.

1. Benefits and Issues to Consider

This credit seeks to recognize construction practices that help ensure high indoor air quality (IAQ) during construction and into occupancy.

Environmental Issues

Reducing indoor air contaminants improves comfort levels, lowers absenteeism, and increases productivity. Demolition and construction practices lead to increased exposure to indoor air pollutants through the introduction of synthetic building materials, power equipment and vehicles, new furnishings, and finish materials. The negative effects of the construction process on indoor air quality can be heightened by reduced ventilation rates (typical during the construction phase) and a lack of attention to pollutant source control. If unaddressed, the contamination can result in poor IAQ extending over the lifetime of the building. Fortunately there are IAQ management strategies that, if instituted during construction and before occupancy, will minimize potential problems (see Implementation).

Economic Issues

Consider the time and labor required to maintain a clean construction site. Protecting the ventilation system and isolating work that involves power equipment are critical methods to preventing the introduction of indoor air contaminants. Clean ventilation systems and building spaces can also extend the lifetime of the ventilation system and improve its efficiency, resulting in reduced energy use. Construction schedule disruption can be avoided through the proper sequencing of material installation, so as to reduce contamination and maintain the project schedule. Early coordination between the contractor and subcontractors can minimize or eliminate scheduling delays.

2. Related Credits

Construction activities can affect the IAQ of the building long after occupancy. Implementing a construction IAQ management plan, selecting low-emitting finish materials and furnishings, and isolating indoor pollutant sources will reduce levels of indoor contaminants. The following credits relate to IAQ management before occupancy:

- IEQ Credit 3.2: Construction Indoor Air Quality Management Plan Before Occupancy
- IEQ Credit 4: Low-Emitting Materials
- IEQ Credit 5: Indoor Chemical and Pollutant Source Control

3. Summary of Referenced Standards

American National Standards Institute (ANSI)/Sheet Metal and Air Conditioning Contractors' National Association (SMACNA) 008-2008, IAQ Guidelines for Occupied Buildings under Construction, 2nd edition, 2007

http://www.smacna.org

The Sheet Metal and Air Conditioning Contractors National Association (SMACNA) is an international organization that developed guidelines for maintaining healthful indoor air quality during demolitions, renovations, and construction. The full document covers air pollutant sources, control measures, IAQ process management, quality control and documentation, interpersonal communication, sample projects, tables, references, resources, and checklists.

American National Standards Institute (ANSI)/ASHRAE 52.2-1999, Method of Testing General Ventilation Air-Cleaning Devices for Removal Efficiency by Particle Size

http://www.ashrae.org

This standard presents methods for testing air cleaners for 2 performance characteristics: the device's capacity for removing particles from the air stream and the device's resistance to airflow.

The minimum efficiency reporting value (MERV) is based on 3 composite average particle size removal efficiency points. Consult the standard for a complete explanation of MERV calculations.

4. Implementation

Complete the construction IAQ management plan before construction begins. The plan should include agenda items to be discussed regularly at preconstruction and construction meetings. Continually educating and providing the proper resources (e.g., collection bins, cleaning tools, and materials) to subcontractors and field personnel reinforces the importance of following the IAQ plan's procedures and encourages their participation. Choose a member of the contractor's team to serve as the IAQ manager; they will be responsible for identifying the cause of the problem and implementing an appropriate solution. The referenced SMACNA standard recommends control measures in 5 areas: HVAC protection, source control, pathway interruption, housekeeping, and scheduling. For each project, the team should review the applicability of each control measure and include those that apply in the final Construction IAQ Management Plan. The control measures are as follows:

HVAC Protection

Ideally, permanently installed HVAC systems should not be used during demolition and construction, because the systems can be contaminated or damaged. In most cases, using the HVAC system during construction activates the clock on the manufacturer's warranty, exposing the contractor to potential out-of-pocket costs if problems occur when the manufacturer's warranty has expired but the warranty for the building has not. Using temporary ventilation units is feasible, practical, and generally inexpensive. Using temporary ventilation units is 1 strategy to meet the SMACNA control measure for HVAC protection. However, it does not satisfy all of the requirements of this credit on its own. Other strategies to mitigate contamination of both HVAC equipment and occupied spaces during construction are detailed below.

The contractor should protect all HVAC equipment from dust and odors and seal all duct and equipment openings with plastic. If the system must be operated to maintain service to other occupied portions of the building or to protect finished work, the contractor should protect the return/negative pressure side of the system. If the returns cannot be closed, the contractor should install and maintain temporary filters over grilles and openings. To comply with the credit requirements, the filtration medium must have a rating of MERV 8 or better. If an plenum without ducts must be used over the construction zone, the construction team should isolate it by having all ceiling tiles in place. The contractor should check for leaks in the return ducts and air handlers and make needed repairs promptly. It is important to avoid using the mechanical rooms for construction storage.

The contractor should replace all filtration media just before occupancy, installing only a single set of final filtration media. Project teams should note that the requirement for MERV 13 rated filters has been moved to IEQ Credit 5: Indoor Chemical and Pollutant Source Control. This credit does not regulate the efficiency of the filters used for the long-term operation of the building.

Source Control

The architect or designer should specify finish materials such as paints, carpet, composite wood, adhesives and sealants that have low-toxicity levels or none at all. (Note that the selection of low-emitting materials is covered under IEQ Credit 4: Low-Emitting Materials). The Construction IAQ Management Plan should specify the control measures for materials containing VOCs. The construction team should recover, isolate, and ventilate containers housing toxic materials. Finally, exhaust fumes from idling vehicles and gasoline-fueled tools to the exterior of the building through the use of funnels or temporary piping.

Pathway Interruption

During construction, isolate occupied work spaces to prevent contamination. Depending on weather conditions, ventilate using 100% outside air to exhaust contaminated air directly from the building during the installation of VOC-emitting materials. Depressurize the work area so that the air pressure differential keeps dust and odors contained in construction areas. Provide temporary barriers to contain the construction area.

Housekeeping

Institute cleaning procedures to control contaminants in building spaces during construction and prior to occupancy. Porous building materials should be protected from exposure to moisture and stored in a clean area before installation. Use vacuum cleaners with high-efficiency particulate filters, clean more frequently, and use wetting agents to control dust.

Scheduling

Coordinate construction activities to minimize or eliminate disruption of operations in the occupied portions of the building. The contractor should sequence construction activities over the duration of the project carefully to minimize the impact on IAQ. It may be necessary to conduct activities with high pollution potential during off-hours, such as on the weekends or in the evenings, to allow time for new materials to air out. The contractor should plan adequate time to conduct flush-out and IAQ test procedures before occupancy. Upon completion of construction, the contractor should replace all filtration media just before occupancy and coordinate this with the activities and requirements addressed in IEQ Credit 3.2, Construction IAQ Management before Occupancy, and IEQ Credit 5, Indoor Chemical and Pollution Source Control.

While core and shell construction is not addressed by LEED for Commercial Interiors, consider minimizing cross contamination of the commercial interior during base construction. The Sheet Metal and Air Conditioning Contractors' National Association's (SMACNA's) IAQ Guidelines for Occupied Buildings Under Construction details many measures to help improve the IAQ of occupied buildings under construction. One measure is to seal off the return air system from the construction-site. Another measure is to exhaust contaminants directly from the project construction-site to the building's exterior. A comprehensive building construction IAQ management plan can help minimize health risks to the existing tenants during construction.

Project teams should also note the following:

- Small, packaged HVAC systems are not excluded from complying with the credit requirements.

- Currently, there is no ASHRAE-approved testing methodology for dynamic air cleaners, and dynamic air cleaners are not an acceptable means of compliance.

- Though the title of the SMACNA guidelines refers to occupied buildings, they constitute the same IAQ management methods to be used on interior construction.

- Using temporary ventilation units is 1 strategy to meet the SMACNA control measure for HVAC protection but does not on its own satisfy all the requirements of this credit.

5. Timeline and Team

Scheduling aspects of this credit are related to the sequencing of demolition and construction procedures as well as the installation of finish materials. It is best to select low-emitting materials and install any products that emit VOCs before installing absorbent materials, such as ceiling tiles, gypsum wallboard, fabric furnishings, carpet, and insulation. If possible, store these materials in an isolated area to minimize contamination.

Give subcontractors and field personnel copies of the construction IAQ management plan prior to the initiation of work, and contractually require them to implement the applicable plan components. Post a copy of the plan in an obvious location on the job site and conduct periodic visual inspections to help enforce compliance. Maintaining a regular photo log of the prescribe strategies is advised.

6. Calculations
There are no calculations required for this credit.

7. Documentation Guidance
As a first step in preparing to complete the LEED Online documentation requirements, work through the following measures. Refer to LEED Online for the complete descriptions of all required documentation.

- Create a written construction IAQ management plan to use during demolition and construction

- Maintain visual documentation (e.g., photos) of the construction IAQ management plan practices followed during construction and indicate which approach is being implemented.

8. Examples

Indoor Air Quality Management Plan (Facility Alterations)
1. Goals and Scope
   To limit indoor air quality problems resulting from construction or renovation projects, (Building) must implement this Indoor Air Quality (IAQ) management plan to sustain the comfort and well-being of occupants and construction workers.
2. SMACNA Guidelines: The following is a list of example procedures. The project team should create a Construction IAQ Management Plan appropriate to the scope of work being completed.
   The following Construction IAQ Management Plan measures must be implemented throughout the construction and occupancy phase of any project.
   A. HVAC Protection: Provide project-specific measures to be employed.
      ■ When possible, HVAC system should be shut down during construction.
   B. Source Control: Provide project-specific measures to be employed.
      ■ Product substitution: low emitting paints, adhesives, sealants,and carpets must be used when feasible.
   C. Pathway Interruption: Provide project specific measures to be employed.
   D. Housekeeping: Provide project-specific measures to be employed.
      ■ Services must utilize best practices for minimizing IAQ problems, such as dust suppression, cleaning frequency, cleaning efficiency, water and spill cleanup, protection of on-site or installed absorptive and porous material.
   E. Scheduling: Provide project specific measures to be employed.
      ■ Building flush out: After construction ends and all interior finishes have been installed, new filtration media must be installed and a flush out of the construction area must be performed. The flush out must comply with the procedure listed within the LEED Rating System
3. Responsible Party
   Teams and individuals involved in activities pertaining to the policy:
   Facility Manager
   General Contractor
   Building Owner
4. Guidance for Resources and Implementation
   A. Sheet Metal and Air Conditioning National Contractors Association (SMACNA) IAQ Guidelines for Occupied Buildings under Construction, second edition, November 2007, Chapter 3
5. Quality Assurance and Quality Control Processes
   During any construction or renovation project the following strategies must be utilized to ensure the implementation of this plan:
   A. A list of filtration media utilized, including the manufacturer, model number, MERV rating, date of installation, and date of replacement.
   B. Photographs documenting the IAQ control measures implemented at 3 time periods during the project (e.g., beginning, middle, and end). The photos will be labeled to highlight the approach taken.
   C. Narrative documenting the flush-out procedure utilized, including airflow and duration.

9. Exemplary Performance
This credit is not eligible for exemplary performance under the Innovation in Design section.

10. Regional Variations
There are no regional variances applicable to this credit.

11. Operations and Maintenance Considerations

Provide the facility manager with a copy of the IAQ management plan used during construction to facilitate adoption of similar practices during future alterations or additions.

12. Resources

Please see USGBC's LEED Resources & Tools (http://www.usgbc.org/projecttools) for additional resources and technical information.

Websites

Controlling Pollutants and Sources
The EPA
http://www.epa.gov/iaq/schooldesign/controlling.html
The EPA website provides information regarding typical sources of indoor andoutdoor pollutants and methods for resolving indoor air quality concerns. Find detailed information on exhaust or spot ventilation practices during construction.

Indoor Air Pollution Report, July 2005
California Air Resources Board
http://www.arb.ca.gov/research/indoor/ab1173/finalreport.htm
This report, released in July 2005, covers the significant health effects caused by indoor air pollution, including respiratory illness and disease, asthma attacks, cancer, and premature death. The report describes the health effects, sources, and concentrations of indoor air pollutants; existing regulations, guidelines, and practices for indoor air pollution; and ways to prevent and reduce indoor air pollution.

The State of Washington Program and IAQ Standards
http://www.aerias.org/DesktopModules/ArticleDetail.aspx?articleId=85
This standard was the first state-initiated program to ensure the design of buildings with acceptable IAQ.

Sheet Metal and Air Conditioning Contractors' National Association, Inc. (SMACNA)
http://www.smacna.org
SMACNA is an international organization that developed guidelines for maintaining healthful indoor air quality during demolitions, renovations, and construction. The professional trade association publishes the referenced standard as well as *Indoor Air Quality: A Systems Approach*, a comprehensive document that covers air pollutant sources, control measures, IAQ process management, quality control and documentation, interpersonal communication , sample projects, tables, references, resources, and checklists.

Print Media

Indoor Air Quality: a Facility Manager's Guide, published by the Construction Technology Centre Atlantic, is written as a comprehensive review of indoor air quality issues and solutions. Purchase the report online at http://ctca.unb.ca/CTCA/communication/IAQ/Order_IAQ.htm.

13. Definitions

A **construction IAQ management plan** outlines measures to minimize contamination in a specific building project during construction and describes procedures to flush the building of contaminants prior to occupancy.

HVAC systems are equipment, distribution systems, and terminals that provide the processes of heating, ventilating, or air-conditioning. (ASHRAE 90.1–2007)

Indoor air quality (IAQ) is the nature of air inside a building that affects the health and well-being of building occupants. It is considered acceptable when there are no known contaminants at harmful concentrations as determined by cognizant authorities and with which a substantial majority (80% or more) of the people exposed do not express dissatisfaction. (ASHRAE 62.1–2007)

Minimum efficiency reporting value (MERV) is a filter rating established by the American Society of Heating, Refrigerating, and Air Conditioning Engineers (ASHRAE 52.2–1999, Method of Testing General Ventilation Air Cleaning Devices for Removal Efficiency by Particle Size). MERV efficiency categories range from 1 (very low efficiency) to 16 (very high).

Tenant space is the area within the LEED project boundary. For more information on what can and must be in the LEED project boundary see the Minimum Program Requirements (MPRs) and LEED 2009 MPR Supplemental Guidance. Note: tenant space is the same as project space.

CONSTRUCTION INDOOR AIR QUALITY MANAGEMENT PLAN— BEFORE OCCUPANCY

	CI
Credit	IEQ Credit 3.2
Points	1 point

Intent

To reduce indoor air quality (IAQ) problems resulting from construction or renovation and promote the comfort and well-being of workers and occupants.

Requirement

Develop an IAQ management plan and implement it after all finishes have been installed and the building has been completely cleaned before occupancy.

OPTION 1. Flush-Out[1]

PATH 1

After construction ends, prior to occupancy and with all interior finishes installed, install new filtration media and flush-out the building by supplying a total air volume of 14,000 cubic feet of outdoor air per square foot of floor area while maintaining an internal temperature of at least 60°F and, where mechanical cooling is operated, relative humidity no higher than 60%.

OR

PATH 2

If occupancy is desired prior to completion of the flush-out, the space may be occupied following delivery of a minimum of 3,500 cubic feet of outdoor air per square foot of floor area. Once the space is occupied, it must be ventilated at a minimum rate of 0.30 cubic feet per minute (cfm) per square foot of outside air or the design minimum outside air rate determined in EQ Prerequisite 1: Minimum IAQ Performance, whichever is greater. During each day of the flush-out period, ventilation must begin a minimum of 3 hours prior to occupancy and continue during occupancy. These conditions must be maintained until a total of 14,000 cubic feet per square foot of outside air has been delivered to the space.

OR

OPTION 2. Air Testing

Conduct baseline IAQ testing after construction ends and prior to occupancy, using testing protocols consistent with the EPA Compendium of Methods for the Determination of Air Pollutants in Indoor Air and as additionally detailed in the LEED Reference Guide for Green Interior Design and Construction, 2009 Edition.

---

1 All finishes must be installed prior to flush-out

IEQ CREDIT 3.2

Demonstrate that the contaminant maximum concentration levels listed below are not exceeded:

Contaminant	Maximum Concentration
Formaldehyde	27 parts per billion
Particulates (PM10)	50 micrograms per cubic meter
Total volatile organic compounds (TVOCs)	500 micrograms per cubic meter
4-Phenylcyclohexene (4-PCH)*	6.5 micrograms per cubic meter
Carbon monoxide (CO)	9 part per million and no greater than 2 parts per million above outdoor levels

*This test is required only if carpets and fabrics with styrene butadiene rubber [SBR] latex backing are installed as part of the base building systems.

For each sampling point where the maximum concentration limits are exceeded, conduct an additional flush-out with outside air and retest the noncompliant concentrations. Repeat until all requirements have been met. When retesting noncompliant building areas, take samples from the same locations as in the first test.

Conduct the air sample testing as follows:

- All measurements must be conducted prior to occupancy, but during normal occupied hours, with the building ventilation system started at the normal daily start time and operated at the minimum outside air flow rate for the occupied mode throughout the test.

- All interior finishes must be installed, including but not limited to millwork, doors, paint, carpet and acoustic tiles. Movable furnishings such as workstations and partitions must be in place.

- The number of sampling locations will depend on the size of the building and number of ventilation systems. For each portion of the building served by a separate ventilation system, the number of sampling points must not be less than 1 per 25,000 square feet or for each contiguous floor area, whichever is larger. Include areas with the least ventilation and greatest presumed source strength.

- Air samples must be collected between 3 and 6 feet from the floor to represent the breathing zone of occupants, and over a minimum 4-hour period.

1. Benefits and Issues to Consider

Environmental Issues

Reducing contaminants inside buildings results in greater occupant comfort, lower absenteeism, and improved productivity. Construction inevitably introduces contaminants to building interiors. If unaddressed, contamination can result in poor IAQ extending over the lifetime of a building. Fortunately, there are IAQ management strategies that, if instituted during construction and before occupancy, will minimize potential problems (see Implementation).

Economic Issues

Additional time and labor may be required during construction to protect and clean ventilation systems and building spaces. These actions can extend the lifetime of ventilation systems and improve their efficiency, resulting in reduced energy use. The sequencing of material installation so as to reduce contamination may require additional time and could potentially delay occupancy. However, early coordination between the design team, contractor, and subcontractors can minimize or eliminate scheduling delays.

2. Related Credits

Comprehensive construction IAQ management consists of best practices both during construction and after construction, prior to occupancy. These activities are typically governed by the same management plan. The following credit also requires development and implementation of a construction IAQ management plan:

- IEQ Credit 3.1: Construction IAQ Management Plan During Construction

The materials that are specified and installed within the external moisture barrier of the building, as well as filtration, can directly affect air quality and influence the results for air quality testing. Refer also to the following credits:

- IEQ Credit 4: Low-Emitting Materials
- IEQ Credit 5: Indoor Chemical and Pollutant Source Control

Dilution of indoor air contaminants can typically be achieved by introducing outdoor air. The following credit and prerequisite deal with ventilation rates:

- IEQ Prerequisite 1: Minimum Indoor Air Quality Performance
- IEQ Credit 2: Increased Ventilation

3. Summary of Referenced Standard

U.S. EPA Compendium of Methods for the Determination of Air Pollutants in Indoor Air

This standard is available from NTIS (800) 553-6847 with the ordering number PB90200288.

According to the Compendium, the EPA created this document to "provide regional, state and local environmental regulatory agencies with step-by-step sampling and analysis procedures for the determination of selected pollutants in indoor air. Determination of pollutants in indoor air is a complex task, primarily because of the wide variety of compounds of interest and the lack of standardized sampling and analysis procedures. The Compendium has been prepared to provide a standardized format for such analytical procedures. A core set of 10 chapters with each chapter containing 1 or more methods are presented in the current document. Compendium covers a variety of active and passive sampling procedures, as well as several analytical techniques both on and off site."

4. Implementation

Flush-Out Procedure

This compliance path uses the building HVAC system to evacuate airborne contaminants. Complete all construction work, including punch-list items, before beginning the flush-out. Finalize all cleaning prior to the flush-out. Complete the final test and balancing of HVAC systems, and make sure the HVAC control is functional, especially if the occupants will be moving in during the second phase of the flush-out. Commissioning can occur during the flush-out if it does not introduce any additional contaminants into the building.

The flush-out procedure discussed below assumes the use of the building's HVAC system, but alternatives are acceptable if they meet the air quantity, temperature, and humidity requirements.

One approach uses temporary supply and exhaust systems placed into windows or window openings. EPA's Indoor Air Quality Tools for Schools website provides information on exhaust and spot ventilation during construction that can be helpful for design teams considering using this approach. Make sure the air flow is not short circuited, which could leave remote corners of the project spaces with inadequate circulation or cause unanticipated increases in other parts of the building, such as a stack effect in elevator shafts.

If the space's central HVAC system is used, the team should remove any temporary filters and duct coverings installed as part of the construction IAQ management plan. The team should replace the HVAC filtration media with new media; if the system is configured to filter only outside air, the filters do not need to be replaced. New filters that meet the design specification and were installed prior to the start of flush-out will also satisfy the requirements of IEQ Credit 3.1, Construction IAQ Management Plan During Construction. Note that these filters must be MERV 13 or better when a project plans to earn IEQ Credit 5, Indoor Chemical and Pollution Source Control. Depending on their condition following flush-out, some or all of the filters might be ready for replacement, but this is not a condition for satisfying the credit requirements.

Outside air is used to dilute and remove off-gassed contaminants. The quantity of outside air that must be introduced to the project space for the flush-out is 14,000 cubic feet of air per square foot of floor area. Occupants may move in only after the initial flush out phase, when 3,500 cubic feet of air per square foot has been replaced (Figure 1). The initial flush-out phase does not signal the completion of the flush-out, however: A total of 14,000 cubic feet of outside air must be supplied per square foot of floor area before the HVAC system is switched to its normal operational mode.

Figure 1. Sample Air Quantity for Flush-Out

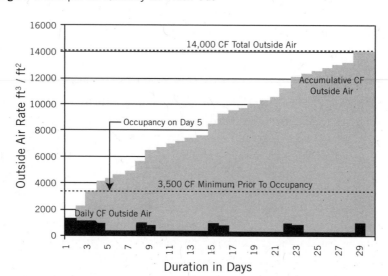

Not all outside air is equal. Depending upon geography and season, outside air can be very cold or damp. Because of this, prudent limits have been set to ensure no harm comes to the building and occupants. The rate of outside air should not cause the interior temperature to drop below 60°F, and relative humidity should not exceed 60%.

During an occupied flush-out phase, a minimum ventilation rate must begin at least 3 hours before daily occupancy and continue while the space is occupied. The rate of outside air must be at least 0.30 cubic feet per minute (cfm) per square foot or the design minimum outside air rate, whichever is greater. The design minimum outside air rate should be determined using ASHRAE 62.1–2007, the same criteria for IEQ Prerequisite 1, Minimum Indoor Air Quality Performance, or the applicable local code if it is more stringent. The 0.30 cfm per square foot rate may be several times the ASHRAE 62.1–2007 requirement for a project's planned occupancy. As a result, consider the minimum flush-out rate during early HVAC design.

There are other thermal comfort, expense, and operational considerations to evaluate when preparing to occupy a space before the end of flush-out. Check to make sure the HVAC system can maintain temperatures within a range that is comfortable for the occupants; opinions formed during this period may last long after the system is operating normally.

There are numerous expense and operational issues to consider, such as the rent or lease details and the existing HVAC system capacity to accommodate the flush-out criteria. Input from the entire project team will help determine the best approach. When completed, make the evaluation and the resulting flush-out strategy part of the project construction IAQ management plan.

When there are multiple HVAC systems that can operate independently, it is acceptable to flush out portions of the building as they are completed, but no additional construction work can occur once the flush-out of an area begins. Isolate completed areas from those under construction per SMACNA IAQ Guidelines for Occupied Buildings under Construction.

Air Quality Testing

The baseline IAQ testing approach is meant to confirm that major contaminants are below recognized acceptable levels before occupancy. While the list included in the credit is not intended to be all-inclusive, it approximates the major forms of postconstruction airborne constituents.

Testing results that meet the credit requirements indicate that the project has implemented a successful construction IAQ management plan, low-emitting materials have been specified, cleanup has been thorough, and the HVAC system is providing adequate ventilation. They can also mean that occupancy can occur sooner than what might have been possible if the flush-out compliance path had been followed. Ideally, the groundwork should be laid for baseline testing during the design process by making sure the testing requirements are included in Division 1 of the project construction specifications. This credit does not establish qualifications for the laboratory or those conducting the sampling; however, the project team should evaluate the capabilities of the IAQ specialist, industrial hygienist, and testing facility being considered for field sampling of IAQ in buildings.

During construction, be vigilant about avoiding substitutions for the specified low-emitting materials. Use low-VOC cleaning supplies to prevent short-term high-VOC levels that may affect test results. Use vacuum cleaners with HEPA filtration to capture particulates.

Projects also following the requirements of IEQ Credit 3.1, Construction IAQ Management Plan During Construction, should replace all filtration media after the final cleaning and complete the air test and balancing of the HVAC system before beginning the baseline IAQ testing. The IAQ maximum contaminant levels are dependent on the HVAC system operating under normal conditions with outdoor airflow rates at the minimum; this stipulation is made so that the air tested is as similar as possible to what the occupants will be breathing. The protocols described in the referenced publication, EPA's Compendium of Methods for the Determination of Air Pollutants in Indoor Air, and the ISO methods are recommended, but others may be used if the project team can provide valid justification. The project team should select the sampling locations carefully to find the concentrations in areas with the least ventilation and, potentially, the greatest presumed contaminant source strength. Determine the number of ventilation systems serving the building. Then, determine if the floor plate is larger or smaller than 25,000 square feet. If it is smaller, take 1 sample every 25,000 square feet. If it is larger, take one per floor plate. For example, a tall 100,000 square foot building with ten 10,000 square foot floors, needs only 4 samples – one per 25,000 square feet because each 10,000 foot floor plate is smaller than 25,000 square feet. However, a building with ten 30,000 square foot floors needs ten samples for the building because each 30,000 floor plate is larger than the 25,000 sq ft criterion. The team should take at least 1 sample per 25,000 square feet in each portion of the building served by a separate ventilation system in a 20,000-square-foot tenant space served by 3 rooftop units—1 each for the north and south elevations (general office area) and the third for a training room and conference rooms—the project team should take samples in at least 3 places, even though 2 units serve 1 general office area. The team should take the samples in the breathing zone, between 3 feet and 6 feet above the floor, during normal occupied hours, with the HVAC system operating at normal daily start times, and with the minimum outside airflow rate. For projects with standardized identical construction, such as classrooms in a school or multifamily residential units, identify which rooms are identical in construction, finishes, configuration, square footage, and HVAC. For these scenarios, project teams can sample the identical spaces by testing 1 in 7. Follow-up samples might be needed, so the project team should record the exact sample locations. If a test sample exceeds the maximum concentration level, the team should flush out the space by increasing the rate of outside air. While the credit requirements do not prescribe the duration of the flush-out, those responsible for testing should make an evaluation based on the contaminant, its concentration, and the potential source. Off-gassing characteristics of sources differ; some deplete rapidly, while others emit at a steady rate over an extended period of time. The project team should resample and confirm compliance before allowing occupancy. The retest may be limited to the chemical contaminants that produced excessive chemical concentration levels in the initial test.

5. Timeline and Team

During the design phase, include language requiring the general contractor to develop and implement a construction IAQ management plan that includes a compliant flush-out procedure and/or air quality testing that meets the requirements of this credit.

After construction and installation of all finishes (including furniture and furnishings), conduct IAQ testing and/or a flush-out following the construction IAQ management plan and in accordance with the requirements of this credit.

Some additional time and labor may be required during and after construction to protect and clean ventilation systems. With early coordination for the sequencing of material installation and coordination between the contractor and subcontractors, the team can minimize or eliminate scheduling delays.

6. Calculations

If a building flush-out is performed before occupancy, the total quantity of outdoor air that must be delivered to the space is calculated as follows:

Phased flush-out:

Phase 1

Building Area (sf)	X	3,500 ft of Outdoor Air	=	Cubic Feet of Air Needed Prior to Occupancy

Phase 2

Building Area (sf)	X	10,500 ft of Outdoor Air	=	Cubic Feet of Air Needed to Complete Flush-Out

Nonphased flush-out:

Building Area (sf)	X	14,000 ft of Outdoor Air	=	Cubic Feet of Air Needed Prior to Occupancy

Note: feet of outdoor air = cubic feet per square foot

7. Documentation Guidance

As a first step in preparing to complete the LEED Online documentation requirements, work through the following measures. Refer to LEED Online for the complete descriptions of all required documentation.

- Maintain a written construction IAQ management plan.

- Record dates, occupancy, outdoor air delivery rates, internal temperature, humidity, and any special considerations for projects completing a flush-out procedure.

- Maintain a copy of the testing report and verify that all required contaminants are accounted for and are reported in the correct unit of measure for projects completing IAQ testing.

8. Examples

Table 1. Time for Flush-Out Options

	Square Foot of Office	Outdoor Air Required for Flush-Out (cfm/sf)	Volume of Air Required Before Occupancy (cu. ft.)	Time Before Occupancy (days)	Minimum Outdoor Air Delivery Rate Post-Occupancy (cfm)	Time to Complete Flush-Out at Minimum Delivery Rate (days)
Pre-Occupancy Option	50,000	14,000	700,000,000	32.4	0	0
Post-Occupancy Option	50,000	14,000	175,000,000	8.1	15,000	24.3
Note: Assuming the building has a 15,000 cfm air handler, capable of operating at 100% OA while maintaining 60° F and 60% RH 24 hr/day						

9. Exemplary Performance

This credit is not eligible for exemplary performance under the Innovation in Design section.

10. Regional Variations

For projects that pursue this credit through the flush-out options in regions where there may be humid and/or cold outdoor air, the project team should be sure to maintain the indoor air temperature at or above 60°F and maintain the relative humidity at or below 60%. When weather conditions may impact the ability to sufficiently heat, cool, or dehumidify the supply air, careful coordination between the project schedule and seasonal variations is crucial.

11. Operations and Maintenance Considerations

Minimize potential sources of indoor air contamination. If such sources must be introduced, consider flushing out the affected areas of the building before those areas are occupied.

Use periodic IAQ testing to verify safe, healthful conditions.

If applicable, provide building operators with information about the flush-out procedures used during construction to facilitate adoption of similar practices following future alterations or additions. Encourage them to draft an IAQ management plan, following the LEED for Existing Buildings: O&M guidance, for any future alterations and additions.

12. Resources

Please see USGBC's LEED Resources & Tools (http://www.usgbc.org/projecttools) for additional resources and technical information.

Websites
Indoor Air Pollution Report, July, 2005
California Air Resources Board
http://www.arb.ca.gov/research/indoor/ab1173/finalreport.htm

Controlling Pollutants and Sources, IAQ Design for Schools
U.S. EPA
http://www.epa.gov/iaq/schooldesign/controlling.html
This EPA website offers detailed information on exhaust or spot ventilation practices during construction activity.

State of Washington Program and IAQ Standards
http://www.aerias.org/DesktopModules/ArticleDetail.aspx?articleId=85
This standard was the first state-initiated program to ensure the design of buildings with acceptable IAQ.

Sheet Metal and Air Conditioning Contractors' National Association
http://www.smacna.org
SMACNA is an international organization that developed guidelines for maintaining healthful indoor air quality during demolitions, renovations, and construction. They publish *Indoor Air Quality: A Systems Approach,* which covers air pollutant sources, control measures, IAQ process management, quality control and documentation, interpersonal communication , sample projects, tables, references, resources, and checklists.

Print Media

Indoor Air Quality: a Facility Manager's Guide, Construction Technology Centre Atlantic, is written as a comprehensive review of IAQ issues and solutions. Purchase the report online at http://ctca.unb.ca/CTCA/communication/IAQ/Order_IAQ.htm.

Compendium of Methods for the Determination of Inorganic Compounds in Ambient Air
U.S. EPA
This standard is available for purchase from NTIS.

13. Definitions

A **construction IAQ management plan** outlines measures to minimize contamination in a specific building during construction and to flush the building of contaminants before occupancy.

Contaminants are unwanted airborne constituents that may reduce air quality (ASHRAE 62.1–2007).

HVAC systems are the equipment, distribution systems, and terminals that provide the processes of heating, ventilating, or air-conditioning (ASHRAE 90.1–2007)

Indoor air quality (IAQ) is the nature of air inside a building that affects the health and well-being of building occupants. It is considered acceptable when there are no known contaminants at harmful concentrations as determined by cognizant authorities and with which a substantial majority (80% or more) of the people exposed do not express dissatisfaction. (ASHRAE 62.1–2007)

Off-gassing is the emission of volatile organic compounds (VOCs) from synthetic and natural products.

Thermal comfort exists when building occupants express satisfaction with the thermal environment.

Outdoor air is the ambient air that enters a building through a ventilation system, either through intentional openings for natural ventilation or by infiltration. (ASHRAE 62.1–2007)

Tenant space is the area within the LEED project boundary. For more information on what can and must be in the LEED project boundary see the Minimum Program Requirements (MPRs) and LEED 2009 MPR Supplemental Guidance. Note: tenant space is the same as project space.

Ventilation the provision and removal of air to control air contaminant levels, humidity, or temperature within an indoor space. Ventilation is measured in air changes per hour—the quantity of infiltration air in cubic feet per minute (cfm) divided by the volume of the room. (ASHRAE 62.1–2007)

	CI
Credit	IEQ Credit 4.1
Points	1 point

Intent

To reduce the quantity of indoor air contaminants that are odorous, potentially irritating and/or harmful to the comfort and well-being of installers and occupants.

Requirements

All adhesives and sealants used on the interior of the building (i.e. inside of the weatherproofing system and applied on-site) must comply with the requirements as applicable to the project scope:[1]

- Adhesives, sealants and sealant primers must comply with South Coast Air Quality Management District (SCAQMD) Rule 1168. Volatile organic compound (VOC) limits listed in the table below were effective July 1, 2005 with a rule amendment date of January 7, 2005.

Architectural Applications	VOC Limit (g/L less water)	Specialty Applications	VOC Limit (g/L less water)
Indoor carpet adhesives	50	PVC welding	510
Carpet pad adhesives	50	CPVC welding	490
Wood flooring adhesives	100	ABS welding	325
Rubber floor adhesives	60	Plastic cement welding	250
Subfloor adhesives	50	Adhesive primer for plastic	550
Ceramic tile adhesives	65	Contact adhesive	80
VCT and asphalt adhesives	50	Special purpose contact adhesive	250
Drywall and panel adhesives	50	Structural wood member adhesive	140
Cove base adhesives	50	Sheet applied rubber lining operations	850
Multipurpose construction adhesives	70	Top and trim adhesive	250
Structural glazing adhesives	100		

Substrate Specific Applications	VOC Limit (g/L less water)	Sealants	VOC Limit (g/L less water)
Metal to metal	30	Architectural	250
Plastic foams	50	Roadway	250
Porous material (except wood)	50	Other	420
Wood	30		
Fiberglass	80		

Sealant Primers	VOC Limit (g/L less water)		
Architectural, nonporous	250		
Architectural, porous	775		
Other	750		

- Aerosol Adhesives must comply with Green Seal Standard for Commercial Adhesives GS-36 requirements in effect on October 19, 2000.

Aerosol Adhesives	VOC weight (g/L minus water)
General purpose mist spray	65% VOCs by weight
General purpose web spray	55% VOCs by weight
Special purpose aerosol adhesives (all types)	70% VOCs by weight

1 The use of a VOC budget is permissible for compliance with this credit.

1. Benefits and Issues to Consider

Many building products contain compounds that have a negative impact on indoor air quality (IAQ) and Earth's atmosphere. The most prominent of these compounds—volatile organic compounds (VOCs)—contribute to smog generation and air pollution as well as adversely affect the well-being of building occupants.

Environmental Issues

VOCs react with sunlight and nitrogen oxides (NOx) in the atmosphere to form ground-level ozone, a chemical that has detrimental effects on human health, agricultural crops, forests, and ecosystems. This ground-level ozone damages lung tissue, reduces lung function, and sensitizes the lungs to other irritants. Additionally, ground-level ozone is also a major component of smog.

Economic Issues

Healthy occupants are more productive and have less illness-related absenteeism. Materials with high VOC content can threaten occupant's health and may decrease their productivity, increasing expenses and liability for building owners, operators, and insurance companies. Because of these issues, the construction market is driving product manufacturers to offer low-VOC alternatives to conventional building products. Costs for these products are generally competitive with conventional materials; however, some low-VOC materials are more expensive than conventional materials, particularly when the products are new to the marketplace. Low-VOC alternatives may also be difficult to obtain for some product types. These issues likely will fade as the use of low-VOC products becomes more commonplace.

2. Related Credits

Because the intent of this credit is to reduce odorous, irritating, or harmful indoor air contaminants, the following other credits may be applicable:

- IEQ Credit 4.2: Low-Emitting Materials—Paints and Coatings
- IEQ Credit 4.3: Low-Emitting Materials—Flooring Systems
- IEQ Credit 4.4: Low-Emitting Materials—Composite Wood and Agrifiber Products
- IEQ Credit 4.5: Low-Emitting Materials—Systems Furniture and Seating

Scheduling strategies relating to the use and tracking of low-emitting materials may be addressed early in construction and prior to occupancy. The following credits also are affected by scheduling considerations:

- IEQ Credit 3.1: Construction IAQ Management Plan During Construction
- IEQ Credit 3.2: Construction IAQ Management Plan Before Occupancy

Project teams may wish to address smoking-related contaminants in the building in conjunction with other sources of air pollutants, as outlined in the following:

- IEQ Prerequisite 2: Environmental Tobacco Smoke (ETS) Control
- IEQ Credit 5: Indoor Chemical and Pollutant Source Control

3. Summary of Referenced Standards

South Coast Air Quality Management District (SCAQMD) Amendment to South Coast Rule 1168, VOC Limits, effective January 7, 2005
South Coast Air Quality Management District
http://www.aqmd.gov/rules/reg/reg11/r1168.pdf

The South Coast Air Quality Management District is a governmental organization in southern California with the mission to maintain healthful air quality for its residents. The organization established source-specific standards to reduce air quality impacts.

Table 1. VOC Limits for Adhesives and Sealants

Architectural Applications	VOC Limit (g/L less water)	Specialty Applications	VOC Limit (g/L less water)
Indoor carpet adhesives	50	PVC welding	510
Carpet pad adhesives	50	CPVC welding	490
Wood flooring adhesives	100	ABS welding	325
Rubber floor adhesives	60	Plastic cement welding	250
Subfloor adhesives	50	Adhesive primer for plastic	550
Ceramic tile adhesives	65	Contact adhesive	80
VCT and asphalt adhesives	50	Special purpose contact adhesive	250
Drywall and panel adhesives	50	Structural wood member adhesive	140
Cove base adhesives	50	Sheet applied rubber lining operations	850
Multipurpose construction adhesives	70	Top and trim adhesive	250
Structural glazing adhesives	100		
Substrate Specific Applications	**VOC Limit (g/L less water)**	**Sealants**	**VOC Limit (g/L less water)**
Metal to metal	30	Architectural	250
Plastic foams	50	Roadway	250
Porous material (except wood)	50	Other	420
Wood	30		
Fiberglass	80		
Sealant Primers	**VOC Limit (g/L less water)**		
Architectural, nonporous	250		
Architectural, porous	775		
Other	750		
This table excludes adhesives and sealants integral to the water-proofing system or that are not building related.			

Green Seal Standard 36 (GS–36), effective October 19, 2000

http://www.greenseal.org/certification/standards/commercial_adhesives_GS_36.cfm
Green Seal is an independent, nonprofit organization that strives to achieve a healthier and cleaner environment by identifying and promoting products and services that cause less toxic pollution and waste, conserve resources and habitats, and minimize global warming and ozone depletion. GS–36 sets VOC limits for commercial adhesives.

Green Seal Standard for Commercial Adhesives GS–36 requirements went in effect on October 19, 2000.

Table 2. VOC Limits for Aerosol Adhesives

Aerosol Adhesives	VOC Limit
General purpose mist spray	65% VOCs by weight
General purpose web spray	55% VOCs by weight
Special purpose aerosol adhesives (all types)	70% VOCs by weight

4. Implementation

The sections under IEQ Credit 4, Low-Emitting Materials, apply to products and installation processes that have the potential to adversely affect the IAQ of a project space and, subsequently, those occupants exposed to the off-gassing of contaminants from these materials.

LEED for Commercial Interiors IEQ Credit 4.1 employs 3 approaches to limit off-gassing: composition limits, emission factors, and performance-based standards. For IEQ Credit 4.1, Low-Emitting Materials—Adhesives and Sealants, project teams may use either the composition limit approach or VOC budgets to determine compliance. For the budget approach, see the Calculations section, below.

Composition Limits

All materials that emit contaminants with the potential to enter the indoor air will be considered indoor contaminant sources. They include all surfaces in contact with indoor air such as: flooring; walls; ceilings; interior furnishings; suspended ceiling systems and the materials above those suspended ceilings; ventilation system components that contact the ventilation supply or return air; and all materials inside wall cavities, ceiling cavities, floor cavities, or horizontal or vertical chases. These materials include caulking materials for windows, as well as insulation in ceilings or walls. An example of a material that has little or no potential to contact indoor air is siding on the exterior of waterproofing membrane. In this approach, the formulation of a product is controlled. Limits are set on the amount of VOCs permitted in a given volume of the product. The threshold limits and the content within a particular product are generally expressed in grams per liter (g/L). 3 IEQ credits use this approach: 4.1, Low-Emitting Materials—Adhesives and Sealants; 4.2, Low-Emitting Materials—Paints and Coatings; and 4.3, Low-Emitting Materials—Flooring Systems. IEQ Credit 4.4, Low-Emitting Materials—Composite Wood and Agrifiber Products, also controls formulation by not allowing any added urea-formaldehyde resins.

5. Timeline and Team

The requirements for products and activities covered in IEQ Credit 4, Low-Emitting Materials—Adhesives and Sealants, should be noted in the project specifications and, ideally, within the specific section applicable to a particular trade or supplier.

Design Phase

Credit requirements should be clearly stated in project specifications. Refer to the credit requirements in both Division 1 and in the technical divisions. Indicate what must be provided in the way of cut sheets, MSD sheets, certificates, and test reports. Consider making submittal of this compliance documentation a condition of product approval.

Construction Phase

Meeting the requirements set in IEQ Credit 4, Low-Emitting Materials—Adhesives and Sealants, is not everyday practice for all construction teams and suppliers. Consider asking the project owner to stress the importance of meeting the LEED requirements during prebid meetings and again at the time of contract award. During these sessions, have LEED Accredited Professionals available and ask for questions. Include requirements in subcontracts and purchase orders. Determine whether the VOC budget compliance path will be necessary and track materials according to the budget planned by the project team. If a product with high VOC levels is used unintentionally, the VOC budget approach may be used to determine whether credit compliance can be attained

Follow-Up during Construction

Consider providing LEED project signage alongside the project safety signage. In progress meetings, address topics relevant to lo w-emitting materials and the LEED requirements. Finally, assign someone on the construction team to provide leadership and ensure compliance in meeting low-emitting materials goals.

6. Calculations

VOC Budget Methodology

Determining a VOC budget is one way to achieve compliance under IEQ Credit 4.1, Low-Emitting Materials—Adhesives and Sealants. To demonstrate that the overall low-VOC performance has been attained for paints and adhesives separately, not in combination, compare the baseline case and the design case. When the design (or actual) is less than the baseline, the credit requirement is satisfied. The values used in the comparison calculation are the total VOCs contained in the products (e.g., sealants) used on the project. To determine total VOCs, multiply the volume of the product used by the threshold VOC level for the baseline case and actual product VOC level for the design case. The baseline application rate should not be greater than that used in the design case. As the term *budget* implies, this compliance path involves an up-front decision. If a product with high VOC levels is used unintentionally, follow the VOC budget approach to determine whether credit compliance can nevertheless be attained.

7. Documentation Guidance

As a first step in preparing to complete the LEED Online documentation requirements, work through the following measures. Refer to LEED Online for the complete descriptions of all required documentation.

- Maintain a list of all indoor aerosol adhesive products, adhesives, sealants, and sealant primers used on the project; include each product's manufacturer's name, product name, specific VOC data (g/L, less water), and the corresponding allowable VOC from the referenced standard

- Track the amount of each product used in the project if the VOC budget approach is taken.

8. Examples

There are no examples for this credit.

9. Exemplary Performance

This credit is not eligible for Exemplary Performance under the Innovation in Design section.

10. Regional Variations

There are no regional variations for this credit.

11. Operations and Maintenance Considerations

Implement a sustainable purchasing policy for the continued use of low-emitting materials during the building's operation. Help building operators find low-emitting products for repairs or alterations by providing them with the list of compliant products used during the construction process.

12. Resources

Please see USGBC's LEED Resources & Tools (http://www.usgbc.org/projecttools) for additional resources and technical information.

Webites

South Coast Air Quality Management District (SCAQMD) South Coast Rule 1168, VOC Limits
http://www.aqmd.gov/rules/reg/reg11/r1168.pdf
The South Coast Air Quality Management District is a governmental organization in southern California with the mission to maintain healthful air quality for its residents. The organization established source-specific standards to reduce air quality impacts.

Green Seal Standard 36 (GS–36)
http://www.greenseal.org/certification/standards/commercial_adhesives_GS_36.cfm
Green Seal is an independent, nonprofit organization that strives to achieve a healthier and cleaner environment by identifying and promoting products and services that cause less toxic pollution and waste, conserve resources and habitats, and minimize global warming and ozone depletion. GS–36 sets VOC limits for commercial adhesives.

13. Definitions

Adhesive is any substance that is used to bond 1 surface to another surface by attachment. Adhesives include adhesive bonding primers, adhesive primers, adhesive primers for plastics, and any other primer. (SCAQMD Rule 1168)

Aerosol adhesive is an aerosol product in which the spray mechanism is permanently housed in a nonrefillable can designed for hand-held application without the need for ancillary hoses or spray equipment. Aerosol adhesives include special-purpose spray adhesives, mist spray adhesives, and web spray adhesives. (SCAQMD Rule 1168)

Architectural nonporous sealant primer is a substance used as a sealant primer on nonporous materials.

Architectural porous sealant primer is a substance used as a sealant on porous materials.

Indoor adhesive, sealant, and/or sealant primer product is as an adhesive or sealant product applied on-site, inside the building's weatherproofing system.

Indoor air quality (IAQ) is the nature of air inside a building that affects the health and well-being of building occupants. It is considered acceptable when there are no known contaminants at harmful concentrations as determined by cognizant authorities and with which a substantial majority (80% or more) of the people exposed do not express dissatisfaction. (ASHRAE 62.1–2007)

Nonporous sealant is a substance used as a sealant on nonporous materials. Nonporous materials, such as plastic and metal, do not have openings in which fluids may be absorbed or discharged.

Occupants in a commercial building are workers who either have a permanent office or workstation or typically spend a minimum of 10 hours per week in the project building; in a residential building, regular occupants also include all persons who live in the building.

Off-gassing is the emission of **volatile organic compounds** (VOCs) from synthetic and natural products.

Ozone (O3) is a gas composed of 3 oxygen atoms. It is not usually emitted directly into the air but at ground-level is created by a chemical reaction between oxides of nitrogen (nox) and volatile organic compounds (VOCs) in the presence of sunlight. Ozone has the same chemical structure whether it occurs miles above the earth or at ground level and can be beneficial or harmful, depending on its location in the atmosphere. (U.S. Environmental Protection Agency)

Porous materials have tiny openings, often microscopic, that can absorb or discharge fluids. Examples include wood, fabric, paper, corrugated paperboard, and plastic foam. (SCAQMD Rule 1168)

A **sealant** has adhesive properties and is formulated primarily to fill, seal, or waterproof gaps or joints between 2 surfaces. Sealants include sealant primers and caulks. (SCAQMD Rule 1168)

A **sealant primer** is applied to a substrate, prior to the application of a sealant, to enhance the bonding surface. (SCAQMD Rule 1168)

Volatile organic compounds (VOCs) are carbon compounds (excluding carbon monoxide, carbon dioxide, carbonic acid, metallic carbides and carbonates, and ammonium carbonate) that participate in atmospheric photochemical reactions. The compounds vaporize (become a gas) at normal room temperatures.

LOW-EMITTING MATERIALS—PAINTS AND COATINGS

	CI
Credit	IEQ Credit 4.2
Points	1 point

Intent

To reduce the quantity of indoor air contaminants that are odorous, irritating and/or harmful to the comfort and well-being of installers and occupants.

Requirements

Paints and coatings used on the interior of the building (i.e. inside the weatherproofing system and applied on-site) must comply with the following criteria as applicable to the project scope[1]:

- Architectural paints and coatings applied to interior walls and ceilings — must not exceed the volatile organic compound (VOC) content limits established in Green Seal Standard GS-11, Paints, 1st Edition, May 20, 1993.

- Anti-corrosive and anti-rust paints applied to interior ferrous metal substrates must not exceed the VOC content limit of 250 g/L established in Green Seal Standard GS-03, Anti-Corrosive Paints, 2nd Edition, January 7, 1997.

- Clear wood finishes, floor coatings, stains, primers, sealers, and shellacs applied to interior elements: must not exceed the VOC content limits established for those coating types in South Coast Air Quality Management District (SCAQMD) Rule 1113, Architectural Coatings, effective January 1, 2004.

---

1   The use of a VOC budget is permissible for compliance with this credit.

1. Benefits and Issues to Consider

Refer to the Benefits and Issues section of IEQ Credit 4.1, Low-Emitting Materials—Adhesives and Sealants.

2. Related Credits

Because the intent of this credit is to reduce odorous, irritating, or harmful indoor air contaminants, the following other credits may be applicable:

- IEQ Credit 4.1: Low Emitting Materials—Adhesives and Sealants
- IEQ Credit 4.3: Low Emitting Materials—Flooring Systems
- IEQ Credit 4.4: Low Emitting Materials—Composite Wood and Agrifiber Products
- IEQ Credit 4.5: Low Emitting Materials—Systems Furniture and Seating

Scheduling strategies relating to the use and tracking of low-emitting materials may be addressed early in construction and prior to occupancy. The following are credits also affected by scheduling considerations:

- IEQ Credit 3.1: Construction IAQ Management Plan, During Construction
- IEQ Credit 3.2: Construction IAQ Management Plan, Before Occupancy

Project teams may wish to address smoking-related contaminants in the building in conjunction with other sources of air pollutants as outlined in the following credits:

- IEQ Prerequisite 2: Environmental Tobacco Smoke (ETS) Control
- IEQ Credit 5: Indoor Chemical and Pollutant Source Control

3. Summary of Referenced Standards

Green Seal Standard GS–11

http://www.greenseal.org/certification/standards/paints_GS_11.pdf

Green Seal is an independent nonprofit organization that strives to achieve a healthier and cleaner environment by identifying and promoting products and services that cause less toxic pollution and waste, conserve resources and habitats, and minimize global warming and ozone depletion. GS–11 sets VOC limits for commercial flat paints and nonflat paints . Tables 1 and 2 summarize Green Seal Standard GS–11.

Green Seal Standard GC–03

http://www.greenseal.org/certification/standards/anti-corrosivepaints.pdf

GC–03 sets VOC limits for anti-corrosive and anti-rust paints.

The GC-03 VOC limits applicable for this credit are summarized in Table 1. IEQc4.2 Applicable VOC Limits.

South Coast Air Quality Management District (SCAQMD) Rule 1113, Architectural Coatings

http://www.aqmd.gov/rules

The South Coast Air Quality Management District is a governmental organization in southern California with the mission to maintain healthful air quality for its residents. The organization established source-specific standards to reduce air quality impacts. The SCAQMD Rule 1113 VOC limits applicable for this credit are summarized in Table 1. IEQc4.2 Applicable VOC Limits.

Table 1. IEQc4.2 Applicable VOC Limits

Product Type	Referenced Standard	VOC Limit (g/L minus water)
Interior Flat Coating or Primer	Green Seal GS-11, 1993	50
Interior Non-Flat Coating or Primer	Green Seal GS-11, 1993	150
Anti-Corrosive/ Anti-Rust Paint	Green Seal GC-03, 2nd Edition, 1997	250
Clear Wood Finish: Lacquer	SCAQMD Rule 1113, 2004	550
Clear Wood Finish: Sanding Sealer	SCAQMD Rule 1113, 2004	350
Clear Wood Finish: Varnish	SCAQMD Rule 1113, 2004	350
Clear Brushing Lacquer	SCAQMD Rule 1113, 2004	680
Floor Coatings	SCAQMD Rule 1113, 2004	100
Sealers and Undercoaters	SCAQMD Rule 1113, 2004	200
Shellac: Clear	SCAQMD Rule 1113, 2004	730
Shellac: Pigmented	SCAQMD Rule 1113, 2004	550
Stain	SCAQMD Rule 1113, 2004	250
Concrete Curing Compounds	SCAQMD Rule 1113, 2004	350
Japans/ Faux Finishing Coatings	SCAQMD Rule 1113, 2004	350
Magnesite Cement Coatings	SCAQMD Rule 1113, 2004	450
Pigmented Lacquer	SCAQMD Rule 1113, 2004	550
Waterproofing Sealers	SCAQMD Rule 1113, 2004	250
Waterproofing Concrete/ Masonry Sealers	SCAQMD Rule 1113, 2004	400
Wood Preservatives	SCAQMD Rule 1113, 2004	350
Low-Solids Coatings	SCAQMD Rule 1113, 2004	120*

*Note: VOC levels for Low-Solids Coatings are measured in grams of VOC per liter of material.

4. Implementation

Refer to the Implementation section of IEQ Credit 4.1, Low-Emitting Materials—Adhesives and Sealants.

5. Timeline and Team

Refer to the Timeline and Team section of IEQ Credit 4.1, Low-Emitting Materials—Adhesives and Sealants.

6. Calculations

Use the VOC budget methodology described in the Calculations section of IEQ Credit 4.1, Low-Emitting Materials—Adhesives and Sealants.

7. Documentation Guidance

As a first step in preparing to complete the LEED Online documentation requirements, work through the following measures. Refer to LEED Online for the complete descriptions of all required documentation.

- Maintain a listing of each indoor paint and coating product used on the project; include each product's manufacturer's name, product name, specific VOC data (in g/L, less water), and the corresponding allowable VOC from the referenced standard.

- Track the amount of each product used if the VOC budget approach is taken.

8. Examples

There are no examples for this credit.

9. Exemplary Performance

This credit is not eligible for exemplary performance under the Innovation in Design section.

10. Regional Variations

There are no regional variations for this credit.

11. Operations and Maintenance Considerations

Implement a sustainable purchasing policy for the continued use of low-emitting materials during the building's operation. Help building operators find low-emitting products for repairs or alterations by providing them with the list of compliant products. Provide maintenance personnel with information about original products to aid in color matching. Using fewer types of paint and coating products in the overall design makes maintenance easier.

12. Resources

Please see USGBC's LEED Resources & Tools (http://www.usgbc.org/projecttools) for additional resources and technical information.

Websites
Green Seal
http://www.greenseal.org

South Coast Air Quality Management District
http://www.aqmd.gov

13. Definitions

Anticorrosive paints are coatings formulated and recommended for use in preventing the corrosion of ferrous metal substrates.

A **coating** is applied to beautify, protect, or provide a barrier to a surface. (SCAQMD Rule 1113)

Flat coatings register a gloss of less than 15 on an 85-degree meter or less than 5 on a 60-degree meter.

Nonflat coatings register a gloss of 5 or greater on a 60-degree meter and a gloss of 15 or greater on an 85-degree meter.

Contaminants are unwanted airborne constituents that may reduce air quality. (ASHRAE 62.1–2007)

Indoor air quality (IAQ) is the nature of air inside a building that affects the health and well-being of building occupants. It is considered acceptable when there are no known contaminants at harmful concentrations as determined by cognizant authorities and with which a substantial majority (80% or more) of the people exposed do not express dissatisfaction. (ASHRAE 62.1–2007)

Indoor paints or **coating products** are applied on-site inside a building's weatherproofing system.

Occupants in a commercial building are workers who either have a permanent office or workstation or typically spend a minimum of 10 hours per week in the project building; in a residential building, regular occupants also include all persons who live in the building.

Paint is a liquid, liquefiable, or mastic composition that is converted to a solid protective, decorative, or functional adherent film after application as a thin layer. These coatings are intended for on-site application to interior or exterior surfaces of residential, commercial, institutional or industrial buildings.

A **primer** is a material applied to a substrate to improve adhesion of subsequently applied coats.

Sealers are coatings applied to either block materials from penetrating into or leaching out of a substrate, to prevent subsequent coatings from being absorbed by the substrate, or to prevent harm to subsequent coatings by materials in the substrate.

Volatile organic compounds (**VOCs**) are carbon compounds (excluding carbon monoxide, carbon dioxide, carbonic acid, metallic carbides and carbonates, and ammonium carbonate) that participate in atmospheric photochemical reactions. The compounds vaporize (become a gas) at normal room temperatures.

	CI
Credit	IEQ Credit 4.3
Points	1 point

Intent

To reduce the quantity of indoor air contaminants that are odorous, irritating and/or harmful to the comfort and well-being of installers and occupants.

Requirements

OPTION 1

All flooring must comply with the following as applicable to the project scope:

- All carpet installed in the building interior must meet the testing and product requirements of the Carpet and Rug Institute Green Label Plus[1] program.

- All carpet cushion installed in the building interior must meet the requirements of the Carpet and Rug Institute Green Label program.

- All carpet adhesive must have less than 50 g/L VOC.

- All hard surface flooring must meet the requirements of the FloorScore[2] standard (current as of the date of this rating system, or more stringent version) as shown with testing by an independent third-party. Mineral-based finish flooring products such as tile, masonry, terrazzo, and cut stone without integral organic-based coatings and sealants and unfinished/untreated solid wood flooring qualify for credit without any IAQ testing requirements. However, associated site-applied adhesives, grouts, finishes and sealers must be compliant for a mineral-based or unfinished/untreated solid wood flooring system to qualify for credit.

- Concrete, wood, bamboo, and cork floor finishes such as sealer, stain and finish must meet the requirements of South Coast Air Quality Management District (SCAQMD) Rule 1113, Architectural Coatings, effective January 1, 2004.

- Tile setting adhesives and grout must meet South Coast Air Quality Management District (SCAQMD) Rule 1168. VOC limits correspond to an effective date of July 1, 2005 and rule amendment date of January 7, 2005.

OR

OPTION 2

All flooring products must meet the testing and product requirements of the California Department of Public Health Standard Practice for the Testing of Volatile Organic Emissions from Various Sources Using Small-Scale Environmental Chambers, including 2004 Addenda. Mineral-based finish flooring products such as tile, masonry, terrazzo, and cut stone without integral organic-based coatings and sealants and unfinished/untreated solid wood flooring qualify for credit without any IAQ testing requirements. However, associated site-applied adhesives, grouts, finishes and sealers must be compliant for a mineral-based or unfinished/untreated solid wood flooring system to qualify for credit.

1 The Green Label Plus program for carpets and its associated VOC emission criteria in micrograms per square meter per hour, along with information on testing method and sample collection developed by the Carpet and Rug Institute (CRI) in coordination with California's Sustainable Building Task Force and the California Department of Public Health, are described in Section 9, Acceptable Emissions Testing for Carpet, DHS Standard Practice CA/DHS/EHLB/R-174, dated 07/15/04.

2 FloorScore is a voluntary, independent certification program that tests and certifies hard surface flooring and associated products for compliance with criteria adopted in California for indoor air emissions of Volatile Organic Compounds (VOCs) with potential health effects. The program uses a small-scale chamber test protocol and incorporates VOC emissions criteria, developed by the California Department of Public Health.

1. Benefits and Issues to Consider

Refer to the Benefits and Issues section of IEQ Credit 4.1, Low-Emitting Materials—Adhesives and Sealants.

2. Related Credits

Because the intent of this credit is to reduce odorous, irritating, or harmful indoor air contaminants, the following other credits may be applicable:

- IEQ Credit 4.1: Low Emitting Materials—Adhesives and Sealants
- IEQ Credit 4.2 Low Emitting Materials—Paints and Coatings
- IEQ Credit 4.4: Low Emitting Materials—Composite Wood and Agrifiber Products
- IEQ Credit 4.5: Low Emitting Materials—Systems Furniture and Seating

Scheduling strategies relating to the use and tracking of Low-Emitting Materials may be addressed early in construction and prior to occupancy. The following are credits also affected by scheduling considerations:

- IEQ Credit 3.1: Construction IAQ Management Plan During Construction
- IEQ Credit 3.2: Construction IAQ Management Plan Before Occupancy

Project teams may wish to address smoking-related contaminants in the building in conjunction with other sources of air pollutants as outlined in the following credits:

- IEQ Prerequisite 2: Environmental Tobacco Smoke (ETS) Control
- IEQ Credit 5: Indoor Chemical and Pollutant Source Control

3. Summary of Referenced Standards

Carpet and Rug Institute (CRI) Green Label Plus Testing Program
Carpet and Rug Institute
http://www.carpet-rug.com
The Carpet and Rug Institute (CRI) is a trade organization representing the carpet and rug industry. Green Label Plus is an independent testing program that identifies carpets with very low VOC emissions. The CRI website describes the program and the associated VOC emission criteria in micrograms per square meter per hour. These criteria were developed by the Carpet and Rug Institute (CRI) in coordination with California's Sustainable Building Task Force and the California Department of Health Services (DHS). In the CRI Green Label Plus Program, emission rates must be verified by annual tests. Approved certification numbers can be reviewed on the CRI website under Indoor Air Quality/Green Label Plus/Approved companies. Approved products are listed under the company heading.

South Coast Air Quality Management District (SCAQMD) Rule 1168, VOC Limits
http://www.aqmd.gov/rules/reg/reg11/r1168.pdf
The South Coast Air Quality Management District is a governmental organization in southern California with the mission to maintain healthful air quality for its residents. The organization established source specific standards to reduce air quality impacts.

South Coast Air Quality Management District (SCAQMD) Rule 1113, Architectural Coatings
http://www.aqmd.gov/rules/reg/reg11/r1113.pdf
The South Coast Air Quality Management District is a governmental organization in southern California with the mission to maintain healthful air quality for its residents. The organization established source specific standards to reduce air quality impacts. The South Coast Rule 1168 VOC limits for adhesives are summarized in Table 1.

FloorScore™ Program
Resilient Floor Covering Institute

http://www.rfci.com/int_FloorScore.htm

According to its website, "The FloorScore program, developed by the Resilient Floor Covering Institute (RFCI) in conjunction with Scientific Certification Systems (SCS), tests and certifies flooring products for compliance with indoor air quality emission requirements adopted in California. Flooring products include vinyl, linoleum, laminate flooring, wood flooring, ceramic flooring, rubber flooring, wall base, and associated sundries."

Carpet Testing Criteria

Carpet must not exceed the maximum target emission factors used in the CRI Green Label program and follow the test protocol used by Green Label Plus. Test results submitted must be no more than 2 years old at the time of submission. Standard Practice for the Testing of Volatile Organic Emissions from Various Sources using Small-Scale Environmental Chambers (State of California Specification Section 01350).

State of California Specification Section 01350
www.ciwmb.ca.gov/GreenBuilding/specs/Section01350/#Indoor

This standard practice document specifies carpet emissions testing criteria that will satisfy the credit requirements.

Environmental Technology Verification (ETV) Large Chamber Test Protocol for Measuring Emissions of VOCs and Aldehydes, effective September 1999
Research Triangle Institute and U.S. EPA

http://www.epa.gov/etv/pdfs/vp/07_vp_furniture.pdf

Under the leadership of the EPA, a testing protocol committee developed the referenced standards. The protocol requires the placement of the seating product or furniture assembly to be tested in a climatically controlled chamberA controlled quantity of conditioned air is drawn through the chamber, and emission concentrations are measured at set intervals over a 4-day period.

4. Implementation
Refer to the Implementation section of IEQ Credit 4.1, Low-Emitting Materials—Adhesives and Sealants.

Emissions Factors
The California Department of Health Services Standard Practice for the Testing of Volatile Organic Emissions from Various Sources Using Small-Scale Environmental Chambers, including 2004 Addenda, sets limits the rate of off-gassing. The rate is stated as the mass of contaminant that may be off-gassed by a given unit quantity of the product in a set period of time. This approach is used for carpet in IEQ Credit 4.3, Low-Emitting Materials—Flooring Systems, where the rate is expressed as micrograms of contaminant per square meter of carpet per hour. These tests, which are now being conducted on an array a variety of product types, place samples of precise size in test chambers.

Air samples are drawn off at set times (generally over several days) and analyzed. There are extensive protocols established to make sure that the testing is representative of actual conditions on a project site and consistent between similar products from multiple manufactures. The Carpet and Rug Institute (CRI) Green Label Plus program uses emissions factor test results for its certifications.

5. Timeline and Team
Refer to the Timeline and Team section of IEQ Credit 4.1, Low-Emitting Materials—Adhesives and Sealants.

	IEQ
CI	Credit 4.3

6. Calculations

There are no calculations required for this credit.

7. Documentation Guidance

As a first step in preparing to complete the LEED Online documentation requirements, work through the following measures. Refer to LEED Online for the complete descriptions of all required documentation.

- Maintain a listing of each carpet, carpet cushion, and carpet adhesive installed on the project in the building interior andrecord the VOC content for each adhesive.

- Maintain a listing of each hard surface flooring product, tile setting adhesive, and grout installed on the project in the building interior andrecord the VOC content for each tile setting adhesive and grout.

8. Examples

Figure 1. Sample Product Information for CRI Green Label Plus Carpeting

Style Number 1111	
Specifications	
Construction	Textured loop pattern
Yarn content	Nylon with 25% recycled content
Dye method	Solution
Machine gauge	1/10 in (39.4 col/10 cm)
Stitch count	11 S.P.I. (43.3/10 cm)
Finished pile thickness	0.124 in (3.15 mm)
Average density	8,710
Yarn weight tufted	30 oz/yd² (1085 g/m²)
Primary backing	Polypropylene
Secondary backing	Woven polypropylene with postconsumer recycled content
Width	12 ft (3.66 m)
Pattern repeat	0.40 in w x .047 in l (1.01 cm x 1.19 cm)
Total recycled content	2.43%
Performance	
Flameresistance	Passes (DOC FF-1-70)
Flooring radiant panel	Class 1 (ASTM E-662)
Smoke density	Less than 450 (ASTM E-662)
CRI Green Label Plus	Certification # GLP 0000
Warranties	
Example nylon warranty	Lifetime carpet static warranty
Example nylon warranty	Lifetime carpet wear, limited warranty
Example nylon certification	Class III, extra heavy traffic
Example nylon content	Minimum 25% recycled content
Example nylon recycling	Available
Additional Information	
Custom colors	Contact sales representative
Coordinating styles	Multiple

9. Exemplary Performance

This credit is not eligible for exemplary performance under the Innovation in Design section.

10. Regional Variations

There are no regional variances for this credit.

11. Operations and Maintenance Considerations

Implement a sustainable purchasing policy for the continued use of low-emitting materials during the building's operation. Help building operators find low-emitting products for repairs or alterations by providing them with the list of compliant products.

Use of carpet tiles saves material over the life of the building because individual tiles can be replaced as needed. Using fewer types of flooring and flooring products makes maintenance easier. If specialized flooring materials are specified, request maintenance information from product manufacturers and installers and give this information to the facilities staff.

12. Resources

Please see USGBC's LEED Resources & Tools (http://www.usgbc.org/projecttools) for additional resources and technical information.

Websites

Carpet and Rug Institute
http://www.carpet-rug.org

Floorscore
http://www.rfci.com/int_FloorScore.htm
http://www.scscertified.com/ecoproducts/indoorairquality/floorscore.html

GreenGuard
http://www.greenguard.org/

Scientific Certification System, Inc.
http://www.scscertified.com/

South Coast Air Quality Management District
http://www.aqmd.gov/rules

13. Definitions

Contaminants are unwanted airborne constituents that may reduce air quality. (ASHRAE 62.1–2007)

Hard surface flooring includes vinyl, linoleum, laminate flooring, wood flooring, rubber flooring, wall base, and associated sundries.

Indoor carpet systems are carpet, carpet adhesive, or carpet cushion products installed on-site inside the building's weatherproofing system.

Indoor air quality (**IAQ**) is the nature of air inside a building that affects the health and well-being of building occupants. It is considered acceptable when there are no known contaminants at harmful concentrations as determined by cognizant authorities and with which a substantial majority (80% or more) of the people exposed do not express dissatisfaction. (ASHRAE 62.1–2007)

Volatile organic compounds (**VOCs**) are carbon compounds (excluding carbon monoxide, carbon dioxide, carbonic acid, metallic carbides and carbonates, and ammonium carbonate) that participate in atmospheric photochemical reactions. The compounds vaporize (become a gas) at normal room temperatures.

LOW-EMITTING MATERIALS—COMPOSITE WOOD AND AGRIFIBER PRODUCTS

	CI
Credit	IEQ Credit 4.4
Points	1 point

Intent

To reduce the quantity of indoor air contaminants that are odorous, irritating and/or harmful to the comfort and well-being of installers and occupants.

Requirements

Composite wood and agrifiber products used on the interior of the building (i.e. inside the weatherproofing system) must contain no added urea-formaldehyde resins. Laminate adhesives used to fabricate on-site and shop-applied composite wood and agrifiber assemblies must not contain added urea-formaldehyde resins.

Composite wood and agrifiber products are defined as: particleboard, medium density fiberboard (MDF), plywood, wheatboard, strawboard, panel substrates and door cores. Materials considered fixtures, furniture, and equipment (FF&E) are not considered base building elements and are not included.

Products covered by IEQ Credit 4.5, Low-Emitting Materials, System Furniture and Seating are excluded from these requirements.

1. Benefits and Issues to Consider

Refer to the Benefits and Issues section of IEQ Credit 4.1, Low-Emitting Materials—Adhesives and Sealants.

2. Related Credits

Because the intent of this credit is to reduce odorous, irritating, or harmful indoor air contaminants, the following other credits may be applicable:

- IEQ Credit 4.1: Low Emitting Materials—Adhesives and Sealants
- IEQ Credit 4.2: Low Emitting Materials—Paints and Coatings
- IEQ Credit 4.3: Low Emitting Materials—Flooring Systems
- IEQ Credit 4.5: Low Emitting Materials—Systems Furniture and Seating

Scheduling strategies relating to the use and tracking of low-emitting materials may be addressed early in construction and prior to occupancy. The following are credits also affected by scheduling considerations:

- IEQ Credit 3.1: Construction IAQ Management Plan—During Construction
- IEQ Credit 3.2: Construction IAQ Management Plan—Before Occupancy

Project teams may wish to address smoking-related contaminants in the building in conjunction with other sources of air pollutants as outlined in the following credits:

- IEQ Prerequisite 2: Environmental Tobacco Smoke (ETS) Control
- IEQ Credit 5: Indoor Chemical and Pollutant Source Control

3. Summary of Referenced Standards

There are no standards referenced for this credit.

4. Implementation

Refer to the Implementation section of IEQ Credit 4.1, Low-Emitting Materials—Adhesives and Sealants.

5. Timeline and Team

Refer to the Timeline and Team section of IEQ Credit 4.1, Low-Emitting Materials—Adhesives and Sealants.

6. Implementation: Calculations

There are no calculations required for this credit.

7. Documentation Guidance

As a first step in preparing to complete the LEED Online documentation requirements, work through the following measures. Refer to LEED Online for the complete descriptions of all required documentation.

- Maintain a listing of each composite wood and agrifiber product installed in the building interior and confirm that each product does not contain any added urea-formaldehyde

8. Examples

There are no examples for this credit.

9. Exemplary Performance

This credit is not eligible for exemplary performance under the Innovation in Design section.

10. Regional Variations

No regional variations have been identified for this credit.

11. Operations and Maintenance Considerations

Implement a sustainable purchasing policy for the continued use of low-emitting materials during the building's operation. Help building operators find low-emitting products for repairs or alterations by providing them with the list of compliant products.

If specialized composite wood or agrifiber materials are specified, request maintenance information from product manufacturers and installers and give this information to the facilities management team.

12. Resources

Please see USGBC's LEED Resources & Tools (http://www.usgbc.org/projecttools) for additional resources and technical information.

Websites

An Update on Formaldehyde
Consumer Product Safety Commission
http://www.cpsc.gov/CPSCPUB/PUBS/725.html
This informational document is from the Consumer Product Safety Commission.

13. Definitions

Agrifiber board is a composite panel product derived from recovered agricultural waste fiber from such sources as cereal straw, sugarcane bagasse, sunflower husk, walnut shells, coconut husks, and agricultural prunings. The raw fibers are processed and mixed with resins to produce panel products with characteristics similar to those derived from wood fiber. The following conditions describe which products must comply with the credit requirements:

1. The product is inside the building's waterproofing system.

2. Composite components used in assemblies are to be included (e.g., door cores, panel substrates).

3. The product is part of the base building systems.

Composite wood consists of wood or plant particles or fibers bonded together by a synthetic resin or binder. Examples include plywood, particle board, oriented-strand board (OSB), medium-density fiberboard (MDF), and composite door cores. The following conditions describe which products must comply with the credit requirements:

1. The product is inside the building's waterproofing system.

2. Composite wood components used in assemblies are included (e.g., door cores, panel substrates, plywood sections of I-beams).

3. The product is part of the base building systems.

Contaminants are unwanted airborne constituents that may reduce air quality. (ASHRAE 62.1–2007)

Formaldehyde is a naturally occurring VOC found in small amounts in animals and plants but carcinogenic and irritating to most people when present in high concentrations, causing headaches, dizziness, mental impairment, and other symptoms. When present in the air at levels above 0.1 ppm parts of air, it can cause watery eyes, burning sensations in the eyes, nose and throat; nausea; coughing; chest tightness; wheezing; skin rashes; and asthmatic and allergic reactions.

Indoor composite wood or **agrifiber** is a composite product installed on-site inside the building's weatherproofing system.

Indoor air quality (**IAQ**) is the nature of air inside a building that affects the health and well-being of building occupants. It is considered acceptable when there are no known contaminants at harmful concentrations as determined by cognizant authorities and with which a substantial majority (80% or more) of the people exposed do not express dissatisfaction. (ASHRAE 62.1–2007)

Laminate adhesive is used in wood or agrifiber products (veneered panels, composite wood products contained in engineered lumber, door assemblies, etc.).

Off-gassing is the emission of volatile organic compounds (VOCs) from synthetic and natural products.

Urea-formaldehyde is a combination of urea and formaldehyde that is used in some glues and may emit formaldehyde at room temperature.

Phenol-formaldehyde, which off-gasses only at high temperature, is used for exterior products, although many of those products are suitable for interior applications.

	CI
Credit	IEQ Credit 4.5
Points	1 point

Intent

To reduce the quantity of indoor air contaminants that are odorous, irritating and/or harmful to the comfort and well-being of installers and occupants.

Requirements

All systems furniture[1] and seating[2] that was manufactured, refurbished or refinished within 1 year prior[3] to occupancy must meet 1 of the options below.

OPTION 1

Furniture and seating are Greenguard Indoor Air Quality Certified.

OR

OPTION 2

Calculated indoor air concentrations that are less than or equal to those listed in Table 1 for furniture systems and seating determined by a procedure based on ANSI/BIFMA M7.1-2007 and ANSI/BIFMA X7.1-2007 testing protocol conducted in an independent third-party air quality testing laboratory.

The requirement in Section 5 of ANSI/BIFMA X7.1-2007 is waived for LEED purposes. Section 5 requires that laboratories used to perform the emissions testing and/or provide analytical results must be independently accredited to ISO/IEC 17025, "General requirements for the competence of testing and calibration laboratories."

Table 1. Maximum Indoor Air Concentrations

Chemical Contaminant	Emission Limits Systems Furniture	Emission Limits Seating
TVOC	0.5 mg/m³	0.25 mg/m³
Formaldehyde	50 parts per billion	25 parts per billion
Total Aldehydes	100 parts per billion	50 parts per billion
4 – Phenylcyclohexene (4-PCH)	0.0065 mg/m³	0.00325 mg/m³

1   Systems furniture is defined as either a panel-based workstation comprised of modular interconnecting panels, hang-on components and drawer/filing components, or a freestanding grouping of furniture items and their components that have been designed to work in concert. Furniture other than systems furniture and task and guest chairs used with systems furniture is defined as occasional furniture and is excluded from the credit requirements.
2   Seating is defined as task and guest chairs used with systems furniture
3   Salvaged and used furniture that is more than 1-year-old at time of occupancy is excluded from the credit requirements.

1. Benefits and Issues to Consider

Refer to the Benefits and Issues section of IEQ Credit 4.1, Low-Emitting Materials—Adhesives and Sealants.

2. Related Credits

Because the intent of this credit is to reduce odorous, irritating, or harmful indoor air contaminants, the following other credits may be applicable:

- IEQ Credit 4.1: Low Emitting Materials—Adhesives and Sealants
- IEQ Credit 4.2: Low Emitting Materials—Paints and Coatings
- IEQ Credit 4.3: Low Emitting Materials—Flooring Systems
- IEQ Credit 4.4: Low Emitting Materials—Composite Wood and Agrifiber Products

Scheduling strategies relating to the use and tracking of low-emitting materials may be addressed early in construction and prior to occupancy. The following are credits also affected by scheduling considerations:

- IEQ Credit 3.1: Construction IAQ Management Plan During Construction
- IEQ Credit 3.2: Construction IAQ Management Plan Before Occupancy

Project teams may wish to address smoking-related contaminants in the building in conjunction with other sources of air pollutants as outlined in the following credits:

- IEQ Prerequisite 2: Environmental Tobacco Smoke (ETS) Control
- IEQ Credit 5: Indoor Chemical and Pollutant Source Control

3. Summary of Referenced Standards

Greenguard™ Certification Program

Greenguard Environmental Institute (GEI)

http://www.greenguard.org

GEI has "established performance-based standards to define goods with low chemical and particle emissions for use indoors," primarily for building materials; interior furnishings; furniture; electronics; and cleaning, maintenance, and personal care products. The standard establishes certification procedures that include "test methods, allowable emissions levels, product sample collection and handling, testing type and frequency, and program application processes and acceptance."

U.S. EPA's Environmental Technology Verification (ETV) Large Chamber Test Protocol for Measuring Emissions of VOCs and Aldehydes, effective September 1999

Research Triangle Institute and U.S. EPA

http://www.epa.gov/nrmrl/std/etv/pubs/07_vp_furniture.pdf

Under the leadership of the EPA, a testing protocol committee developed the referenced standards. The protocol requires the placement of the seating product or furniture assembly to be tested in a climatically controlled chamber. A controlled quantity of conditioned air is drawn through the chamber, and emission concentrations are measured at set intervals over a 4-day period.

4. Implementation

The sections under IEQ Credit 4, Low-Emitting Materials, apply to products and installation processes that have the potential to adversely affect the IAQ of a project space and, consequently, those occupants exposed to the off-gassing of contaminants.

LEED for Commercial Interiors IEQ Credit 4 employs 3 approaches to limit off-gassing: composition limits, emission factors, and performance-based standards. For IEQ Credit 4.5, Low-Emitting Materials—Systems Furniture and Seating, the performance-based standards approach applies.

Performance-Based Standards

This approach calculates the amount of contaminants each product will add to the air. The protocols are very similar to those for emission factor testing, but are crafted to allow for testing of more complex assemblies such as systems furniture. Again, groups of products are placed in a test chamber. Air is circulated in the chamber, simulating the conditions where the product would normally be used. At set intervals, samples of the air are taken and analyzed. The results are reported in the same units of measure established for air quality and used in the IAQ testing procedure of IEQ Credit 3.2, Construction IAQ Management Plan Before Occupancy—parts per million, parts per billion, or micrograms per cubic meter of air. The performance-based standards approach is used in IEQ Credit 4.5, Low-Emitting Materials—Systems Furniture and Seating. The Greenguard Institute testing program for systems furniture and office seating uses performance-based standards. Using products listed as Greenguard certified is 1 means of compliance for IEQ Credit 4.5, Low-Emitting Materials—Systems Furniture and Seating. They are certified as having test results below the threshold contaminant amounts.

In the selection of systems furniture and multiple office seating, the specifier should confirm that the desired product will meet the testing requirements at the time it is manufactured.

The Greenguard Environmental Institute provides a listing of the products it has certified. Additional manufacturers may also have met the testing requirements set out in this credit.

Performance-Based Emissions Limits

By satisfying the test results referenced in LEED for Commercial Interiors IEQ Credit 4.5, Low-Emitting Materials—Systems Furniture and Seating, the product should not increase the concentration of contaminants in the air around it by more than the threshold limits; the values are expressed as either mg/m^3 or parts per billion.

The testing protocol that covers systems furniture uses a large chamber where a full workstation is assembled. The workstation size, mix of components, and types of materials (including fabrics and finishes) are intended to be representative of what is most commonly used in actual installations. Product specifiers may want to confer with the manufacturer when considering substitutions or if the density of the components will be higher than in a normal application.

For the performance-based standard used in this credit to be applicable at the project site, other considerations need to be satisfied. The air velocity and outdoor air rate introduced into the work place should meet ASHRAE 62.1–2007, the same standard referenced in IEQ Prerequisite 1, Minimum Indoor Air Quality Performance. Adequate ventilation during installation helps dissipate early off-gassing. The flush-out period called for in IEQ Credit 3.2, Construction IAQ Management Plan Before Occupancy, is not to begin until furniture installation is complete.

Remember that systems furniture may be either a panel-based workstation comprising modular interconnecting panels, hang-on components, and drawer/filing components, or a free-standing grouping of furniture items and their components that have been designed to work in concert. Seating covered by this credit is defined as task and guest chairs used with systems furniture.

Work tools often attached to systems furniture are not included in the credit requirement. Other furniture is considered occasional furniture and does not need to be included in the credit documentation. Also, salvaged and used furniture that is more than 1 year old at the time of occupancy is excluded from the credit. Refurbishment of systems furniture or multiple office seating occurring within the 12-month period prior to occupancy must meet the credit requirements.

5. Timeline and Team

Refer to the Timeline and Team section of IEQ Credit 4.1, Low-Emitting Materials—Adhesives and Sealants.

6. Calculations

There are no calculations required for this credit.

7. Documentation Guidance

As a first step in preparing to complete the LEED Online documentation requirements, work through the following measures. Refer to LEED Online for the complete descriptions of all required documentation.

- Confirm that systems furniture and seating products specified for the project are Greenguard Indoor Air Quality certified

- Comply with U.S. Environmental Protection Agency's Environmental Technology Verification Large Chamber Test Protocol for Measuring Emissions of VOCs and Aldehydes (September 1999) testing protocol, or comply with ANSI/BIFMA M7.1–2007 and ANSI/BIFMA X7.1–2007 testing protocol.

8. Examples

There are no examples for this credit.

9. Exemplary Performance

This credit is not eligible for exemplary performance under the Innovation in Design section.

10. Regional Variations

There are no regional variations for this credit.

11. Operations and Maintenance Considerations

Implement a sustainable purchasing policy for low-emitting materials during the building's operation. Help building operators find low-emitting furniture systems for future installations by providing them with the list of compliant products.

12. Resources

Please see USGBC's LEED Resources & Tools (http://www.usgbc.org/projecttools) for additional resources and technical information.

Websites
Greenguard™ Certification Program
Greenguard Environmental Institute
http://www.greenguard.org/

U.S. EPA's Environmental Technology Verification (ETV) Large Chamber Test Protocol for Measuring Emissions of VOCs and Aldehydes, effective September, 1999
Research Triangle Institute and U.S. EPA
http://www.epa.gov/nrmrl/std/etv/pubs/07_vp_furniture.pdf
Under the leadership of EPA, a testing protocol committee developed the referenced standards. The protocol requires the placement of the seating product or furniture assembly to be tested in a climatically controlled chamber. A controlled quantity of conditioned air is drawn through the chamber, and emission concentrations are measured at set intervals over a 4-day period.

13. Definitions

Contaminants are unwanted airborne constituents that may reduce air quality (ASHRAE 62.1–2007).

Indoor air quality (IAQ) is the nature of air inside a building that affects the health and well-being of building occupants. It is considered acceptable when there are no known contaminants at harmful concentrations as determined by cognizant authorities and with which a substantial majority (80% or more) of the people exposed do not express dissatisfaction. (ASHRAE 62.1–2007)

Occasional furniture is located in lobbies and in conference rooms.

Off-gassing is the emission of volatile organic compounds (VOCs) from synthetic and natural products.

Systems furniture includes panel-based workstations comprising modular interconnecting panels, hang-on components, and drawer and filing components or a free-standing grouping of furniture items designed to work in concert.

Seating consists of task and guest chairs used with systems furniture.

Volatile organic compounds (VOCs) are carbon compounds that participate in atmospheric photochemical reactions (excluding carbon monoxide, carbon dioxide, carbonic acid, metallic carbides and carbonates, and ammonium carbonate). The compounds vaporize (become a gas) at normal room temperatures.

INDOOR CHEMICAL AND POLLUTANT SOURCE CONTROL

	CI
Credit	IEQ Credit 5
Points	1 point

Intent

To minimize building occupant exposure to potentially hazardous particulates, biological contaminants and chemical pollutants that degrade air and water quality.

Requirements

Design to minimize and control the entry of pollutants into the tenant space and later cross-contamination of regularly occupied areas through the following strategies:

- Employ permanent entryway systems at least 10 feet long in the primary direction of travel to capture dirt and particulates entering the building at regularly used exterior entryways. Acceptable entryway systems include permanently installed grates, grills and slotted systems that allow for cleaning underneath. Roll-out mats are acceptable only when maintained on a weekly basis by a contracted service organization.

- Sufficiently exhaust each space where hazardous gases or chemicals may be present or used (e.g. garages, housekeeping and laundry areas copying and printing rooms) to create negative pressure with respect to adjacent spaces when the doors to the room are closed. For each of these spaces, provide self-closing doors and deck-to-deck partitions or a hard-lid ceiling. The exhaust rate must be at least 0.50 cubic feet per minute (cfm) per square foot, with no air recirculation. The pressure differential with the surrounding spaces must be at least 5 Pascals (Pa) (0.02 inches of water gauge) on average and 1 Pa (0.004 inches of water) at a minimum when the doors to the rooms are closed.

- In mechanically ventilated buildings, each ventilations system that supplies outdoor air shall comply with the following:

  - Particle filters or air cleaning devices shall be provided to clean the outdoor air at any location prior to its introduction to occupied spaces.

  - These filters or devices shall be rated a minimum efficiency reporting value (MERV) of 13 or better in accordance with ASHRAE Standard 52.2.

  - Clean air filtration media shall be installed in all air systems after completion of construction and prior to occupancy.

1. Benefits and Issues to Consider

Environmental Issues

This credit recognizes projects that reduce or mitigate human contact with airborne chemicals and particles. Additional materials and energy may be required to provide entryway systems and isolate chemical-use areas.

Economic Issues

Additional sinks, drains, room separations, and separate exhaust systems for copying and housekeeping areas can increase the project's overall initial cost. Dedicated ventilation and exhaust systems may require additional ductwork and associated installation costs. Effective housekeeping processes, however, coupled with good human health initiatives, should prove economically sound over the lifetime of the project. Clean air can promote occupants' productivity, increasing profitability for the company. Reducing the potential for spills can avoid costly environmental cleanups. An environmentally sound building also supports the well-being of occupants, which may contribute to lowering health insurance rates and health care costs.

2. Related Credits

Coordinate minimum efficiency reporting values (MERVs) in final filtration media with these other credits:

- IEQ Credit 3.1: Construction IAQ Management Plan During Construction

- IEQ Credit 3.2: Construction IAQ Management Plan Before Occupancy

Additional ventilation systems designed to mitigate contaminating space activities may affect building energy performance and commissioning; these issues are covered under the following credits:

- EA Credit 1.3: Optimized Energy Performance—HVAC

- EA Prerequisite 2: Minimum Energy Performance

- EA Prerequisite 1: Fundamental Commissioning of Building Energy Systems

- EA Credit 2: Enhanced Commissioning

Ventilation system design will also be affected; installed systems must be capable of accommodating filtration media required for credit compliance. Refer to these credits:

- IEQ Prerequisite 1: Minimum Indoor Air Quality Performance

- IEQ Credit 1: Outdoor Air Delivery Monitoring

3. Summary of Referenced Standard

American National Standards Institute (ANSI)/ASHRAE 52.2–1999, Method of Testing General Ventilation Air-Cleaning Devices for Removal Efficiency by Particle Size

American Society of Heating, Refrigerating, and Air-Conditioning Engineers (ASHRAE)
http://www.ashrae.org

This standard presents methods for testing air cleaners for 2 performance characteristics: the device's capacity for removing particles from the air stream and the device's resistance to airflow. The minimum efficiency reporting value (MERV) is based on 3 composite average particle size removal efficiency points. Consult the standard for a complete explanation of MERV value calculations. Table 1 summarizes the requirements for MERV 13.

Table 1. Requirements for MERV 13

Composite Average Particle Size Efficiency (%)				Minimum Final Resistance (in. of water)
0.30 - 0.10 μm	1.0 - 3.0 μm	3.0 - 10.0 μm	(Pa)	
<75%	≥90%	≥90%	350	1.4

4. Implementation

The indoor air quality of buildings can be adversely affected by daily occupancy and operations. Occupants and building visitors contribute to indoor IAQ issues by introducing contaminants via shoes and clothing. Daily copier, fax, and printer operations add contaminants to the building's interior environment. This credit seeks to mitigate the amount of particulate, chemical, and biological contaminants that occupants are exposed to inside buildings and improve the indoor air quality.

Entryway Systems

Not all LEED for Commercial Interiors projects will need to satisfy all the requirements of this credit. When the project space does not have direct access to the exterior, the requirement for a permanent entryway system may be waived.

However, to earn this credit, the project team must demonstrate that if there is a need for a segregated area for hazardous gasses or chemicals, the requirements for its construction and ventilation are met. Finally, the project team must demonstrate that new air filtration media with a MERV 13 or better rating has been installed prior to occupancy.

The project team should incorporate permanent entryway systems, at all regularly used exterior access points to reduce the amount of contaminants tracked into the occupied space. The entryway systems should be designed to capture and remove particles from shoes without allowing buildup of contaminants.

Regularly used exterior access points will always include, but may not be limited to, the main building entry. Buildings that have entries from structured parking will have high use in these locations. In some instances, these entry points are inside a garage structure. While a covered garage does provide protection from the elements, it is a source of possible contaminants, and it functions as a direct connection to the outdoors. Buildings that have distinct employee and visitor entry points should include permanent entryway systems in these locations as well. The project team should evaluate all building entry points to determine whether permanent entryway systems should be incorporated.

Equip all exterior to interior entrances with entryway systems (e.g., grilles, grates, or mats) to catch and hold dirt particles and prevent contamination of the building interior. Entryway systems must extend 10 feet from the building entrance into the building interior. Open grates and grilles or other entryway systems that have a recessed collection area are generally thought to be most effective.

Mat systems should be appropriate for the climate. For example, durable coarse mats with large open loops are appropriate for capturing sand, mud or snow and should have a Class I fire-retardant rating.

High-void volume within fibers provides space for trapping dirt below the mat surface and enables water to spread to a larger area for improved drying. This inhibits dirt retracing and mold and mildew growth. High-void volume mats are also easier to vacuum or shake out. Fiber height provides maximum scraping surface at the shoe and mat interface and improves vacuum efficiency.

Entryway mats with solid backings capture dirt and moisture and help prevent soiling under the center of a mat and dirtying the floor after cleaning. A nonporous backing inhibits mold and mildew growth. The use of mold- and mildew-resistant materials in the mat construction can also prevent mold and mildew growth. Other recommended performance features for an entryway system include the following:

- Fire-retardant ratings that exceed DOC-FF-1-70, such as National Fire Protection Association (NFPA) -253 Class I and II, which can reduce insurance costs

- Electrostatic propensity levels of less than 2.5 kV, which means that the mat should not produce electrical discharges when a user touches other people or objects

Entryway systems constructed with recycled-content and rubber backings are preferable.

Hazardous Chemical Areas

The design team should locate high-volume copy, print, and fax equipment in enclosed rooms away from regularly occupied spaces. In order to effectively remove airborne contaminants generated by this type of equipment, the rooms must be physically separated from adjacent spaces. This may be accomplished through installation of deck-to-deck partitions or sealed gypsum board enclosures. Rooms with large openings but no doors will not meet the credit requirement. Installation of a self-closing door is an option for such spaces. To remove airborne contaminants and prevent cross-contamination into occupied spaces, copy, print, and fax rooms must be equipped with a dedicated exhaust system that creates negative pressure within the room, meeting the requirements of this credit. Convenience copier and printer use should be minimized if possible. Although encouraged, designing exhaust systems that account for convenience copier and printer use is not required for credit.

Chemical storage and mixing areas, such as janitor's closets and photo labs, should also be located away from occupant work areas. Additionally, these rooms must be physically separated from adjacent spaces via installation of deck-to-deck partitions or sealed gypsum board enclosures. Rooms must be equipped with a dedicated exhaust system that creates the required negative pressurization to ensure that cross-contamination into adjacent occupied spaces will not occur. Drywall ceilings may be used in place of full-height partitions, but acoustical lay-in ceilings are not adequate.

The definition of convenience printers and copiers, which are not required to be segregated in a chemical use area, is left to the discretion of the design team; convenience machines are generally smaller units shared by many office personnel for short print and copy jobs.

Battery banks used to provide temporary back-up power must be segregated to satisfy credit requirements.

Housekeeping facilities that are part of a common laundry room in residential or hospitality buildings must meet the chemical storage requirements.

All building HVAC systems must be able to accommodate filtration systems with a minimum MERV 13 rating. This may be difficult to achieve for spaces with low-capacity, packaged air-handling systems because of the size of these filters and their associated pressure drop.

5. Timeline and Team

During the early planning stage of a project, ask questions about the client's equipment requirements and usage patterns. This information will be critical in determining whether dedicated, isolated rooms will be required to house copy, fax, and print equipment.

During the schematic design phase, the architect or designer should identify locations for entryway systems and incorporate project-specific details to ensure their proper performance. Confirm the locations of areas where chemicals and high-volume copy, fax, and print equipment will be used. It may be possible to locate such rooms above or adjacent to 1 another to make individual exhaust systems unnecessary and thereby minimize exhaust ductwork. Also confirm that chemical and equipment rooms are properly isolated from adjacent spaces. The layout may prohibit deck-to-deck separation and separate ventilation systems for chemical use areas. Storage areas for recyclable materials might also be considered sources of contaminants, depending on the items recycled.

During the design development phase, the mechanical engineer should incorporate MERV 13 filters, dedicated exhaust systems; these elements will affect the fan sizing, shaft layout, and underground coordination.

Indoor chemical and pollutant source control is primarily a planning, design, and operations issue. In the construction phase, the space exhaust systems are installed and commissioned to ensure they meet the owner's requirements and the design intent.

6. Calculations

There are no calculations required for this credit.

7. Documentation Guidance

As a first step in preparing to complete the LEED Online documentation requirements, work through the following measures. Refer to LEED Online for the complete descriptions of all required documentation.

- Retain drawings showing the location and size of all permanent entryway systems and/or walk-off mats.

- Detail deck-to-deck partitions or hard-lid conditions at rooms known to have contaminates.

- Review negative pressure calculations at hazardous chemical areas to assure proper depressurization as the project evolves.

- Maintain product literature for MERV 13 or higher filters.

8. Examples

Figure 1. Requirements for Isolation Areas for Hazardous Gases or Chemicals

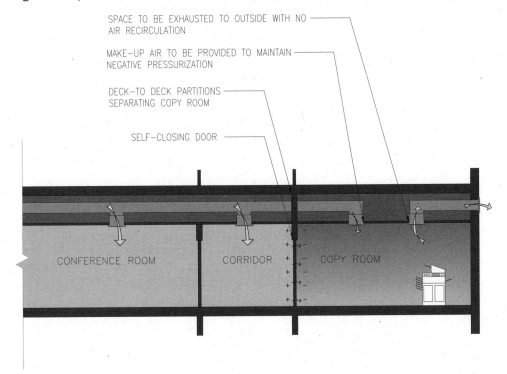

SPACE TO BE EXHAUSTED TO OUTSIDE WITH NO AIR RECIRCULATION

MAKE-UP AIR TO BE PROVIDED TO MAINTAIN NEGATIVE PRESSURIZATION

DECK-TO DECK PARTITIONS SEPARATING COPY ROOM

SELF-CLOSING DOOR

CONFERENCE ROOM   CORRIDOR   COPY ROOM

9. Exemplary Performance

This credit is not eligible for exemplary performance under the Innovation in Design section.

10. Regional Variations

Local weather conditions should be factored into determining the location and type of entryway systems. For example, in areas that receive heavy rain or snow, it may be prudent to locate entryway systems in an enclosed vestibule or inside the building. A floor drain beneath the grille may also be necessary.

11. Operations and Maintenance Considerations

Establish procedures and schedules for replacing filtration media and testing and maintaining exhaust systems and include them in the building's preventive maintenance plan.

Systems that require regular maintenance should be designed to be easily accessible to operations staff. Ensure that protocols for selecting, storing, and handling hazardous waste are clearly communicated to building operators; some janitorial supplies can degrade indoor air quality.

Develop, document, and record entryway maintenance practices in accordance with the manufacturer's specifications. These practices should specify cleaning strategies for the exterior and interior of entryways, general maintenance of entryway systems, and cleaning during inclement weather. Operations staff can reduce maintenance and replacement needs for entryway systems by keeping exterior walkways clean and using high-quality mats. Cleaning mats frequently can prolong the life of carpets and other flooring materials.

12. Resources

Please see USGBC's LEED Resources & Tools (http://www.usgbc.org/projecttools) for additional resources and technical information.

Websites

Green Seal

http://www.greenseal.org/findaproduct/index.cfm

Green Seal is an independent, nonprofit organization that promotes the manufacture and sale of environmentally responsible consumer products. This webite contains product recommendations for general purpose cleaning solutions.

Janitorial Products Pollution Prevention Project

http://www.westp2net.org/janitorial/jp4.cfm

The Janitorial Products Pollution Prevention Project is a governmental and nonprofit project that provides fact sheets, tools, and links.

EPA Environmentally Preferable Purchasing Information

http://www.epa.gov/opptintr/epp/tools/index.htm

This list of tools includes a database of environmental information on more than 600 products, including janitorial and pest control products.

Print Media

Clean and Green: The Complete Guide to Non-Toxic and Environmentally Safe Housekeeping, by Annie Berthold-Bond (Ceres Press, 1994).

13. Definitions

Air-handling units are mechanical indirect heating, ventilating, or air-conditioning systems in which the air is treated or handled by equipment located outside the rooms served, usually at a central location, and conveyed to and from the rooms by a fan and a system of distributing ducts. (NEEB 1997 edition)

Indoor air quality (IAQ) is the nature of air inside a building that affects the health and well-being of building occupants. It is considered acceptable when there are no known contaminants at harmful concentrations as determined by cognizant authorities and with which a substantial majority (80% or more) of the people exposed do not express dissatisfaction. (ASHRAE 62.1–2007)

Minimum efficiency reporting value (MERV) is a filter rating established by the American Society of Heating, Refrigerating, and Air Conditioning Engineers (ASHRAE 52.2–1999, Method of Testing General Ventilation Air Cleaning Devices for Removal Efficiency by Particle Size). MERV categories range from 1 (very low efficiency) to 16 (very high).

Permanent entryway systems can be open floor grates or grilles with a recessed area designed to capture dirt and other debris from shoes and clothing.

Regularly occupied spaces in commercial buildings are areas where people sit or stand as they work. In residential applications these spaces include all living and family rooms and exclude bathrooms, closets, or other storage or utility areas.

Tenant space is the area within the LEED project boundary. For more information on what can and must be in the LEED project boundary see the Minimum Program Requirements (MPRs) and LEED 2009 MPR Supplemental Guidance. Note: tenant space is the same as project space.

Walk-off mats are placed inside building entrances to capture dirt, water, and other materials tracked inside by people and equipment.

	CI
Credit	IEQ Credit 6.1
Points	1 point

Intent

To provide a high level of lighting system control for individual occupants or groups in multi-occupant spaces (e.g., classrooms and conference areas) and promote their productivity, comfort and well-being.

Requirements

Provide individual lighting controls for: 90% (minimum) of the tenant space occupants to enable adjustments to suit individual task needs and preferences.

Provide lighting system controls for all shared multi-occupant spaces to enable adjustments that meet group needs and preferences.

1. Benefits and Issues to Consider

Environmental Issues

Providing individual controls for lighting increases occupant comfort by enabling them to adjust the workspace to their individual lighting needs. Individual controls also allow for multiple lighting possibilities—lighting for specific tasks, general overhead lighting, lighting with consideration for A/V needs, and lecture-style lighting with emphasis on the learning walls or presentation screens, for example. By balancing ambient light levels and providing user-controlled, flexible, task-appropriate lighting, project teams can reduce the overall lighting energy consumption and the heat loads associated with unnecessarily high or uneven levels of indoor lighting.

Effective lighting is important to human comfort, productivity, and communication. In classroom and presentation settings, building occupants must be able to see material on which they are working, as well as material that is presented on white boards and projected onto screens.

Economic Issues

Additional task lights and lighting controls might increase initial costs for the project. These costs are generally offset by a reduced heat load and may enable designers to minimize ambient light levels, as well as the number of installed fixtures and lamps. Abuse of personal controls, such as leaving task lights on when not in the room, has the potential to increase energy costs. Integrating individual controls with occupancy sensors provides project teams with an opportunity to reduce the overall energy cost. Integrating light-reflecting (or light-absorbing) surface materials with lighting design may create opportunities to reduce the number of installed luminaries, resulting in potential energy savings.

2. Related Credits

Task lighting can be affected by numerous factors; the following credit requirements should be considered when designing the lighting systems:

- IEQ Credit 8: Daylight and Views
- IEQ Credit 6.2: Controllability of Systems—Thermal Comfort

Additionally, energy performance is significantly affected by lighting systems. Consider the following related credits:

- EA Prerequisite 2: Minimum Energy Performance
- EA Credit 1.1: Optimize Energy Performance—Lighting Power
- EA Credit 1.2: Optimize Energy Performance—Lighting Controls
- EA Prerequisite 1: Fundamental Commissioning of Building Energy Systems
- EA Credit 2: Enhanced Commissioning

3. Summary of Referenced Standards

There are no standards referenced for this credit.

4. Implementation

Many conventional buildings have only fixed-intensity general lighting systems that illuminate indoor spaces without consideration for specific tasks and individual occupant comfort or needs. A better approach provides uniform, general ambient lighting, augmented with individually controlled task fixtures.

When developing a task-ambient approach, the lighting designer should investigate methods for providing uniform ambient light. Increased uniformity will reduce the perception of decreased light levels in open spaces by minimizing high contrast areas. Designers should investigate the benefits of direct and indirect or pendant-mounted systems coupled with high reflectance ceiling surfaces and finishes. Integrating surface material and lighting design might reduce the number of necessary lighting fixtures, resulting in potential energy savings. To comply with ASHRAE 90.1–2007, task lighting must be included in the lighting allowance for EA Prerequisite 2 and EA Credit 1.2. Daylighting can be integrated with this credit by using daylighting technologies and strategies where possible to balance artificial light levels in the space as detailed in IEQ Credits 8.1 and 8.2. The office equipment and layout should be carefully analyzed to ensure that 90% of the occupants have lighting controls. Task lights come in several varieties, from desktop lamps to fixtures that are permanently attached to workstations. Ideally these task lights will have multiple lighting levels and automatic shutoff switching. Task lighting does not need to be hardwired to meet the requirements of this credit: Outlet-powered task lighting provides a simple and effective way to add additional control.

The anticipated space uses, as well as any special needs or lighting preferences of the expected building users should be documented and given to the lighting designer. This will enable the designer to provide sufficient controllability and create light levels that match the needs and desires and for all users.

5. Timeline and Team

During design, the layout of lighting and controls is the responsibility of the architect or lighting designer in consultation with the owner. Consider occupants' lighting needs and desires. Document the tasks specific to each space and the tools and equipment that occupants will use on a daily basis. A large open space, such as a 24-hour data center, might have special design needs because of round-the-clock use. Ensuring consistent, ergonomic, and operable lighting is a fundamental part of design decision making and project infrastructure.

In design development, project teams should involve electrical engineers and coordinate power and circuitry requirements. Design should include lighting professionals and electrical engineers to ensure that white boards and screens are free from glare. Improperly lit surfaces can prevent participants from seeing important information. Lighting for audiovisual presentations should be dark enough that images are clearly visible on the screen but not so dark that the audience cannot take notes.

Early in the construction phase, coordinate the final calibration of the lighting controls with the installer and commissioning agent to ensure that the system operates as intended. Once the fixtures are installed, lighting systems and controls should be commissioned for specific calibration.

During building operation, the owner should provide training for building maintenance staff in the calibration of systems and relamping. Property management and building engineers should periodically review lighting systems, as well as conduct surveys to ensure that occupants' needs are met and that lighting is working according to design.

6. Calculations

Adjustable Task Lighting

Identify workstation locations intended for individual use. Include every individual workspace (e.g., private offices, open-plan workstations, reception stations, ticket booths). Confirm that 90% or more of occupants of these spaces have task lighting that enables adjustment to suit individual needs. Adjustability, at a minimum, the occupants must be able to turn the fixture on and off. Ideally, the occupant can easily reposition the fixture and have multiple light levels. The fixture should be appropriate for the task.

Shared Multioccupant Spaces

In conference rooms, classrooms, and other indoor spaces used for functions such as presentations and training, the group should have access to adequate controls to suit its activities. Specific types or numbers of controls are not listed in the credit requirements to allow for flexibility in designing to the unique uses of each project. Meeting spaces must be designed so that occupants have control of their individual area; subdivide these spaces with movable walls or partitions. When daylighting is used as a component of an ambient lighting scheme in either type of space, provide glare control, lighting level controls, and room-darkening shades if appropriate.

Offices and Other Regularly Occupied Spaces

Count the workstation locations intended for individual use. The office and equipment layout should be carefully analyzed to ensure that 90% or more of occupants of these spaces have individual lighting controls that enable adjustment to suit individual needs. Adjustability, at a minimum, must enable the occupant to turn the fixture on and off.

Individual Workstation Lighting Controls

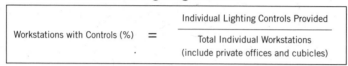

$$\text{Workstations with Controls (\%)} = \frac{\text{Individual Lighting Controls Provided}}{\text{Total Individual Workstations (include private offices and cubicles)}}$$

7. Documentation Guidance

As a first step in preparing to complete the LEED Online documentation requirements, work through the following measures. Refer to LEED Online for the complete descriptions of all required documentation.

- Maintain a floor plan that indicates the location, zoning, and type of lighting controls. The floor plan should also include furniture layout and indicate individual and shared work areas.

- Retain design information on task lighting, sensors, and lighting controls.

8. Examples

Figure 1. Workstations with Individually Adjustable Task Lighting

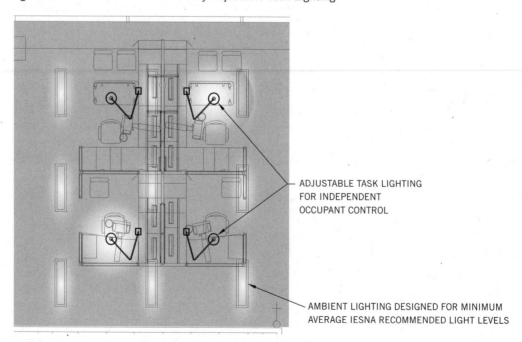

ADJUSTABLE TASK LIGHTING FOR INDEPENDENT OCCUPANT CONTROL

AMBIENT LIGHTING DESIGNED FOR MINIMUM AVERAGE IESNA RECOMMENDED LIGHT LEVELS

Figure 2. Multioccupant Space with Access to Lighting Controls

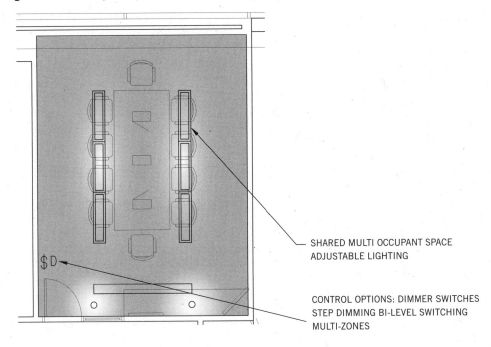

SHARED MULTI OCCUPANT SPACE
ADJUSTABLE LIGHTING

CONTROL OPTIONS: DIMMER SWITCHES
STEP DIMMING BI-LEVEL SWITCHING
MULTI-ZONES

Daylight harvesting and lighting control have been linked to higher productivity and lower energy bills. A lighting control system that either is remotely programmed or uses occupancy sensors (with a delay) to turn lamps on and off can save energy when areas are not in use.

9. Exemplary Performance

This credit is not eligible for exemplary performance under the Innovation in Design section.

10. Regional Variations

Buildings in regions with strong sunlight may need to use less electric lighting by day but require greater controllability in their lighting systems. Because daylight levels may range from the low to the intense during the course of a day, building occupants may experience discomfort if light levels fluctuate widely. Project teams in these regions should consider incorporating passive design strategies, such as good building orientation and the use of light-shielding devices like canopies, to control daylight. Daylight sensors that automatically adjust artificial lighting to compensate are also effective.

11. Operations and Maintenance Considerations

Building owners and architects should work with the lighting engineers and building operators in specifying the number and type of lighting controls to be installed.

For automatic controls, provide appropriate setpoints and schedules in the facility's building operation plan. Establish procedures and schedules for recalibrating sensors based on the manufacturer's requirements, and include them in the building's preventive maintenance plan.

When specifying automatic controls, consider the intended space use and choose an option suited to expected conditions. A utility room, for example, may have moving parts that can falsely trigger motion-based sensors.

12. Resources

Please see USGBC's LEED Resources & Tools (http://www.usgbc.org/projecttools) for additional resources and technical information.

Websites

A Field Study of Personal Environmental Module Performance in Bank of America's San Francisco Office Buildings

http://www.cbe.berkeley.edu/research/pdf_files/bauman1998_bofa.pdf

This University of California, Berkeley research center provides information about underfloor air distribution technologies and other topics.

Association of Lighting and Mercury Recyclers

http://www.almr.org

Energy-10™

National Renewable Energy Laboratory

http://www.nrel.gov/buildings/energy10.html

Print Media

Controls and Automation for Facilities Managers: Applications Engineering, by Viktor Boed (CRC Press, 1998).

Advanced Lighting Guidelines, 2003 edition, by New Buildings Institute (NBI, 2003):http://www.newbuildings.org/lighting.htm.

Controls and Automation for Facilities Managers: Applications Engineering, by Viktor Boed (CRC Press, 1998).

IESNA Lighting Handbook, 9th edition, by Illuminating Engineering Society of North America (IESNA, 2000): Document ID HB-9-00, at http://www.iesna.org.

13. Definitions

Audiovisual (A/V) media are slides, film, video, sound recordings, and other such devices used to present information.

Commissioning is the process of verifying and documenting that the facility and all of its systems and assemblies are planned, designed, installed, tested, operated, and maintained to meet the owner's project requirements.

Controls are operating mechanisms that enable a person to turn on or off devices (e.g., lights, heaters) or adjust systems within a range (e.g., lighting, temperature).

Daylighting is the controlled admission of natural light into a space through glazing to reduce or eliminate electric lighting.

Glare is any excessively bright source of light within the visual field that creates discomfort or loss in visibility.

In **individual occupant spaces,** workers use standard workstations to conduct individual tasks. Examples are private offices and open office areas with multiple workers.

Nonoccupied spaces include all rooms used by maintenance personnel that are not open for use by occupants. Examples are closets and janitorial, storage, and equipment rooms.

Outdoor air is the ambient air that enters a building through a ventilation system, either through intentional openings for natural ventilation or by infiltration. (ASHRAE 62.1–2007)

Shared (group) multioccupant spaces include conference rooms, classrooms, and other indoor spaces used as places of congregation.

Sensors are devices that undergo a measurable change in response to a change in the environment and communicate this to the appropriate equipment or control system.

Tenant space is the area within the LEED project boundary. For more information on what can and must be in the LEED project boundary see the Minimum Program Requirements (MPRs) and LEED 2009 MPR Supplemental Guidance. Note: tenant space is the same as project space.

CONTROLLABILITY OF SYSTEMS—THERMAL COMFORT

	CI
Credit	IEQ Credit 6.2
Points	1 point

Intent

To provide a high level of thermal comfort system control[1] for individual occupants or groups in multi-occupant spaces (e.g., classrooms and conference areas) and promote their productivity, comfort and well-being.

Requirements

Provide individual controls for 50% (minimum) of the tenant occupants to enable adjustment to suit individual needs and preferences, Operable windows may be used in lieu of individual controls for occupants located 20 feet inside and 10 feet to either side of the operable part of the window. The areas of operable window must meet the requirements of ASHRAE Standard 62.1-2007 paragraph 5.1 Natural Ventilation (with errata but without addenda[2]).

Provide comfort system controls for all shared multi-occupant spaces to enable adjustments that meet group needs and preferences.

Conditions for thermal comfort are described in ASHRAE Standard 55-2004 (with errata but without addenda) and include air temperature, radiant temperature, air speed and humidity.

1   For the purposes of this credit comfort system control is defined as control over at least 1 of these primary factors in the occupant's local environment: air temperature, radiant temperature, air speed and humidity.
2   Project teams wishing to use ASHRAE approved addenda for the purposes of this credit may do so at their discretion. Addenda must be applied consistently across all LEED credits.

1. Benefits and Issues to Consider

Environmental Issues

Providing acceptable levels of temperature control and ventilation air to building occupants will promote a healthy work environment and improve the quality of life for tenants. A typical commercial interior project may not be able to adjust major base building components of the HVAC system, but the designers can maximize the thermostatic control and the amount of outside air provided by following ASHRAE 62.1–2007 and by incorporating an adequate number of thermostats for the space. Allowing occupants the ability to control the temperature in their space will likely result in reduced energy consumption and associated negative environmental impacts.

Economic Issues

Occupant complaints frequently include thermal discomfort. Greater thermal comfort may increase occupant performance and attendance and, at least, will reduce complaints. According to the Rocky Mountain Institute's Green Developments in Real Estate, office worker salaries are estimated to be 72 times higher than energy costs,[18] and they account for 92% of the life-cycle costs of a building. With this in mind, thermal comfort can have a tremendous effect on overall costs.[19] Case studies have shown productivity increases from 1% to 16%, saving companies millions of dollars per year.[20]

Additional controllability may add to a project's initial costs, however, these costs are generally offset by energy savings from lower-conditioned temperatures, automatic occupancy detectors, natural ventilation, and shading devices. Conversely, abuse of personal controls, such as setting thermostats too high or leaving windows open during nonworking hours, increases energy costs. Therefore, it is important to educate occupants on the design and function of system controls.

2. Related Credits

The intent of this credit is to enable individuals and, in multioccupant spaces, groups to control their thermal comfort. The following prerequisites and credits also address building occupants' ability to control systems, maintenance, and other factors:

- EA Prerequisite 1: Fundamental Commissioning of Building Systems

- EA Prerequisite 2: Minimum Energy Performance

- EA Credit 1.3: Optimize Energy Performance—HVAC

- EA Credit 2: Enhanced Commissioning

- EA Credit 3: Measurement and Verification

- IEQ Credit 6.1: Controllability of Systems—Lighting

- IEQ Credit 8: Daylight and Views

3. Summary of Referenced Standards

American National Standards Institute (ANSI)/ASHRAE Standard 62.1–2007, Ventilation for Acceptable Indoor Air Quality
ASHRAE
http://www.ashrae.org

Section 5.1 of the standard provides minimum requirements for operable openings. The portion of the window that can be opened must be 4% of the net occupiable floor area. Building occupants must have ready access to the means of opening the windows.

American National Standards Institute (ANSI)/ASHRAE Standard 55-2004: Thermal Environmental Conditions for Human Occupancy

ASHRAE

http://www.ashrae.org

ASHRAE 55-2004 identifies the factors of thermal comfort and the process for developing comfort criteria for a building space and its occupants. ASHRAE states, "This standard specifies the combinations of indoor space environment and personal factors that will produce thermal environmental conditions acceptable to 80% or more of the occupants within a space. The environmental factors addressed are temperature, thermal radiation, humidity, and air speed; the personal factors are those of activity and clothing."

4. Implementation

Many conventional buildings are built as sealed spaces in which the occupants have no control over thermal conditions. A better approach would give individuals the freedom to adjust the thermal conditions for a more comfortable environment. An individual's thermal comfort can depend on air velocity, the direction and temperature of indoor air, and moisture content.

Mechanical systems that allow for individual control of comfort can be integrated into the overall systems design by enabling individual adjustment of selected comfort parameters, such as individual thermostats, individual diffusers (located on the floor, desk or overhead), and individual radiant panels. Occupancy sensors can also be integrated into the design to automatically turn down the thermostat and reduce airflow when occupants are away, which helps reduce energy use.

Individual comfort plug-in devices are acceptable for meeting the intent of this credit provided they are included in EA Prerequisite 2: Minimum Energy Performance and the proposed design model but not in the baseline model for EA Credit 1.3: Optimize Energy Performance, and EA Credit 1.4: Optimize Energy Performance--Equipment and Appliances as appropriate.

Operable windows are often 1 of the occupants' most desired building features. In commercial interior projects where the space is being selected, the project team will have some say. Other means of providing thermal comfort involve planning and design consideration. When the control method is chosen and the space occupied, project teams take time to educate occupants on the individual controls of their office space, as well as facility managers on maintaining the HVAC equipment and recalibrating controls as recommended by the manufacturers.

5. Timeline and Team

By surveying the building tenants, the design team can determine the level of individual control desired. Confirm that the central HVAC systems will be able to provide the desired level of thermal comfort. During design development, locate the thermal comfort controls with electrical and mechanical engineers as well as the construction or development manager. Consider thermal comfort needs as they pertain to ASHRAE 55-2004 requirements. Evaluate the controls for each space, considering the specific tools and equipment that occupants will use on a daily basis. When evaluating shared occupant spaces, consider the occupancy schedule.

If possible, include comfort controls that meet both individual needs and those of groups in shared spaces. ASHRAE 55-2004 identifies the factors of thermal comfort and the process for developing comfort criteria for a building space and its occupants. Strategies to consider include designs with mechanical systems only, operable windows, and hybrid designs incorporating operable windows and mechanical systems.

Postinstallation commissioning of all thermal comfort systems will ensure proper operation. During building operation, the owner should provide training for building maintenance staff in using the controls. Property management and building engineers should periodically review comfort control systems to ensure that occupants' needs are met and that controls are working according to design.

6. Calculations

Individual Thermal Comfort

Identify workstations intended for individual use, such as private offices, open-plan workstations, reception stations, and ticket booths. Confirm that 50% or more of individuals occupying these locations have at least 1 means of individual control over thermal comfort.

Operable windows may be used in lieu of individual controls for occupants located within 20 feet of the exterior wall and within 10 feet of either side of the operable part of the window. The operable portion of the window must comply with the free-opening size criterion of ASHRAE 62.1–2007, Section 5.1; the minimum area of the window that may be opened is 4% of the net occupiable floor area. For the limits used in this credit (i.e., an area 20 feet by 20 feet per window), the opening size would need to be 16 square feet.

Shared Multioccupant Spaces

For conference rooms and lecture halls, confirm that there is at least 1 accessible means of control over thermal comfort. For meeting spaces that can be subdivided, such as a convention hall with a movable wall, occupants in each area have control of their individual area.

7. Documentation Guidance

As a first step in preparing to complete the LEED Online documentation requirements, work through the following measures. Refer to LEED Online for the complete descriptions of all required documentation.

- Maintain a list of the total number of individual workstations and thermal controls in individual workstations.

- Maintain a list of the project's group multioccupant spaces and a description of the installed thermal controls in shared, multioccupant spaces.

8. Examples

Figure 1. Underfloor Air Distribution System with Individual Controls for Air Velocity and Temperature

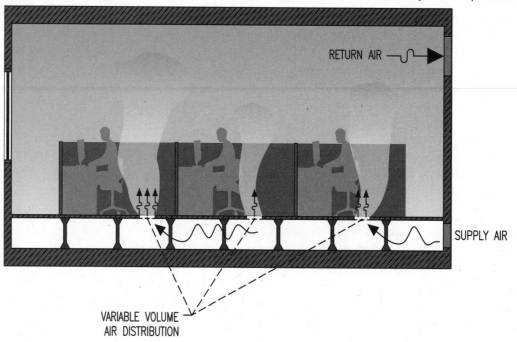

Some examples to help achieve thermal comfort for building occupants include thermostat controls; local diffusers at the floor, desk, or overhead levels; or control of individual radiant panels. Radiant heating may be a good option to pursue. More specifically, room thermostats, natural ventilation actuators, and ceiling fans can have the capability for local occupant override or bypass.

9. Exemplary Performance

This credit is not eligible for exemplary performance under the Innovation in Design section.

10. Regional Variations

Local weather and ambient air conditions may determine the feasibility of operable windows within existing projects. For example, in areas that are prone to extreme temperatures for a majority of the year, or urban areas where traffic and air pollution are problematic, operable windows may not be an appropriate addition to a building.

11. Operations and Maintenance Considerations

Inform building operators about the number and type of thermal comfort controls installed.

Include the default setpoints and schedules in the facility's building operation plan. Establish procedures and schedules for recalibrating controls, based on the manufacturer's recommendations, and include them in the building's preventive maintenance plan. Train building operators in using and maintaining specialty equipment.

If windows are operable, the facility managers should educate tenants on the security and HVAC consequences of leaving windows open when the building is not occupied. Explain how this affects the HVAC systems and ultimately comfort. Maintenance staff should also plan to clean or replace HVAC filters more frequently if building occupants use operable windows.

12. Resources

Please see USGBC's LEED Resources & Tools (http://www.usgbc.org/projecttools) for additional resources and technical information.

Websites

A Field Study of Personal Environmental Module Performance in Bank of America's San Francisco Office Buildings
http://www.cbe.berkeley.edu/research/pdf_files/bauman1998_bofa.pdf
This University of California, Berkeley research center provides information about underfloor air distribution technologies and other topics.

Do Green Buildings Enhance the Well-Being of Workers? Yes
Environmental Design + Construction
http://www.edcmag.com/Articles/Cover_Story/fb077b7338697010VgnVCM100000f932a8c0. This article by Judith Heerwagen in the July/August 2000 edition of *Environmental Design + Construction* quantifies the effects of green building environments on productivity.

Print Media

Controls and Automation for Facilities Managers: Applications Engineering, by Viktor Boed (CRC Press, 1998).

13. Definitions

The **building envelope**, or shell, is the exterior surface of a building's construction—the walls, windows, roof, and floor.

Comfort criteria are the specific original design conditions that at minimum include temperature (air, radiant, and surface), humidity, and air speed as well as outdoor temperature design conditions, outdoor humidity design conditions, clothing, and expected activity. (ASHRAE 55-2004)

Commissioning is the process of verifying and documenting that the facility and all of its systems and assemblies are planned, designed, installed, tested, operated, and maintained to meet the owner's project requirements.

Controls are considered to be operating devices that enable the occupant to turn on or off other devices (e.g., lighting) or adjust other devices or systems within in a range (e.g., temperature).

Daylighting is the controlled admission of natural light into a space through glazing to reduce or eliminate electric lighting.

HVAC systems are equipment, distribution systems, and terminals that provide the processes of heating, ventilating, or air-conditioning. (ASHRAE 90.1-2007)

In **individual occupant spaces,** workers use standard workstations to conduct individual tasks. Examples are private offices and open office areas with multiple workers.

Natural ventilation relies on a range of techniques that maximize the potential of the stack effect, using air passages through doors, windows, or other intentional openings at differing heights and wind effects.

Nonoccupied spaces include all rooms used by maintenance personnel that are not open for use by occupants. Examples are janitorial, storage and equipment rooms, and closets.

Outdoor air is the ambient air that enters a building through a ventilation system, either through intentional openings for natural ventilation or by infiltration. (ASHRAE 62.1-2007)

Regularly occupied spaces in commercial buildings are areas where people sit or stand as they work. In residential applications these spaces include all living and family rooms and exclude bathrooms, closets, or other storage or utility areas.

Shared (group) multioccupant spaces include conference rooms, classrooms and other indoor spaces used as places of congregation.

Sensors are devices that undergo a measurable change in response to a change in the environment and communicates this to the appropriate equipment or control system.

Thermal comfort exists when occupants express satisfaction with the thermal environment.

	CI
Credit	IEQ Credit 7.1
Points	1 point

Intent

To provide a comfortable thermal environment that promotes occupant productivity and well-being.

Requirements

Design heating, ventilating and air-conditioning (HVAC) systems to meet the requirements of ASHRAE Standard 55-2004, Thermal Comfort Conditions for Human Occupancy (with errata but without addenda[1]). Demonstrate design compliance in accordance with the Section 6.1.1 documentation.

---

1 Project teams wishing to use ASHRAE approved addenda for the purposes of this credit may do so at their discretion. Addenda must be applied consistently across all LEED credits.

1. Benefits and Issues to Consider

Environmental Issues

Maintaining an acceptable level of thermal comfort for building occupants should be considered a necessity for any building or space with regular occupancy. Studies have shown that people who are comfortable are more productive and generally happier. In a work environment, increases in productivity can reduce the amount of time and energy required for an individual task. Over the course of a year, that can translate to fewer hours running equipment such as computers or task lighting, resulting in energy savings that reduce the strain on the environment.

Economic Issues

Generally, HVAC and building envelope systems that do not adequately address the thermal comfort of occupants are less energy efficient than their more robust counterparts—with the exception of passive or naturally ventilated spaces. Mechanical systems relying on natural ventilation typically have lower capital and construction costs and use less energy than mechanically ventilated systems. In climates with extreme seasonal temperature swings, occupants' comfort can suffer in a naturally ventilated building, but a well-designed building envelope and HVAC system can help compensate. Buildings with poor envelopes might struggle to maintain a comfortable environment for occupants near the building perimeter. The building HVAC system will expend more energy trying to maintain a comfortable environment for those occupants on the perimeter, increasing the annual energy cost of the building.

HVAC systems with poorly located or inadequate numbers of thermostats or control zones can significantly impact occupant comfort. Occupants using areas that could otherwise have been provided individual temperature controls may have to share a thermostat or may use space heaters, which can increase energy use. When spaces have not been properly thermally zoned, occupants may try to heat and cool the same area at the same time, potentially resulting in greater energy use and additional costs to operate the building.

2. Related Credits

The thermal comfort of building occupants is affected by environmental conditions (air temperature, radiant temperature, relative humidity, and air speed), personal factors (metabolic rate and clothing), and personal preferences. Thermal comfort can be controlled through both active (mechanical) systems and passive (natural ventilation) systems, with the best results often achieved through a combination of the 2 systems: Using both can help reduce the building's energy consumption, as well as achieve optimum comfort levels. For all these reasons, this credit is related to the following other prerequisites and credits:

- EA Prerequisite 2: Minimum Energy Performance

- EA Credit 1.3: Optimize Energy Performance—HVAC

- EA Credit 3: Measurement and Verification

To address the issue of commissioning thermal comfort features, refer to the following:

- EA Prerequisite 1: Fundamental Commissioning of Building Energy Systems

- EA Credit 2: Enhanced Commissioning

The following prerequisite and credits also pertain to occupants' comfort:

- IEQ Prerequisite 1: Minimum Indoor Air Quality Performance

- IEQ Credit 2: Increased Ventilation

- IEQ Credit 6.2: Controllability of Thermal Systems—Thermal Comfort
- IEQ Credit 7.2: Thermal Comfort—Verification

3. Summary of Referenced Standard

American National Standards Institute (ANSI)/ASHRAE Standard 55-2004, Thermal Comfort Conditions for Human Occupancy

ASHRAE

http://www.ashrae.org

According to ASHRAE, this standard "specifies the combinations of indoor space environment and personal factors that will produce thermal environmental conditions acceptable to 80% or more of the occupants within a space. The environmental factors addressed are temperature, thermal radiation, humidity, and air speed; the personal factors are those of activity and clothing."

4. Implementation

Although often associated only with air temperature, thermal comfort is a complex issue, affected by environmental conditions (e.g., air temperature, radiant temperature, humidity, and air speed) and personal factors (e.g., metabolic rate, clothing, and preferences). There are 3 basic approaches to providing thermal comfort in project space:

- Mechanical Ventilation (i.e., active ventilation).
- Natural Ventilation (i.e., passive ventilation).
- Mixed-Mode Ventilation (i.e., both mechanical and natural ventilation).

The owner should decide which conditioning approach to use and find an appropriate space for that conditioning system. ASHRAE 55-2004 provides thermal comfort standards with an optional alternate approach specifically for naturally ventilated spaces. The selected space should be evaluated to determine whether it can be made to meet the desired comfort criteria identified by the future occupant.

ASHRAE 55-2004 uses the predicted mean vote model, which incorporates heat balance principles to relate the personal and environmental thermal comfort factors based on the thermal sensation scale that shows 7 levels ranging from +3 (hot) to -3 (cold). The predicted mean vote model is applicable to air speeds not greater than 0.20 meters per second (40 feet per minute). For naturally ventilated spaces, the standard indicates that field experiments have shown that the occupants' thermal responses depend in part on the outdoor climate and may differ from thermal responses in buildings with centralized HVAC systems. This is primarily because of the occupant's different thermal experiences, clothing, availability of control, and shifts expectations. The standard provides an optional method of compliance, intended for naturally ventilated spaces. This optional method provides indoor temperature ranges as a function of mean monthly outdoor temperatures, assuming light, sedentary activity but independent of humidity, air speed, and clothing considerations. The optional method in Section 5.3 of the standard uses a chart with a broad temperature range and is based on the adaptive model of thermal comfort (which also accounts for occupants' clothing adaptation). The chart is derived from a global database with measures being taken in office buildings.

There are many well established HVAC load calculation methodologies to assist designers in sizing and selecting HVAC equipment in order to provide thermal comfort conditions. Natural ventilation may be more difficult to evaluate and require more intensive analysis and/or reliance on experience and precedents. For naturally ventilated buildings, CIBSE AM10 presents strategies that can be implemented to the selected space; however, attention should be given to the lease requirements of the building to ensure the modifications desired by the owner and the design team may be implemented.

For mechanical conditioning, the operating set points and parameters of the HVAC system will be a primary influence on thermal comfort conditions in the project space. Many facility operators in mechanically air conditioned spaces spend significant time and effort adjusting thermostat set points and other operational parameters in order to limit complaints associated with poor thermal comfort. Systems where individual occupants are provided some amount of direct control over temperature and/or air movement generally yield fewer thermal comfort complaints.

The maxim "passive buildings, active occupants" fits the natural ventilation model well. Occupants generally take a primary role in managing thermal comfort conditions in naturally ventilated buildings by opening and closing windows as necessary. Thermal comfort in naturally conditioned buildings is also somewhat more variable than in mechanically conditioned buildings, where systems are often designed to maintain consistent conditions through all periods of occupancy.

5. Timeline and Team

The project owner and design team need to work together to achieve this credit, but responsibility for meeting the requirements and ensuring the thermal comfort of occupants resides with the HVAC design engineer. Start early in the design development stage. Discuss the local climate, energy efficiency, and occupant comfort ranges.

The design team should decide whether thermal comfort conditions can be met with a passive approach or an active HVAC system or mixed-mode approach. This decision may be influenced by the type of space and cost considerations.

Using ASHRAE 55–2004, the design team and the owner should together identify the environmental parameters required to maintain the desired thermal comfort in the project space and then identify the conditioning systems (whether active or passive) available at the leased space to provide these conditions.

6. Calculations

There are no calculations required for this credit.

7. Documentation Guidance

As a first step in preparing to complete the LEED Online documentation requirements, work through the following measures. Refer to LEED Online for the complete descriptions of all required documentation.

- Design mechanical systems within the comfort criteria of ASHRAE 55-2004.

- Describe how thermal comfort conditions were established for the project and how the design of conditioning systems addresses the thermal comfort design criteria.

8. Examples

Figure 1 presents the ASHRAE 55–2004 comfort zone charts for summer and winter. They take into consideration factors like temperature and humidity and are most applicable to occupants who are appropriately dressed and involved in light work (e.g., office workers). The variations in the charts reflect the assumption that occupants are dressed according to the seasons.

Figure 1. (ASHRAE 55)

Summer Comfort Zone

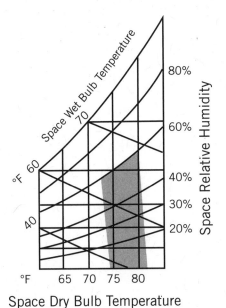

Winter Comfort Zone

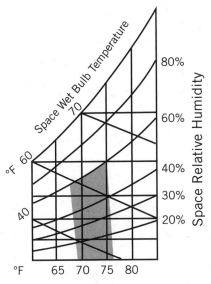

These charts can help the building owner and facility manager identify optimum interior comfort levels as well as identify deviations in thermal comfort that are specific to the building, the occupants and their type of work.

9. Exemplary Performance

This credit is not eligible for exemplary performance under the Innovation in Design section.

10. Regional Variations

When considering occupant comfort, anticipate how climatic and seasonal variations will affect the thermal comfort of occupants. Climate variations play an important role in passively ventilated buildings because of the introduction of unconditioned outside air. In mechanically ventilated buildings, regional variations have an impact on the temperature range that an occupant considers comfortable. Warmer climates typically have higher design temperatures than colder climates to match the conditions that would normally be considered comfortable for the occupants.

11. Operations and Maintenance Considerations

Provide the building owner, facility manager, and occupants with the information needed to understand, maintain, and adjust the HVAC system for thermal comfort. Establish appropriate setpoints and control sequences, as well as recommendations for typical corrective actions, and include them in the facility's building operating plan and sequence of operations document.

Establish procedures and schedules for inspecting and recalibrating sensors and controls, based on the manufacturer's recommendations, and include them in the building's preventive maintenance plan.

12. Resources

Please see the USGBC's LEED Resources & Tools (http://www.usgbc.org/projecttools) for additional resources and technical information.

Websites

Advanced Desiccant Cooling and Dehumidification Program

http://www.nrel.gov/docs/fy99osti/26300.pdf

This U.S. Department of Energy research and development program works with companies to realize the potential of desiccant systems for reducing energy consumption and improving indoor air quality and comfort.

NIST Multizone Modeling Software

http://www.bfrl.nist.gov/IAQanalysis/software

The National Institute of Standards and Technology (NIST) provides software such as CONTAM, a multizone indoor air quality and ventilation analysis computer program designed to predict airflows and contaminant concentrations.

Enhance Indoor Environmental Quality, The Whole Building Design Guide

http://www.wbdg.org/design/ieq.php

The Indoor Environmental Quality section provides a wealth of resources including definitions, fundamentals, materials, and tools.

Print Media

ASHRAE 55–2004: Thermal Environmental Conditions for Human Occupancy (ASHRAE, 2004).

ASHRAE 111–1988: Practices for Measurement, Testing, Adjusting and Balancing of Building Heating, Ventilation, Air-Conditioning and Refrigeration Systems (ASHRAE, 1988).

Dehumidification Enhancements for 100-%-Outside-Air AHUs: Parts I, II and III, by Donald Gatley, *Heating Piping and Air Conditioning Magazine* (September, October, and November 2000): http://www.HPAC.com.

Humidity Control Design Guide, by L. Harriman, G.W. Brundett, and R. Kittler (ASHRAE, 2000).

The Impact of Part-Load Air-Conditioner Operation on Dehumidification Performance: Validating a Latent Capacity Degradation Model, by Hugh Henderson, IAQ and Energy (1998). Using ASHRAE 62 and 90.1 Conference Papers (ASHRAE, 1998).

The New Comfort Equation For Indoor Air Quality, by P.O. Fanger, *ASHRAE Journal* (October 1989): 33-38.

Selecting HVAC Systems for Schools, by Arthur Wheeler and Walter Kunz, Jr. (Maryland State Department of Education, 1994).

Thermal Comfort, by P.O. Fanger (Mc-Graw Hill, 1973).

Thermal Delight in Architecture, by Lisa Heschong (MIT Press, 1979).

Unplanned Airflows and Moisture Problems, by T. Brennan, J. Cummings, and J. Lstiburek, *ASHRAE Journal* (November 2000).

13. Definitions

Comfort Criteria are the specific original design conditions that at a minimum include temperature (air, radiant and surface), humidity and air speed as well as outdoor temperature design conditions, outdoor humidity design conditions, clothing, and expected activity. (ASHRAE 55–2004)

Commissioning is the process of verifying and documenting that the facility and all of its systems and assemblies are planned, designed, installed, tested, operated, and maintained to meet the owner's project requirements.

Mixed-mode ventilation combines natural ventilation with mechanical systems; the latter are used only when necessary. Mixed-mode ventilation strategies include 3 distinct approaches; contingency, complementary, and zoned. (CIBSE Guide F–2008)

Mechanical ventilation is provided by mechanically powered equipment, such as motor-driven fans and blowers, but not by devices such as wind-driven turbine ventilators and mechanically operated windows. (ASHRAE 62.1–2004)

Natural ventilation is provided by thermal, wind, or diffusion effects through doors, windows, or other intentional openings in the building. (ASHRAE 62.1–2007)

Occupants in a commercial building are workers who either have a permanent office or workstation or typically spend a minimum of 10 hours per week in the project building; in a residential building, regular occupants also include all persons who live in the building.

Predicted mean vote is an empirical equation for predicting the mean vote on a rating scale of thermal comfort of a large population of people exposed to a certain environment.

Relative humidity is the ratio of partial density of water vapor in the air to the saturation density of water vapor at the same temperature and the same total pressure. (ASHRAE 55–2004).

Thermal comfort exists when building occupants express satisfaction with the thermal environment.

THERMAL COMFORT—VERIFICATION

	CI
Credit	IEQ Credit 7.2
Points	1 point*

*1 point in addition to IEQ Credit 7.1

Intent

To provide for the assessment of occupant thermal comfort over time.

Requirements

Achieve IEQ Credit 7.1: Thermal Comfort – Design

Provide a permanent monitoring system and process for corrective action to ensure that building performance meets the desired comfort criteria as determined by IEQ Credit 7.1: Thermal Comfort—Design.

Agree to conduct a thermal comfort survey of tenant space occupants within 6 to 18 months after occupancy. This survey should collect anonymous responses about thermal comfort in the tenant space including an assessment of overall satisfaction with thermal performance and identification of thermal comfort problems. Agree to develop a plan for corrective action if the survey results indicate that more than 20% of occupants are dissatisfied with thermal comfort in the tenant space This plan should include measurement of relevant environmental variables in problem areas in accordance with ASHRAE Standard 55-2004 (with errata but without addenda[1]).

---

1 Project teams wishing to use ASHRAE approved addenda for the purposes of this credit may to do so at their discretion. Addenda must be applied consistently across all LEED credits.

1. Benefits and Issues to Consider

Environmental Issues

For many facilities, the HVAC systems that maintain indoor thermal comfort are the largest energy users. A successful green building should minimize the energy use associated with building conditioning—along with the associated energy cost, fuel consumption, and air emissions—while maintaining thermal comfort conditions that enhance occupant well-being.

Economic Issues

Depending on the specific approach and project space limitations, providing the thermal comfort conditions as defined by ASHRAE 55-2004 may increase or decrease the cost of designing, constructing, and operating the facility.

The choices that are made while finding the project space will shape the cost implications of this credit. If the owner selects a space that has mechanical systems, the project team must evaluate the existing system to determine if maintaining the comfort criteria is feasible from a system operations and monitoring point of view as well as whether there is a need for modifications or changes to the overall system. This might affect lease agreements, which could reduce or increase the overall cost of the project.

Thermal comfort monitoring (via occupant surveying or monitoring environmental variables) may add capital, operations, and maintenance costs to a facility. The building systems, use, and occupants change with time, requiring ongoing maintenance and perhaps improvements to thermal comfort performance. Reducing thermal comfort problems and complaints contributes to occupant performance and may allow facility operations and maintenance staff to focus on other critical areas.

If the owner selects a space that has a natural ventilation system, the above mentioned feasibility procedure should be carried out to evaluate cost implications. The selected space might have operable windows but may or may not provide the comfort criteria established by the owner and the design team. Natural ventilation systems consume less energy, and may have reduced maintenance costs compared with the HVAC systems.

2. Related Credits

The thermal comfort of building occupants is affected by environmental conditions (air temperature, radiant temperature, relative humidity, and air speed), personal factors (metabolic rate and clothing), and personal preference. Thermal comfort can be controlled through the use of active (mechanical) systems and passive (natural ventilation) systems, with the best results often achieved through a combination of the 2 systems. Using both active and passive features can help reduce the energy consumption of the building as well as achieve optimum comfort levels in a building. Refer to the requirements in the following:

- EA Prerequisite 2: Minimum Energy Performance

- EA Credit 1.3: Optimize Energy Performance—HVAC

- EA Credit 3: Measurement and Verification

Another prerequisite and credit address the issue of commissioning thermal comfort:

- EA Prerequisite 1: Fundamental Commissioning of Building Energy Systems

- EA Credit 2: Enhanced Commissioning

This credit also works in synergy with the following prerequisite and credits that pertain directly to occupant comfort:

- IEQ Prerequisite 1: Minimum Indoor Air Quality Performance

- IEQ Credit 2: Increased Ventilation

- IEQ Credit 6.2: Controllability of Thermal Systems—Thermal Comfort

- IEQ Credit 7.1: Thermal Comfort—Design

3. Summary of Referenced Standard

American National Standards Institute (ANSI)/ASHRAE Standard 55-2004, Thermal Comfort Conditions for Human Occupancy

American Society of Heating, Refrigerating, and Air-Conditioning Engineers

http://www.ashrae.org

"This standard specifies the combinations of indoor space environment and personal factors that will produce thermal environmental conditions acceptable to 80% or more of the occupants within a space. The environmental factors addressed are temperature, thermal radiation, humidity and air speed; the personal factors are those of activity and clothing." (ASHRAE)

4. Implementation

Since thermal comfort is inherently subjective and is psychological as much as physiological, regularly surveying occupants may be the best way to determine whether a facility is comfortable. Sporadic complaints about thermal comfort may not be an appropriate indicator of overall thermal comfort, but rather an indicator of local or personal dissatisfaction. Providing a systematic process and mechanism for all occupants to provide feedback about their thermal comfort will help building operators adjust and maintain thermal comfort in the building.

Analyzing environment variables (typically by monitoring space temperature and relative humidity) is an alternate approach to determining if a facility is providing thermal comfort for its occupants. Temperature, humidity, and other environmental monitoring systems provide facility operators with objective data to determine if the building space conditions meet the design intent and/or if they are being maintained consistently through the occupied periods.

The building systems, building use, and occupants change with time, which means that requiring ongoing maintenance and improvements may be necessary to maintain thermal comfort. Reducing thermal comfort problems and complaints contributes to occupant performance and may allow facility operations and maintenance staff to focus on other critical areas.

Employing a monitoring system will control nondirectional air speed, air temperature, and humidity under all expected operating conditions. Maintenance and operations personnel need to verify that the system is functioning properly and that the comfort criteria determined earlier is being maintained by taking readings and assessing the thermal comfort parameters that are identified by the owner and the design team. Periodic verifications and adjustments to the system help maintain the set comfort criteria, contributes to occupant performance, and keeps the systems up to date.

5. Timeline and Team

The design and engineering team are primarily responsible for achieving this credit, which is based on the requirements of ASHRAE 55-2004. Additionally, a member of the building operations team, an owner agent, or a commissioning authority should carry out the followup survey to meet the requirements of this credit.

During the design phase, identify the environmental parameters in IEQ Credit 7.1, Thermal Comfort—Design, that will affect comfort in the project building. Any space temperature sensors, humidity sensors, or other sensors needed to monitor thermal comfort conditions should be integrated into the HVAC design. For the survey, consult the guidelines and a sample thermal environment survey in ASHRAE 55-2004.

During the operations phase, facility managers should develop procedures to survey building occupants about thermal comfort conditions for every operating mode. These regular surveys may be administered in person, over the phone, over networked computers, or on paper but should be consistently applied and available for participation by all regular occupants. The survey may encompass other indoor environmental quality considerations (such as lighting or acoustics) as well, although this is not required for this credit.

6. Calculations

There are no calculations associated with this credit.

7. Documentation Guidance

As a first step in preparing to complete the LEED Online documentation requirements, work through the following measures. Refer to LEED Online for the complete descriptions of all required documentation.

- Create a written plan for corrective action if 20 % or more of a building's occupants are dissatisfied with thermal comfort in the building

- Create a thermal comfort survey for the building's occupants

8. Examples

There are no examples for this credit.

9. Exemplary Performance

This credit is not eligible for exemplary performance under the Innovation in Design section.

10. Regional Variations

ASHRAE 55-2004 provides alternate thermal comfort criteria based on presumed seasonal changes in occupants' dress. This assumption may or may not be valid for facilities and for different regions of the country. Designers should consider and anticipate occupants' clothing and likely metabolic rate in determining the indoor thermal comfort criteria.

A natural ventilation approach is more typical in mild and temperate climates, although there are precedents for naturally conditioned buildings in all climates.

11. Operations and Maintenance Considerations

Provide the building owner, maintenance personnel, and occupants with the information needed to understand, maintain, and adjust the HVAC system for thermal comfort. Establish appropriate setpoints and control sequences, as well as recommendations for typical corrective actions, and include them in the building operating plan and sequence of operations document.

Establish procedures and schedules for inspecting and recalibrating sensors and controls, based on the manufacturer's recommendations, and include them in the building's preventive maintenance plan.

12. Resources

Please see the USGBC's LEED Resources & Tools (http://www.usgbc.org/projecttools) for additional resources and technical information.

Websites

Advanced Desiccant Cooling and Dehumidification Program
http://www.nrel.gov/docs/fy99osti/26300.pdf
This U.S. Department of Energy research and development program works with companies to realize the potential of desiccant systems for reducing energy consumption and improving indoor air quality and comfort.

NIST Multizone Modeling Software

http://www.bfrl.nist.gov/IAQanalysis/software

The National Institute of Standards and Technology (NIST) provides software such as CONTAM, a multizone indoor air quality and ventilation analysis computer program designed to predict airflows and contaminant concentrations.

Enhance Indoor Environmental Quality, The Whole Building Design Guide

http://www.wbdg.org/design/ieq.php

The Indoor Environmental Quality section provides a wealth of resources including definitions, fundamentals, materials, and tools.

Print Media

ASHRAE 55–2004: Thermal Environmental Considerations for Human Occupancy (ASHRAE, 2004).

ASHRAE 111–1988: Practices for Measurement, Testing, Adjusting and Balancing of Building Heating, Ventilation, Air-Conditioning, and Refrigeration Systems (ASHRAE, 1988).

Dehumidification Enhancements for 100-%-Outside-Air AHUs: Parts I, II and III, by Donald Gatley, *Heating Piping and Air Conditioning Magazine* (September, October, and November 2000): http://www.HPAC.com.

Humidity Control Design Guide, by L. Harriman, G.W. Brundett, and R. Kittler (ASHRAE, 2000).

The Impact of Part-Load Air-Conditioner Operation on Dehumidification Performance: Validating a Latent Capacity Degradation Model, by Hugh Henderson, IAQ and Energy (1998). Using ASHRAE 62 and 90.1 Conference Papers (ASHRAE, 1998).

The New Comfort Equation For Indoor Air Quality, by P.O. Fanger, *ASHRAE Journal,* October (1989): pp. 33-38.

Selecting HVAC Systems for Schools, by Arthur Wheeler and Walter Kunz, Jr. (Maryland State Department of Education, 1994).

Thermal Comfort, by P.O. Fanger (McGraw Hill, 1973).

Thermal Delight in Architecture, by Lisa Heschong (MIT Press, 1979).

Unplanned Airflows and Moisture Problems, by T. Brennan, J. Cummings, and J. Lstiburek, *ASHRAE Journal* (November 2000).

13. Definitions

Comfort criteria are the specific original design conditions that at a minimum include temperature (air, radiant and surface), humidity and air speed as well as outdoor temperature design conditions, outdoor humidity design conditions, clothing, and expected activity. (ASHRAE 55–2004)

Commissioning is the process of verifying and documenting that the facility and all of its systems and assemblies are planned, designed, installed, tested, operated, and maintained to meet the owner's project requirements.

Mechanical ventilation is provided by mechanically powered equipment, such as motor-driven fans and blowers, but not by devices such as wind-driven turbine ventilators and mechanically operated windows. (ASHRAE 62.1–2004)

Mixed-mode ventilation combines mechanical and natural ventilation methods.

Natural Ventilation is a ventilation design relying on a range of techniques which maximize the potential of the stack effect, using air passages through doors, windows, or other intentional openings at differing heights and wind effects.

Occupants in a commercial building are workers who either have a permanent office or workstation or typically spend a minimum of 10 hours per week in the project building; in a residential building, regular occupants also include all persons who live in the building.

Predicted mean vote is an empirical equation for predicting the mean vote on a rating scale of thermal comfort of a large population of people exposed to a certain environment.

Relative humidity is the ratio of partial density of water vapor in the air to the saturation density of water vapor at the same temperature and the same total pressure. (ASHRAE 55–2004).

Tenant space is the area within the LEED project boundary. For more information on what can and must be in the LEED project boundary see the Minimum Program Requirements (MPRs) and LEED 2009 MPR Supplemental Guidance. Note: tenant space is the same as project space.

Thermal comfort exists when occupants express satisfaction with the thermal environment.

DAYLIGHT AND VIEWS—DAYLIGHT

	CI
Credit	IEQ Credit 8.1
Points	1-2 points

Intent

To provide occupants with a connection between indoor spaces and the outdoors through the introduction of daylight and views into the regularly occupied areas of the tenant space.

Requirements

Through 1 of the 4 options, achieve daylighting in at least the following spaces[1]:

Regularly Occupied Spaces	Points
75%	1
90%	2

OPTION 1. Simulation

Demonstrate through computer simulations that the applicable spaces achieve daylight illuminance levels of a minimum of 10 footcandles (fc) and a maximum of 500 fc in a clear sky condition on September 21 at 9 a.m. and 3 p.m.

Provide glare control devices to avoid high-contrast situations that could impede visual tasks. However, designs that incorporate view-preserving automated shades for glare control may demonstrate compliance for only the minimum 10 fc illuminance level.

OR

OPTION 2. Prescriptive

For sidelighting zones:

- Achieve a value, calculated as the product of the visible light transmittance (VLT) and window-to-floor area ratio (WFR) between 0.150 and 0.180.

$$0.150 \quad < \quad VLT \quad X \quad WFR \quad < \quad 0.180$$

- The window area included in the calculation must be at least 30 inches above the floor.

- In section, the ceiling must not obstruct a line that extends from the window-head to a point on the floor that is located twice the height of the window-head from the exterior wall as measured perpendicular to the glass (see diagram on next page).

---

1 Exceptions for areas where tasks would be hindered by the use of daylight will be considered on their merits.

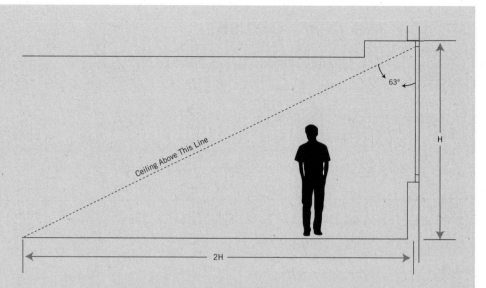

- Provide glare control devices to avoid high-contrast situations that could impede visual tasks. However, designs that incorporate view-preserving automated shades for glare control may demonstrate compliance for only the minimum 0.150 value.

For toplighting zones:

- The toplighting zone under a skylight is the outline of the opening beneath the skylight, plus in each direction the lesser of (see diagram below):

  - 70% of the ceiling height

  - 1/2 the distance to the edge of the nearest skylight

  - The distance to any permanent partition that is closer than 70% of the distance between the top of the partition and the ceiling.

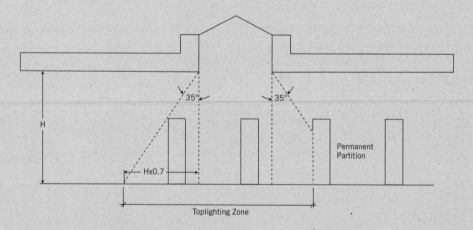

- Achieve a skylight coverage for the applicable space (containing the toplighting zone) between 3% and 6% of the total floor area.

- The skylights must have a with a minimum 0.5 VLT.

- A skylight diffuser, if used, must have a measured haze value of greater than 90% when tested according to ASTM D1003.

OR

OPTION 3. Measurement

Demonstrate, through records of indoor light measurements that a minimum daylight illumination level of 10 fc and a maximum of 500 fc has been achieved in the applicable spaces. Measurements must be taken on a 10-foot grid and recorded on building floor plans.

Provide glare control devices to avoid high contrast situations that could impede visual tasks. However, designs that incorporate view-preserving automated shades for glare control may demonstrate compliance for only the minimum 10 fc illuminance level.

OR

OPTION 4. Combination

Any of the above calculation methods may be combined to document the minimum daylight illumination in the applicable spaces.

1. Benefits and Issues to Consider

This credit addresses the availability of daylight to a building's occupants. When designing for maximum daylight, designers must evaluate and balance a number of environmental factors, such as heat gain and loss, glare control, visual quality, and variations in daylight availability.

Environmental Issues

Buildings emphasizing daylighting may often depend on the introduction of larger daylighting apertures. Daylighting reduces the need for electric lighting of building interiors, which, if integrated into the overall approach to lighting, can result in decreased energy use. A well-designed daylighted building is estimated to reduce lighting energy use by 50% to 80%.[21] This conserves natural resources and reduces air pollution impacts due to energy production and consumption.

Daylighting design involves a careful balance of heat gain and loss, glare control, visual quality, and variations in daylight availability. Shading devices, light shelves, courtyards, atriums, and glazing materials are all strategies employed in daylighting design. Important considerations include selected buildings' orientation, glazing size and spacing, glazing selection, reflectance of interior finishes, and locations of interior walls.

Large expanses of unfragmented or untreated glazing can give the illusion of transparency or reflect sky and habitat, causing birds in flight to collide into the glazing. See the Implementation sections for measures to reduce bird collisions.

Economic Issues

Adequate daylighting creates environments that are more pleasant and comfortable for building occupants, while also providing opportunities to reduce on-going energy demand. Research has demonstrated that direct access to daylighting results in greater overall occupant satisfaction (Environmental Building News, 1999; Figueiro, M.G., et al. 2002; California Energy Commission, 2003b). Improved occupant comfort and satisfaction can reduce absenteeism, result in greater productivity, and create greater employee retention than in comparable poorly-lit spaces. Similarly, research conducted in a variety of elementary school classrooms concluded that students in day-litghted schools consistently performed better on math and reading tests (California Energy Commission, 2003a). In some cases, extensive glazing may lead to over-lighting due to the combination of interior lighting and daylight, resulting in unnecessary energy use within the space. This condition can be addressed by designing interior lighting systems to effectively respond to daylighting levels via dimmers that maintain optimal lighting for occupants, while also producing energy savings. Additionally, excessive heat gain can be avoided through the installation of shading and glare control devices. Good daylighting design integrates with the effective lighting design to create more productive spaces that use less energy

2. Related Credits

Increasing the area of vision glazing is likely to provide greater access to views from the building interior, which is covered under the following credit:

- IEQ Credit 8.2: Daylight and Views—Views for Seated Spaces

Incorporate HVAC perimeter zones to address temperature differences adjacent to glazing, and to effectively accommodate their associated heating and cooling affects. This credit also has a direct correlation to related lighting design energy conservation strategies. The interior lighting systems design can be used to maximize the energy savings by providing daylighting controls.

- EA Credit 1.1: Optimize Energy Performance—Lighting Power

- EA Credit 1.2: Optimize Energy Performance—Lighting Controls

- EA Credit 1.3: Optimize Energy Performance—HVAC
- IEQ Credit 6.1: Controllability of Systems—Lighting

3. Summary of Referenced Standard

ASTM D1003–07E1, Standard Test Method for Haze and Luminous Transmittance of Transparent Plastics

http://www.astm.org

This test method covers the evaluation of specific light-transmitting and wide-angle-light-scattering properties of planar sections of materials such as essentially transparent plastic.

4. Implementation

Daylighting is affected by design decisions that start with building massing and orientation, shape of floorplate design, floor to ceiling heights. For commercial interiors projects where the project team may not have had the opportunity to design the fenestration, it is critical to select a building that supports daylighting. The project team should determine if daylighting and direct line of sight to the outdoors is available. Some buildings' potential for natural daylighting is limited by site constraints or structures that prohibit daylight penetration.

The project team should consider how the building's orientation could affect daylighting options and opt for designs with higher ceiling heights, shallow floor plates, courtyards, atriums, clerestory windows, and toplighting. The team should evaluate the potential to add exterior shading devices, interior light shelves, louvers, and view-preserving shades.

Attention to daylight should also be addressed during the interior design phase of the building.

Furniture systems, wall partitions, surface color, and texture all have the ability to reflect daylight into the space. High surface reflections should also be considered, as they can improve the daylight distribution in a space.

The desired amount of daylight will differ depending on the how each space is used. Daylighted spaces often have several daylight zones with differing target light levels. In addition to light levels, daylighting strategies should address interior color schemes, direct sun penetration, and integration with the electric lighting system. Unwanted glare without occupant control over it is a common failure. Typically low luminance ratios and lighting of primary surfaces will enhance visual quality. Glare control should be designed for all glazing areas that affect tasks.

Computer modeling software can be used to simulate daylighting conditions and can provide valuable input into the development of an effective, integrated daylighting design. Daylighting software simulates the daylighting conditions of interior spaces at various times during the day and shows the combined effects of multiple windows within a daylighted space.

Photo-responsive controls for dimming electric lighting can be incorporated into daylighting strategies to maintain consistent light levels and help save energy by reducing electric lighting in high daylight conditions while preserving illuminance levels on the task surface. These types of automatic controls require commissioning attention to avoid over-dimming, under-dimming or cycling of electric lights.

The selected building may have limited daylighting potential because of its orientation, number and size of building openings, and floor plate dimensions. Vertical site elements such as neighboring buildings and trees may reduce the potential for daylighting.

Effectively managing glare in a space should not be perceived as requiring a trade-off with occupant views. Many manufacturers offer view-preserving shades and blinds that control glare while also allowing occupants to see directly to the outdoors. The preservation of both daylighting and views can significantly increase occupant comfort and productivity.

Despite the known benefits of views in buildings, a potential downside is the likelihood that birds will fly into the windows. Larger areas of unfragmented or untreated glazing increase the risk. To reduce these collisions, consider treating the window glazing. Use exterior shading devices, introduce etched or fritt patterns, and/or create appropriate visual markers, such as differentiated planes, materials, textures, colors, opacity, or other features that help fragment glass reflections and reduce apparent overall transparency and reflectivity.

Common glare control devices are:

- Fixed exterior shading devices such as overhangs or fins

- Exterior light shelves

- Interior light shelves preferably with some translucency (3 to 5%) to avoid dark shadows under the light shelves.

- Louvers

- View preserving blinds with manual, motorized or automated controls

- Operable draperies

5. Timeline and Team

During the predesign stage, the owner, architect, and engineers should discuss general lighting design and the goals for occupants' work environment. Daylighting performance of a potential tenant space should be considered during leasing.

During schematic design and programming efforts, identify regularly occupied spaces and rooms as primary candidates for access to daylighting. The design team should work with the existing building envelope to determine how to allocate the spaces and maximize their access to daylight. Also at this time, identify initial glare control device strategies and run daylighting simulations to assist in the design decisions.

During the preparation of construction documents, the LEED calculations and/or computer simulation model should be developed in greater detail to inform the design decisions and verify compliance of the design. Refer again to the owner's project requirements. Use preliminary calculations to guide specifications for glare control devices. Once the design is complete, finalize the LEED calculations and supporting documentation.

During construction, the design and construction team should confirm that the submitted products and systems meet the owner's project requirements, the design performance specifications, and the original design intent.

During building operations, the owner should verify that occupants are not subject to glare and ensure that the installed glare control devices are performing as intended.

6. Calculations

To calculate the daylighting zone prercentage of regularly occupied spaces, divide the total daylighted regularly occupied area by the total regularly occupied area. If the percentage is 75% or more, the credit requirements are met for 1 point. If the percentage is 90% or more, the credit requirements are met for 2 points.

Calculating Regularly Occupied Areas

Identify all regularly occupied spaces within the project and calculate their associated floor areas. The regularly occupied spaces and total area calculated for this credit should be consistent with the regularly occupied areas identified in other credits, such as IEQ Credit 8.2.

Any spaces dedicated to tasks that would be compromised or hindered by the inclusion of daylighting should be identified and the reason for their exclusion should be explained, for documentation purposes, in a supporting narrative. Any exclusion must be based solely on the basis of the task performed in the space, not the length of time an occupant will spend there. In addition, exceptions to the requirement are solely based on visual considerations, not based on sound.

Multipurpose rooms must be included in the credit calculations. Because some activities in these spaces may be hindered by daylighting, effective shades, view preserving blinds, and lighting controls should be included in the design.

For veterinary, boarding, or animal shelter facilities, include the area regularly occupied by the animals.

Calculating Daylighting Performance

The requirements for any option can be met even if 100% of each room does not meet the minimum requirement when using the daylight simulation, prescriptive, or measurement approaches. The portion of the room within the daylight zone or meeting the illumination level requirements counts toward the percentage of daylighted area, and the rest of the space is included in the calculation of total area. The floor area of all compliant spaces is tallied and then divided by the floor area of all regularly occupied spaces:

OPTION 1. Simulation

- Create a daylight simulation model for the building or for each regularly occupied space with glazing. The model should include glazing properties, as well as representative surface reflectance settings for interior finishes.

- For each applicable area, include a horizontal calculation grid at 30 inches above the floor, or measured at the appropriate desk or work height level for the intended use of the space. This represents the typical work plane height. It is recommended that the calculation grid should be set with a regular size interval so that the grid has at least 9 measuring points in a room but with a maximum interval of 5-feet to provide a detailed illumination diagram for each room.

- Calculate the daylight illumination for each applicable space using the following daylight criterion: clear-sky conditions at both 9:00 a.m. and 3:00 p.m. on September 21 for the project's geographic location.

- Identify the area of the room that has daylight illumination between 10 footcandles and 500 footcandles at both times (9:00 am and 3:00 pm). Spaces that do not meet the daylight illumination levels at both times do not qualify.

- If the space uses automated view-preserving shades, the maximum footcandle requirement does not apply.

- Sum the square footage of all daylighted rooms or areas and divide by the total square footage of all regularly occupied spaces.

OPTION 2. Prescriptive

To demonstrate compliance via Option 2, project floor plans should be evaluated to categorize internal areas as Sidelighting or Toplighting daylight zones. Per the methodologies below, daylighted areas adjacent side windows (i.e. vision and daylighting glazing) and below any skylights/top-lights should be calculated. These two areas taken together represent the compliant area for the project and are divided by the total floor area to demonstrate credit compliance. Care should be taken not to double-count compliant areas that may fall under both categories.

Sidelighting

This option provides a relatively simple method of determining whether the daylighting requirements are met. It is applicable to many standard building designs, primarily rectangular floor plates with a central core. The project team needs the following basic information to determine compliance:

- Window head height
- Window sill height
- Window area
- Visible light transmittance (abbreviated as VLT or T_{vis})
- Floor area

Perform the following calculation for each bay applicable space.

- Determine the eligible window area (WA) for the space.

  - Determine whether a modified head height must be used. As shown in Figure 1 draw a 63-degree angle from the vertical, in section, from the window head to the floor. If the ceiling obstructs this line, a modified head height must be used.

  - Draw a 63-degree angle from the vertical, in section, using the ceiling corner that obstructed the previous line as a starting point. The point at which this line intersects the window is the modified head height. See Figure 1.

- Determine the floor area (FA).
- Determine the ratio of the window area to the floor area (WFR)—that is, WA/FA.
- Determine the ratio of visible light transmittance to window to floor area—that is, $(T_{vis})(WFR)$.
- If the result is between 0.150 and 0.180, the space counts as a daylight zone. If the result is between 0.000 and 0.150 a portion of the space is compliance. Calculate the compliance floor area as follows:

  - Divide the calculated result by 0.150 and multiply by the floor area of the space. This fractional result represents the floor area to be counted as qualifying daylit area.

- When using this method in conjunction with toplighting, the qualifying floor area from sidelighting is assumed to be the floor area immediately adjacent to the windows.

An example of the sidelighting calculation is shown in Table 1.

Figure 1. Sample Modified Window Head Height

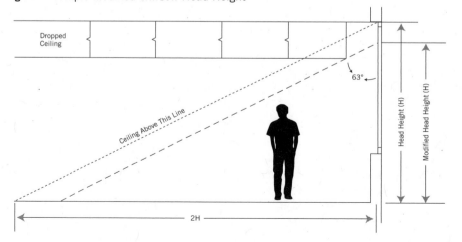

Toplighting Daylight Zone

This method is applicable for many standard building designs and may be particularly useful for single-floor retail developments. The project team needs the following basic information to determine compliance:

- Area of skylights or toplighting (SA)
- Visible light transmittance (VLT or T_{vis}) of skylights or toplighting
- Floor area of the space (FA)
- Measured haze value of skylight or toplighting diffuser

Perform the following calculation for each space:

- Determine the skylight or toplighting coverage, which is the ratio of skylights or toplighting are to floor area—that is, (SA/FA) (100).
- Determine the top-light daylight zone area, which is the outline of the opening beneath the skylight, plus in each direction the lesser of- 70% of the ceiling height, 1/2 the distance to the edge of the nearest skylight, the distance to any permanent partition that is closer than 70% of the distance between the top of the partition and the ceiling.
- Confirm a minimum 0.5 VLT for skylights or toplight.
- Confirm that the skylight or toplighting diffuser has a measured haze value greater than 90% per the ASTM D1003 testing methodology.
- The area of the toplighting zone complies if the skylight or toplight roof coverage is between 3% and 6%, the measured haze value is greater than 90%, and the minimum 0.5 VLT criteria is achieved.

An example of the toplighting calculation is shown in Table 1.

Figure 2. Toplighting Daylight Zone

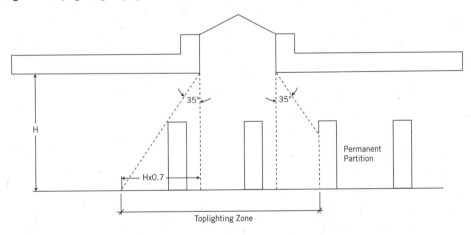

Combined Sidelighting and Toplighting Daylight Zone

For buildings that have both sidelighting and toplighting conditions, a combination of the above 2 methodologies can be utilized to demonstrate compliance.

OPTION 3

- Take field measurements of illuminance levels at 30 inches above the floor within all regularly occupied areas, or measured at the appropriate desk or work height level for the intended use of the space.

- Record indoor light measurements of all regularly occupied spaces on a grid that has at least 4 points in a room and with a maximum grid interval of 10-feet.

- Enter the floor area with daylight illuminance levels of 10 footcandles or above into a summary table. See Table 2.

- For spaces where some of the measurements meet the minimum 10 footcandle requirement, only the floor area meeting the minimum criteria is counted as the daylight zone.

OPTION 4

The above calculation methods may be combined to document the minimum daylight percentage of applicable spaces. To combine the methods, determine for each space which single method will be used to determine the daylight zone. Once the daylight zone has been determined for each applicable space, sum the daylight zone areas, this sum is the total daylighted area.

Divide the total daylighted area by the total combined floor area for all applicable spaces to determine the qualifying floor area percentage.

7. Documentation Guidance

As a first step in preparing to complete the LEED Online documentation requirements, work through the following measures. Refer to LEED Online for the complete descriptions of all required documentation.

- Develop documentation—such as floor plans, sections, and elevations—showing the glare control methods used on the project.

- Maintain documentation—such as floor plans, sections, and elevations—showing the location of regularly occupied spaces with a qualifying amount of daylight.

- If using daylight simulation, update the computer model as the design progresses.

- If using measurement, record indoor light measurements of all applicable spaces on a maximum 10-foot grid on project floor plans.

8. Examples

Figure 3 provides an example of a daylight simulation model.

Figure 3. Sample Daylight Simulation Model Output

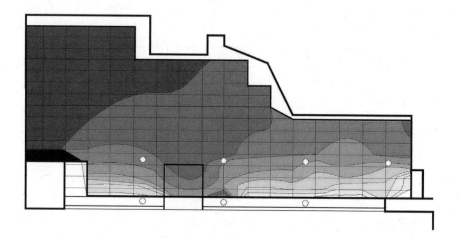

Figure 4. Sample Prescriptive Diagram

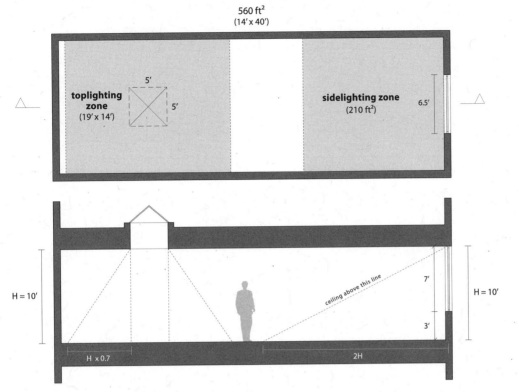

560 ft²
(14' x 40')

toplighting zone
(19' x 14')

sidelighting zone
(210 ft²)

Table 1. Sample Prescriptive Calculation

Regularly Occupied Space ID	Space Type	Floor Area (sf)	Sidelighting Daylight Zones						Toplighting Daylight Zones					Total Daylighted Area, Prescriptive (sf)
			Zone Floor Area (sf)	Window Area (sf)	Window to Floor Area Ratio (WFR)	VLT (T$_{vis}$) of Window	VLT x WFR	Sidelighted Area Subtotal (sf)	Zone Floor Area (sf)	Total Area of Skylight Openings (sf)	Skylight Coverage	VLT (T$_{vis}$) of Skylight	Toplighted Area Subtotal (sf)	
Room 119	Conference/ Meeting	1,090.00	1090.00	248.00	0.23	0.68	0.155	1090.00	0.00				0.00	1090.00
Room 123	Office: Private	455.00	298.00	64.00	0.21	0.70	0.150	298.00	0.00				0.00	298.00
Room 129	Office: Private	680.00	466.60	100.00	0.21	0.70	0.150	466.60	150.00	25.00	0.04	0.60	150.00	616.60
Room 144	Conference/ Meeting	905.00	905.00	200.00	0.22	0.70	0.155	905.00	0.00				0.00	905.00
Room 201	Other	220.00						0.00	220.00	8.00	0.04	0.60	220.00	220.00
Room 206	Office: Open	930.00						0.00	870.00	35.00	0.04	0.60	870.00	870.00
Room 210	Office: Open	1,180.00						0.00	1030.00	44.00	0.04	0.55	1030.00	1030.00
Picture Ex.	Conference/ Meeting	560.00	210.00	45.00	0.21	0.70	0.150	210.00	266.00	25.00	0.04	0.60	266.00	476.00
	Total regularly occupied area (sf)	6,020.00	Total daylighted area, prescriptive (sf)											5505.60

Table 2. Sample Daylighting Measurement

Regularly Occupied Space ID	Space Type	Floor Area (sf)	Floor Area with Daylight Illuminance Levels between 10 fc and 500 fc
Room 101	Office- Private	400	400
Room 102	Office- Private	600	500
Room 103	Other	240	0
Room 104	Conference/Meeting	975	975
Room 110	Office- Open	2420	2120
Room 112	Office- Private	330	330
Room 114	Conference/Meeting	720	0
Room 115	Office- Private	604	604
TOTAL		6,289	4,929

9. Exemplary Performance

The availability of 2 points in IEQ Credit 8.1, Daylight and Views—Daylight, precludes the opportunity to earn a third point using the same criteria.

10. Regional Variations

The building site orientation and its specific regional location will directly influence the available daylight throughout the day and during the year. For instance, in northern latitudes, winter days are short, and building occupants might spend the entire period of daylight inside. Seasonal variances in the sun's daily path should be evaluated during the project design development to minimize the potential for glare inside the building while maximizing the use of functional daylighting. The consistent availability of adequate daylight at a particular project site will also affect the potential for reduction in lighting power demand through the use of daylighting strategies, such as incorporation of photoresponsive controls for perimeter lighting zones. When building glazing systems, balance the visible light transmittance with overall building energy performance goals to minimize undesirable heat loss and/or gain through the glazing.

11. Operations and Maintenance Considerations

Glazing and shading systems should be regularly cleaned and maintained. Likewise, windows and skylights require periodic sealant and flashing inspections to ensure water tightness.

12. Resources

Please see USGBC's LEED Resources & Tools (http://www.usgbc.org/projecttools) for additional resources and technical information.

Websites

The Art of Daylighting
http://www.edcmag.com/Articles/Feature_Article/10e5869a47697010VgnVCM100000f932a8c0
This Environmental Design + Construction article provides a solid introduction to daylighting.

New Buildings Institute's Productivity and Building Science Program
http://www.newbuildings.org/downloads/photometrics/5D5.3.5a_photometry.pdf
This report provides case studies and information on the benefits of daylighting.

Radiance Software
http://radsite.lbl.gov/radiance/
This site offers free daylighting simulation software from the Lawrence Berkeley National Laboratory.

Tips for Daylighting with Windows

http://btech.lbl.gov/pub/designguide/

This site offers a comprehensive daylighting guide from Lawrence Berkeley National Laboratory.

Whole Building Design Guide, Daylighting

Whole Building Design Guide, Electric Lighting Controls

http://www.wbdg.org/resources/electriclighting.php?r=school_library

The Daylighting and Electric Lighting Controls sections provide a wealth of resources including definitions, fundamentals, materials, and tools.

Print Media

Architectural Lighting, 2nd edition, by M. David Egan and Victor Olgyay, (McGraw-Hill, 2002).

Daylighting Design, by Benjamin Evans, *Time-Saver Standards for Architectural Design Data* (McGraw-Hill, Inc., 1997).

Daylighting for Sustainable Design, by Mary Guzowski (McGraw-Hill, Inc., 1999).

Daylighting Performance and Design, by Gregg D. Ander (John Wiley & Sons, 1997).

Sustainable Building Technical Manual (Public Technology Institute, 1996): http://www.pti.org.

Biophilic Design: The Theory, Science and Practice of Bringing Buildings to Life, by Kellert, Heerwagen, and Mador (John Wiley & Sons, 2008).

13. Definitions

A **bay** is a component of a standard, rectilinear building design. It is the open area defined by a building element such as columns or a window. Typically, there are multiple identical bays in succession.

Daylighting is the controlled admission of natural light into a space through glazing to reduce or eliminate electric lighting. Daylighting creates a stimulating and productive environment for building occupants.

Daylighting zone is the total floor area that meets the performance requirements for daylighting.

Glare is any excessively bright source of light within the visual field that creates discomfort or loss in visibility.

Regularly occupied spaces in commercial buildings are areas where people sit or stand as they work. In residential applications these spaces include all living and family rooms and exclude bathrooms, closets, or other storage or utility areas.

Tenant space is the area within the LEED project boundary. For more information on what can and must be in the LEED project boundary see the Minimum Program Requirements (MPRs) and LEED 2009 MPR Supplemental Guidance. Note: tenant space is the same as project space.

Visible light transmittance (T_{vis}) is the ratio of total transmitted light to total incident light. (I.e., the amount of visible spectrum light passing through a glazing surface divided by the amount of light striking the glazing surface. The higher T_{vis} value, the more incident light passes through the glazing.

Vision glazing is that portion of exterior windows between 30 and 90 inches above the floor that permits a view to the exterior of the project space.

Window-to-floor ratio (**WFR**) is the total area of the window (measured vertically from 30 inches above the finished floor to the top of the glass, multiplied by the width of the glass) divided by the floor area.

DAYLIGHT AND VIEWS—VIEWS FOR SEATED SPACES

	CI
Credit	IEQ Credit 8.2
Points	1 point

Intent

To provide the building occupants a connection to the outdoors through the introduction of daylight and views into the regularly occupied areas of the tenant space.

Requirements

Achieve a direct line of sight to the outdoor environment via vision glazing between 30 inches and 90 inches above the finish floor for building occupants in 90% of all regularly occupied areas. Determine the area with a direct line of sight by totaling the regularly occupied square footage that meets the following criteria:

- In plan view, the area is within sight lines drawn from perimeter vision glazing.

- In section view, a direct sight line can be drawn from a point 42 inches above the floor (typical seated eye height) to perimeter vision glazing.

The line of sight may be drawn through interior glazing. For private offices, the entire square footage of the office may be counted if 75% or more of the area has a direct line of sight to perimeter vision glazing. If less than 75% of the area has a direct line of sight, only the area with the direct line of sight count toward meeting the credit requirement. For multi-occupant spaces, the actual square footage with a direct line of sight to perimeter vision glazing is counted.

1. Benefits and Issues to Consider

Environmental Issues

Providing access to views of the outdoors through the incorporation of vision glazing enables building occupants to maintain a visual connection to the surrounding environment. The additional glazed area may reduce the need for interior electric lighting, resulting in decreased energy use. This conserves natural resources and reduces air pollution impacts due to energy production and consumption.

When designing for maximum views and daylighting, designers must evaluate and balance a number of environmental factors, including heat gain and loss, glare control, visual quality, and variations in daylight availability. Appropriate shading devices to control glare must be utilized to provide a high level of visual comfort.

Economic Issues

Refer to the Economic Issues section in IEQ Credits 8.1.

2. Related Credits

Increasing the area of vision glazing is likely to provide greater daylight access to the building interior. The following credit has related requirements:

- IEQ Credit 8.1: Daylight and Views—Daylight 75% of Spaces

Vision glazing has a direct correlation to lighting design energy conservation strategies. The interior lighting systems design can be used to maximize the energy savings by providing daylighting controls, and HVAC perimeter zones may be required to address temperature differences adjacent to glazing. Refer to these 2 credits:

- EA Credit 1.2: Optimize Energy Performance—Lighting Controls

- EA Credit 1.3: Optimize Energy Performance—HVAC

3. Summary of Referenced Standards

There are no standards referenced for this credit.

4. Implementation

1 successful strategy is to locate open plan areas along the exterior walls while placing private offices and areas not regularly occupied in the core of the building. This configuration maintains the optimum number of available views. The line of sight used for the determination of horizontal views is assumed to be 42 inches (the average height of one's eyes when sitting). Maintaining the views for spaces near the core is an important design objective. See Figure 1.

Figure 1. Horizontal View at 42 Inches

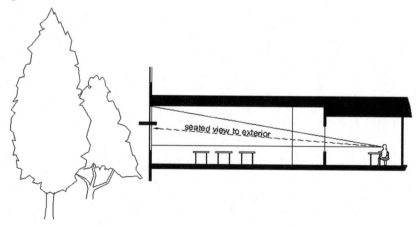

seated view to exterior

Regularly occupied spaces include office spaces, conference rooms, and cafeterias. Areas that need not be considered include support areas for copying, storage, mechanical equipment, laundry, and restrooms.

5. Timeline and Team

During space planning, regularly occupied spaces and rooms should be identified as high-priority candidates for access to views. During the design phase, the entire design team—the owner, architect, and interior designer—should take an integrated approach to allocating regularly occupied spaces along the interior building perimeter.

During the preparation of construction documents, the LEED calculations should be developed in greater detail to inform the design decisions and verify the compliance of the building design. Once the design is complete, finalize the LEED calculations and supporting documentation.

6. Calculations

Two calculations are required to determine compliance. One, using the direct line of sight to perimeter glazing, determines whether 90% of the regularly occupied area has the potential for views. It is based on vision glazing between 30 inches and 90 inches above the floor and the location of full-height interior partitions. Movable furniture and partitions are not included in the scope of this credit calculation. See Figure 2. Movable furniture and partitions are those that can moved to provide access to the view by the user without the need for tools or assistance from special trades and facilities management. The other uses the horizontal view at a typical seated eye height to determine access to views.

Figure 2. Direct Line of Sight to Perimeter Vision Glazing

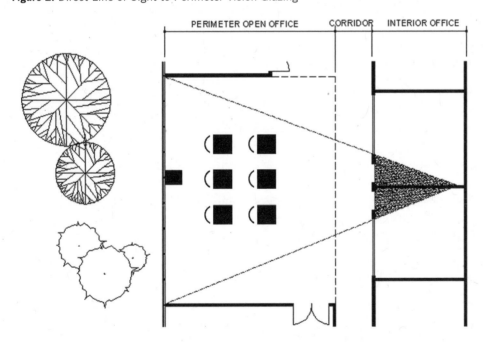

Determining Direct Line of Sight to Perimeter Vision Glazing

- Create a spreadsheet and identify all regularly occupied areas. Determine the floor area (square footage) of each applicable space using construction documents.

- Using a floor plan, determine the fraction of the regularly occupied area that has direct line of sight to the outdoors for each window. The line of sight can pass through 2 interior glazing surfaces but not through doorways with solid doors. See Figure 2.

- For private offices, if the percentage of floor area with direct line of sight is 75% or more (i.e., only the corners are noncompliant), enter the entire square footage of that room in the spreadsheet (Table 1) as meeting the credit requirement. If less than 75% of the room has a direct line of sight, estimate the compliant floor area and enter that value.

- For multioccupant spaces, such as conference rooms and classrooms, estimate the actual square footage with a direct line of sight to perimeter vision glazing.

Determining Horizontal View at Seated Eye Height

- Using representative building sections, draw a line at 42 inches (typical seated eye height) across the section to establish eye height and any obstruction to the perimeter glazing. Draw 1 or more representative sight lines from a point at eye height in the regularly occupied space to the perimeter vision glazing (Figure 1).

- For each space with a horizontal view at seated eye height, enter yes in the spreadsheet (Table 1). If a room has direct line of sight on the floor plan but does not have an unobstructed view at eye height, the floor area does not count toward the requirement; enter no.

- Total the areas that meet all the above criteria and divide the sum by the total regularly occupied area to determine whether the building meets the 90% access to views requirement.

Table 1. Views Compliance

Room	Regularly Occupied Floor Area (sf)	Plan Area of Direct Line of Sight to Perimeter Vision Glazing (sf)	Calculated Area of Direct Line of Sight to Perimeter Vision Glazing (sf)	Horizoinatal View at 42 Inches (Yes/No)	Compliant Area (sf)
101 Office	820	790	820	Yes	820
102 Office	330	280	330	Yes	330
103 Open office	4,935	4,641	4,641	Yes	4,641
104 Office	250	201	250	No	0
105 Office	250	175	175	Yes	175
Total	6,585				5,966
Percent access to views (5,966/6,585)					90.5% credit earned

7. Documentation Guidance

As a first step in preparing to complete the LEED Online documentation requirements, work through the following measures. Refer to LEED Online for the complete descriptions of all required documentation.

- Maintain documentation—such as floor plans, sections, and elevations—showing the location of regularly occupied spaces with views.

- Maintain a spreadsheet documenting the view area as outlined in the Calculations section to account for any changes in design.

8. Examples

The following example demonstrates the percentage of spaces with access to views that could be realized for an 80,000 square foot office building. The floor plan was designed to locate private offices toward the inside the building. 96% of views are achieved, which meets the threshold for this credit.

Figure 3. Sample Floor Plan Excerpt

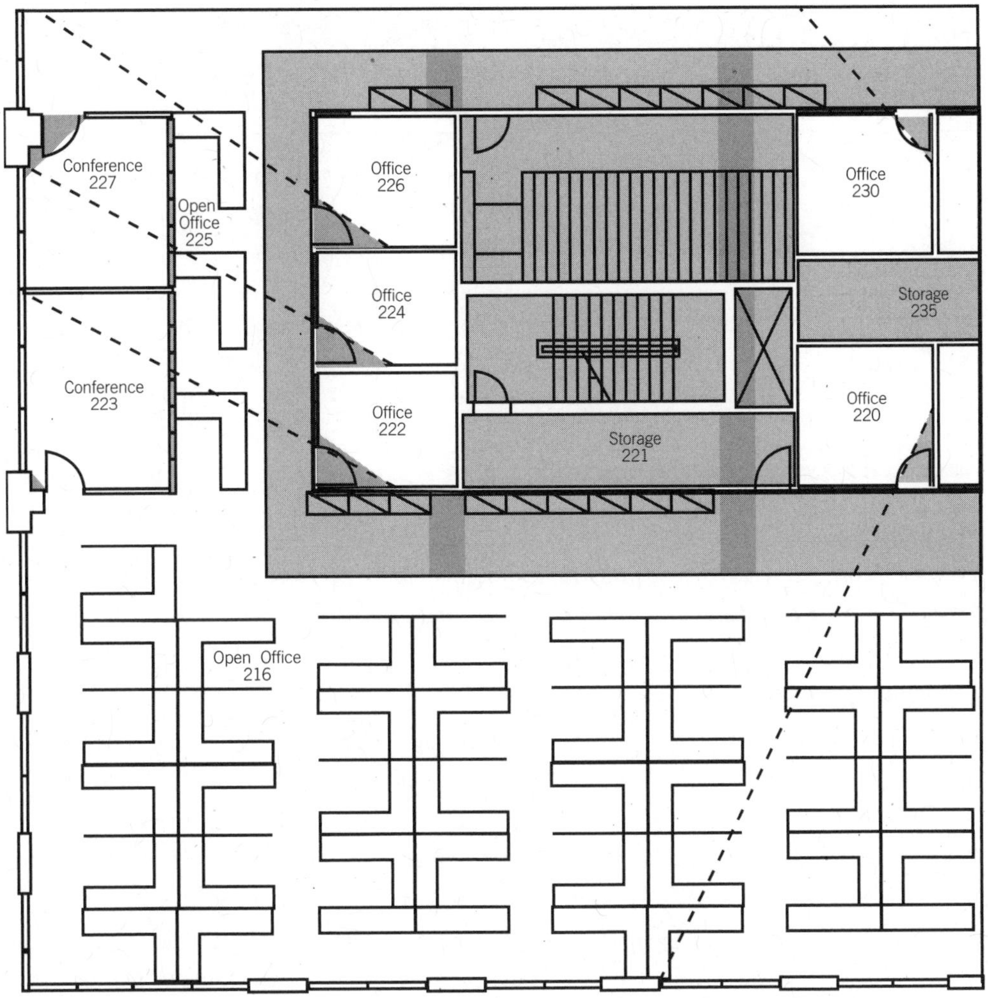

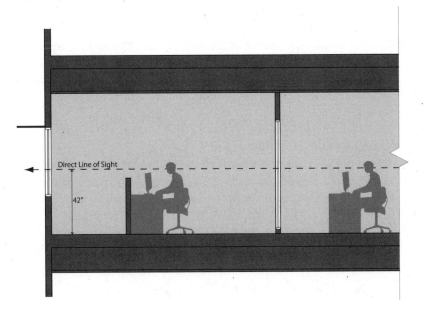

Conference 227

Open Office 225

Conference 223

Office 226

Office 224

Office 222

Office 230

Storage 235

Office 220

Storage 221

Open Office 216

Figure 4. Unobstructed View through Window over Low Partition

Direct Line of Sight

42"

Table 2. Sample Calculations Excerpt

Room	Descripton	Floor area (sf)	Horizontal view at 42"	Views (sf)
216	Open office	4,405	Y	4,405
220	Office	136	Y	136
222	Office	115	Y	115
223	Conference	198	Y	197
224	Office	115	Y	115
225	Open office	224	Y	0
226	Office	120	Y	120
227	Conference	169	Y	161
232	Office	132	Y	132
Totals		5,634		5,381
Percentages of Area with Views: (5,381/5,634)				96%

9. Exemplary Performance

Exemplary performance may be demonstrated for this credit by meeting 2 of the 4 following measures:

1. 90% or more of regularly occupied spaces have multiple lines of sight to vision glazing in different directions at least 90 degrees apart.

2. 90% or more of regularly occupied spaces have views that include views of at least 2 of the following: 1) vegetation, 2) human activity or 3) objects at least 70 feet from the exterior of the glazing.

3. 90% or more of regularly occupied spaces have access to unobstructed views located within the distance of 3 times the head height of the vision glazing.

4. 90% or more of regularly occupied spaces have access to views with a view factor of 3 or greater, per the Heschong Mahone Group study, *Windows and Offices; A Study of Office Worker Performance and the Indoor Environment*, page 47, for their primary view (seated at workstation, facing computer screen). See: http://h-m-g.com/downloads/Daylighting/day_registration_form.htm to download the report at no charge.

10. Regional Variations

Available duration and potency of solar radiation can directly impact the heat gain through glazing systems. Consideration should be given when selecting glazing systems to minimize undesirable heat loss and gain through the glazing. The visual appeal of the exterior environment greatly impacts the subjective quality of the views.

11. Operations and Maintenance Considerations

Glazing and shading systems should be regularly cleaned and maintained. Windows and skylights require periodic sealant and flashing inspections to ensure water tightness. Additionally, any landscaping that may provide for high-quality views should be well maintained.

12. Resources

See USGBC's LEED Resources & Tools (http://www.usgbc.org/projecttools) for additional resources and technical information.

Websites

Whole Building Design Guide, Daylighting
http://www.wbdg.org/resources/daylighting.php

Whole Building Design Guide, Electric Lighting Controls
http://www.wbdg.org/resources/electriclighting.php?r=school_library
The Daylighting and Electric Lighting Controls sections provide a wealth of resources including definitions, fundamentals, materials, and tools.

Print Media

Sustainable Building Technical Manual (Public Technology Institute, 1996): http://www.pti.org.

Biophilic Design: The Theory, Science and Practice of Bringing Buildings to Life, by Kellert, Heerwagen, and Mador (John Wiley & Sons, 2008).

13. Definitions

Daylighting is the controlled admission of natural light into a space through glazing to reduce or eliminate electric lighting.

Direct Line of Sight to Perimeter Vision Glazing is the approach used to determine the calculated area of regularly occupied areas with direct line of sight to perimeter vision glazing. The area determination includes full height partitions and other fixed construction prior to installation of furniture.

Glare is any excessively bright source of light within the visual field that creates discomfort or loss in visibility.

Movable furniture and partitions are those that can moved to provide access to the view by the user without the need for tools or assistance from special trades and facilities management.

Regularly occupied spaces in commercial buildings are areas where people sit or stand as they work; in residential applications these spaces are living and family rooms.

Tenant space is the area within the LEED project boundary. For more information on what can and must be in the LEED project boundary see the Minimum Program Requirements (MPRs) and LEED 2009 MPR Supplemental Guidance. Note: tenant space is the same as project space.

Visible light transmittance (T_{vis}) is the ratio of total transmitted light to total incident light (i.e., the amount of visible spectrum, 380–780 nanomater light passing through a glazing surface divided by the amount of light striking the glazing surface). The higher the T_{vis} value, the more incident light is passing through the glazing.

Vision glazing is that portion of exterior windows above 30 inches and below 90 inches that permits a view to the outside.

Endnotes

[1]   U.S. Environmental Protection Agency. Health Buildings, Healthy People: A Vision for the 21st Century. 2001. http://www.epa.gov/iaq/hbhp/hbhptoc.html (accessed May 2008).

[2]   U.S. Environmental Protection Agency. Unfinished Business: A Comparative Assessment of Environmental Problems. Washington, DC: U.S. EPA, 1987.

[3]   U.S. Environmental Protection Agency. Reducing Risk: Setting Priorities and Strategies for Environmental Protection. Washington, DC: U.S. EPA, 1990.

[4]   U.S. Environmental Protection Agency. Indoor Air in Large Buildings. 2002. http://www.epa.gov/iaq/largebldgs/i-beam/text/budgets_accounts.html (accessed May 2008).

5   Fisk, W.J. "Health and Productivity Gains from Better Indoor Environments and Their
     Relationship with Building Energy Efficiency." Annual Rev. Energy Environ. 25 (2000): 537–66.

6   Rocky Mountain Institute. "Greening the Building and the Bottom Line." http://www.rmi.org/
     images/PDFs/BuildingsLand/D94-27_GBBL.pdf (accessed November 2008).

7   This assumes that $100,000 in IAQ improvements are invested. Damiano, Leonard, and
     David Dougan. The Big Carrots: Productivity and Health. Ebtron, Inc., 2003. http://www.
     automatedbuildings.com/news/apr03/articles/ebtron/ebtron.htm. (accessed May 2008).

8   U.S. Department of Health and Human Services, National Institutes of Health, National Cancer
     Institute. "Smoking and Tobacco Control Monograph 10." Health Effects of Exposure to
     Environmental Tobacco Smoke. NIH, 1999. http://cancercontrol.cancer.gov/tcrb/monographs/10/
     m10_complete.pdf (accessed May 2008).

9   Ibid.

10   U.S. Department of Health and Human Services, Public Health Service, Office of the Surgeon
     General. Women and Smoking: A Report of the Surgeon General. 2001. http://www.cdc.gov/
     tobacco/sgr/sgr_forwomen/index.htm. (accessed May 2008).

11   Prill, Rich. Why Measure Carbon Dioxide in Buildings?. Washington State University Extension
     Energy Program. 2000. http://www.energy.wsu.edu/documents/building/iaq/CO2inbuildings.pdf
     (accessed November 2008).

12   Goren, A., S. Hellman, A. Gabbay, and S. Brenner. "Respiratory problems associated with exposure
     to airborne particles in the community." Archives of Environmental Health 54 (1999).

13   Chen, Allen, and Edward L. Vine. A Scoping Study on the *Costs of Indoor Air Quality Illnesses: An
     Insurance Loss Reduction Perspective*. 1998. http://eetd.lbl.gov/insurance-research/PUBS/LBNL-
     41919.pdf. (accessed May 2008).

14   Department of Health and Human Services, National Institutes of Health, National Cancer
     Institute. *Health Effects of Exposure to Environmental Tobacco Smoke—Smoking and Tobacco Control
     Monograph 10*. 1999. http://cancercontrol.cancer.gov/tcrb/monographs/10/m10_complete.pdf
     (accessed May 2008).

15   Americans for Non-Smokers' Rights. "Americans for Non-Smokers' Rights: Smoke-free Lists, Maps, and
     Data." http://www.no-smoke.org.goingsmokefree.php?id=519. (accessed September 2008).
     This information is subject to change based on the ongoing indoor smoking legislation of each
     state.

16   Canadian Centre for Occupational Health and Safety. "Health Effects of Carbon Dioxide Gas."
     1997. http://www.ccohs.ca/oshanswers/chemicals/chem_profiles/carbon_dioxide/health_cd.html
     (accessed May 2008).

17   U.S. Environmental Protection Agency. "Why Study Human Health Indoors?" Healthy Buildings,
     Healthy People: A Vision for the 21st Century. 2001. http://www.epa.gov/iaq/hbhp/section_1.pdf
     (accessed May 2008).

18   Rocky Mountain Institute. "Greening the Building and the Bottom Line." http://www.rmi.org/
     images/PDFs/BuildingsLand/D94-27_GBBL.pdf (accessed November 2008).

19   Rocky Mountain Institute. *Green Development: Integrating Ecology and Real Estate*. Wiley, 1998.

20   Rocky Mountain Institute. "Greening the Building and the Bottom Line." http://www.rmi.org/
     images/PDFs/BuildingsLand/D94-27_GBBL.pdf (accessed November 2008).

21   Abraham, Loren E. Sustainable Building Technical Manual: Green Building Design, Construction,
     and Operations. Public Technology Inc. and U.S. Green Building Council, 1996.

Overview

Sustainable design strategies and measures are constantly evolving and improving. New technologies are continually introduced to the marketplace, and up-to-date scientific research influences building design strategies. The purpose of this LEED category is to recognize projects for innovative features and sustainable building strategies and practices.

Occasionally, a strategy results in performance that greatly exceeds what is required in an existing LEED credit. Other strategies may not be addressed by any LEED prerequisite or credit but warrant consideration for their sustainability benefits. In addition, LEED is most effectively implemented as part of an integrated design process, and this category addresses the role of a LEED Accredited Professional in facilitating that process.

Implementing New Technologies and Methods

As the building design and construction industry introduces new strategies for sustainable development, opportunities leading to additional environmental benefits will continue to emerge. Opportunities that are not currently addressed by LEED for Commercial Interiors may include environmental solutions specific to a particular location, condition, or region. With all sustainable strategies and measures, it is important to consider related environmental impacts. Project teams must be prepared to demonstrate the environmental benefit of innovative strategies and are encouraged to pursue opportunities that provide benefits of particular significance. Project teams can earn exemplary performance points by implementing strategies that result in performance that greatly exceeds the level or scope required by an existing LEED prerequisite or credit. Exemplary performance opportunities are noted throughout this reference guide.

CREDIT	TITLE
ID Credit 1	Innovation in Design
ID Credit 2	LEED® Accredited Professional

	CI
Credit	ID Credit 1
Points	1-5 points

Intent

To provide design teams and projects the opportunity to achieve exceptional performance above the requirements set by the LEED Green Building Rating System and/or innovative performance in Green Building categories not specifically addressed by the LEED Green Building Rating System.

Requirements

Credit can be achieved through any combination of the Innovation in Design and Exemplary Performance paths as described below:

PATH 1. Innovation in Design (1-5 points)

Achieve significant, measurable environmental performance using a strategy not addressed in the LEED 2009 for Commercial Interiors Rating System.

One point is awarded for each innovation achieved. No more than 5 points under IDc1 may be earned through PATH 1—Innovation in Design.

Identify the following in writing:

- The intent of the proposed innovation credit
- The proposed requirements for compliance
- The proposed submittals to demonstrate compliance
- The design approach (strategies) used to meet the requirements.

PATH 2. Exemplary Performance (1-3 points)

Achieve exemplary performance in an existing LEED 2009 for Commercial Interiors prerequisite or credit that allows exemplary performance as specified in the LEED Reference Guide for Green Building Interior Design, 2009 Edition. An exemplary performance point may be earned for achieving double the credit requirements and/or achieving the next incremental percentage threshold of an existing credit in LEED.

One point is awarded for each exemplary performance achieved. No more than 3 points under IDc1 may be earned through PATH 2— Exemplary Performance.

PATH 3. Pilot Credit (1-5 points)

Attempt a pilot credit available in the Pilot Credit Library at www.usgbc.org/pilotcreditlibrary. Register as a pilot credit participant and complete the required documentation. Projects may pursue up to 5 Pilot Credits total.

ID	
CI	Credit 1

1. Benefits and Issues to Consider

Sustainable design comes from innovative strategies and thinking. Institutional measures to reward such thinking—like the achievement of this credit—benefit our environment. Recognition of the exceptional will spur further innovation.

2. Related Credits

Every LEED for Commercial Interiors (CI) credit holds ideas for Innovation in Design points and strategies. Refer to the Exemplary Performance section of each credit in this reference guide.

3. Summary of Referenced Standards

There is no standard referenced for this credit. Please refer to the Summary of Referenced Standards section in each credit for relevant standards.

4. Implementation

Credits in this section may be earned by documenting increased benefits to the environment in 1 of 2 ways:

Exemplary Performance Strategy

Exemplary performance strategies result in performance that greatly exceeds the level or scope required by existing LEED for Commercial Interiors prerequisites or credits.

As a rule of thumb, ID credits for exemplary performance are awarded for doubling the credit requirements and/or achieving the next incremental percentage threshold. For instance, to achieve an ID credit for exemplary performance in MR Credit 4, Recycled Content, the total recycled value must be 30% or greater.

Exemplary performance is not available for all credits in LEED CI. Credits that allow exemplary performance through a predetermined approach are noted throughout this reference guide and the LEED Online credit templates. A maximum of 3 ID points can be earned for exemplary performance.

Innovative Strategies

Innovative strategies are those that are not addressed by any existing LEED credits. Only those strategies that demonstrate a comprehensive approach and have significant, measurable environmental benefits are applicable.

There are 3 basic criteria for achieving an innovation credit for a category not specifically addressed by LEED:

1. The project must demonstrate quantitative performance improvements for environmental benefit (establishing a baseline of standard performance for comparison with the final design).

2. The process or specification must be comprehensive. For example, a team that is considering applying for an innovation credit for a green housekeeping program would need to demonstrate that the program applies to the entire project being certified under LEED. Measures that address a limited portion of a project or are not comprehensive in other ways are not eligible.

3. The concept the project team develops for the innovation credit must be applicable to other projects and must be significantly better than standard sustainable design practices.

ID credits awarded for 1 project at a specific point in time do not constitute automatic approval for similar strategies in a future project.

ID credits are not awarded for the use of a particular product or design strategy if the technology aids in the achievement of an existing LEED credit.

Approved ID credits may be pursued by any LEED project, but the project team must sufficiently document the achievement using the LEED credit equivalence process.

5. Timeline and Team

Innovation in Design ideally begins at a project's conception, but it can become part of the project at any step of the process and come from any member of the project team. Open-mindedness, creativity, and rigor in follow-through are the critical ingredients. Options for innovation may come from the spheres of the technological—for example, an inventive wall section for climate control—or the general, such as educational outreach measures. Thus, team members with a variety of skills and interests will be able to contribute to the achievement of this credit.

6. Calculations

For exemplary performance, please refer to the Calculations section in each credit.

7. Documentation Guidance

As a first step in preparing to complete the LEED Online documentation requirements, work through the following measures. Refer to LEED Online for the complete descriptions of all required documentation.

- Document the process by which the project team has worked to develop and/or implement environmental benefits beyond the requirements set by the LEED Green Building Rating System and/or innovative performance in other areas.

- Track development and implementation of the specific exceptional and innovative strategies used.

8. Examples

The level of effort involved in achieving an ID credit should be extraordinary. For example, installing a single green product or addressing a single aspect of a sustainability issue is not a sufficient level of effort. An environmental educational program consisting of simple signage in a building would not by itself be considered a significant benefit. Conversely, a visitor's center interactive display, coupled with an educational website and video highlighting the project's environmental strategies, would be eligible for an ID credit.

Suggested Topics for Innovation Credits

The following list illustrates sample actions and concepts that may be viable candidates for an ID credit, given appropriate implementation and documentation. It is the responsibility of the project team to determine the feasibility of possible ID-related programs or initiatives, develop and execute the program in a manner that yields a meaningful environmental benefit, and provide documentation and calculations that substantiate the validity of the project team's approach and implementation. Project teams are encouraged to explore the full range of innovative opportunities within their buildings.

This list provides examples only and does not constitute formal preapproval of any ID strategy. Project teams desiring formal preapproval of an ID strategy must submit a Credit Interpretation Request and explain the proposal in detail.

- Provide an educational program on the environmental and human health benefits of green building practices and how building occupants or the public can help improve green performance. Evaluate results and refine the program to increase its impact and audience as appropriate. The program must be actively instructional and include at least 2 instructional initiatives that have ongoing components. Types of initiatives might include the following:

1. A comprehensive signage program or displays inside the building to educate occupants and visitors on the benefits of green buildings. Examples include windows to view energy-saving mechanical equipment, signs that call attention to water-conserving landscape features, and digital screens showing real-time energy consumption or building performance data.

2. A case study highlighting the successes of the LEED project that could be used to inform the operations of other buildings.

3. Guided tours focusing on sustainability, using the project as an example.

4. An educational outreach program that engages occupants or the public through periodic events covering green building topics.

5. A website or electronic newsletter that informs building occupants and visitors about the building's features and green strategies they can practice at home.

- Evaluate a substantial quantity of products or materials being used (or being considered for use in the building) on the basis of an ISO 14040 life-cycle assessment.

- Divert significant volumes of waste generated from sources other than the project building site and associated grounds via expanded waste management and diversion programs. For example, provide a collection and recycling program that allows building occupants or members of the community to bring in end-of-life home electronic equipment for recycling.

9. Regional Variations

ID credits may have regional content. For example, in temperate climates, projects with operable windows may elect to install ceiling fans and eliminate central air-conditioning altogether. The exclusive use of natural ventilation in this instance might be worthy of an ID point.

Extraordinary designs that use the vernacular architectural strategies of the region may be among the most environmentally sound. Project teams should look to the characteristic buildings of their region as a source for innovation.

LEED® ACCREDITED PROFESSIONAL

	CI
Credit	ID Credit 2
Points	1 point

Intent

To support and encourage the design integration required by LEED to streamline the application and certification process.

Requirements

At least 1 principal participant of the project team shall be a LEED Accredited Professional (AP).

1. Benefits and Issues to Consider

LEED APs have the expertise required to design a building to LEED standards and to coordinate the documentation process that is necessary for LEED certification. The LEED AP understands the importance of integrated design and the need to consider interactions between the prerequisites and credits and their respective criteria. Architects, engineers, consultants, owners, and others who have a strong interest in sustainable building design are all appropriate candidates for accreditation. The LEED AP should champion the project's LEED application and be an integral member of the project team. The LEED AP can also educate other team members about LEED and green buildings.

2. Summary of Referenced Standards

LEED Accredited Professional

Green Building Certification Institute

www.gbci.org

Individuals who successfully complete the LEED professional accreditation exam are LEED APs. Accreditation certifies that the individual has the knowledge and skills necessary to participate in the LEED application and certification process, holds a firm understanding of green building practices and principles, and is familiar with LEED requirements, resources, and processes. The Green Building Certification Institute (GBCI), established with the support of the U.S. Green Building Council (USGBC), handles exam development and delivery to ensure objective and balanced management of the credentialing program.

3. Implementation

A LEED AP is a valuable resource in the LEED for Commercial Interiors process. Although not required, the presence of a LEED AP aids the project team in understanding the elements of the rating system, the importance of considering interactions among the prerequisites and credits, and the LEED application process.

Including a LEED AP on the project team meets the credit requirements and can be accomplished in either of 2 ways:

- Engaging an individual within the organization who is already a LEED AP to participate in the certification application process.

- Hiring a LEED AP to support the project. Consider selecting a LEED AP experienced with LEED CI and industry best green practices in interior design and construction.

4. Documentation Guidance

As a first step in preparing to complete the LEED Online documentation requirements, work through the following measures. Refer to LEED Online for the complete descriptions of all required documentation.

- Obtain confirmation from team members who are LEED APs or are planning to become LEED APs.

5. Resources

Please see USGBC's LEED Resources & Tools (http://www.usgbc.org/projecttools) for additional resources and other technical information.

Websites

Green Building Certification Institute

www.gbci.org

GBCI administers the LEED Professional Accreditation program to ensure objective management of the credential. GBCI manages exam development, registration, and delivery. It was established as a separately incorporated entity with the support of the USGBC. See the GBCI website for more information on workshops, testing locations, fees, and topics covered on the accreditation exam.

ID	
CI	Credit 2

6. Definitions

LEED **Accredited Professionals** (**APs**) are individuals who have successfully completed the LEED professional accreditation exam.

Overview

Because some environmental issues are unique to a locale, USGBC regional councils have identified distinct environmental zones within their areas and allocated six credits to encourage design teams to focus on regional priorities. A project that earns a Regional Priority credit automatically earns one point in addition to any points awarded for that credit. Up to four extra points can be earned in this way.

Go to www.usgbc.org to learn more about the Regional Priority credits in your area.

CREDIT	TITLE
RP Credit 1	Regional Priority

	CI
Credit	RP Credit 1
Points	1-4 points

Intent

To provide an incentive for the achievement of credits that address geographically specific environmental priorities.

Requirements

Earn 1-4 of the 6 Regional Priority credits identified by the USGBC regional councils and chapters as having environmental importance for a project's region. A database of Regional Priority Credits and their geographic applicability is available on the USGBC website, http://www.usgbc.org/.

One point is awarded for each Regional Priority Credit achieved; no more than 4 credits identified as Regional Priority credits may be earned. The USGBC has prioritized credits for projects located in the U.S., Puerto Rico, the U.S. Virgin Islands, and Guam. All other international projects should check the database for eligible Regional Priority credits.

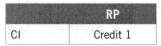
1. Benefits and Issues to Consider

Refer to the Benefits and Issues section under a particular Regional Priority credit.

2. Related Credits

For a list of applicable credits, visit the Regional Priority database at www.usgbc.org.

3. Summary of Referenced Standards

Refer to the standards for a particular Regional Priority credit.

4. Implementation

Refer to the Implementation section under a particular Regional Priority credit.

5. Timeline and Team

Identify Regional Priority credits early in the project timeline.

6. Calculations

Refer to the Calculations section under a particular Regional Priority credit.

7. Documentation Guidance

The Documentation Guidance section helps project teams prepare for formal certification application and complete the LEED Online documentation requirements. Refer to the Documentation Guidance section under each Regional Priority credit and refer to LEED Online for complete descriptions of all required documentation.

8. Examples

Refer to the Examples section under a particular Regional Priority credit.

9. Regional Variations

Refer to the Regional Variations section under a particular Regional Priority credit.

10. Operations and Maintenance Considerations

Refer to the Operations and Maintenance section under a particular Regional Priority credit.

11. Resources

See USGBC's LEED Resources & Tools (http://www.usgbc.org/projecttools) for additional resources and technical information.

12. Definitions

Refer to the Definitions section under a particular Regional Priority credit.

Adapted (or introduced) plants reliably grow well in a given habitat with minimal winter protection, pest control, fertilization, or irrigation once their root systems are established. Adapted plants are considered low maintenance and not invasive.

Adaptive reuse is the renovation of a space for a purpose different from the original.

An a**dhesive** is any substance used to bond 1 surface to another by attachment. Adhesives include bonding primers, adhesive primers, and adhesive primers for plastics. (SCAQMD Rule 1168)

Aerosol adhesive is an aerosol product in which the spray mechanism is permanently housed in a nonrefillable can. Designed for hand-held application, these products do not need ancillary hoses or spray equipment. Aerosol adhesives include special-purpose spray adhesives, mist spray adhesives, and web spray adhesives. (SCAQMD Rule 1168)

Agrifiber products are made from agricultural fiber. Examples include particleboard, medium-density fiberboard (MDF), plywood, oriented-strand board (OSB), wheatboard, and strawboard.

Air-conditioning is the process of treating air to meet the requirements of a conditioned space by controlling its temperature, humidity, cleanliness, and distribution. (ASHRAE 62.1–2007)

Air-handling units (AHUs) are mechanical indirect heating, ventilating, or air-conditioning systems in which the air is treated or handled by equipment located outside the rooms served, usually at a central location, and conveyed to and from the rooms by a fan and a system of distributing ducts. (NEEB, 1997 edition)

Albedo is synonymous with **solar reflectance.**

Alternative daily cover is material (other than earthen material) that is placed on the surface of the active face of a municipal solid waste landfill at the end of each operating day to control vectors, fires, odors, blowing litter, and scavenging.

Alternative-fuel vehicles use low-polluting, nongasoline fuels such as electricity, hydrogen, propane, compressed natural gas, liquid natural gas, methanol, and ethanol. In LEED, efficient gas-electric hybrid vehicles are included in this group.

Anticorrosive paints are coatings formulated and recommended for use in preventing the corrosion of ferrous metal substrates.

Aquatic systems are ecologically designed treatment systems in which a diverse community of biological organisms (e.g., bacteria, plants, fish) treat wastewater.

An **aquifer** is an underground water-bearing rock formation or group of formations that supply groundwater, wells, or springs.

An **area-weighted SRI is** a weighted average calculation that may be performed for buildings with multiple roof surfaces to demonstrate that the total roof area has an average solar reflectance index equal to or greater than that of a theoretical roof 75% of whose surfaces have an SRI of 78 and 25% have an SRI of 30.

Architectural porous sealant primer is a substance used as a sealant on porous materials.

An **assembly** can be either a product formulated from multiple materials (e.g., concrete) or a product made up of subcomponents (e.g., a workstation).

GLOSSARY

Assembly recycled content is the percentage of material in a product that is either postconsumer or preconsumer recycled content. It is determined by dividing the weight of the recycled content by the overall weight of the assembly.

The **attendance boundary** is used by school districts to determine which students attend what school based on where they live.

Automatic fixture sensors are motion detectors that automatically turn on and turn off lavatories, sinks, water closets, and urinals. Sensors can be hard wired or battery operated.

Baseline building performance is the annual energy cost for a building design intended for use as a baseline for rating above standard design, as defined in ANSI/ASHRAE/IESNA Standard 90.1–2007, Informative Appendix G.

Baseline irrigation water use is the amount of water used by conventional irrigation in the region.

Basis of design includes design information necessary to accomplish the owner's project requirements, including system descriptions, indoor environmental quality criteria, design assumptions, and references to applicable codes, standards, regulations, and guidelines.

A **bay** is a component of a standard, rectilinear building design. It is the open area defined by a building element such as columns or a window. Typically, there are multiple identical bays in succession.

Bicycle racks, in LEED, include outdoor bicycle racks, bicycle lockers, and indoor bicycle storage rooms.

Biochemical oxygen demand is a measure of how fast biological organisms use up oxygen in a body of water. It is used in water quality management and assessment, ecology, and environmental science.

Biodiversity is the variety of life in all forms, levels, and combinations, including ecosystem diversity, species diversity, and genetic diversity.

Biofuel-based energy systems are electrical power systems that run on renewable fuels derived from organic materials, such as wood by-products and agricultural waste. In LEED, biofuels include untreated wood waste (e.g., mill residues), agricultural crops or waste, animal waste and other organic waste, and landfill gas.

Biofuel-based systems are power systems that run on renewable fuels derived from organic materials, such as wood by-products and agricultural waste. Examples of biofuels include untreated wood waste, agricultural crops and residues, animal waste, other organic waste, and landfill gas.

Biological control is the use of chemical or physical water treatments to inhibit bacterial growth in cooling towers.

Biomass is plant material from trees, grasses, or crops that can be converted to heat energy to produce electricity.

Blackwater definitions vary, but wastewater from toilets and urinals is always considered blackwater. Wastewater from kitchen sinks (perhaps differentiated by the use of a garbage disposal), showers, or bathtubs is considered blackwater under some state or local codes.

Bleed-off, or **blowdown,** is the release of a portion of the recirculating water from a cooling tower; this water carries dissolved solids that can cause mineral buildup.

Breathing zone is the region within an occupied space between 3 and 6 feet above the floor. Note that this definition varies from that of ASHRAE 62.1-2007, which states that the breathing zone is between 3 inches and 6 feet from the floor, and 2 feet from the walls as well as fixed air conditioning equipment.

A **brownfield** is real property whose use may be complicated by the presence or possible presence of a hazardous substance, pollutant, or contaminant.

A **building automation system** (**BAS**) uses computer-based monitoring to coordinate, organize, and optimize building control subsystems, including lighting, equipment scheduling, and alarm reporting.

Building density is the floor area of the building divided by the total area of the site (square feet per acre).

Building footprint is the area on a project site used by the building structure, defined by the perimeter of the building plan. Parking lots, landscapes, and other nonbuilding facilities are not included in the building footprint.

A **campus** or **private bus** is a bus or shuttle service that is privately operated and not available to the general public. In LEED, a campus or private bus line that falls within 1/4 mile of the project site and provides transportation service to the public can contribute to earning credits.

Carbon dioxide (**CO2**) **levels** are an indicator of ventilation effectiveness inside buildings. CO2 concentrations greater than 530 ppm above outdoor CO2 conditions generally indicate inadequate ventilation. Absolute concentrations of CO2 greater than 800 to 1,000 ppm generally indicate poor air quality for breathing.

A **carpool** is an arrangement by which 2 or more people share a vehicle for transportation.

Chain-of-custody (**COC**) is a tracking procedure for a product from the point of harvest or extraction to its end use, including all successive stages of processing, transformation, manufacturing, and distribution.

Chain-of-custody certification is awarded to companies that produce, sell, promote, or trade forest products after audits verify proper accounting of material flows and proper use of the Forest Stewardship Council name and logo. The COC certificate number is listed on invoices for nonlabeled products to document that an entity has followed FSC guidelines for product accounting.

Chemical treatment includes the use of biocidal, conditioning, dispersant, and scale-inhibiting chemicals to control biological growth, scale, and corrosion in cooling towers. Alternatives to conventional chemical treatment include ozonation, ionization, and exposure to ultraviolet light.

Chlorofluorocarbons (**CFCs**) are hydrocarbons that are used as refrigerants and cause depletion of the stratospheric ozone layer.

Churn is the movement of workstations and people within a space.

Climate change refers to any significant change in measures of climate (such as temperature, precipitation, or wind) lasting for an extended period (decades or longer). (U.S. Environmental Protection Agency, 2008)

A **coating** is applied to beautify, protect, or provide a barrier to a surface. **Flat coatings** register a gloss of less than 15 on an 85-degree meter or less than 5 on a 60-degree meter. **Nonflat coatings** register a gloss of 5 or greater on a 60-degree meter and a gloss of 15 or greater on an 85-degree meter. (SCAQMD Rule 1113)

Combined heat and power (**CHP**), or **cogeneration**, generates both electrical power and thermal energy from a single fuel source.

Comfort criteria are specific design conditions that take into account temperature, humidity, air speed, outdoor temperature, outdoor humidity, seasonal clothing, and expected activity. (ASHRAE 55–2004)

GLOSSARY

Commissioning (Cx) is the process of verifying and documenting that a building and all of its systems and assemblies are planned, designed, installed, tested, operated, and maintained to meet the owner's project requirements.

The **commissioning authority (CxA)** is the individual designated to organize, lead, and review the completion of commissioning process activities. The CxA facilitates communication among the owner, designer, and contractor to ensure that complex systems are installed and function in accordance with the owner's project requirements.

The **commissioning cycle** is the schedule of activities related to existing building commissioning, including the investigation and analysis, implementation, and ongoing commissioning.

The **commissioning plan** is a document that outlines the organization, schedule, allocation of resources, and documentation requirements of the commissioning process.

The **commissioning process** is a systematic quality-focused effort to ensure that building systems are designed, specified, procured, installed, and functioning in accordance with the owner's intent. The process uses planning, documentation, and verification of testing to review and oversee the activities of both designer and constructor.

The **commissioning report** documents the commissioning process, including a commissioning program overview, identification of the commissioning team, and description of the commissioning process activities.

Commissioning specification is the contract language used in the construction documents to detail the objective, scope, and implementation of the construction and acceptance phases of the commissioning process as developed in the design phase of the commissioning plan. This allows the construction contractor to ensure that these activities are considered in proposals for the construction work.

The **commissioning team** includes those people responsible for working together to carry out the commissioning process.

Completed design area is the total area of finished ceilings, floors, full-height walls and demountable partitions, interior doors, and built-in case goods in the completed project. It does not include exterior windows and doors.

Composite wood consists of wood or plant particles or fibers bonded by a synthetic resin or binder. Examples include particleboard, medium-density fiberboard (MDF), plywood, oriented-strand board (OSB), wheatboard, and strawboard.

Composting toilet system. See **nonwater toilet system.**

The **Comprehensive Environmental Response, Compensation, and Liability Act**, or CERCLA, is more commonly known as Superfund. Enacted in 1980, CERCLA addresses abandoned or historical waste sites and contamination by taxing the chemical and petroleum industries and providing federal authority to respond to releases of hazardous substances.

A **compressed workweek** rearranges the standard workweek (5 consecutive 8-hour days in a week), increasing the daily hours and decreasing the number of days in the work cycle. For example, instead of working 8-hour days Monday through Friday, employees work 10-hour days for 4 days per week, or 9-hour days for 9 of 10 consecutive days.

Concentration ratio is the ratio of the level of dissolved solids in the recirculating water to the level found in the entering makeup water. A higher concentration ratio results from a lower bleed-off rate; increasing the ratio above a certain point, however, leads to scaling, and water savings diminish after a certain level. This ratio is also called the cycles of concentration. Cycles refers to the number of times dissolved minerals in the water are concentrated compared with makeup water, not to water flow over the tower or to on-off cycles.

Conditioned space is the part of a building that is heated or cooled, or both, for the comfort of occupants. (ASHRAE 62.1–2007)

A **constructed wetland** is an engineered system designed to simulate natural wetland functions for water purification. In LEED, constructed wetlands are essentially treatment systems that remove contaminants from wastewater.

Construction and demolition debris includes waste and recyclables generated from construction and from the renovation, demolition, or deconstruction of preexisting structures. It does not include land-clearing debris, such as soil, vegetation, and rocks.

Construction, demolition, and land-clearing debris includes all of the above plus soil, vegetation, and rock from land clearing.

A **construction IAQ management plan** outlines measures to minimize contamination in a specific project building during construction and describes procedures to flush the building of contaminants prior to occupancy.

Contaminants are unwanted airborne elements that may reduce indoor air quality. (ASHRAE 62.1–2007)

Controls are mechanisms that allow occupants to direct power to devices (e.g., lights, heaters) or adjust devices or systems within in a range (e.g., brightness, temperature).

Conventional irrigation refers to the most common irrigation system used in the region where the building is located. A conventional irrigation system commonly uses pressure to deliver water and distributes it through sprinkler heads above the ground.

A **cooling tower** uses water to absorb heat from air-conditioning systems and regulate air temperature in a facility.

Curfew hours are locally determined times when lighting restrictions are imposed. When no local or regional restrictions are in place, 10:00 p.m. is regarded as a default curfew time.

Daylighting is the controlled admission of natural light into a space, used to reduce or eliminate electric lighting.

Daylight-responsive lighting controls are photosensors used in conjunction with other switching and dimming devices to control the amount of artificial lighting in relationship to the amount and quality of natural daylight.

Densely occupied space is an area with a design occupant density of 25 people or more per 1,000 square feet (40 square feet or less per person).

Density factor (k_d) is a coefficient used in calculating the landscape coefficient. It modifies the evapotranspiration rate to reflect the water use of a plant or group of plants, particularly with reference to the density of the plant material.

Design light output is the light output of lamps at 40% of their useful life.

The **development footprint** is the area affected by development or by project site activity. Hardscape, access roads, parking lots, nonbuilding facilities, and the building itself are all included in the development footprint.

A **district energy system** is a central energy conversion plant and transmission and distribution system that provides thermal energy to a group of buildings (e.g., a central cooling plant on a university campus). Central energy systems that provide only electricity are not included.

Downstream equipment consists of all heating or cooling systems, equipment, and controls located within the project building and site associated with transporting thermal energy into heated or cooled spaces. This includes the thermal connection or interface with the district energy system, secondary distribution systems in the building, and terminal units.

Drip irrigation delivers water at low pressure through buried mains and submains. From the submains, water is distributed to the soil through a network of perforated tubes or emitters. Drip irrigation is a high-efficiency type of microirrigation.

Durable goods have a useful life of 2 years or more and are replaced infrequently or may require capital program outlays. Examples include furniture, office equipment, appliances, external power adapters, televisions, and audiovisual equipment.

The **durable goods waste stream** consists of durable goods leaving the project site that are fully depreciated and have reached the end of their useful lives for normal business operations.

Ecological restoration is the process of assisting in the recovery and management of ecological integrity and includes biodiversity, ecological processes and structures, regional and historical context, and sustainable cultural practices.

Ecologically appropriate site features are natural site elements that maintain or restore the ecological integrity of the site. Examples include native or adapted vegetation, water bodies, exposed rock, unvegetated ground, and other features that provide habitat value and are part of the historic natural landscape.

An **economizer** is a device used to make building systems more energy efficient. Examples include HVAC enthalpy controls, which are based on humidity and temperature.

An **ecosystem** is a basic unit of nature that includes a community of organisms and their nonliving environment linked by biological, chemical, and physical processes.

An **electrical conductivity (EC) meter** measures the amount of nutrients and salt in water.

Elemental mercury is pure mercury (rather than a mercury-containing compound), the vapor of which is commonly used in fluorescent and other lamp types.

Embodied energy is the energy used during the entire life cycle of a product, including its manufacture, transportation, and disposal, as well as the inherent energy captured within the product itself.

Emergency lighting as defined by the Illuminating Engineering Society of North America is lighting designed to supply illumination essential to the safety of life and property in the event of failure of the normal supply.

Emissions reduction reporting is the calculating, tracking, and documenting of the greenhouse gas emissions that result directly from energy use and other operations of a building.

Emissivity is the ratio of the radiation emitted by a surface to the radiation emitted by a black body at the same temperature.

An **endangered species** is threatened with extinction because of harmful human activities or environmental factors.

An **energy audit** identifies how much energy a building uses and the purposes for which it is used, and identifies efficiency and cost-reduction opportunities. The American Society of Heating, Refrigerating and Air-Conditioning Engineers uses 3 levels of energy audits: walk-through analysis, energy survey and analysis, and detailed analysis of capital-intensive modifications.

Energy conservation measures are installations or modifications of equipment or systems intended to reduce energy use and costs.

An **energy simulation model, or energy model**, is a computer-generated representation of the anticipated energy consumption of a building. It permits a comparison of energy performance, given proposed energy efficiency measures, with the baseline.

An **ENERGY STAR®** rating is a measure of a building's energy performance compared with that of similar buildings, as determined by the ENERGY STAR® Portfolio Manager. A score of 50 represents average building performance.

Enhanced commissioning is a set of best practices that go beyond fundamental commissioning to ensure that building systems perform as intended by the owner. These practices include designating a commissioning authority prior to the construction documents phase, conducting commissioning design reviews, reviewing contractor submittals, developing a systems manual, verifying operator training, and performing a postoccupancy operations review.

Entryway systems are designed to capture dirt and other debris from occupants entering the building; they can be open floor grates or grilles set over a recessed area.

Environmental tobacco smoke (ETS), or **secondhand smoke**, consists of airborne particles emitted from the burning end of cigarettes, pipes, and cigars, and is exhaled by smokers. These particles contain about 4,000 compounds, up to 50 of which are known to cause cancer.

Erosion is a combination of processes or events by which materials of the earth's surface are loosened, dissolved, or worn away and transported by natural agents (e.g., water, wind, or gravity).

Eutrophication is the increase in chemical nutrients, such as the nitrogen and phosphorus often found in fertilizers, in an ecosystem. The added nutrients stimulate excessive plant growth, promoting algal blooms or weeds. The enhanced plant growth reduces oxygen in the land and water, reducing water quality and fish and other animal populations.

Evapotranspiration is the loss of water by evaporation from the soil and by transpiration from plants. It is expressed in millimeters per unit of time.

Evapotranspiration (ET) rate is the amount of water lost from a vegetated surface in units of water depth. It is expressed in millimeters per unit of time.

Exfiltration is air leakage through cracks and interstices and through the ceilings, floors, and walls.

Exhaust air is removed from a space and discharged outside the building by mechanical or natural ventilation systems.

Existing area is the total area of the building structure, core, and envelope that existed when the project area was selected. Exterior windows and doors are not included.

Existing building commissioning, or retrocommissioning, involves developing a building operation plan that identifies current operating requirements and needs, conducting tests to determine whether building systems are performing optimally in accordance with the plan, and making any necessary repairs or changes.

Extraction, harvest or recovery point refers to the location of raw materials prior to manufacturing of the building material or product that is furnished and installed in the project building.

Facility alterations and additions are discussed in the Introduction of the LEED for Green Building Operations & Maintenance.

Fairtrade is a product certification system overseen by FLO International, which identifies products that meet certain environmental, labor, and development standards.

Fly ash is the solid residue derived from incineration processes. Fly ash can be used as a substitute for Portland cement in concrete.

The **Food Alliance** certifies foods from sustainable farms and ranches that produce natural products, ensure quality control and food safety, responsibly manage water and energy resources, emphasize recycling and responsible waste management, provide a safe work environment, and commit to continuous improvement of sustainable practices.

A **footcandle** (**fc**) is a measure of light falling on a given surface. One footcandle is defined as the quantity of light falling on a 1-square-foot area from a 1 candela light source at a distance of 1 foot (which equals 1 lumen per square foot). Footcandles can be measured both horizontally and vertically by a footcandle meter or light meter.

Formaldehyde is a naturally occurring VOC found in small amounts in animals and plants but is carcinogenic and an irritant to most people when present in high concentrations, causing headaches, dizziness, mental impairment, and other symptoms. When present in the air at levels above 0.1 ppm, it can cause watery eyes; burning sensations in the eyes, nose, and throat; nausea; coughing; chest tightness; wheezing; skin rashes; and asthmatic and allergic reactions.

Fuel-efficient vehicles have achieved a minimum green score of 40 according to the annual vehicle-rating guide of the American Council for an Energy Efficient Economy.

A **full cutoff luminaire** has zero candela intensity at an angle of 90 degrees above the vertical axis (nadir or straight down) and at all angles greater than 90 degrees from straight down. Additionally, the candela per 1,000 lamp lumens does not numerically exceed 100 (10%) at an angle of 80 degrees above nadir. This applies to all lateral angles around the luminaire.

Full-time equivalent (**FTE**) represents a regular building occupant who spends 40 hours per week in the project building. Part-time or overtime occupants have FTE values based on their hours per week divided by 40. Multiple shifts are included or excluded depending on the intent and requirements of the credit.

Full-time-equivalent building occupants is a measure equal to the total number of hours all building occupants spend in the building during the peak 8-hour occupancy period divided by 8 hours.

In a **fully shielded** exterior light fixture, the lower edge of the shield is at or below the lowest edge of the lamp, such that all light shines down.

Fundamental commissioning is a set of essential best practices used to ensure that building performance requirements have been identified early in the project's development and to verify that the designed systems have been installed in compliance with those requirements. These practices include designating a commissioning authority, documenting the owner's project requirements and basis of design, incorporating commissioning requirements into the construction documents, establishing a commissioning plan, verifying installation and performance of specified building systems, and completing a summary commissioning report.

Furniture, fixtures, and equipment are all items that are not base-building elements. Examples include lamps, electronics, desks, chairs, and tables.

Geothermal energy is electricity generated by harnessing hot water or steam from within the earth.

Geothermal heating systems use pipes to transfer heat from underground steam or hot water for heating, cooling, and hot water. The system retrieves heat during cool months and returns heat in summer months.

Glare is any excessively bright source of light within the visual field that creates discomfort or loss in visibility.

Graywater is defined by the Uniform Plumbing Code (UPC) in its Appendix G, Gray Water Systems for Single-Family Dwellings, as "untreated household waste water which has not come into contact with toilet waste. Greywater includes used water from bathtubs, showers, bathroom wash basins, and water from clothes-washer and laundry tubs. It must not include waste water from kitchen sinks or dishwashers." The International Plumbing Code (IPC) defines graywater in its Appendix C, Gray Water Recycling Systems, as "waste water discharged from lavatories, bathtubs, showers, clothes washers and laundry sinks." Some states and local authorities allow kitchen sink wastewater to be included in graywater. Other differences with the UPC and IPC definitions can likely be found in state and local codes. Project teams should comply with graywater definitions as established by the authority having jurisdiction in the project area.

Green cleaning is the use of cleaning products and practices that have lower environmental impacts and more positive indoor air quality impacts than conventional products and practices.

Green power is synonymous with **renewable energy.**

Green-e is a program established by the Center for Resource Solutions to both promote green electricity products and provide consumers with a rigorous and nationally recognized method to identify those products.

Greenfields are sites not previously developed or graded that could support open space, habitat, or agriculture.

Greenhouse gases (**GHGs**) absorb and emit radiation at specific wavelengths within the spectrum of thermal infrared radiation emitted by Earth's surface, clouds, and the atmosphere itself. Increased concentrations of greenhouse gases are a root cause of global climate change.

Group (**shared**) **multioccupant spaces** include conference rooms, classrooms, and other indoor spaces used as a place of congregation.

Halons are substances, used in fire-suppression systems and fire extinguishers, that deplete the stratospheric ozone layer.

Hardscape consists of the inanimate elements of the building landscaping. Examples include pavement, roadways, stone walls, concrete paths and sidewalks, and concrete, brick, and tile patios.

Hard surface flooring includes vinyl, linoleum, laminate flooring, wood flooring, rubber flooring, wall base, and associated sundries.

Heat island effect refers to the absorption of heat by hardscapes, such as dark, nonreflective pavement and buildings, and its radiation to surrounding areas. Particularly in urban areas, other sources may include vehicle exhaust, air-conditioners, and street equipment; reduced airflow from tall buildings and narrow streets exacerbates the effect.

Horizontal footcandles occur on a horizontal surface. They can be added together arithmetically when more than 1 source provides light to the same surface.

The **hospitality industry** consists of companies within the food services, accommodations, recreation, and entertainment sectors.

HVAC systems are equipment, distribution systems, and terminals that provide the processes of heating, ventilating, or air-conditioning. (ASHRAE 90.1–2007)

Hybrid vehicles use a gasoline engine to drive an electric generator and use the electric generator and/or storage batteries to power electric motors that drive the vehicle's wheels.

Hydro energy is electricity produced from the downhill flow of water from rivers or lakes.

Hydrochlorofluorocarbons (**HCFCs**) are refrigerants that cause significantly less depletion of the stratospheric ozone layer than chlorofluorocarbons.

Hydrofluorocarbons (HFCs) are refrigerants that do not deplete the stratospheric ozone layer but may have high global warming potential. HFCs are not considered environmentally benign.

Hydrology is the study of water occurrence, distribution, movement, and balances in an ecosystem.

Hydropower is electricity produced from the downhill flow of water from rivers or lakes.

Impervious surfaces have a perviousness of less than 50% and promote runoff of water instead of infiltration into the subsurface. Examples include parking lots, roads, sidewalks, and plazas.

An **incinerator** is a furnace or container for burning waste materials.

Individual occupant spaces are standard workstations where workers conduct individual tasks.

Indoor adhesive, sealant, or **sealant primer** product is an adhesive or sealant product applied on-site, inside the building's weatherproofing system.

Indoor air quality (IAQ) is the nature of air inside the space that affects the health and well-being of building occupants. It is considered acceptable when there are no known contaminants at harmful concentrations and a substantial majority (80% or more) of the occupants do not express dissatisfaction. (ASHRAE 62.1–2007)

Indoor carpet systems are carpet, carpet adhesive, or carpet cushion products installed on-site inside the building's weatherproofing system.

Indoor composite wood or **agrifiber is a** product installed inside the building's weatherproofing system.

Indoor paints or **coating products** are applied inside a building's weatherproofing system.

Infiltration is uncontrolled air leakage into conditioned spaces through unintentional openings in ceilings, floors, and walls from unconditioned spaces or the outdoors. (ASHRAE 62.1–2007)

Infiltration basins and trenches are devices used to encourage subsurface infiltration of runoff volumes through temporary surface storage. Basins are ponds that can store large volumes of stormwater. They need to drain within 72 hours to maintain aerobic conditions and be available for future storm events. Trenches are similar to infiltration basins but are shallower and function as a subsurface reservoir for stormwater volumes. Pretreatment to remove sediment and oil may be necessary to avoid clogging infiltration devices. Infiltration trenches are more common in areas where infiltration basins are not possible.

Infrared (or thermal) emittance is a parameter between 0 and 1 (or 0% and 100%) that indicates the ability of a material to shed infrared radiation (heat). The wavelength range for this radiant energy is roughly 5 to 40 micrometers. Most building materials (including glass) are opaque in this part of the spectrum and have an emittance of roughly 0.9. Materials such as clean, bare metals are the most important exceptions to the 0.9 rule. Thus clean, untarnished galvanized steel has low emittance, and aluminum roof coatings have intermediate emittance levels.

In situ remediation involves treatment of contaminants using technologies such as injection wells or reactive trenches. These methods employ the natural hydraulic gradient of groundwater and usually require only minimal disturbance of the site.

An **installation inspection** examines components of the building systems to determine whether they are installed properly and ready for systems performance testing.

Integrated pest management (IPM) is the coordinated use of knowledge about pests, the environment, and pest prevention and control methods to minimize pest infestation and damage by the most economical means while minimizing hazards to people, property, and the environment.

Interior lighting power allowance is the maximum lighting power (in watts) allowed for the interior of a building.

Interior nonstructural components reuse is determined by dividing the area of retained components by the larger of (1) the area of the prior condition or (2) the area of the completed design.

Invasive plants are nonnative to the ecosystem and likely to cause harm once introduced. These species are characteristically adaptable and aggressive, have a high reproductive capacity, and tend to overrun the ecosystems they enter. Collectively, they are among the greatest threats to biodiversity and ecosystem stability.

Laminate adhesive is used in wood or agrifiber products, such as veneered panels, composite wood products contained in engineered lumber, and door assemblies.

Lamps use electricity to produce light in any of several ways: by heating a wire for incandescence; by exciting a gas that produces ultraviolet light from a luminescent material; by generating an arc that emits visible light and some ultraviolet light; or by inducing excitation of mercury through radio frequencies. Light-emitting diodes packaged as traditional lamps also meet this definition.

Lamp life is the useful operating life of the sources of artificial light, such as bulbs.

Landfills are waste disposal sites for solid waste from human activities.

The **landscape area** is the total site area less the building footprint, paved surfaces, water bodies, and patios.

The **landscape coefficient** (K_L) is a constant used to calculate the evapotranspiration rate. It takes into account the species factor, density factor, and microclimate factor of the area.

The **leakage rate** is the speed at which an appliance loses refrigerant, measured between refrigerant charges or over 12 months, whichever is shorter. The leakage rate is expressed in terms of the percentage of the appliance's full charge that would be lost over a 12-month period if the rate stabilized. (EPA Clean Air Act, Title VI, Rule 608)

A **least toxic chemical pesticide** is any pesticide product for which all active ingredients and known inert ingredients meet the least toxic Tier 3 hazard criteria under the City and County of San Francisco's hazard screening protocol. Least toxic also applies to any pesticide product, other than rodent bait, that is applied in a self-contained, enclosed bait station placed in an inaccessible location or applied in a gel that is neither visible nor accessible.

The **LEED project boundary** is the portion of the project site submitted for LEED certification. For single building developments, this is the entire project scope and is generally limited to the site boundary. For multiple building developments, the LEED project boundary may be a portion of the development as determined by the project team.

Legionella pneumophila is a waterborne bacterium that causes Legionnaire's disease. It grows in slow-moving or still warm water and can be found in plumbing, showerheads, and water storage tanks. Outbreaks of Legionella pneumonia have been attributed to evaporative condensers and cooling towers.

Life-cycle assessment is an analysis of the environmental aspects and potential impacts associated with a product, process, or service.

Life-cycle costing is an accounting methodology used to evaluate the economic performance of a product or system over its useful life. It considers operating costs, maintenance expenses, and other economic factors.

Light pollution is waste light from building sites that produces glare, is directed upward to the sky, or is directed off the site. Waste light does not increase nighttime safety, utility, or security and needlessly consumes energy.

Light trespass is obtrusive light that is unwanted because of quantitative, directional, or spectral attributes. Light trespass can cause annoyance, discomfort, distraction, or loss of visibility.

Lighting power density is the installed lighting power, per unit area.

Local zoning requirements are local government regulations imposed to promote orderly development of private lands and prevent land-use conflicts.

Low-emitting vehicles are classified as zero-emission vehicles (ZEVs) by the California Air Resources Board.

A **lumen** is a unit of luminous flux equal to the light emitted in a unit solid angle by a uniform point source of 1 candle intensity.

A **luminaire** is a complete lighting unit consisting of a lamp (or lamps) with the housing designed to distribute the light, position, and protect the lamp and connect it to the power supply.

Luminous opening refers to the part of the outer surface of a luminaire (lighting fixture) through which light is emitted (i.e., the opening where the lamps are).

Makeup water is fed into a cooling tower system to replace water lost through evaporation, drift, bleed-off, or other causes.

Management staff includes employees or contractors involved in operating and maintaining a project building and site.

Marine Stewardship Council Blue Eco-Label applies to products that meet certain principles and criteria for sustainable fishing, including sustainable harvest of the target stock, acceptable impact of the fishery on the ecosystem, effectiveness of the fishery management system (including all relevant biological, technological, economic, social, environmental, and commercial aspects), and compliance with relevant laws and standards.

Market value, presumed to be less than replacement value, is the amount that either was paid or would have been paid for a used product.

Mass transit is designed to transport large groups of persons in a single vehicle, such as a bus or train.

Material safety data sheets (**MSDS**) are detailed, written instructions documenting a method to achieve uniformity of performance.

Mechanical ventilation, or **active ventilation**, is provided by mechanically powered equipment, such as motor-driven fans and blowers, but not by devices such as wind-driven turbine ventilators and mechanically operated windows. (ASHRAE 62.1–2004)

Metering controls limit the flow time of water. They are generally manual-on and automatic-off devices, most commonly installed on lavatory faucets and showers.

Microclimate factor (k_{mc}) is a constant used in calculating the landscape coefficient. It adjusts the evapotranspiration rate to reflect the climate of the immediate area.

Microirrigation involves irrigation systems with small sprinklers and microjets or drippers designed to apply small volumes of water. The sprinklers and microjets are installed within a few centimeters of the ground; drippers are laid on or below grade.

Minimum efficiency reporting value (**MERV**) is a filter rating established by the American Society of Heating, Refrigerating, and Air-Conditioning Engineers (ASHRAE 52.2–1999, Method of Testing General Ventilation Air Cleaning Devices for Removal Efficiency by Particle Size). MERV categories range from 1 (very low efficiency) to 16 (very high).

Mixed-mode ventilation combines mechanical and natural ventilation methods.

A **mixed-use** project involves a combination of residential and commercial or retail components.

Movable furniture and partitions are those that can moved to provide access to the view by the user without the need for tools or assistance from special trades and facilities management.

The **National Pollutant Discharge Elimination System** (**NPDES**) is a permit program that controls water pollution by regulating point sources that discharge pollutants into waters of the United States. Industrial, municipal, and other facilities must obtain permits if their discharges go directly to surface waters.

Native (**or indigenous**) **plants** are adapted to a given area during a defined time period and are not invasive. In North America, the term often refers to plants growing in a region prior to the time of settlement by people of European descent.

Natural areas feature native or adapted vegetation or other ecologically appropriate features.

Natural ventilation, or **passive ventilation**, is provided by thermal, wind, or diffusion effects through doors, windows, or other intentional openings in the building; it uses the building layout, fabric, and form to achieve heat transfer and air movement.

Neighborhood is synonymous with **residential area.**

Net metering is a metering and billing arrangement that allows on-site generators to send excess electricity flows to the regional power grid. These electricity flows offset a portion of those drawn from the grid.

Net project material value includes the construction material value and the CSI Division 12 (Furniture and Furnishings) material value, the lesser of material values for mechanical and electric components, and the salvage value identified in the MR credits.

Nonoccupied spaces include all rooms used by maintenance personnel that are not open for use by occupants. Examples are closets and janitorial, storage, and equipment rooms.

Nonporous sealant is a substance used as a sealant on nonporous materials. Nonporous materials, such as plastic and metal, do not have openings in which fluids may be absorbed or discharged.

Nonpotable water. See **potable water.**

Nonwater (**or composting**) **toilet systems** are dry plumbing fixtures and fittings that contain and treat human waste via microbiological processes.

A **nonwater** (**or dry**) **urinal** replaces a water flush with a trap containing a layer of buoyant liquid that floats above the urine, blocking sewer gas and odors.

Occasional furniture is located in lobbies and in conference rooms.

Occupants in a commercial building are workers who either have a permanent office or workstation in the building or typically spend a minimum of 10 hours per week in the building. In a residential building, occupants also include all persons who live in the building.

Off-gassing is the emission of volatile organic compounds (VOCs) from synthetic and natural products.

Off-site renewable energy is derived from renewable energy sources and generated outside the project site perimeter; it is delivered through a private agreement with the energy-generating entity.

Off-site salvaged materials are recovered from a source different from the project site.

On-demand (or tankless) heaters heat water only when it is needed and then apply only the amount of heat required to satisfy the immediate need.

Ongoing commissioning is a continuous process that methodically identifies and corrects system problems to maintain optimal building performance; it includes regular measurement and comparative analysis of building energy data over time.

Ongoing consumables have a low cost per unit and are regularly used and replaced in the course of business. Examples include paper, toner cartridges, binders, batteries, and desk accessories.

On-site renewable energy is energy derived from renewable sources located within the project site perimeter.

On-site salvaged materials are recovered from and reused at the same building site.

On-site wastewater treatment is the transport, storage, treatment, and disposal of wastewater generated on the project site.

Open space area is usually defined by local zoning requirements. If local zoning requirements do not clearly define open space, it is defined for the purposes of LEED calculations as the property area minus the development footprint; it must be vegetated and pervious, with exceptions only as noted in the credit requirements section. Only ground areas are calculated as open space. For projects located in urban areas that earn a Development Density and Community Connectivity credit, open space also includes nonvehicular, pedestrian-oriented hardscape spaces.

Open-grid pavement is less than 50% impervious and accommodates vegetation in the open cells.

Outdoor air is the ambient air that enters a building through a ventilation system, either through natural ventilation or by infiltration. (ASHRAE 62.1–2007)

The **owner** is the person directly employed by the organization holding title to the project building and recognized by law as having rights, responsibilities, and ultimate control over the building.

Owner's project requirements is a written document that details the ideas, concepts, and criteria that are determined by the owner to be important to the success of the project.

Ozone (O_3) is a gas composed of 3 oxygen atoms. It is not usually emitted directly into the air, but at ground-level it is created by a chemical reaction between oxides of nitrogen (NOx) and volatile organic compounds (VOCs) in the presence of sunlight. Ozone has the same chemical structure whether it occurs in the atmosphere or at ground level and can have positive or negative effects, depending on its location. (U.S. Environmental Protection Agency)

Paint is a liquid, liquefiable, or mastic composition that is converted to a solid protective, decorative, or functional adherent film after application as a thin layer. These coatings are intended for application to interior or exterior surfaces of residential, commercial, institutional, or industrial buildings.

Parking footprint refers to the area of the project site occupied by the parking areas and structures.

Parking subsidies are the costs of providing occupant parking that are not recovered in parking fees.

In a **partially shielded** exterior light fixture, the lower edge of the shield is at or below the centerline of the lamp, to minimize light emitted above the horizontal plane.

Pedestrian access allows people to walk to services without being blocked by walls, freeways, or other barriers.

Percentage improvement measures the energy cost savings for the proposed building performance compared with the baseline building performance.

Permeable. See **porous pavement.**

Perviousness is the percentage of the surface area of a paving system that is open and allows moisture to soak into the ground below.

Phenol formaldehyde, which off-gasses only at high temperature, is used for exterior products, although many of these products are suitable for interior applications.

Photovoltaic (PV) energy is electricity from photovoltaic cells that convert the energy in sunlight into electricity.

A **picogram** is 1 trillionth of a gram.

Picograms per lumen-hour is a measure of the amount of mercury in a lamp per unit of light delivered over its useful life.

Plug load is synonymous with **receptacle load.**

Pollutants include emissions of carbon dioxide (CO_2), sulfur dioxide (SO_2), nitrogen oxides (NO_x), mercury (Hg), small particulates (PM2.5), and large particulates (PM10).

Porous materials have tiny openings, often microscopic, that can absorb or discharge fluids. Examples include wood, fabric, paper, corrugated paperboard, and plastic foam. (SCAQMD Rule 1168)

Porous pavement and **permeable surfaces** allow runoff to infiltrate into the ground.

Postconsumer fiber consists of paper, paperboard, and fibrous wastes that are collected from municipal solid waste streams.

Postconsumer material is recycled from consumer waste.

Postconsumer recycled content is the percentage of material in a product that was consumer waste. The recycled material was generated by household, commercial, industrial, or institutional end-users and can no longer be used for its intended purpose. It includes returns of materials from the distribution chain. Examples include construction and demolition debris, materials collected through recycling programs, discarded products (e.g., furniture, cabinetry, decking), and landscaping waste (e.g., leaves, grass clippings, tree trimmings). (ISO 14021)

Potable water meets or exceeds EPA's drinking water quality standards and is approved for human consumption by the state or local authorities having jurisdiction; it may be supplied from wells or municipal water systems.

ppm stands for parts per million.

Preconsumer recycled content, formerly known as postindustrial content, is the percentage of material in a product that is recycled from manufacturing waste. Examples include planer shavings, sawdust, bagasse, walnut shells, culls, trimmed materials, overissue publications, and obsolete inventories. Excluded are rework, regrind, or scrap materials capable of being reclaimed within the same process that generated them. (ISO 14021)

Predicted mean vote is an empirical equation for predicting the mean vote on a rating scale of thermal comfort of a large population of people exposed to a certain environment.

Preferred parking, available to particular users, includes designated spaces close to the building (aside from designated handicapped spots), designated covered spaces, discounted parking passes, and guaranteed passes in a lottery system.

Preventive maintenance is routinely scheduled equipment inspection, cleaning, and repair conducted to detect and prevent equipment failure and keep materials and systems in working order.

Previously developed sites once had buildings, roadways, parking lots, or were graded or otherwise altered by direct human activities.

A **primer** is a material applied to a substrate to improve the adhesion of subsequently applied coats.

Prior condition area is the total area of finished ceilings, floors, and full-height walls that existed when the project area was selected. It does not include exterior windows and doors.

Prior condition is the state of the project space at the time it was selected.

Private or private use applies to plumbing fixtures in residences, apartments, and dormitories, to private (non-public) bathrooms in transient lodging facilities (hotels and motels), and to private bathrooms in hospitals and nursing facilities.

Process water is used for industrial processes and building systems such as cooling towers, boilers, and chillers. It can also refer to water used in operational processes, such as dishwashing, clothes washing, and ice making.

Property area is the total area within the legal property boundaries of a site; it encompasses all areas of the site, including constructed and nonconstructed areas.

Proposed building performance is the annual energy cost calculated for a proposed design, as defined in ANSI/ASHRAE/IESNA Standard 90.1–2007, Appendix G.

Protected Harvest certification standards reflect the growing requirements and environmental considerations of different crops and bioregions. Each crop- and region-specific standard addresses production, toxicity, and chain-of-custody.

Public or public use applies to all buildings, structures, or uses that are not defined as private or private use.

Public transportation consists of bus, rail, or other transit services for the general public that operate on a regular, continual basis.

Rainforest Alliance certification is awarded to farms that protect wildlife by planting trees, control erosion, limit agrochemicals, protect native vegetation, hire local workers, and pay fair wages.

Rapidly renewable materials are agricultural products, both fiber and animal, that take 10 years or less to grow or raise and can be harvested in a sustainable fashion.

Rated power is the nameplate power on a piece of equipment. It represents the capacity of the unit and is the maximum that it will draw.

Receptacle (or plug) load is the current drawn by all equipment that is plugged into the electrical system.

Recirculated air is removed from a space and reused as supply air, delivered by mechanical or natural ventilation.

Reclaimed water is wastewater that has been treated and purified for reuse.

Recommissioning applies to buildings that were previously commissioned as part of new construction or buildings covered by existing building commissioning.

Recovered fiber includes both postconsumer fiber and waste fiber from the manufacturing process.

Recycled content is the proportion, by mass, of preconsumer or postconsumer recycled material in a product. (ISO 14021)

Recycling is the collection, reprocessing, marketing, and use of materials that were diverted or recovered from the solid waste stream.

A **recycling collection area** is located in regularly occupied space in the building for the collection of occupants' recyclables. A building may have numerous collection areas from which recyclable materials are typically removed to a central collection and storage area.

Refrigerants are the working fluids of refrigeration cycles that absorb heat from a reservoir at low temperatures and reject heat at higher temperatures.

Refurbished materials are products that could have been disposed of as solid waste. These products have completed their life cycle as consumer items and are then refurbished for reuse without substantial alteration of their form. Refurbishing includes renovating, repairing, restoring, or generally improving the appearance, performance, quality, functionality, or value of a product.

Regionally extracted materials are raw materials taken from within a 500-mile radius of the project site.

Regionally manufactured materials are assembled as finished products within a 500-mile radius of the project site. Assembly does not include on-site assembly, erection, or installation of finished components.

Regularly occupied spaces are areas where workers are seated or standing as they work inside a building. In residential applications, these areas are all spaces except bathrooms, utility areas, and closets or other storage rooms. In schools, they are areas where students, teachers, or administrators are seated or standing as they work or study inside a building.

Relative humidity is the ratio of partial density of airborne water vapor to the saturation density of water vapor at the same temperature and total pressure.

Remanufactured materials are items that are made into other products. One example is concrete that is crushed and used as subbase.

Remediation is the process of cleaning up a contaminated site by physical, chemical, or biological means. Remediation processes are typically applied to contaminated soil and groundwater.

Renewable energy comes from sources that are not depleted by use. Examples include energy from the sun, wind, and small (low-impact) hydropower, plus geothermal energy and wave and tidal systems. Ways to capture energy from the sun include photovoltaic, solar thermal, and bioenergy systems based on wood waste, agricultural crops or residue, animal and other organic waste, or landfill gas.

Renewable energy certificates (RECs) are tradable commodities representing proof that a unit of electricity was generated from a renewable energy resource. RECs are sold separately from electricity itself and thus allow the purchase of green power by a user of conventionally generated electricity.

Replacement value is the estimated cost of replacing a used product. This value may be equal to the cost of a similar new product or based on a new product with comparable features.

A **residential area** is land zoned primarily for housing at a density of 10 units per acre or greater. These areas may have single-family and multifamily housing and include building types such as townhomes, apartments, duplexes, condominiums, or mobile homes.

The **Resource Conservation and Recovery Act (RCRA)** addresses active and future facilities and was enacted in 1976 to give EPA authority to control hazardous wastes from cradle to grave, including generation, transportation, treatment, storage, and disposal. Some nonhazardous wastes are also covered under RCRA.

Retained components are portions of the finished ceilings, finished floors, full-height walls and demountable partitions, interior doors, and built-in case goods that existed in the prior condition area and remain in the completed design.

Retention ponds capture stormwater runoff and clear it of pollutants before its release. Some retention pond designs use gravity only; others use mechanical equipment, such as pipes and pumps, to facilitate transport. Some ponds are dry except during storm events; others permanently store water.

A **retrofit** is any change to an existing facility, such as the addition or removal of equipment or an adjustment, connection, or disconnection of equipment.

Return air is removed from a space and then recirculated or exhausted. (ASHRAE 62.1–2007)

Reuse returns materials to active use in the same or a related capacity as their original use, thus extending the lifetime of materials that would otherwise be discarded. Examples of construction materials that can be reused include extra insulation, drywall, and paints.

Reused area is the total area of the building structure, core, and envelope that existed in the prior condition and remains in the completed design.

Ridesharing is synonymous with carpooling.

Safety and comfort light levels meet local code requirements and must be adequate to provide a safe path for egress without overlighting the area.

Salvaged materials or **reused materials** are construction materials recovered from existing buildings or construction sites and reused. Common salvaged materials include structural beams and posts, flooring, doors, cabinetry, brick, and decorative items.

A **sealant** has adhesive properties and is formulated primarily to fill, seal, or waterproof gaps or joints between 2 surfaces. Sealants include sealant primers and caulks. (SCAQMD Rule 1168)

A **sealant primer** is applied to a substrate, prior to the application of a sealant, to enhance the bonding surface. (SCAQMD Rule 1168)

Sealers are coatings applied to either block materials from penetrating into or leaching out of a substrate, to prevent subsequent coatings from being absorbed by the substrate, or to prevent harm to subsequent coatings by materials in the substrate.

Seating consists of task and guest chairs used with systems furniture.

Secure bicycle storage is an internal or external space that keeps bicycles safe from theft. It may include lockers and storage rooms.

Sedimentation is the addition of soil particles to water bodies by natural and human-related activities. Sedimentation often decreases water quality and can accelerate the aging process of lakes, rivers, and streams.

Sensors are devices that undergo a measurable change in response to environmental changes and communicate this change to a control system.

Setpoints are normal operating ranges for building systems and indoor environmental quality. When the building systems are outside of their normal operating range, action is taken by the building operator or automation system.

Shielding is a nontechnical term that describes devices or techniques that are used as part of a luminaire or lamp to limit glare, light trespass, or sky glow.

Site area is synonymous with **property area**.

A **site assessment** is an evaluation of a site's aboveground and subsurface characteristics, including its structures, geology, and hydrology. Site assessments are typically used to determine whether contamination has occurred, as well as the extent and concentration of any release of pollutants. Information generated during a site assessment is used to make remedial action decisions.

Site energy is the amount of heat and electricity consumed by a building, as reflected in utility bills.

Sky glow is caused by stray light from unshielded light sources and light reflecting off surfaces that then enter the atmosphere and illuminate and reflect off dust, debris, and water vapor. Sky glow can substantially limit observation of the night sky, compromise astronomical research, and adversely affect nocturnal environments.

Soft costs are expense items that are not considered direct construction costs. Examples include architectural, engineering, financing, and legal fees.

Solar reflectance, or **albedo**, is a measure of the ability of a surface material to reflect sunlight—visible, infrared, and ultraviolet wavelengths—on a scale of 0 to 1. Solar reflectance is also called albedo. Black paint has a solar reflectance of 0; white paint (titanium dioxide) has a solar reflectance of 1.

Solar thermal systems collect or absorb sunlight via solar collectors to heat water that is then circulated to the building's hot water tank. Solar thermal systems can be used to warm swimming pools or heat water for residential and commercial use.

The **solar reflectance index** (**SRI**) is a measure of a material's ability to reject solar heat, as shown by a small temperature rise. Standard black (reflectance 0.05, emittance 0.90) is 0 and standard white (reflectance 0.80, emittance 0.90) is 100. For example, a standard black surface has a temperature rise of 90°F (50°C) in full sun, and a standard white surface has a temperature rise of 14.6°F (8.1°C). Once the maximum temperature rise of a given material has been computed, the SRI can be calculated by interpolating between the values for white and black. Materials with the highest SRI values are the coolest choices for paving. Because of the way SRI is defined, particularly hot materials can even take slightly negative values, and particularly cool materials can even exceed 100. (Lawrence Berkeley National Laboratory Cool Roofing Materials Database)

Source energy is the total amount of raw fuel required to operate a building; it incorporates all transmission, delivery, and production losses for a complete assessment of a building's energy use.

Source reduction reduces the amount of unnecessary material brought into a building. Examples include purchasing products with less packaging.

Species factor (k_s) is a constant used to adjust the evapotranspiration rate to reflect the biological features of a specific plant species.

The **square footage** of a building is the total area in square feet (sf) of all rooms, including corridors, elevators, stairwells, and shaft spaces.

Standard operating procedures are detailed, written instructions documenting a method to achieve uniformity of performance.

Stormwater runoff consists of water from precipitation that flows over surfaces into sewer systems or receiving water bodies. All precipitation that leaves project site boundaries on the surface is considered stormwater runoff.

A **stormwater pollution prevention plan** describes all measures to prevent stormwater contamination, control sedimentation and erosion during construction, and comply with the requirements of the Clean Water Act.

Stratified random sampling categorizes members of a population into discrete subgroups, based on characteristics that may affect their responses to a survey. For example, a survey of building occupants' commuting behavior might separate people by income level and commuting distance. To yield representative results, the survey should sample subgroups according to their proportions in the total population.

Submetering is used to determine the proportion of energy use within a building attributable to specific end uses or subsystems (e.g., the heating subsystem of an HVAC system).

Supply air is delivered by mechanical or natural ventilation to a space, composed of any combination of outdoor air, recirculated air, or transfer air. (ASHRAE 62.1-2007)

Sustainable forestry is the practice of managing forest resources to meet the long-term forest product needs of humans while maintaining the biodiversity of forested landscapes. The primary goal is to restore, enhance, and sustain a full range of forest values, including economic, social, and ecological considerations.

A **sustainable purchasing policy** gives preference to products that have little to no negative impact on the environment and society throughout their life cycle, and to the companies that supply them.

A **sustainable purchasing program** is the development, adoption, and implementation of a procurement strategy that supports an organization's sustainable purchasing policy.

Systematic sampling surveys every xth person in a population, using a constant skip interval. It relies on random sampling order or an order with no direct relationship to the variable under analysis (e.g., alphabetical order when sampling for commuting behavior).

Systems furniture includes panel-based workstations comprising modular interconnecting panels, hang-on components, and drawer and filing components or a free-standing grouping of furniture items designed to work in concert.

Systems performance testing is the process of determining the ability of commissioned systems to perform in accordance with the owner's project requirements, the basis of design, and construction documents.

Telecommuting is working by using telecommunications and computer technology from a location other than the usual or traditional place of business—for example, from home, a satellite office, or a telework center.

A **tenant** is a person or entity that pays to occupy land or space that is owned by someone else.

Tenant space is the area within the LEED project boundary. For more information on what can and must be in the LEED project boundary see the Minimum Program Requirements (MPRs) and LEED 2009 MPR Supplemental Guidance. Note: tenant space is the same as project space.

Tertiary treatment is the highest form of wastewater treatment and includes removal of organics, solids, and nutrients as well as biological or chemical polishing, generally to effluent limits of 10 mg/L biological oxygen demand (BOD) 5 and 10 mg/L total suspended solids (TSS).

Thermal comfort exists when occupants express satisfaction with the thermal environment.

Tipping fees are charged by a landfill for disposal of waste, typically quoted per ton.

Total phosphorus (TP) consists of organically bound phosphates, polyphosphates, and orthophosphates in stormwater, the majority of which originates from fertilizer application. Chemical precipitation is the typical removal mechanism for phosphorus.

Total suspended solids (TSS) are particles that are too small or light to be removed from stormwater via gravity settling. Suspended solid concentrations are typically removed via filtration.

Transient users are occupants who do not use a facility on a consistent, regular, daily basis. Examples include students in higher education settings, customers in retail settings, and visitors in institutional settings.

A 2-year, 24-hour design storm is a nationally accepted rate that represents the largest amount of rainfall expected over a 24-hour period during a 2-year interval. The rate is the basis for planning and designing stormwater management facilities and features.

Undercover parking is underground or under a deck, roof, or building; its hardscape surfaces are shaded.

Universal notification means notifying building occupants not less than 72 hours before a pesticide is applied in a building or on surrounding grounds under normal conditions, and within 24 hours after application of a pesticide in emergency conditions. Use of a least toxic pesticide or self-contained nonrodent bait does not require universal notification; all other pesticide applications do.

Upstream equipment consists of all heating or cooling systems, equipment, and controls that are associated with a district energy system but are not part of the project building's thermal connection or do not interface with the district energy system. It includes the central energy plant and all transmission and distribution equipment associated with transporting the thermal energy to the project building and site.

Urea formaldehyde is a combination of urea and formaldehyde that is used in some glues and may emit formaldehyde at room temperature.

USDA Organic is the U.S. Department of Agriculture's certification for products that contain at least 95% organically produced ingredients (excluding water and salt). Any remaining ingredients must consist of approved nonagricultural substances (as listed by USDA) or be nonorganically produced agricultural products that are not commercially available in organic form.

Vegetation-containing artifices are planters, gardens, or other constructs intended to host flora.

A vendor of certified wood is the company that supplies wood products to contractors or subcontractors for on-site installation. A vendor needs a chain-of-custody number if it is selling FSC-certified products that are not individually labeled; this includes most lumber.

Ventilation is the process of supplying air to or removing air from a space for the purpose of controlling air contaminant levels, humidity, or temperature within the space. (ASHRAE 62.1-2007).

Verification is the range of checks and tests carried out to determine whether components, subsystems, systems, and interfaces between systems operate in accordance with the contract documents.

Vertical footcandles occur on a vertical surface. They can be added together arithmetically when more than 1 source provides light to the same surface.

Visible light transmittance (VLT) (T_{vis}) is the ratio of total transmitted light to total incident light (i.e., the amount of visible spectrum, 380–780 nanometers of light passing through a glazing surface divided by the amount of light striking the glazing surface). The higher the T_{vis} value, the more incident light passes through the glazing.

Vision glazing is the portion of an exterior window between 30 and 90 inches above the floor that permits a view to the outside.

Volatile organic compounds (VOCs) are carbon compounds that participate in atmospheric photochemical reactions (excluding carbon monoxide, carbon dioxide, carbonic acid, metallic carbides and carbonates, and ammonium carbonate). The compounds vaporize (become a gas) at normal room temperatures.

Walking distance is the length of the walkable pathway between the building and public transportation.

Walk-off mats are placed inside building entrances to capture dirt, water, and other materials tracked inside by people and equipment.

Waste comprises all materials that flow from the building to final disposal. Examples include paper, grass trimmings, food scraps, and plastics. In LEED, waste refers to all materials that are capable of being diverted from the building's waste stream through waste reduction.

Waste disposal eliminates waste by means of burial in a landfill, combustion in an incinerator, or any other way that is not recycling or reuse.

Waste diversion is a management activity that disposes of waste other than through incineration or the use of landfills. Examples include reuse and recycling.

Waste reduction includes both source reduction and waste diversion through reuse or recycling.

A **waste reduction program** encompasses source reduction, reuse, and recycling. Such a program assigns responsibility within the organization for implementation, lists the general actions that will be taken to reduce waste, and describes tracking and review procedures to monitor waste reduction and improve performance.

The **waste stream** is the overall flow of waste from the building to a landfill, incinerator, or other disposal site.

Wastewater is the spent or used water from a home, community, farm, or industry that contains dissolved or suspended matter. (Federal Remediation Technologies Roundtable)

Waterless urinals are dry plumbing fixtures that use advanced hydraulic design and a buoyant fluid to maintain sanitary conditions.

A **water meter** measures the volume of water usage. Most commercial building water meters are designed to measure cold potable water.

Wave and tidal power systems capture energy from waves and the diurnal flux of tidal power, respectively. The captured energy is commonly used for desalination, water pumping, and electricity generation.

Wind energy is electricity generated by wind turbines.

Window-to-floor ratio (WFR) is the total area of the window (measured vertically from 30 inches above the finished floor to the top of the glass, multiplied by the width of the glass) divided by the floor area.

Xeriscaping is a landscaping method that makes routine irrigation unnecessary. It uses drought-adaptable and low-water plants as well as soil amendments such as compost and mulches to reduce evaporation.

RECYCLED
Paper made from
recycled material
FSC® C014174

This reference guide was printed on 100% postconsumer waste paper, processed chlorine free, and printed with non-toxic, soybased inks using 100% wind power. By using these materials and production processes, the U.S. Green Building Council saved the following resources:

Trees*	Solid Waste	Liquid Waste	Electricity	Greenhouse Gases	Sulfur & Nitrogen Oxides
83,464 lbs. of virgin wood, equal to 145 trees	13,086 lbs.	122,734 gallons	18,780 kWh	23,789 lbs.	45 lbs.

*one harvested tree = aprox. 575 lbs